The Racing Motorcycle

The Racing Motorcycle

A technical guide for constructors

John Bradley

Volume 1

Gearing, geometry, aerodynamics and suspension

Broadland Leisure Publications

PO Box 72, Whitby YO21 3YE, England

Tel. 01947 893356

First published 1996

IMPORTANT NOTICE

Motorcycle racing is an inherently dangerous activity and when building or modifying a bike for this purpose it is easy to overstep the fine line that exists between performance and reliability. It is therefore the reader's responsibility to ensure his or her own safety when participating in such activities. Every effort has been made to ensure that the information contained in this book is accurate but no liability can be accepted by the publisher or author for any loss, damage or injury that results from the reader's use of, or reliance upon, this material.

Readers should adopt all appropriate safety precautions that might be indicated by the activities described in this book and the reader assumes full responsibility for all risks connected with any instructions or suggestions given. The author and publisher cannot guarantee any of the standard products described herein and disclaim any obligation to obtain information on those products, other than that provided to them by the manufacturer.

British Library Cataloguing in Publication Data

A CIP record for this book is available from the British Library

ISBN for complete set of two volumes: 0 9512929 1 9

ISBN for this volume: 0 9512929 2 7

Cover picture: This racing special was designed and built by Andy Stevenson. It is powered by an FZR1000 engine and features hub-centre steering. Andy is now building road bikes to a similar design. Contact A.S.P. on 0115 9535410. Illustration by Scott Macfarlane c/o Maltings Partnership, 18 King Alfred Street, Derby DE22 3QJ (tel 01332 291377).

Design and illustration by the author

Printed by Sessions of York, The Ebor Press, York YO31 9HS, England

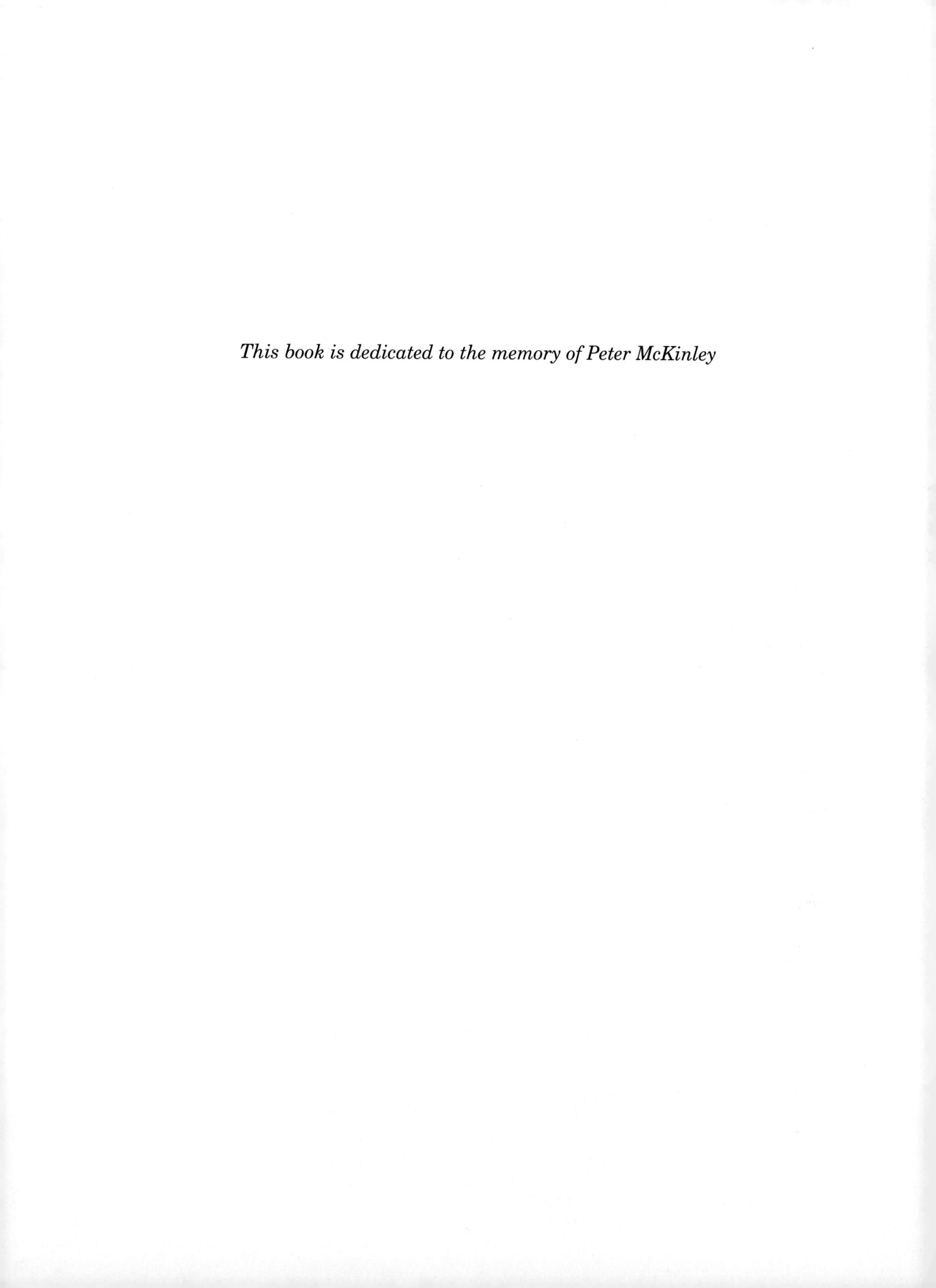

This book is dedicated to the memory of Peter McKinley

Contents

Section 7. Appendices

Acknowledgments

I am deeply indebted to everyone who has helped to make this book possible. Without them, it would have been a much more difficult task. I would particularly like to thank Liz for her tireless encouragement, support and assistance. Tudor Powell has also devoted most of his recent life to proof-reading the text and for this I am extremely grateful. I would also like to thank the following people who have been of great assistance.

Roy Kiviet and Eric Lindeman (WP Suspension Netherlands), Peter Babbage (WP Suspension UK), Roger Titchmarsh, Derek Stripling (Hagon Products), Dan White and Peter Murray (Suspension supplies), Pete Spence (M.R.Holland), Kevin Cooper (National Research Council, Canada), Dave Clark (Michelin Competition Dept.), Graham Dyson (Nova Transmissions), Peter Brooks (University of Leeds), Prof. Robin Sharp (University of Cranfield), Martin Hughes (BMW), Alan Thompson (Gear Technology), Paul Blanchard (Monroe Europe (UK) Ltd), Reynold Chains, Andy Stevenson, Maltings Partnership, Dave Sault, Norman Wood, Rob Shuker, Nick Carpenter, Fernando Mendez, Trevor Bousfield, John Hall, Mike Wood, Charlie Cotterell, David Broadley, John Pitt, Frank Swan, and Gary Hall.

Preface

Competition motorcycles bring pleasure to thousands of people in a variety of pursuits that include trials, motocross, enduro, grasstrack, speedway and roadracing.

Bikes and riders vary enormously covering both the classic and modern eras but everyone concerned likes to reduce their lap times. This search for success is often long and painful, especially when funds are limited. Engine development is always a focal point but there are many other aspects involved and enthusiasm has no bounds when it comes to experimenting.

For many riders this is limited to developing a standard bike. For others there are more major developments, particularly the use of different engines, while some people finish up designing and building their own bike, a special, in pursuit of success and personal satisfaction.

Designing and modifying motorcycles has always been a sort of love affair, a blend of art, science, engineering, hearsay and gut feelings, but in this age of increasing efficiency the requirements are ever more demanding and decisions need to be analysed carefully.

This book is the first in a series of books that are aimed at people who want to design or develop motorcycles. It is not a motorcycle book in the conventional sense but an engineering book, a text book if you like, that tries to provide basic technical support. This volume covers some of the 'timeless principles' that always have been, and always will be, the basis of a competitive motorcycle. It does not include anything on engine development and will,1 hope, complement the many books on engine tuning that are available. A second volume covering engineering materials, standard components and practical construction techniques is currently being written.

My book is based on roadracing but all the ideas can be applied to any type of motorcycle, from any era, given suitable dimensional and aesthetic adaptations. Some non-roadrace data is included so that you can make the necessary comparisons between different specialisms.

Various guidelines are given which are based on my own experience and that of friends. I am certainly no motorcycle 'expert' and bikes have always been just a hobby, but after many years of building and racing them there is bound to be something of use to someone who is new to all this. My guidelines only represent a starting point. Developing bikes is all about experimenting, writing things down and eventually deciding what works best for you. This book is designed to help you focus on the things that matter as far as general performance is concerned.

Finally I must express my sincere thanks to everyone who has contributed to this book either directly or indirectly. It would be impossible to identify all of them since it is now some thirty years since I manufactured my first special and set off for the race track as a naive sixteen year old.

Lots of things have changed in that time but I am still just as indebted to those who helped me then as to those who have helped me in more recent times. If this book helps someone else to achieve success or satisfaction then it will have been worth the effort involved.

John Bradley
York
1996

1.1 Overview

Introduction

The design of a motorcycle can be as simple or as complicated as you care to make it. Most bikes are built from a predominantly practical point of view, selecting components on the grounds of availability, cost, etc. These are then combined in what seems to be the most sensible and convenient manner, given the physical constraints imposed on their location.

Thousands of bikes have been built in this way by people who never agonised over any technicalities and they often perform very well. When I first started grasstrack racing at the age of sixteen I knew two people who could neither read nor write and yet they built very nice looking motorcycles using their considerable practical skills, enthusiasm and experience. However, as we all know, times have changed. Perhaps the greatest change is one of availability, at a price, and there are now numerous very sophisticated bikes available to anyone who can afford them.

Engines are highly developed, even in road bikes, and there are very few people who can come up with quantum leaps in engine performance. Everything is more refined, more gradual and more expensive because the only gains possible are small gains.

There are two side effects to this. Firstly, it has opened the door to some very expensive components aimed at making small but crucial improvements. Suspension is the obvious example where it is possible to spend large sums of money seeking small but vital reductions in lap times, assuming of course that you are capable of outriding your existing suspension set-up. Instrumentation and data logging equipment are also commonplace, helping to optimise every setting to the nth degree

Fig 1.1 *If you cannot buy what you want you have to build it. Aprilia started by doing just that and now produce some of the best motorcycles in the world. This is Jean-Philippe Ruggia on the 250cc GP bike.*

when in the hands of the more experienced. All such matters are of course bad news for those who are running on a very restricted budget, but there is also some good news. For the majority of riders, financial constraints impose limits and there are many bikes on the track, in every class, that have roughly the same power available. In addition, although the riders are undoubtedly quick in general terms, they do not fall into the category of GP riders who can corner at whatever speed technology allows them to.

As a result of this, it is possible for most club racers to climb up the finishing order by making more of the simple and relatively inexpensive components available to them. At club level, spending a fortune does not always lead to success because certain things need to be right to get the best from any bike, irrespective of what the bits cost or how appealing it may look.

One of the main purposes of this book is therefore to highlight these things and offer some guidelines. The information can then be applied to an existing bike or to a new bike, in an attempt to get better performance for the same financial outlay.

Functional design

There are two main aspects to the design of anything, functionality and aesthetic appeal. In the case of a motorcycle, the fact that a bike is particularly attractive to look at is unlikely to affect its ability to perform either way, though it is usually indicative of attention to detail, hence reliability, and will of course affect the resale value as far as many people are concerned.

State-of-the-art components like the examples in Fig 1.2 are both functional and beautiful. Quality oozes from every corner. However, if you intend to make many of the parts yourself, then some sort of compromise has to be reached or the bike will never get finished. I am a great believer in the KIS (keep it simple) philosophy which decrees that everything will be neat, simple and functional.

Fig 1.2 *They could be works of art, but they are also highly functional. After-market forks for superbikes (photograph WP Suspension).*

- **Engine performance**
- **Gearbox ratios**
- **Overall gearing**
- **Chassis geometry**
- **Centre of gravity**
- **Rider positioning**
- **Suspension behaviour**
- **Structural stiffness**
- **Weight**
- **Resistance to motion**
- **Braking response**
- **Tyres**

Table 1.1 *Key performance elements.*

Functionality is not a debatable issue. Any racing motorcycle must be functional and that function must be refined to a high level if the bike is to be competitive against others in its class. Functional aspects can be further subdivided.

Firstly there is the fundamental design which provides the baseline for performance. No amount of good looks can compensate for deficiencies in this area. Secondly there is the detail design, the selection of materials and manufacturing techniques that will render the basic design workable, reliable and safe. This book only concerns itself with the fundamental design and Table 1.1 lists some of the most important design areas that will influence how competitive the bike is. We have to assume that the rider is capable of getting the best from what is available but if all other things remain equal, then changing the items listed will alter the lap times achieved, often quite dramatically. Some of the more important aspects such as tyres are not entirely under your control, often for financial reasons, but there are still plenty of things you can work at on a limited budget.

Engine performance is an obvious starting point and while this book makes no attempt to deal with engine tuning it does outline how such tuning might affect the engine characteristics and how these will subsequently affect performance. If nothing else, I would hope the text shows that there is more to engine performance than peak power figures alone.

Gearing could be regarded as being even more important than engine development because unless you have suitable gear ratios available, the performance of the engine will be somewhat restricted. In certain cases, the use of inappropriate gearing may impose a complete block on further engine development, at least in terms of peak power. Many racing bikes are built around engines that were originally intended for other applications, eg motocross, and in such cases it is particularly important to look at the suitability of the gearbox internals available to you. Alterations can be very expensive.

The need for appropriate steering geometry is well documented and most riders have a clear preference for the way a particular configuration feels. This could be purely psychological but if the bike feels right then confidence is inspired and lap times reduce. It is usually fairly easy to alter things like steering geometry on an existing bike and it is therefore commonplace to continue development of this area indefinitely. This is fortunate because steering is all about what feels right and the use of different tyres or track conditions will change that feel. Having appropriate adjustments allows optimum settings to be achieved for each rider under different track conditions.

However, other critical areas are much harder to adapt once a bike is completed. Centre of gravity location is a crucial factor that greatly affects acceleration and braking as well as interacting with other things to influence the feel of the bike. It is not usually easy to alter it significantly once the bike is finished. This book shows you how to predict the centre of gravity location as the bike is evolving, thereby giving control over another important aspect.

One key area that frequently receives less attention than it deserves is aerodynamic drag. Some people spend a fortune on engine development without ever giving any thought to the forces that the engine has to overcome, yet reducing these will allow the same level of performance from less power. This is especially important for competition bikes because road speeds are high and aerodynamic forces increase rapidly as you travel faster. Developing the aerodynamic efficiency of a motorcycle is a major challenge because it requires knowledge, patience, ingenuity and a willingness to battle against something that is rather abstract and difficult to quantify without the use of a wind tunnel. The difficulty is further compounded by regulations that severely limit some of the more obvious improvements. Nevertheless, some improvement is possible in most cases and this is one aspect which separates GP bikes from the rest.

The area that seems to have received the most attention in recent years is of course suspension. One could perhaps be rather cynical and suggest that the marketing machine has overcome reality in many cases and it is by no means certain that spending a lot of money on complex suspension systems will reduce lap times.

Simple systems that are well engineered and set up correctly can be just as effective for the majority of riders. After all, only a very good rider is capable of genuinely outriding any well set up system. Fortunately for the manufacturers, there are a lot of people who think they can!

One area which does normally receive the attention it deserves is weight. Weight and bulk are without doubt some of the most influential factors in terms of performance. Low weight reduces the inertia of the bike, ie it makes it easier to accelerate, but it also reduces the forces that oppose acceleration. Rolling resistance is proportional to weight and, if the low weight is the result of a small rider, then considerable reductions in aerodynamic drag may also be possible via reduced frontal area. Anyone who has raced small capacity bikes knows the difference this can make. A light bike is also more manoeuvrable.

At GP level all bikes have weight limits. It has always mildly irritated me that these limits only apply to the bike thereby giving a massive advantage to very small riders but at last we are beginning to see changes. For 1996, the 125 class has a combined weight limit, ie bike and rider, of 130kgf (286lbf). Under normal ACU solo regulations no minimum weight is specified so you are limited by safety and expense. The importance of keeping all weight to a minimum, including that of the rider, cannot be over-emphasised. Assuming you are on a limited budget, and that applies to the majority, then one of the most important things to do is to sit down and try to work out where money is best spent. For example, if you know hand on heart that cornering speed is limited by you rather than the bike then there is nothing to be gained from exotic suspension other than a certain amount of credibility. Perhaps the money would be better spent on a quick shifter that will certainly reduce the lap times at some tracks. Similarly, if you can build a bike that is safe and light using simple materials there is little point in spending a fortune on carbon this and titanium that when funds are limited. A better selection of tyres and sprockets will do a lot more for your results. I am not anti high-technology, indeed I have made a good living out of it for thirty years, but when you see people on vintage bikes with rigid frames overtaking the latest exotica on the corners it does make you wonder if some riders can really capitalise on their vast expense!

Given this mass of variables that a motorcycle implies, it can be difficult to know where to start or how to quantify the numerous decisions that have to be made. I hope this book provides at least some of the answers, especially for those people who want to build specials of their own design.

Initially, it is probably sensible to start somewhere close to any guidelines given but the real aim is to experiment and document results until you are able to formulate your own guidelines based on experience. As I said earlier, a lot of this is subjective.

Copying something else is one way to get started but it automatically puts you behind in terms of development. Innovation rather than replication is the only real way forward. There is also the problem that what suits one person may feel strangely odd and uninspiring to another.

Even with some guidelines to follow, any new bike can be a source of great frustration. There are no set rules and it is sometimes difficult to keep a balance between agonising over things while doing nothing or producing a bike that you wish you had thought more about in the first place. A great deal of time can be spent going round in circles trying to find a compromise. Despite these problems, decisions have to be made and I have tried to arrange the chapters in this book so that they reflect at least one possible route to completion of the initial layout. You can of course read the book in any order you see fit, though this may present certain difficulties for those who are not familiar with all the terminology.

1.2 General notes

Special builders

There are a number of points I would like to discuss very briefly before embarking on the rest of this book. The first is a word of warning for anyone contemplating a special as opposed to a more standard bike. I am not talking about simple engine changes, but complete bikes where you design and manufacture most of it, eg frame, seat, tank, fairing, exhausts etc.

Building specials is very time consuming. It requires skill and facilities. It is rarely less expensive than buying something and it may not appeal to anyone when you subsequently try to sell it.

The bike will only be worth something if you finish it. Those rusty lengths of metal in the shed may well be '531' tubing that cost £100 but the local scrap man will not share your sense of value and neither will anyone else.

It is also easy to become buried in swarf all day and never actually get to the race track because you are always making things. By the time you do the organisers have decided not to run your class anymore! If you have built bikes in the past you will know all about this. I don't want to put anyone off but there can be a lot of problems with going down this route. You must do it for the right reasons which are personal satisfaction and the chance to own and ride something that you alone have created.

Having said this, building specials can be the most satisfying thing imaginable, especially when you win races on them. I have always built specials, sometimes to the detriment of success, but having won races and set lap records I am aware that no amount of money could yield the same degree of satisfaction. Indeed, this book was originally intended specifically for special builders but it became obvious that the information could also be applied to any type of bike, special or otherwise.

Calculations

Throughout this book there are numerous calculations and this will not be to everyone's taste. Some readers will completely dismiss such matters as a total waste of time.

This is simply not true. There are areas where it is often very difficult to get a handle on things without some form of calculation and others where the alternatives are both time consuming and expensive. The idea is to save time and produce something that you have faith in. A compromise is therefore necessary and I have done what I can to facilitate this. All formulae are 'ready to use' with options for both metric and imperial units of measure. Everything has been arranged so that calculations can all be done on a very elementary calculator and any formula given is of real practical use. You may argue that such effort is wasted because just about everything on a motorcycle is subjective, ie what suits one person does not suit another, but again this is not an issue. The idea of the calculations is not to give some magical result but to provide a basis for comparison. By doing this you are better able to decide what factors contribute to your personal preference and hence have some chance of reproducing them on different types of bike.

If the sums required to get a useful practical result are too complex to justify the effort then I have said so or left them out. You have to find a balance. I would be the first to admit to making hundreds of bits without drawings because that would have taken longer than actually doing the job. Conversely, I would never think of building a new bike without making some attempt to assess the gear ratios, determine possible sprocket sizes or estimate the centre of gravity location because failure to do this in the early days proved to be very time consuming and expensive to alter.

When I first started writing this book I was adamant that there would be a balance between practical metal bashing and the things that some readers may classify as purely theoretical. Unfortunately, by the time the book was written it had become clear that there was too much information to include in one book and the only logical split was between this book, which is predominantly technical, and the one I hope to follow it with which is almost totally practical!

In my experience, it is always best to think about the general layout first and that is really what this book is about. Only then can you move on to more detailed design and manufacture.

Rounding errors

Readers who take a keen interest in numerical matters will notice that the figures quoted in many of the examples are not exact. This is due to rounding errors that occur at various points. The main problem concerns calculations that involve several stages of working. In general, I have retained an appropriate number of decimal places throughout the series of calculations and then rounded the final answer. However, if the results of each stage are printed, eg in a table, then they too have been rounded, purely for the sake of appearance, even though the full value has been used to get the final result. This means that if you use the intermediate results from the table, you will get a slightly different final answer. This is unlikely to cause any practical problems but it seemed sensible to point it out.

Going metric

The decision to write this book using predominantly metric units was not taken lightly. I do appreciate that some readers consider anything metric as 'funny money' and will despair at things like kW. However I don't think there was any real choice. We are gradually going metric and anyone at school or college in the last fifteen years or so will have been taught nothing else. The good news for imperial stalwarts is that I have duplicated everything that matters in good old pounds, feet and inches. I have also mixed the units where it seems appropriate, eg most people who use horsepower still talk about engine capacity in cubic centimetres! The correct use of scientific units does present serious problems for anyone who only dabbles with these matters on rare occasions and I have included Appendix 1 to try and explain some of the basic ideas associated with each system of units.

Use of computers

The use of a computer with purpose written software or a standard spreadsheet program will greatly facilitate some of the calculations in this book by removing the more tedious aspects. However for many people computers are still something of a mystery when they are not running standard software and therefore the book is generally written assuming that you only have a simple calculator.

This does impose certain restrictions and there is one section on predicting speed-time history which is really totally impractical unless you use a computer to do the tedious bits for you. Despite this, I have indicated the general ideas so that those with suitable expertise can take the matter further. If this book proves to be popular then I will probably release some appropriate software to go with it.

2.1 Engine characteristics

Introduction

Selecting the engine/gearbox unit for a bike is a very important decision because in most cases everything will be built around it. If the unit chosen proves to be unsuitable, or uncompetitive, then a lot of time, money and inconvenience may be involved in sorting it out. It may even be necessary to abandon the first choice altogether and seek an alternative, the choice of which is now further restricted by the rolling chassis you have just produced.

Engine selection is clearly a matter of personal preference, cost, availability and eligibility, together with dozens of more practical aspects which are outlined in Chapters 2.3 and 2.4, but there is also the basic performance to consider. Today, all forms of racing are so competitive that virtually every successful rider or bike builder has to get involved in engine development and testing at some level, either directly or by paying someone else to do it. Standards are very high and in most cases development has passed well beyond the garden shed era that was adequate in the past.

This book makes no attempt to cover engine development since there are numerous tuners and tuning books available. However, to clarify the basic ideas involved, this Section looks at the engine characteristics that will develop from tuning and outlines how these will influence the gearing requirements and straight line performance.

Overview

The engine tries to drive the motorcycle forward by means of the force that can be generated at the rear tyre's contact patch. Unfortunately this is not the only force involved because the moving motorcycle also experiences a significant amount of resistance from the air it has to pass through, as well as other forms of resistance which are conveniently lumped together and called rolling resistance - Fig 2.1.

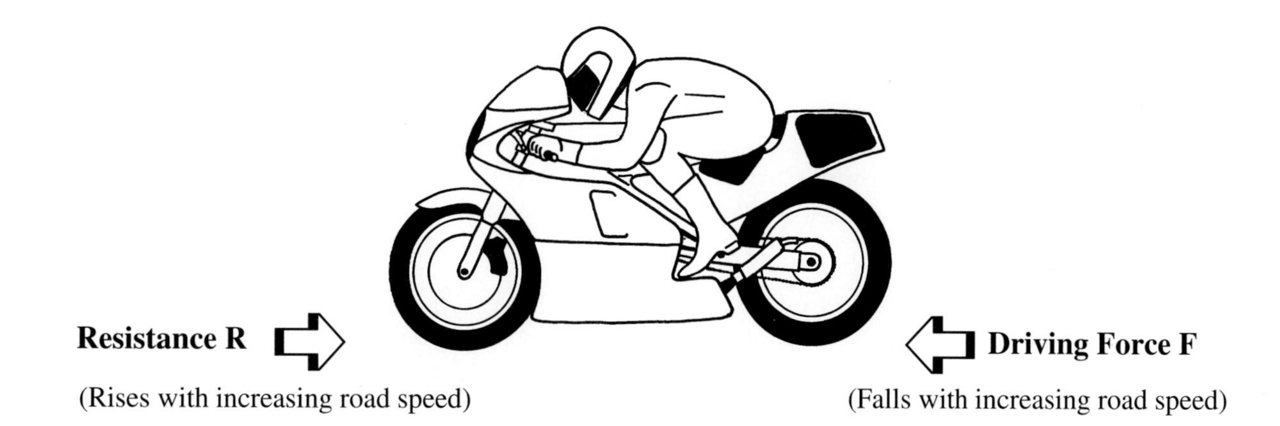

The acceleration from any road speed is proportional to the value of (F - R) at that road speed. If the value of (F - R) is zero then top speed has been reached.

Fig 2.1 *The motorcycle is accelerated by the difference between the driving force and the total amount of resistance present. Resistance is normally dominated by aerodynamic drag and rises with speed.*

The total force resisting motion rises very rapidly as the speed of the bike increases, the air resistance being largely responsible for this depressing aspect. Furthermore, for reasons which will become clear later on, the driving force that the engine is able to generate at the rear wheel under full throttle conditions will fall as the speed of the bike increases.

The bike responds to the difference between these two forces. If the driving force is greater than the resistance then the bike will accelerate, ie it increases its speed. The greater the difference is between the forces, the greater the acceleration will be. This does of course assume that the rear tyre is able to grip and the front wheel can be kept close enough to the ground for the rider to stay in control at full throttle.

In addition, for a given net accelerating force a lighter bike/rider combination will produce a greater acceleration so the need to keep weight to a minimum is added to our list of priorities. It is worth mentioning that there is a bit more to the weight aspect than has been implied here because not only do we have to accelerate the bike and rider down the road but to do so the engine also has to accelerate all the bits that rotate around their spindles. More of this later.

At some road speed the increasing resistance and falling driving force will become equal. Now there is no force difference, hence no acceleration, and the bike has reached its maximum speed. On short circuits no respectable racing bike will reach the true maximum speed of which it is capable because the straights are not long enough to reach maximum engine revs in the highest gearing the bike is capable of pulling. This immediately introduces another aspect, gearing, into our list of basic straight line performance factors which now looks something like this.

- Maximise the driving force at all road speeds.
- Minimise the resistance at all road speeds.
- Keep the overall weight to a minimum.
- Seek the most appropriate balance between rear wheel spin and front wheel lift.
- Select suitable gear ratios and overall gearing.
- Ride the bike in the best possible way.

All of these aspects receive due attention somewhere in this book but the one I want to concentrate on first is the driving force produced by the engine at the rear wheel. As you might expect, there is a lot more to it than the flash power figures commonly quoted.

Torque

Torque is the engineering term for a 'turning effect', hence the name 'torque wrench'. A torque wrench is used to produce a controlled turning effort and hence avoid overtightening, or undertightening, critical fasteners. One reason we need this aid is that while most people develop a good feel for the force they apply to a spanner, the turning effect this produces depends not just on the force but also the radius at which it acts, as shown in Fig 2.2. The torque produced is equal to force x effective radius.

In each case, the effective radius is that which meets the line of action of the force at 90 degrees. If this radius is zero then the torque is zero, irrespective of the force applied. Conversely, a small force can exert a large torque if the radius is substantial.

The driving force that tries to accelerate the bike has its origins in a similar turning effect that is produced at the crankshaft of the engine. Engine torque is fundamentally the same as that associated with a torque wrench but the big difference lies in the fact that the turning effort has to be maintained while the shaft rotates at high speed. Doing this requires power rather than just force and so torque and power are both fundamental requirements for performance.

Right. Fig 2.2 *Torque is produced by the combination of a force and an effective radius. Torque = F x r in each case.*

The crankshaft torque is transferred to the rear wheel via the gearbox and final drive system. In doing so, the torque will normally be altered and is generally greater at the rear wheel than it is at the engine for reasons discussed in Chapter 2.2. It is probably worth pointing out immediately that such torque increases do not come 'free' and are only obtained if rotational speed can be reduced.

Whatever the case, this final torque at the rear wheel is effectively represented by the combination of chain tension and sprocket radius as shown in Fig 2.3.

For the moment, it is sufficient to acknowledge that torque is what we need to produce the driving force that will accelerate the motorcycle and that to do so at anything other than a standstill requires power. I shall therefore consider both aspects in this chapter.

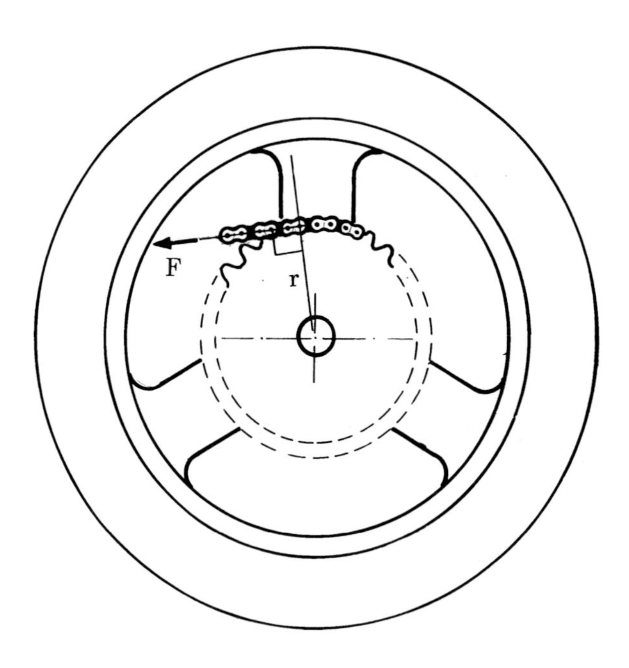

Above. Fig 2.3 *The torque finally arriving at the back wheel is in the form of chain tension acting at sprocket radius.*

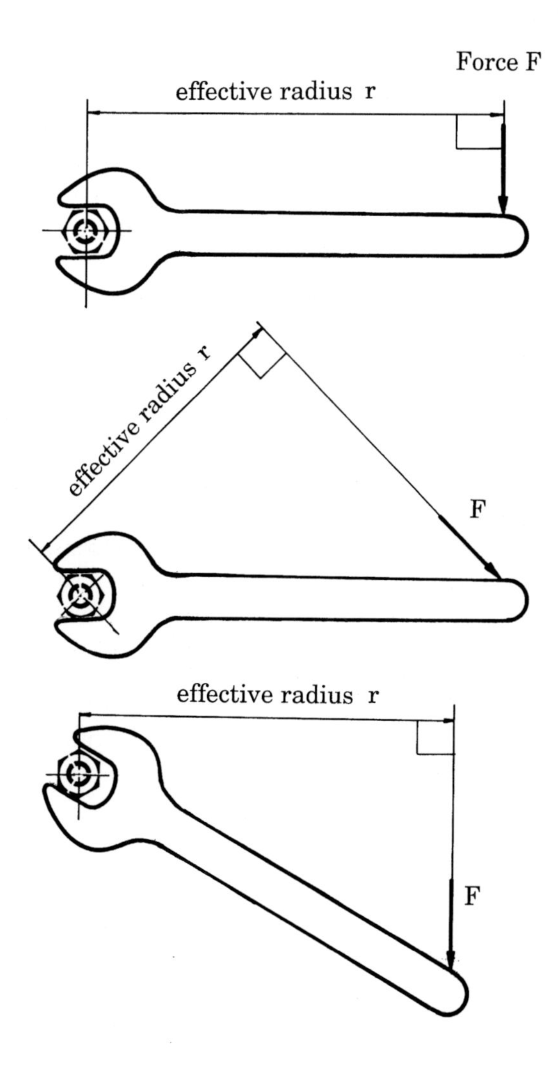

Torque generation

There are two distinct aspects of engine torque output that need to be considered. The first, which is rarely discussed, is the variation of torque output during each complete engine cycle, ie one crankshaft revolution for a two stroke and two crankshaft revolutions for a four stroke. This aspect, which is further influenced by the number of cylinders and firing sequence, plays a key role in the way the rider perceives the engine and the ability to control traction, especially on slippery off-road surfaces.

The second aspect, which is commonly discussed, is the variation in the average torque per complete engine cycle as the speed of the engine is varied over its entire working range.

The torque produced by the engine is a result of the combustion forces being transmitted to the crankshaft at some particular radius via the connecting rod and crankpin. Both the force and the radius alter considerably during each revolution of the crankshaft - Fig 2.4. Following ignition on the power stroke, the combustion process generates very high cylinder pressures (and hence piston forces) but these will decay very rapidly throughout the stroke and return to somewhere around atmospheric when the exhaust port is opened. The force involved therefore varies considerably.

Similarly, the radius at which this is effective varies from zero at top and bottom dead centre to a maximum that is equal to half the stroke. This maximum occurs somewhere in the region of mid stroke, according to the ratio of connecting rod length to crankpin radius. Clearly the combination of changing force and radius produces a very variable torque during the power stroke but even worse there is no useful production of torque during any idle strokes. To illustrate this, Fig 2.5 shows the general form of torque variation produced by both two and four stroke single cylinder engines during one complete engine cycle.

Fig 2.4 *The torque produced during the power stroke varies with cylinder pressure and crank angle.*

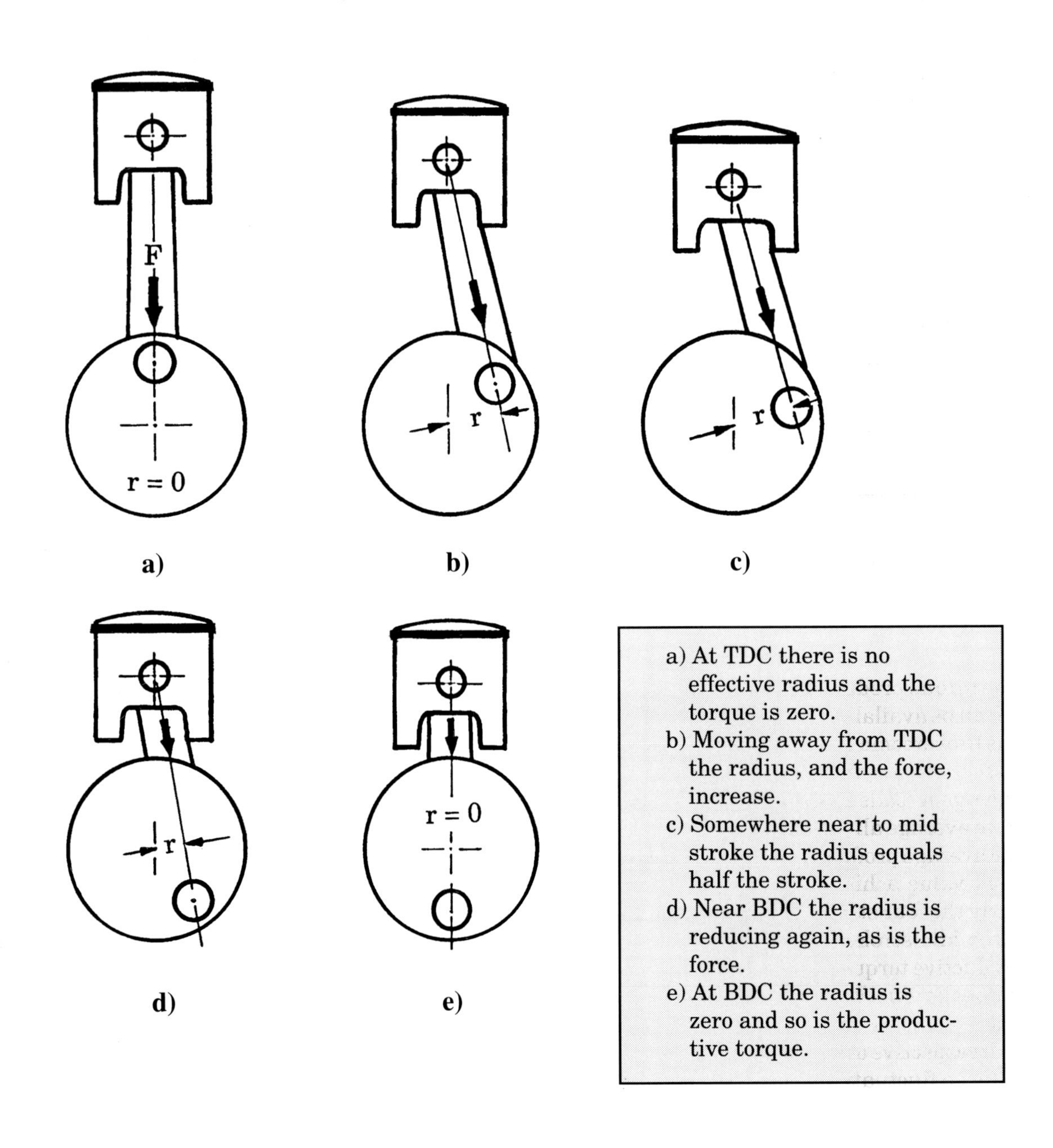

a) At TDC there is no effective radius and the torque is zero.
b) Moving away from TDC the radius, and the force, increase.
c) Somewhere near to mid stroke the radius equals half the stroke.
d) Near BDC the radius is reducing again, as is the force.
e) At BDC the radius is zero and so is the productive torque.

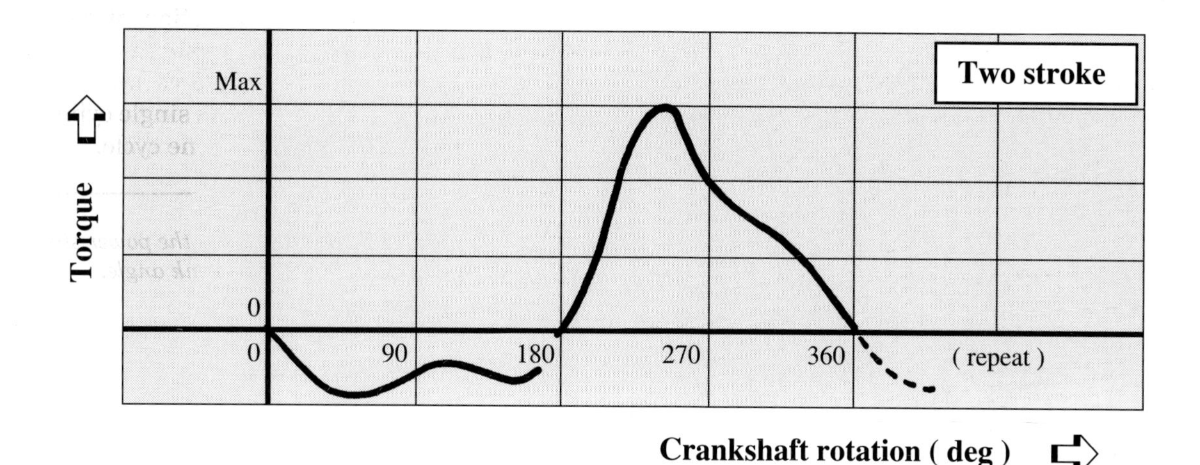

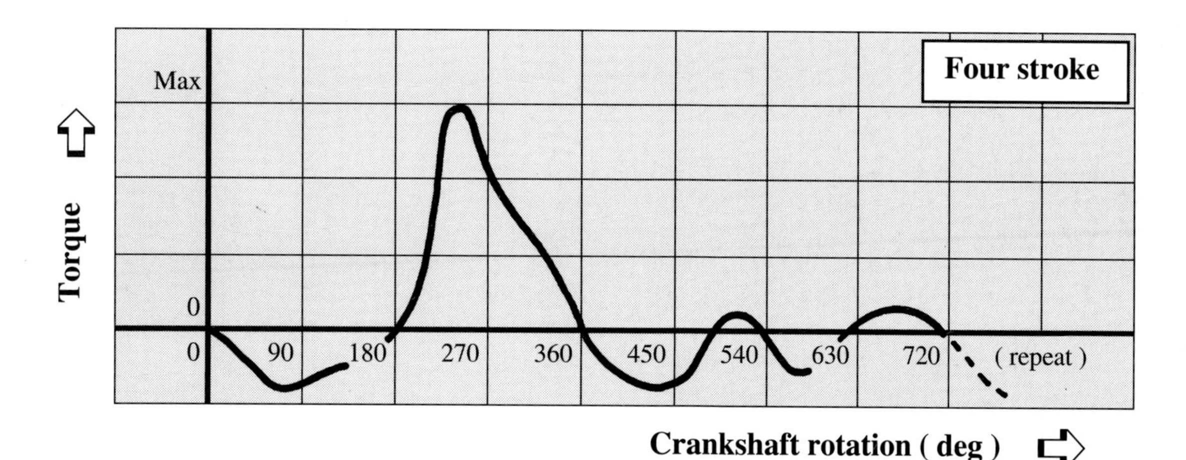

Fig 2.5 *Typical variations in crankshaft torque for one cycle of a) Two stroke and b) Four stroke engines.*

The torque produced during the power stroke will not all be available to drive the bike because it also has to overcome compression resistance, pumping losses, friction and, in the case of the four stroke, valve gear loads that occur during the idle strokes. If we average all this out over the whole cycle then the average productive torque is a lot less than the peak value achieved on the power stroke. Obviously the four stroke is the worst example, having three idle strokes, and in this case the average productive torque per cycle may only be 10 -15% of the peak value! Fortunately, the peak torque value is usually relatively high with four stroke engines.

Irrespective of how we might seek to average all of these fluctuations out, large torque variations cannot be ignored because they greatly influence the way the engine feels, especially at low revs. The four stroke single is clearly more of a thumper than its two stroke counterpart at the same engine speed and this fact has other implications as well.

Erratic torque production tends to produce a crankshaft speed that fluctuates significantly on a rev by rev basis and with a single cylinder engine the only simple way to limit this is by increasing the inertia of the flywheels. If the flywheels are made larger and/or heavier then they possess more inertia, ie a greater reluctance to change speed. During the power stroke they will of course speed up but during the idle strokes they are more reluctant to slow down.

However you cannot have it both ways. Just as the crankshaft is reluctant to slow down so it is reluctant to speed up in the first place and therefore excessive flywheel effect gives a smoother running engine but one that does not accelerate itself easily and is therefore sluggish.

Going the other way, and finishing up with inadequate flywheel inertia, leads to a motor with more of a bang bang bang characteristic but which can accelerate itself very quickly. Unfortunately, it is also likely to stop dead and lock up the back wheel when braking on a closed throttle or over-rev very easily during acceleration! Both aspects increase the degree of rider concentration required. This whole business of torque variation and flywheel matching is very influential. Off-road, there are many conditions where the intermittent torque output of a moderately flywheeled four stroke single finds more grip in the mud than a two stroke with the same average torque but a lot less flywheel (possible because the torque variation is substantially less). The fact that the two stroke accelerates itself easily may not always be an advantage in such cases and there is a reasonable market in external flywheels for trials riders whose low speed activities often highlight these matters more clearly.

This discussion suggests that obtaining the best performance involves more than simply maximising the average torque we can get from the engine, though fortunately for roadracers grip is relatively consistent and many potential problems do not show up until there is plenty of surplus torque.

Multi-cylinders

One way of avoiding the need for excessive flywheel inertia is of course to go for more cylinders. On paper this has everything going for it apart from the obvious cost and complexity implications. Small cylinders have fewer thermal problems and small, light, reciprocating parts can be run at much higher engine speeds before they self destruct. In theory and in practice multi-cylinder engines can produce more power, the details of which follow shortly. As far as torque is concerned, more cylinders give closer spacing of the power strokes and with more than four cylinders the power strokes received by the crankshaft will actually overlap. Because of this, the average torque produced is now a much higher percentage of the peak value, the running is smooth, and only relatively light flywheels are involved giving a motor that can accelerate itself very quickly.

Fortunately for the average enthusiast, regulations have restricted the number of cylinders allowed. If these were not enforced then ludicrously complex multicylinder engines might be necessary for success. It is not too long ago that four cylinder 125's won everything in their class.

However, even with the current restrictions the manufacturers have demonstrated that supersmooth delivery of massive torque is not necessarily desirable, even on tarmac. 500cc four cylinder GP engines have now adopted revised firing arrangements that reportedly make such monsters easier to control during acceleration and give the tyres a better chance of survival by providing some breathing space between each almighty bang. The term used to describe this modification is 'big bang', a very apt description and the engines have been likened by some to a motor with the power of a two stroke but a torque delivery that is more akin to a four stroke single.

In these engines, cylinders one and two fire together and are rapidly followed by cylinders three and four (within ninety degrees of crank rotation). This leaves the rest of the revolution for the tyre to settle down, thus aiding traction and tyre longevity. This technique does of course place serious loads on crankshafts and gearboxes.

It is most unlikely that anyone will supply you with individual figures relating to the torque variations that are described here because when an engine is tested on a conventional dynamometer (brake) then only the average torque at a particular engine speed is revealed. This is one of several reasons why, essential as it is, dynamometer testing does not give a totally clear picture of what the bike will be like to ride.

Nevertheless, as a constructor you will have to think about these aspects when selecting a suitable engine, especially if it was originally built for a different application. Flywheel sizing, conrod length, bore:stroke ratio, balance factor and firing sequence are all aspects that will influence the torque delivery and such factors should be well understood when developing an 'untried' motor.

Average torque and engine speed

Commercial tests generally ignore the torque variations that occur during each engine cycle and only detect the average values. The average value obtained will vary with both engine speed and throttle setting. Most of the tests, which are carried out on a dynamometer or 'brake', are conducted at full throttle and seek to reveal the engine's maximum capability. Although figures may well be tabulated, it is more usual to present the results as a graph of torque against engine speed. Values are frequently published for maximum torque (and power) but on their own they are usually fairly meaningless because they relate to just one specific engine speed and there is no way you will be able to hold the engine at that speed all the way round the track. Obviously the maximum figures obtained must be of a useful order but, assuming this to be the case, it is the variation with engine speed that is important.

Other things being equal, the average torque produced by the engine is primarily determined by the engine's ability to breathe, ie to take in fresh fuel/air mixture, burn it and exhaust the waste products.

To achieve good breathing it is necessary to get the maximum mass flow of air into the cylinder in the first place. We could easily measure the rate of flow of the air during testing and hence come up with a figure for what is termed volumetric efficiency. This indicates what percentage of the air required to completely fill the cylinder at ambient pressure and temperature we are actually getting in there. Conducting such a test at different engine speeds would produce data along the lines of that shown in Fig 2.6.

The peak value is particularly pronounced for racing two strokes because their ability to fill the cylinder is dominated by resonance effects. What this means is that when the timing of the various pressure changes in exhaust, inlet, cylinder and crankcase is precisely synchronised then a great deal more air/fuel mixture is trapped inside the cylinder. Since such synchronisation depends on

Fig 2.6 *The volumetric efficiency of the engine always shows a distinct peak and will control the average torque delivered at any given engine speed. Note that volumetric efficiency can, and often does, exceed 100%.*

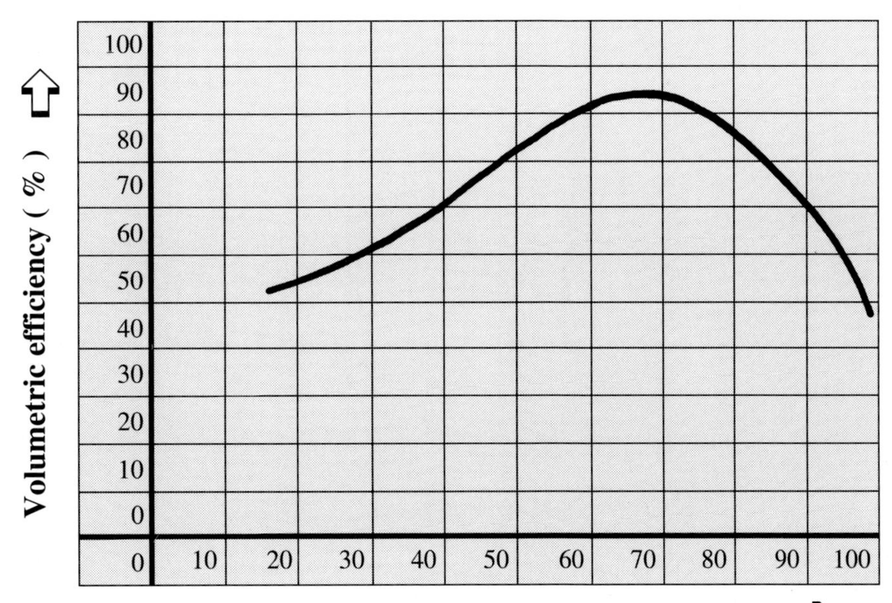

engine speed, the results at other engine speeds may be grossly inferior, just as trying to push a child on a swing at the wrong time gives very little response. The other major factor controlling the torque production is mechanical efficiency. Increased engine speeds involve extra pumping work and rising frictional loads so that these aspects further compound the decline in torque at higher engine speeds.

Because of this it is not possible to produce a torque that is constant, ie independent of engine speed, and the more general characteristic is very much along the lines of the volumetric efficiency curve given earlier in Fig 2.6 with extra fall off near peak engine speed.

In practice, a large number of deviations from this basic characteristic might be observed. Some of the changes are introduced deliberately using careful development to tailor the curve precisely according to application. Other variations may be the result of various inadequacies. Resonance effects can lead to a series of small peaks rather than a smooth curve and there can also be some substantial dips in the delivery due to poor tuning, carburation/ignition limitations or possibly even interaction between cylinders when exhaust pipes are shared.

Before I discuss the shape of various torque curves a word of warning. You cannot reliably compare the shape of any graphs unless they are all drawn to the same scale. Ideally, they need to be on the same sheet of paper as well. Fig 2.7 illustrates this clearly by presenting the torque curve for a 125cc Honda racer on different scales. The impression given by the graphs is very different but they are plotted from identical data.

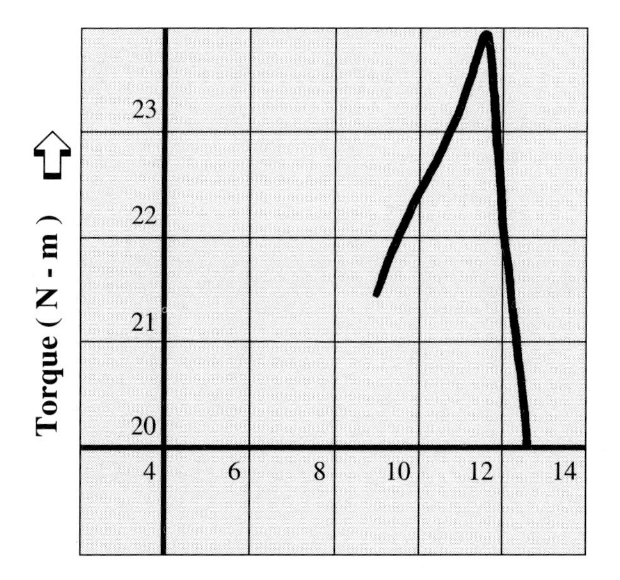

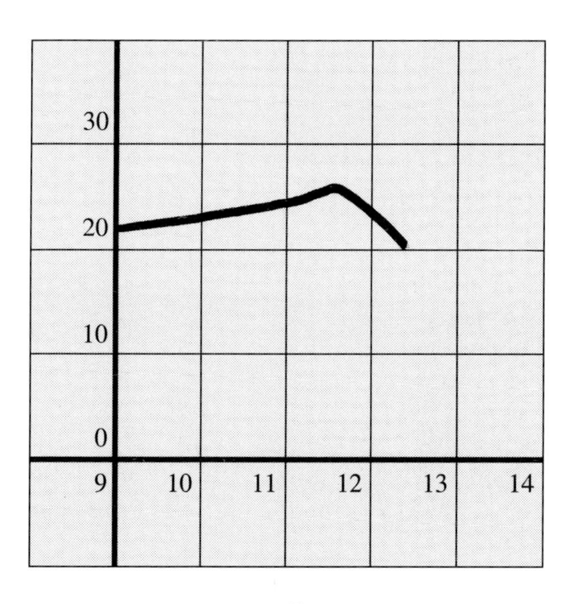

Fig 2.7 *The shape of graphs should only be compared when they are drawn to the same scale. These graphs are drawn from the same data.*

Torque curve shape

Accepting the need to use the same graph scales when making comparisons, we can make some general observations about shape by reference to Fig 2.8 overleaf in which several very different curves are shown. The first objective is of course to produce sufficient torque to be competitive and there are several avenues to explore with this aim in mind.

- Using a more potent fuel (this option will be less applicable as regulations tighten).
- Burning the fuel more efficiently (combustion chamber design/ ignition performance).
- Raising the volumetric efficiency (porting, valving, pipes, induction).
- Reducing mechanical losses (oil drag, pumping loads, gear mesh).
- Revising the basic mechanical design layout (bore, stroke, conrod length).

Whatever the case, you will not continually succeed in raising the torque values without changing the shape of the curve produced because most of the variables alter with engine speed. There comes a point where the shape has more influence on performance than the actual peak values obtained and you would be ill advised to ignore this.

The maximum speed at which the engine can run is determined by mechanical reliability. The limit is usually imposed by piston speed and acceleration which in turn depend on engine stroke. Valve gear reliability may also be a problem in some cases.

If we can obtain high torque outputs in this high speed region then the engine is producing a lot of power (discussed shortly) but the usual consequence of doing this is to render the engine useless at low speeds. The engine develops a narrow 'power band'. In Fig 2.8, the most obvious example of this is the Honda 125 racer where in order to obtain high torque values (for a 125) at high crankshaft speeds the engine is rendered virtually useless at all speeds below 9000revs/min. This implies the need for a low first gear and the use of a lot of clutch slip. Furthermore, because the working range of the engine is only about 3500revs/min the choice of internal gearbox ratios is critical. If the 'jump' to the next gear is too great then the engine speed will drop to a value below 9000revs/min following a gearchange and the engine will 'bog down' or 'drop out of the powerband', to use common expressions.

Gearing considerations are of paramount importance when developing engines to this level and they are discussed in detail later on.

The fact that this engine is unable to perform below 9000revs/min has important implications for less obvious cases. Let us suppose that the little Honda produces virtually no torque at 7000revs/min. If we were able to record torque data in the range 7000 - 9000revs/min then the graph would be one with a very steep rise, much steeper than anything else in Fig 2.8.

In this region, any increase in load on the engine causes the engine speed to drop and that produces a substantial drop in torque. With less torque available the speed drops further still and the whole output collapses (which is why the dyno operator cannot get reliable data in this region!)

Clearly, a torque curve with a very steep rise is bad news, especially if the values are not particularly great. For the Honda this is a fact of life. The torque curve is actually relatively flat, providing you stay above 9000revs/min!

A complete contrast to the Honda racer characteristic is shown by the Kawasaki KLX650 trail bike engine. In this case peak torque is delivered at low speed and from there on the value falls continuously. At first you may consider this to be poor but it is in fact a good characteristic for the application concerned.

For example, imagine you are tearing down a forest track with the KLX motor running at 7000revs/min. If you suddenly hit heavy sand then extra load is put on the engine and its speed will drop. Unlike the Honda, a drop in speed will produce increasing torque delivery from the Kawasaki and that extra torque will help drive the bike through the sand without the need to change down continuously. Variable conditions like this are encountered all the time when riding off road and so a good proportion of the torque characteristic should be on a falling curve. The roadracer, which does not normally experience sudden changes in load like this, can make more use of a high speed torque peak and the rising curve that this will imply. These examples show just how important it is to match the curves to the applications.

Roadbikes obviously come somewhere in-between these extremes because they have moderately varying requirements for cruising, acceleration etc. The Triumph Trident data in Fig 2.8 is an excellent example of a good roadbike torque curve. It is relatively flat and the peak is just past the centre of the useful range of engine speeds. This engine would be excellent for touring.

The torque curve for the Ducati is particularly noteworthy for its overall working range - about 8000revs/min. It manages this even though there is still about 2500revs/min of useful range beyond the point of peak torque. There is a very obvious trough in the delivery around 6000revs/min and the rise beyond it is somewhat steep suggesting that for best results the motor ought to be kept above 8000revs/min if performance is what you are after. This curve is an excellent attempt to marry high performance torque together with reasonable flexibility.

I hope that these examples illustrate the diverse range of requirements and make the point that it is no good trying to raise the peak torque if you cannot maintain a suitable characteristic. Combining the two is what separates good tuners from bad ones.

Fig 2.8 *Contrasting torque curves from different engines due to requirements discussed in the text.*

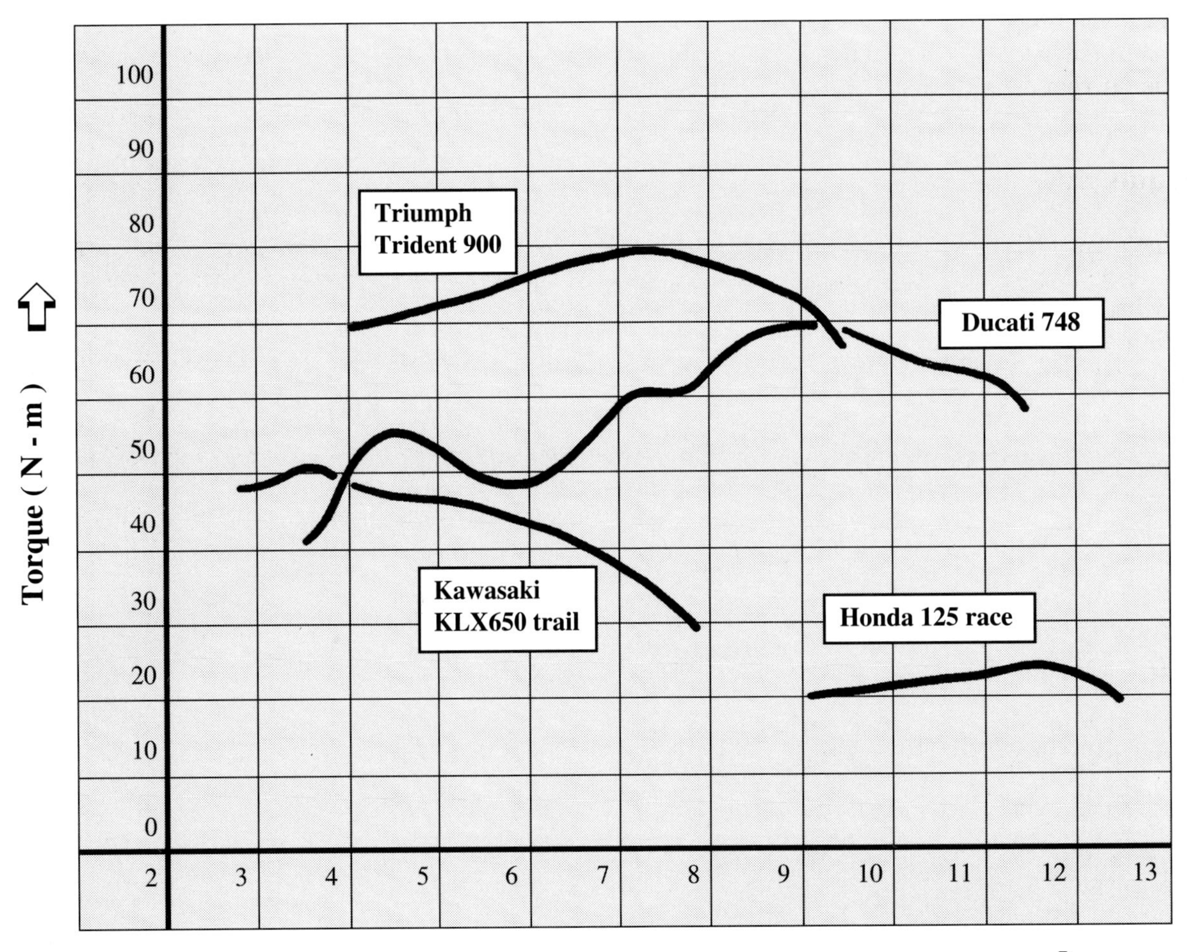

As far as roadracing is concerned there is obviously a lot more emphasis on pushing for peak torque at high engine speeds. This is possible because the load changes tend to be gradual rather than sudden though the gearing implications remain very serious.

If the torque peak is close to maximum engine speed then the drop in torque, when it comes, will be sudden and may almost give the impression that the brakes have been applied. In a sense this is useful, it discourages over-revving, but success depends heavily on rider skill. If the bike is slightly undergeared overall you are in trouble!

For most riders of average ability a gradual torque fall off over at least 1500 - 2000revs/min can prove beneficial and the need to gear the bike spot on will be relaxed somewhat.

At GP level, where factors such as wheelspin through corners need to be considered, the situation is not simple and tailoring gearing and torque curves to rider style becomes a serious business that is far removed from this basic introduction.

Torque units

We have come this far without delving into the units used to measure torque but if you have to deal with it in practice then the units may well be the first stumbling block.

Because torque is effectively the product of a force and a radius the units can be any suitable combination that complies with this, though in general they will be chosen to yield sensible values, eg 70 rather than 0.00007 or 700000!

Using metric units the preferred form is newton-metres (N-m) and the torque produced by most normal bikes is likely to lie in the range of 10 to 120N-m. To give you some idea, a 125cc racer might develop a peak torque of around 20N-m and a 750cc road bike around 70N-m.

For very small road bikes the torque might alternatively be given in kilogramforce centimetres (kgf-cm). Each kgf-cm is approximately 0.1N-m, see Table 2.1, so although it is not a technically preferred unit, it is sometimes used for relatively small torque outputs.

You will frequently find this unit written with the 'f' missing, ie kilogram centimetres (kg-cm). This is not strictly correct, but in the context of torque it is not a practical problem because the numbers will be unchanged. Instances where the difference is important do arise and Appendix 1 should help explain what is going on.

The final metric torque unit worth mentioning is the kilogramforce-metre (kgf-m) which is roughly ten times larger than the N-m. This unit is much more likely to appear in a manual of torque wrench settings and as usual you may well find that the 'f' has gone missing.

For imperial units, poundsforce-feet (lbf-ft) are the most common and values in the range 10 - 90lbf-ft are typical. Again, the 'f' might be missing thus giving lb-ft though the history is a bit more involved here than for metric units (Appendix 1). Finally, small torques are sometimes given in lbf-in, there being twelve of these to every lbf-ft.

Generally speaking you would be well advised to stick to N-m or lbf-ft and Table 2.1 gives you all the conversion factors you are likely to need to get values into one of these two forms.

I should also point out that the force and length units may be written in reverse order, ie 20lbf-ft is equal to 20ft-lbf. It is very likely that you will have no practical feel for these units whatsoever and the scientific definitions of what newtons or pounds really are will not help. The only way to get a practical handle on such things is to work with them on paper, on the dyno, and on the track. That way you can relate what you feel to what is written down.

Table 2.1 *Torque units and conversions.*

To convert	to	multiply by
lbf - ft	N - m	1.3557
lbf - in	N - m	0.1130
kgf - cm	N - m	0.0981
kgf - m	N - m	9.8100
N - m	lbf - ft	0.7376
lbf - in	lbf - ft	0.0833
kgf - cm	lbf - ft	0.0724
kgf - m	lbf - ft	7.2425

B.M.E.P.

Torque is what accelerates the bike and comparing torque curves is an important aspect of engine selection. However if you want to compare the state of development of two engines with different capacities then torque is not a very good basis. You would expect a 500 to produce a bit more than a 125. Once you get down to doing this seriously then you will be comparing curves for the same engine in different states of tune rather than concerning yourself with the output of another engine in a totally different class, however it can be very useful to get some idea of where you stand in terms of overall development.

The best indicator of the level of engine development is a value known as 'brake mean effective pressure' or bmep. This rather exotic title hides the simple concept of looking at how much torque we get per engine cylinder, per mechanical cycle, per unit cylinder volume. In other words it gives us a means of comparison that is independent of engine size or number of cylinders. We do have to make a distinction between two stroke and four stroke when working things out because the two stroke cycle only occupies one revolution while the four stroke cycle takes two revolutions but even this distinction is effectively eradicated in the final answers. Most four strokes will do better than two strokes because of the way they operate.

You can calculate the bmep associated with a given engine by using any of the formulae given that are appropriate. The bmep is so called because it has units of pressure and you will frequently read that it represents various forms of 'average' cylinder pressure. This is not the case because mechanical efficiency is buried within the figure (unlike indicated mean effective pressure, imep, which can be deduced from the cylinder's pressure-time history) and so the figures obtained are simply a basis for comparing the specific output of various engines.

In recent years the bmep figures produced have risen to values beyond anything we expected a few years ago. In the mid 80's most competitive two strokes gave values in the range 690 - 828kN/m^2 (100 - 120lbf/in^2) while the majority of their four stroke counterparts were around 966 - 1242kN/m^2 (140 - 180lbf/in^2). The best two strokes have advanced considerably with some small capacity engines now running at almost 1173kN/m^2 (170lbf/in^2). Four strokes have also improved with 1311 - 1518kN/m^2 (190 - 220 lbf/in^2) being realistic figures for very highly developed engines. These are of course peak figures corresponding to maximum torque. The variation with engine speed will be identical to the torque curve because for a

Four Stroke

$$\text{bmep (kN/m}^2\text{)} = \frac{12573.3T}{V}$$

where T = torque in N-m
V = engine capacity in cm^3

or

$$\text{bmep (lbf/in}^2\text{)} = \frac{2475T}{V}$$

where T = torque in lbf-ft
V = engine capacity in cm^3

Two Stroke

$$\text{bmep (kN/m}^2\text{)} = \frac{6286.7T}{V}$$

where T = torque in N-m
V = engine capacity in cm^3

or

$$\text{bmep (lbf/in}^2\text{)} = \frac{1237.5T}{V}$$

where T = torque in lbf-ft
V = engine capacity in cm^3

given engine capacity the bmep graph is simply a scaled version of the torque figures.

Example. The Yamaha YZF750R four stroke road bike has a peak torque output of 78N-m. What is the peak bmep?

$$\text{bmep (kN/m}^2) = \frac{12573.3T}{V}$$

$$= \frac{12573.3 \times 78}{750}$$

$$= 1308\text{kN/m}^2$$

Example. A 500cc JAP single cylinder four stroke speedway engine gives a peak torque of 56N-m when running on methanol. What is the peak bmep?

$$\text{bmep (kN/m}^2) = \frac{12573.3 \times 56}{500}$$

$$= 1408\text{kN/m}^2$$

Example. A 1960's 124cc single cylinder two stroke road racer produced a peak torque of 13.2lbf-ft. Compare the bmep with a 1994 Honda 125 producing 17lbf-ft, again from 124cc.

$$\text{1960's bmep (lbf/in}^2) = \frac{1237.5T}{V}$$

$$= \frac{1237.5 \times 13.2}{124}$$

$$= 131.73 \text{ lbf/in}^2$$

$$\text{1994 bmep (lbf/in}^2) = \frac{1237.5 \times 17}{124}$$

$$= 169.66\text{lbf/in}^2$$

Example. If you could obtain a maximum bmep of 150lbf/in^2 from a 250cc two stroke, what would the peak torque be?

Rearranging the appropriate formula,

$$\text{Torque (lbf-ft)} = \frac{\text{bmep} \times \text{Volume}}{1237.5}$$

$$= \frac{150 \times 250}{1237.5}$$

$$= 30.3\text{lbf-ft.}$$

Power

Although the ability to provide torque is essential to accelerate the motorcycle it is only half the story. Unlike the relatively static torque wrench we discussed earlier, the engine of a motorcycle has to be able to deliver the required torque while the bike is travelling at speed.

Since the engine and rear wheel are positively connected by the transmission, any road speed will have a corresponding engine speed (in each gear) at which the torque must be provided. The ability of the engine to produce a combination of torque and speed is called power.

In effect, the torque values indicate the amount of turning effort that can be applied to the crankshaft but you need to know the crankshaft speed involved in order to deduce the performance potential. This information can all be obtained from the torque - engine speed graphs discussed earlier but you will have to work it out. Access to power curves can save a bit of work.

The basic relationship between torque, power and crankshaft speed is power = torque x speed but we will need to adapt this with suitable constants to ensure that the units come out correctly. Nevertheless, it is immediately obvious that two engines producing the same power output could be as different as chalk and cheese, one delivering loads of torque at relatively low revs while the other screams along like a turbine with high revs and much less torque.

The question 'which will give the best lap times' cannot be answered on the basis of the peak power figures alone, even if the bikes are otherwise identical. Power is essential for performance, irrespective of the torque figures, but we need to look at the way the power is developed over the whole range of engine speeds and examine the gearing arrangements available before we can make realistic comparisons. The only thing we can say for the moment is that the top speed obtainable in an unrestricted space will be near enough identical if we get the gearing right in both cases.

To illustrate this dilemma, you might ponder the case of a new 125cc Honda roadrace engine up against a 500cc JAP speedway engine from the 1970's. Both produce about the same peak power but you could probably run the JAP up to top speed on tarmac using a two speed gearbox and a lot of clutch slip. The Honda on the other hand, produces nothing below about 9000revs/min and would be next to impossible to coax along the road with anything less than the six gears it has, irrespective of how many clutches you were prepared to sacrifice. Clearly the peak power figures tell you which ballpark you are in but they do not provide all the answers.

In the metric system, power is measured in watts (W) but, since a watt is a very small amount of power, engine data is usually given in kilowatts (kW). Each kW is 1000W. To calculate the power produced in kilowatts use the following formula.

$$\text{Power (kW)} = \frac{NT}{9549}$$

where N = crankshaft speed in revs/min
T = torque in N-m

In the imperial system, power is measured in horsepower (hp). Most figures are written as brake horse power (bhp) to emphasise the fact that this is true output as measured on a brake, rather than that theoretically developed in the cylinder.

One horsepower corresponds to a workrate of 33000lbf-ft per minute though mounting a suitable thoroughbred on the dyno is unlikely to confirm this! As usual it is all a matter of history.

To calculate the power in horsepower use the following formula.

$$\text{Power (hp)} = \frac{NT}{5252}$$

where N = crankshaft speed in revs/min
T = torque in lbf-ft

The metric and imperial units are related by,

1hp = 745.7W = 0.7457kW

Therefore to convert hp to kW multiply the hp value by 0.7457. To convert kW to hp, multiply the kW value by 1.341 (ie 1/0.7457).

Example. An engine produces a torque of 20N-m at 10000revs/min. How much power does it produce at this speed?

$$\text{Power (kW)} = \frac{10000 \times 20}{9549}$$

$$= 20.94\text{kW}$$

$$\text{or } 20.94 \times 1.341 = 28.08\text{hp}$$

Example. An engine produces a power output of 40hp at 12000revs/min. What torque is available?

$$\text{Power (hp)} = \frac{NT}{5252}$$

so rearranging,

$$\text{Torque (lbf-ft)} = \frac{\text{hp} \times 5252}{N}$$

$$= \frac{40 \times 5252}{12000}$$

$$= 17.5\text{lbf-ft}$$

Just to complicate the issue even further, it is extremely likely that you will find the power figures of Japanese motorcycles quoted in a unit that is not the basic 'scientific' unit in either the imperial or metric systems.

This is the PS, which stands for Pferdestärke, and it does have the ability to make the figures look a bit better in the brochures. The PS is sometimes referred to as a 'metric horsepower' and it relates to the normal scientific units as follows.

1PS = 0.735kW = 0.9863hp

Thus to convert PS to horsepower you multiply by 0.9863 and to convert PS to kW you multiply by 0.735. Going the other way, convert bhp to PS by multiplying by 1.014 and kW to PS by multiplying by 1.360. These conversions are summarised in Table 2.2.

Example. An engine produces 60PS. What is this in kW and bhp?

60PS = 60 x 0.735kW = 44.1kW

60PS = 60 x 0.9863bhp = 59.2bhp

Example. An engine produces 130bhp. What is this in PS and kW?

130bhp = 130 x 1.014PS = 131.82PS

130bhp = 130 x 0.7457kW = 96.94kW

In general, only convert figures once. All the conversion factors given are rounded up and repeated conversions will gradually introduce significant errors.

Like torque, power data is usually shown graphically against engine speed. Taking the theoretical case of a constant torque output, the basic relationship of power = torque x speed will produce a

Table 2.2 *Conversion factors for power data.*

To convert	to	multiply by
bhp	kW	0.7457
bhp	PS	1.014
kW	bhp	1.341
kW	PS	1.360
PS	kW	0.735
PS	bhp	0.986

power graph that is a straight sloping line as shown in Fig 2.9. The higher the torque figure is, the steeper the power line would be on a given graph scale. However, as we have already found out, the torque value is not constant and so the power curve will deviate from the straight sloping line in sympathy with the torque variations, only touching it at peak torque.

Fig 2.9 *A constant torque output would produce a power 'curve' that is a straight line. The line becomes steeper if the torque is increased.*

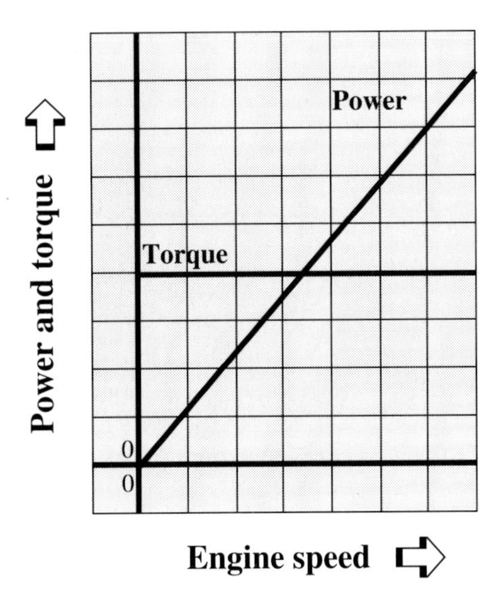

Fig 2.10 demonstrates this with data from a Yamaha YZF750R. If you only have a power curve available you can quickly determine the point of peak torque by simply drawing in a line as shown. This line is one which, when rotated clockwise about the origin, stops where it first touches the power curve. This technique often saves plotting out a torque graph but note that the graph scales must start from zero for this to work.

In all cases we can begin by studying power graphs at the low speed end, noting that 'low speed' might well be 8000revs/min plus for a racing engine. In this region, both the torque and the speed are increasing so power, which is equal to torque x speed, builds up rapidly. At some engine speed peak torque is reached, however it is usually the case that this engine speed is below that at which peak power occurs.

The reason for this is that the rise in engine speed beyond that at which peak torque occurs may be able to compensate for the drop in torque that takes place. For example, suppose that peak torque is 60N-m at 10000revs/min and that the torque has fallen to 52N-m at 12000revs/min. The power at 10000revs/min is nominally 63kW (84hp) but at 12000revs/min it has risen to 65kW (87.5hp) so clearly the power is still increasing in this region.

Eventually , the fall off in torque is too rapid to be offset in this way and so the power curve also peaks. It then drops off either slowly or quickly according to how the torque output collapses. Without delving further into the role of the gear-box we can only make general observations regarding different power curves at this stage.

Firstly, any development that adds area under the curve will be productive providing that peak power does not suffer significantly. In practice this usually reduces to the original objective of raising torque figures because most racing engines already run their crankshafts close to the mechanical limit.

Riders speak of engines having a lot of torque or power. In general, the reference to torque relates to the low-mid range of engine speeds while the impression of power is generally associated with high engine speeds. In reality, power is torque dependent so the torque information is there in the power/engine speed curve once you know how to find it. The power curve of an engine giving high mid-range torque will touch the straight line (shown in Fig 2.10) at relatively low engine speeds. It may touch, or almost touch, the line several times and the distance from the line is a measure of the torque shortfall from its peak value. The

Right. Fig 2.10 *These are power and torque curves for a Yamaha YZF750R. Note how a straight line drawn from the origin so that it just touches the power curve will pin point the engine speed for maximum torque. Also note how the power continues to rise beyond the speed for peak torque.*

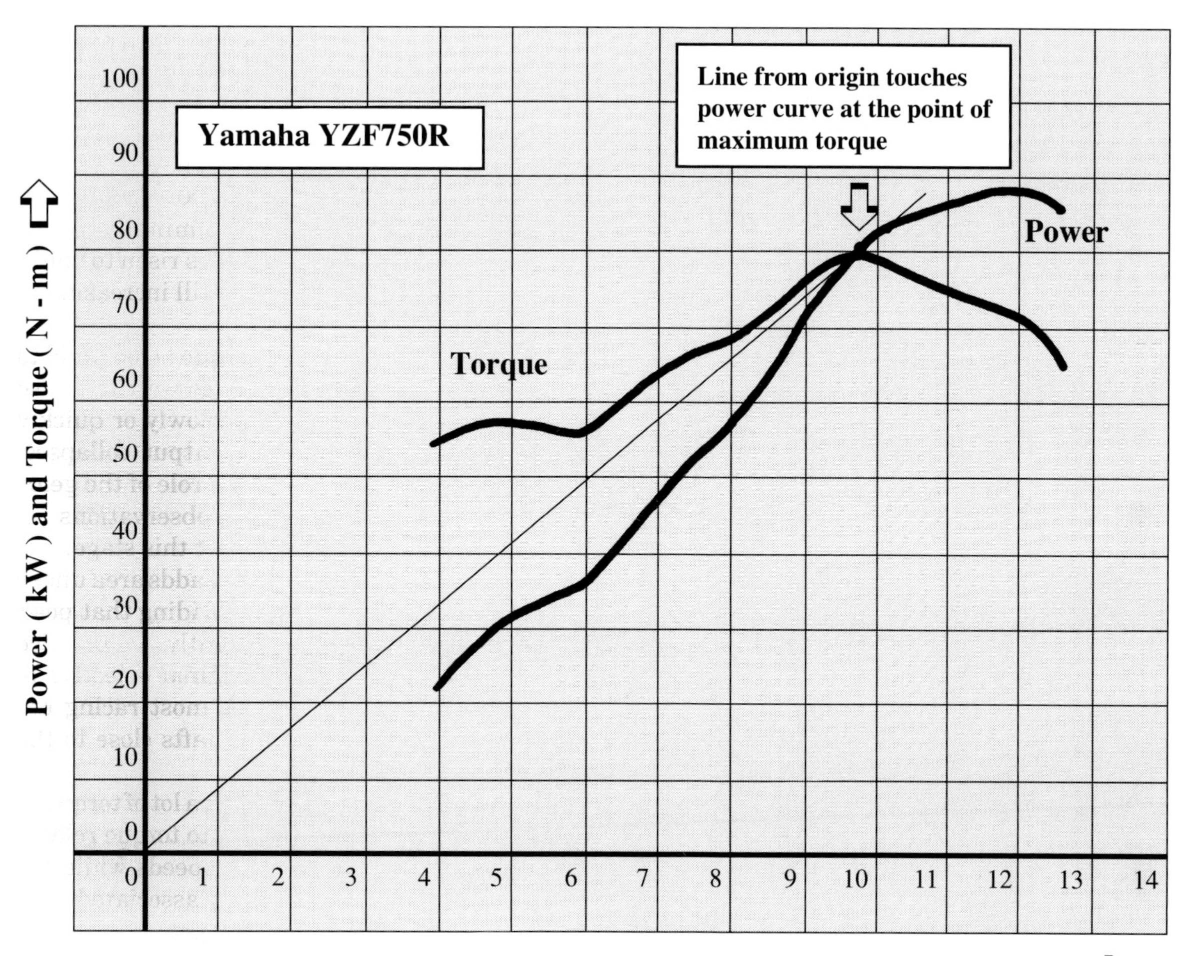

closer the power curve tracks this line, the flatter the torque curve is. In effect, an engine described as having lots of torque is one that is producing a relatively high power output at the lower range of engine speeds. If it continues to do this then the area under the power curve will be high for a given peak power value. This is the main thing to look for but it becomes harder to achieve as the peak power increases.

Road bike and motocross engines generally give peak torque at well below maximum engine speed to aid flexibility but coaxing the peaks upwards, without losing too much of them, is the tuner's greatest challenge. With suitable experience you will soon realise that this can be very difficult. To obtain a high torque figure which occurs at a high crankshaft speed (and thereby get maximum power) the engine has to be ported and piped to resonate strongly in this region. As a result of this it will be much less enthusiastic about lower speeds as I have already pointed out. Low speed torque delivery is sacrificed and the range of speeds over which the engine really pulls, commonly known as the 'power band', will start to narrow considerably if you are not careful. The result may well be an engine that is totally useless given the gearbox options that are available. Fig 2.11 gives several examples of power curves and in each case I have used the technique of drawing a tangent to the curve in order to identify the point of maximum torque.

All of these graphs have very different characteristics. Starting with the Honda 125 racer, the narrow power band is immediately obvious, together with the fact that there is no useful power below about 9500revs/min. Also note that the peak torque occurs almost at the point of maximum power; only about 250revs/min separates the two. This is a pure racing engine in a high state of development and its gearing requirements will be very critical, especially in terms of internal ratios. Now consider the Moto Guzzi 750. It produces about the same power as the Honda but

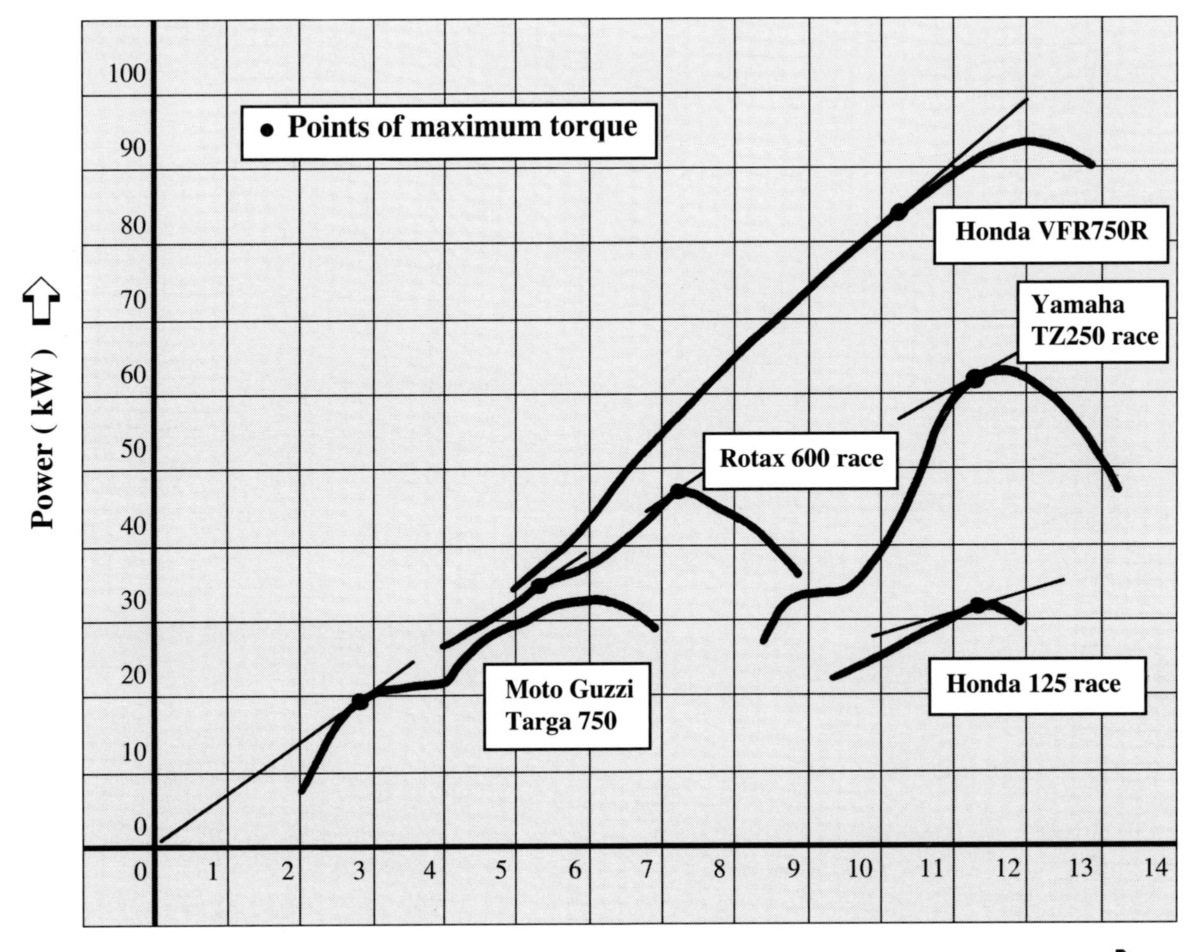

Fig 2.11 *Power curves for a variety of applications. The differences are not as obvious as they are on the torque curves and it is always a good idea to study both.*

there the similarity ends. Although the peak power figures are similar, the Guzzi produces it at about half the engine speed of the Honda and therefore gives about twice as much torque at this point. However the big feature of the Guzzi is the production of peak torque right down the speed range, somewhere around 2800revs/min. This engine, though lacking outright performance for its capacity, produces substantial low speed torque that many riders would enjoy. The Guzzi and the Honda may have roughly equal power but compare the areas under the power curves.

The Rotax 600cc single cylinder racer exhibits another interesting torque characteristic. Because the tangent touches at two points this engine is giving as much torque at 5500revs/min as it does at 7200revs/min where peak power is also developed. This engine provides good 'race' performance while maintaining rideability and flexibility.

The main feature of the Honda VFR750R, apart from its sheer power, is how close to a straight line the power curve is between engine speeds of 5000 and 11000revs/min. This means that the torque curve is virtually flat over a wide range of engine speeds. The bike is very rideable for this level of power, good on road or track.

The final example is a 1995 Yamaha TZ250 racer. I have left this until last because it illustrates some very important aspects. Peak power is obviously high and the spread of power is wide for a two stroke racing engine. Despite this, the engine has problems for all but the most experienced riders. Using the straight line to pinpoint peak torque, it is clear that there is a massive drop in torque at the bottom end and mid range. The actual values are not the problem, it is the rate at which it returns!

Look at the slope of the graph. It is much steeper than anything else on the page and the output actually rises at a peak rate of about 16kW per 1000revs per minute (21.5bhp/1000revs per min). Almost everywhere between 9500revs/min and 11500revs/min it is rising at a rate which exceeds 11kW/1000revs per minute (15bhp/1000revs per min). This is a most violent power delivery and the bike is very hard to ride well. Even Aprilias do not increase their power at such a rate despite what you may have been told about disc valves. Compare the slope of the graph to that of the Honda VFR750R and you get some idea of how significant this is. Obviously, in the hands of a highly skilled rider on GP type tracks the power delivery would be tolerable but for an average British rider buzzing round airfields it would be a nightmare that could lose a lot of time. This example clearly shows another aspect to look for when comparing power curves. Anything that rises at more than perhaps 9kW/1000 revs per minute (12bhp/1000revs per minute) needs thinking about, especially if the slope is long lasting and occurs just below peak torque. It is all very well to say that the rider should keep the engine buzzing but it would take a very good rider indeed to ensure that the Yamaha did not find itself below 10000revs per minute at some point on the circuit.

Based on these observations, you should be able to make a reasonable assessment of any power curves available to you. The basic things to check are as follows.

- What is the minimum engine speed for useful power? As this increases rideability reduces and gearing becomes more critical.

- What are the peak power and torque? These need to be reasonable when compared with the competition but shape is equally important.

- At what speed does the engine cease to perform? Is this a mechanical limit? Will raising it compromise the reliability beyond what you are prepared to accept?

- Is there a reasonable range of engine speeds between peak torque and peak power? If there is then the engine will be more flexible but this is hard to obtain along with high peak values. If there is little difference, eg the Honda 125, then the internal gear ratios need to be checked out carefully.

- What is the shape of the torque curve? If you cannot be bothered to plot it, look at how the power curve tracks the tangent line. The closer the power curve runs to this line the better. If the fall off is large at low speed, check the rate at which power is delivered from there on.

- What happens beyond peak power? Is the fall off fast or slow and is there a reasonable range of engine speeds? If the fall off is fast and the range is short the overall gearing will be more critical. Over-revving will increase lap times.

One question that still remains unanswered is 'which power or torque curve gives the best performance'. The reason it remains unanswered is that we really need to look at the effects of gearing to understand the situation fully. Power is a transferable quantity. What I mean by this is that engine power can be transferred directly to the back wheel, albeit subject to some reduction that goes to overcome transmission 'losses' (ie power has to be used to overcome bearing friction, oil drag etc). Even so more than 90% should get through to the wheel.

Torque is different. If the speed changes then the torque changes so the torque we get through to the back wheel from one engine could be very different to that from another, even if the engines produce the same peak torque values. It all depends on the gearing required and that in turn depends on the speed at which the engine produces peak power. The only conclusion we can draw at present is that power is what you need for top speed and, if the engine produces it at high crankshaft speeds, we can gear it down substantially and thereby raise the torque at the wheel, thus improving acceleration. I will clarify this in Chapter 2.4.

Testing

Dynamometer testing is now a much more common activity than it used to be, partially because of greater awareness, but also because the need is greater and dynos are more readily available to the general public than they used to be.

It would be possible to produce a complete book on engine testing alone, indeed there are such books, and therefore I will confine the discussion here to the more important practical points.

Engine testing is a very specialised activity and getting reliable results can be heavily dependent on the skill of the operator even though many modern dynamometers have automated certain aspects. It is particularly important that the instrumentation is reliable and properly calibrated. Always go to test centres run by people with a proven track record of quality engine development, rather than those who see the dynamometer as just another source of income. In general, repeatability is much more important than absolute accuracy. The data you will get from different dynamometers will vary by several percent, some being conveniently optimistic. This should not concern you too much - comparing published figures always was a bit of a lottery - but what you should try to ensure is that the figures obtained from a given dyno are repeatable.

Once you have found this to be the case then stick to that dynamometer and, ideally, the same operator. By doing this you have the best chance of making reliable comparisons as the engine is developed. One very important aspect to consider when making comparisons with other data is to ensure that you know how the figures were obtained. Although results may be listed as engine output they could have been obtained at the crankshaft, the gearbox sprocket, or the back wheel and it is most unlikely that they will be accurately corrected for transmission efficiency should this be relevant. Thus a rear wheel test is quoting actual net useful power and this may differ significantly from crankshaft power. 10% of any output produced by a racing engine is a big difference.

If you are hooked on comparing different manufacturers' figures then you need to know a lot more about the data than most articles will tell you. Different manufacturers not only use different dynos, they conduct their tests to different standards. There are a mass of British, American, ISO and DIN procedures to choose from. DIN figures are commonly higher than most and you will need to read the standards to find out why. For example, one particular engine that was originally tested to BS5514 gave 4.3% more power when it was subsequently tested to DIN 70020.

As far as your engines are concerned the secret is to agree a standard procedure with the test house and stick to it rigidly. It is no good running the engine for five minutes one week and then expecting it to be the same if you run for half an hour the week after.

In short, I don't think it matters too much where or how you obtain the figures. What matters is that once you have found a reliable source and a reliable procedure, you stick with it throughout development of the engine.

2.2 Gearing terminology

The need for gearing

In the previous chapter outlining engine characteristics, the subject of gearing was raised on several occasions for the the simple reason that it is not possible, or at best very foolish, to consider the engine in isolation from its gearbox.

In general, the restrictions placed on gearing by availability of parts and competition regulations form a significant constraint on the engine characteristics which will prove to be acceptable and so checking out the suitability of the gearbox should always come before any serious engine development. Failing to follow this rule can lead to great expense or disappointment. One-off gears of suitable quality are far from cheap.

The practical side of gearbox assessment is covered in Chapters 2.3 and 2.4. The purpose of this chapter is to outline the terminology and ideas associated with gearing for those who are somewhat unsure about this vital area. There are two basic reasons why we need some form of gearing between the engine and rear wheel.

Firstly, the majority of motorcycle engines are designed to perform best at crankshaft speeds between about 6000 and 14000revs/min. The engine then has to drive the back wheel at a speed which corresponds to the actual road speed unless we happen to have clutch slip or wheelspin. This road speed will be infinitely variable up to its maximum value and if we assume typical tyre sizes we could easily show that the rear wheel will be rotating at a speed of perhaps 0 - 2500revs/min according to the road speed and tyre size.

Clearly there is a considerable difference between the speed at which the engine rotates and that at which the wheel rotates so some form of speed reduction between the two is essential. This is the most basic requirement of the gearing.

Secondly, there is the problem of 'power band' to consider. All readers will be aware that the range of useful engine speeds may be quite limited and in the previous chapter I have tried to outline the reasons for this. In recent years the spread of power from racing engines has increased considerably but it is still narrow in general terms. Although a roadbike engine may be flexible over perhaps 6000revs/min, many of the small capacity racing engines can only offer a powerband of perhaps 3000revs/min and a lot less if you really want the best out of the motor. To illustrate the problem this causes, assume that a bike is geared to do 200km/hr and has the power to achieve this. If the engine is running at 10000revs/min at this point then when the bike slows to 100km/hr, in the same gear, the engine will have to run at 5000revs/min. Unless the powerband is very wide it will not be able to cope and the lower the road speed the worse things will become. In short, we need a choice of gears to allow the engine to remain within its working range over the whole spectrum of road speeds and conditions.

Current regulations allow a maximum of six gears. This is more than adequate for a typical road bike and many large capacity bikes of this type would be perfectly acceptable with five or even four gears to choose from.

Racing is very different. The search for more power leads to narrow powerbands and for small capacity engines even six gears may involve a lot of compromise around the circuit. However, before getting too involved with how the gears will affect track performance, some discussion of basic terminology may help.

Motorcycle transmission

Conventional motorcycles use three separate stages of speed change between the engine and rear wheel as shown in Fig 2.12 overleaf.

Firstly, there is the so-called primary drive between the crankshaft and clutch. This is always a speed reduction and causes the clutch shaft to run at a speed that is about 22 - 50% of crankshaft speed. This stage is implemented by gears, chains and sprockets, or toothed belts. Most modern engines use gears while classic bikes use chains, or, if the chains are a problem, toothed belts.

Secondly, there is the actual gearbox itself. This will determine how fast the gearbox final drive sprocket runs in relation to the clutch and most gearboxes offer a choice of five or six different 'gears'. When in 'top gear', the sprocket usually runs at roughly the same speed as the clutch. Moving down towards 'bottom gear' gives a progressively greater speed reduction. Finally we have the chain and sprocket drive between the gearbox and rear wheel. This is also invariably a speed reduction and will normally be referred to as the final drive or secondary drive.

In this type of transmission the gearing can be altered by making changes to any of the individual stages, ie primary, internal or final drive. Changes to the primary drive or final drive will obviously affect every 'gear' that is available and only by changing the pinions inside the gearbox can we modify just one of the gears available in isolation from everything else.

For Club and National racing most gearing changes are carried out by altering the final drive sprockets. Unless a cassette type gearbox is fitted it is usually impractical to alter the gearbox internals at the circuit, though this aspect is virtually essential to get the best performance, hence the use of such gearboxes at GP level. On modern bikes, changes in the primary drive are also difficult, if only due to the cost of the gears. Classic bikes with chain drives are easier to deal with in this respect and as such another means of modification is made available. In general, the primary drive remains unaltered and you should take note that off-road engines normally provide a much greater speed reduction via the primary drive than road engines do. This aspect can catch you out, or cost you a lot of money, when building a special that utilises a moto-cross engine for roadracing.

Fig 2.12 *A typical motorcycle transmission consists of three stages: primary, internal (gearbox) and final drive. All three can be modified to suit the application.*

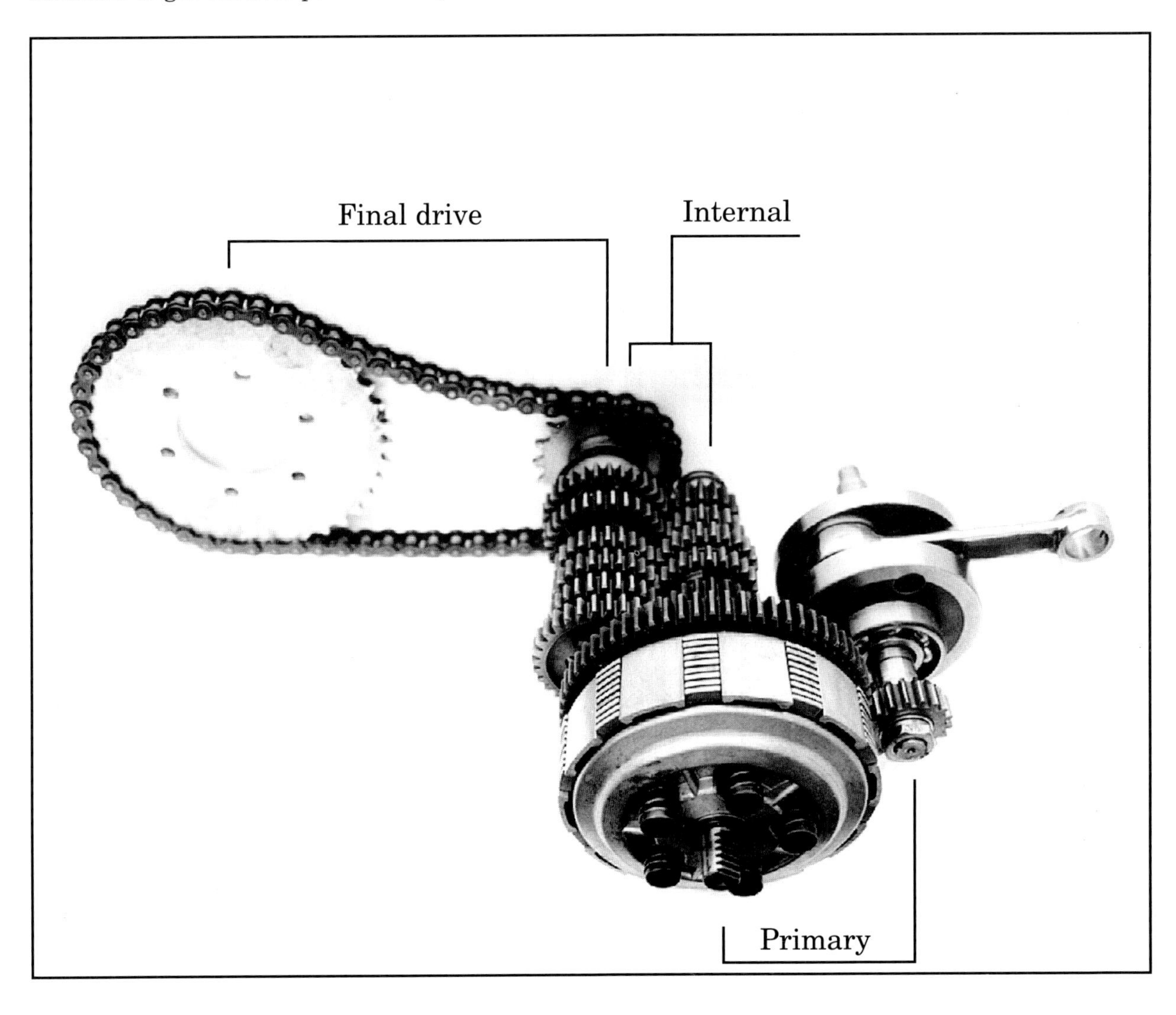

Gear ratios

A ratio is a means of expressing how one thing relates to another and when drive is transmitted via gears, sprockets or pulleys, the effect of the 'gearing' is normally expressed in terms of a gear ratio. Ratios can mean all sorts of things and be expressed in various ways so some standardisation is necessary to ensure that everyone understands what is going on.

We can begin by looking at the gear ratio associated with a simple gear pair and can then extend the idea to cover the entire motorcycle transmission. When two shafts are coupled by a pair of meshing gears or a chain/toothed belt drive, then the first thing to do is to identify which shaft is the driver and which one is being driven. By definition, the driver is the shaft that instigates the motion, the input shaft if you like.

Any driver/driven pairing in which the number of teeth are unequal will cause the driven shaft to run at a speed which is different from that of the driver. If there are more teeth on the driven gear than the driver then the shaft speed will be reduced, ie the driven shaft runs slower than the one driving it. Conversely, if the driven gear has less teeth than the driver, the driven shaft will run more quickly. Fig 2.13 illustrates both these possibilities.

These speed changes are frequently expressed in the form of a 'gear ratio'. The ratio can be determined by measuring the speed of rotation or, much more conveniently, by counting the number of teeth on each gear or sprocket.

Given such data, the value of the gear ratio is then expressed as follows.

$$\textbf{Gear Ratio} = \frac{\textbf{Speed of driving gear}}{\textbf{Speed of driven gear}}$$

or

$$\textbf{Gear Ratio} = \frac{\textbf{Teeth on driven gear}}{\textbf{Teeth on driving gear}}$$

Speed reduction

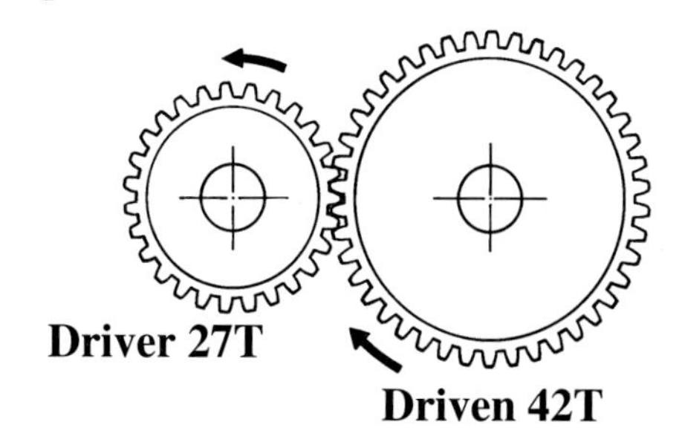

$$\text{Gear ratio} = \frac{\text{Teeth on driven gear}}{\text{Teeth on driving gear}}$$

$$= 42/27$$

$$= 1.555:1$$

Speed increase

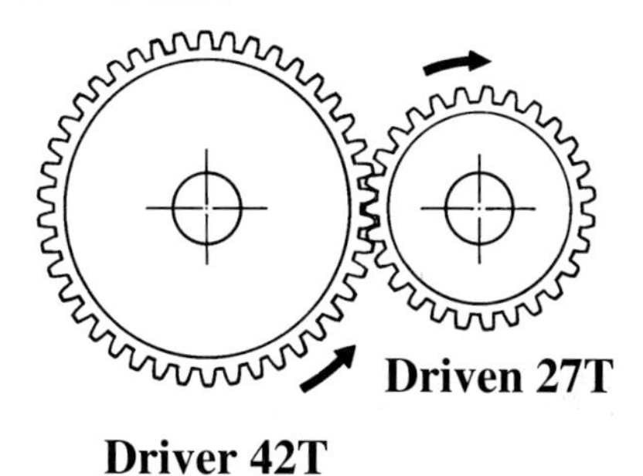

$$\text{Gear ratio} = \frac{\text{Teeth on driven gear}}{\text{Teeth on driving gear}}$$

$$= 27/42$$

$$= 0.643:1$$

Fig 2.13 *The effect of gearing on shaft speed is expressed as a ratio. Using standard terminology any ratio greater than 1:1, eg 3:1, indicates a speed reduction while ratios less than 1:1, eg 0.7:1 indicate a speed increase.*

These definitions are almost universal now and are used by all the Japanese manufacturers. As usual, it is possible to find rare exceptions that employ a different system but I will deal with the normal one first.

Example. A crankshaft with a 20 tooth pinion drives a clutch with 40 teeth. What is the gear ratio involved?

$$\text{Gear ratio} = \frac{\text{Teeth on driven gear}}{\text{Teeth on driving gear}}$$

$$= \frac{40}{20}$$

$$= \frac{2}{1}$$

This would be referred to as a '2 to 1' gear ratio and written as 2:1.

Example. A gear ratio is given as 0.8:1. If the driving gear has 30 teeth how many teeth are on the driven gear?

$$\text{Gear ratio} = \frac{\text{Teeth on driven gear}}{\text{Teeth on driving gear}}$$

$$\text{hence} \quad 0.8 = \frac{\text{Teeth on driven gear}}{30}$$

$$\text{so Teeth on driven gear} = 0.8 \times 30$$

$$= 24 \text{ teeth}$$

Example. A final drive uses a 15 tooth gearbox sprocket and a 36 tooth rear wheel sprocket. What is the final drive ratio?

$$\text{Gear ratio} = \frac{\text{Teeth on driven sprocket}}{\text{Teeth on driver}}$$

$$= \frac{36}{15}$$

$$= 2.4:1$$

From these ratios you can calculate the speed of one shaft if you know the speed of the other and the ratio involved. For those who are not too keen on transposing such formulae the following rules, plus common sense, should solve most problems.

- If the ratio is equal to one then both shafts run at the same speed.
- If the ratio given is greater than one then the driven shaft runs more slowly than the driver by a factor equal to the ratio. eg if the ratio is 4:1 then the driven shaft runs at driver speed/4.
- If the ratio given is less than one then the driven shaft runs faster than the driver. To find the speed of the driven gear divide the driver speed by the gear ratio figure. eg driver 1000revs/min, ratio 0.5:1, driven shaft speed = 1000/0.5 = 2000revs/min.

Example. A crankshaft with a 20 tooth gear drives a clutch with 45 teeth. If the crank rotates at 10000revs/min how fast does the clutch rotate?

The ratio is 45/20 = 2.25:1

This is greater than 1:1 so speed is reduced

Clutch speed = 10000/2.25

= 4444revs/min

Idler gears

In some primary drives you will find an arrangement like that shown in Fig 2.14 where an intermediate gear is placed between the crankshaft and clutch gears. A gear like this is called an idler gear and it serves two main functions.

- It produces a change in the direction of rotation. In the example shown the final driven gear would rotate counter clockwise if no idler gear was included.
- It allows the drive to span a greater centre distance without using excessively large gearwheels.

Drive reversal can be useful to give a crankshaft rotation that directs the piston sidethrust onto the exhaust port side during the power stroke. This improves sealing in two stroke cylinders.

What the idler gear does not do is to affect the gear ratio relating the two gears on either side of it. In the example, the ratio is still 1:1 irrespective of how many teeth the idler has. Indeed, you can put in as many idler gears as you like and still not change this ratio. Note however that if the number of idlers is odd (1,3,5 etc) then the rotation of the final driven gear will be the same as that of the driver. If the number of idler gears is even (2,4,6 etc) then the rotation of the final driven gear is in the opposite direction to the driver.

It is quite possible that the idler gear drives something such as a water pump. This does not change any of the comments above. It is still an idler gear as far as the pairing on either side of it is concerned. Its speed can of course be calculated by treating it as a driven gear.

Returning to the basic ideas, virtually all the gear ratios you will encounter on a motorcycle will be greater than one, ie a speed reduction is involved. The only likely exceptions to this are the internal gearbox ratios in either fifth or sixth gear where ratios between 0.8:1 and 1:1 are common. In these gears, the gearbox sprocket shaft will be running faster than the clutch shaft.

At the begining of this discussion I mentioned the fact that you might encounter a different system of calculating ratios. To my knowlege this is only applicable to some Italian engines but I may be wrong. In such cases it is possible that a ratio is always calculated by dividing the number of teeth on the largest gear by the number on the smallest gear. This will have no effect for speed reductions but can leave you very confused for small speed increases. I can offer no help other than suggesting you look carefully at such cases and will assume the normal system throughout this book.

Fig 2.14 *A gear placed between two others as shown acts as an idler gear which does not affect the ratio between the outer pair.*

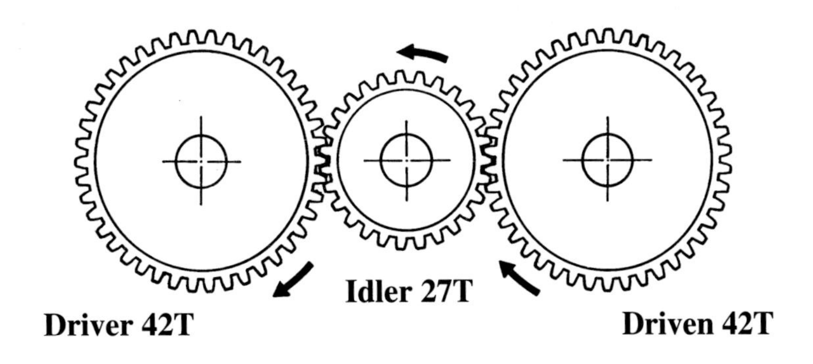

$$\text{Gear ratio} = \frac{\text{Teeth on driven gear}}{\text{Teeth on driving gear}} = \frac{42}{42} = 1.000:1$$

Power and torque

Any driving shaft will exert a torque and the combination of its torque and speed is the power available. This power is transmitted to the driven gear relatively efficiently with only a small amount of the power being converted to heat or noise so to begin the discussion we could say that the same power is available at the driven shaft.

However, the driven shaft is, in general, running at a different speed so the torque must be different for the same power. If the speed has been reduced then the torque will increase. Conversely, if the speed has been increased then the torque will be reduced. In general,

$$\textbf{Gear Ratio} = \frac{\textbf{Torque at driven shaft}}{\textbf{Torque at driving shaft}}$$

As before, common sense avoids too much handling of such formulae.

Example. An engine produces a crankshaft torque of 20N-m at 10000revs/min. What is the speed and torque at the clutch if the primary reduction ratio is 4:1?

4:1 is greater than one so speed is reduced by a factor of 4 to 10000/4 = 2500revs/min.

Since speed reduces by four the torque increases by four (ignoring inefficiencies) to 20N-m x 4 = 80N-m.

When the real drive is considered there is always an efficiency of less than 100%. This will reduce the torque and hence the power but it does not affect the speed ratio because gear and chain drives are of a positive nature. Efficiency will vary with speed and load but a ballpark figure for average quality gears, well lubricated, is a loss of 2% for every pair of gears in mesh and transmitting power. Additional losses will be incurred due to bearing friction and oil drag.

Overall gear ratios

Thus far we have only considered one stage of transmission. In the case of a motorcycle there are normally three such stages as outlined earlier and these all combine together to produce an overall effect. An overall gear ratio is one which gives us the combined effect of all three stages and as such it determines the relationship between engine speed and rear wheel speed. To find this overall ratio you simply multiply together the ratios at each individual stage, ie

$$\textbf{Overall Ratio} = \frac{\textbf{Engine speed}}{\textbf{Rear wheel speed}}$$

and

$$\textbf{Overall Ratio} = \textbf{primary x internal x final}$$

In arriving at this from the basic ideas given earlier, you may wish to note that,

- The crankshaft acts as a driver.
- The clutch shaft is driven but then acts as a driver as well.
- The gearbox output shaft is driven via the clutch shaft but then acts as a driver to the back wheel.
- The rear wheel is driven.

Clearly there will be as many overall ratios as there are 'gears' available and all of them will be affected together if you alter either the primary or final drive ratios.

Example. A bike has a primary ratio of 4:1 and a final drive ratio of 3:1. What is the overall gear ratio in sixth gear if the internal ratio in that gear is 0.9:1?

Overall ratio = primary x internal x final

= 4 x 0.9 x 3

= 10.8:1

Example. The following data is given for a TZ250. Determine the overall gear ratio in each gear.

Crankshaft pinion 20T

Clutch gear 52T

Rear wheel sprocket 36T

Gearbox sprocket 15T

Teeth on gearbox output shaft in first = 28, on clutch shaft = 14

Teeth on gearbox output shaft in second= 31, on clutch shaft = 21

Teeth on gearbox output shaft in third = 26, on clutch shaft = 21

Teeth on gearbox output shaft in fourth = 27, on clutch shaft = 25

Teeth on gearbox output shaft in fifth = 26, on clutch shaft = 27

Teeth on gearbox output shaft in sixth = 20, on clutch shaft = 22

Solution,

The primary ratio is 52/20	= 2.6:1
The final drive ratio is 36/15	= 2.4:1
Internal first gear is 28/14	= 2:1
Second is 31/21	= 1.476:1
Third is 26/21	= 1.238:1
Fourth is 27/25	= 1.080:1
Fifth is 26/27	= 0.963:1
Sixth is 20/22	= 0.909:1

This gives overall ratios of,

First gear	= 2.6 x 2.4 x 2.000 = 12.48:1
Second	= 2.6 x 2.4 x 1.476 = 9.21:1
Third	= 2.6 x 2.4 x 1.238 = 7.73:1
Fourth	= 2.6 x 2.4 x 1.080 = 6.74:1
Fifth	= 2.6 x 2.4 x 0.963 = 6.01:1
Sixth	= 2.6 x 2.4 x 0.909 = 5.67:1

This is probably a reasonable point to comment on the practical implications of this. If we assume that the TZ250 motor peaks at 12000revs/min then in sixth gear the back wheel will rotate at 12000/5.67 = 2116revs/min, provided that the engine produces sufficient power to run the bike at the corresponding road speed. If it does not then the engine speed will not reach this peak in sixth gear. A further calculation would show that this wheel speed equates to a road speed of around 239km/hr (148miles/hr).

The torque available at the rear wheel under these conditions will be 5.67 times that produced by the engine, less anything used to run the transmission itself. If this torque provides more driving force than is necessary to achieve the stated speed then the bike may be capable of reaching a greater speed if the gearing is modified.

In first gear the overall reduction is much greater and in this gear the road speed corresponding to 12000revs/min is somewhere around 109km/hr (68miles/hr). Although the road speed in this gear is restricted, the rear wheel torque is now 12.48 times what the engine produces (neglecting transmission losses) and the acceleration potential is therefore much greater.

General terminology

Motorcyclists use a variety of expressions to describe gearing so some clarification of these terms may help avoid confusion.

A 'low' gear is one in which the wheel runs much slower than the engine. It is sometimes called a 'short' gear and it will have a large numerical overall ratio value, eg 20:1. The larger the ratio is, the lower the gear so 24:1 is lower than 20:1. If the gear is too low then the bike is said to be undergeared. 'First gear' is, conventionally, the lowest gear.

A 'high' or 'tall' gear is one in which the rear wheel speed is closer to that of the engine and this therefore corresponds to a smaller ratio value, eg 7:1. 'Top gear' is the highest gear and if it is too high the bike is said to be overgeared. No wonder people get confused!

In general, if I refer to a 'low gear' it is in the general terminology of a motorcyclist and implies that the reduction ratio will be a high numerical value leading to limited road speed but good acceleration.

Internal ratios

The internal ratios are normally given in an engine manual as implied by the TZ250 example, however if you do not have this information then you will have to count the teeth on appropriate gears in order to work them out.

I do not propose to discuss the mechanics of gearboxes in detail since all have minor differences and the manufacturer's manual is the place to look, however some general ideas may help. Modern gearboxes are usually of a type known as a cross-over all indirect layout.

The term cross-over simply implies that the drive comes in at one side of the gearbox (at the clutch) and leaves it at the other side (where the sprocket is).

The indirect transmission can be a little bit harder to follow but the following principles apply. There are two shafts. The clutch shaft is the input shaft and the one with the sprocket on it is the output shaft. In a six speed gearbox there are six internal gears on each of these shafts and all of them are in mesh with their opposite number. However, if you look at the gears in more detail you will find that some are splined to rotate the shaft with them while others are free to rotate on the shafts. Some of the gears which are splined to the shafts are free to move along the shaft by small amounts and such movement is produced by selector forks. When these gears are moved they have 'dogs' on them which engage in slots on adjacent gears that are not splined to the shafts. As such, these gears, which normally rotate free from the shaft, now rotate with the shaft.

By arranging for the selectors to move appropriate gears in this way it is possible to transmit power through any of the gear pairings, thereby giving the range of ratios we need. It is easy to investigate this in any engine with a horizontally split gearbox housing.

Finding the internal ratios for this type of gearbox is straightforward once you have decided which gears are involved in transferring drive between the shafts for each 'gear' selected. You either have to look in the manual or fathom it out from the bits!

Once you have decided which pairs correspond to each 'gear' selected then the ratios are calculated as shown in Fig 2.15. The example given is for a five speed cluster.

With classic and vintage gearboxes the situation is rather more involved. In most of these gearboxes the basic mechanism is rather different and uses what is known as a mainshaft/layshaft system. Power comes into the mainshaft via the clutch and is then transferred to the layshaft via a gear pairing. It is then further transferred via another gear pair onto what is termed a sleeve gear. This gear, which carries the final drive sprocket, is concentric with the mainshaft which runs inside it. In top gear, the mainshaft and sleeve gear are normally directly coupled together via dogs to give a 1:1 ratio.

In this type of layout it is necessary to find the ratio at each stage, ie as power goes from the mainshaft to the layshaft and again as it goes back from the layshaft to the sleeve gear. It can all be a bit frustrating to sort out while the bits lurk at the bottom of a gearbox casting but that is the only way, short of making a special housing for inspection purposes. Fig 2.16 overleaf gives an example of what to do once you have sorted it all out.

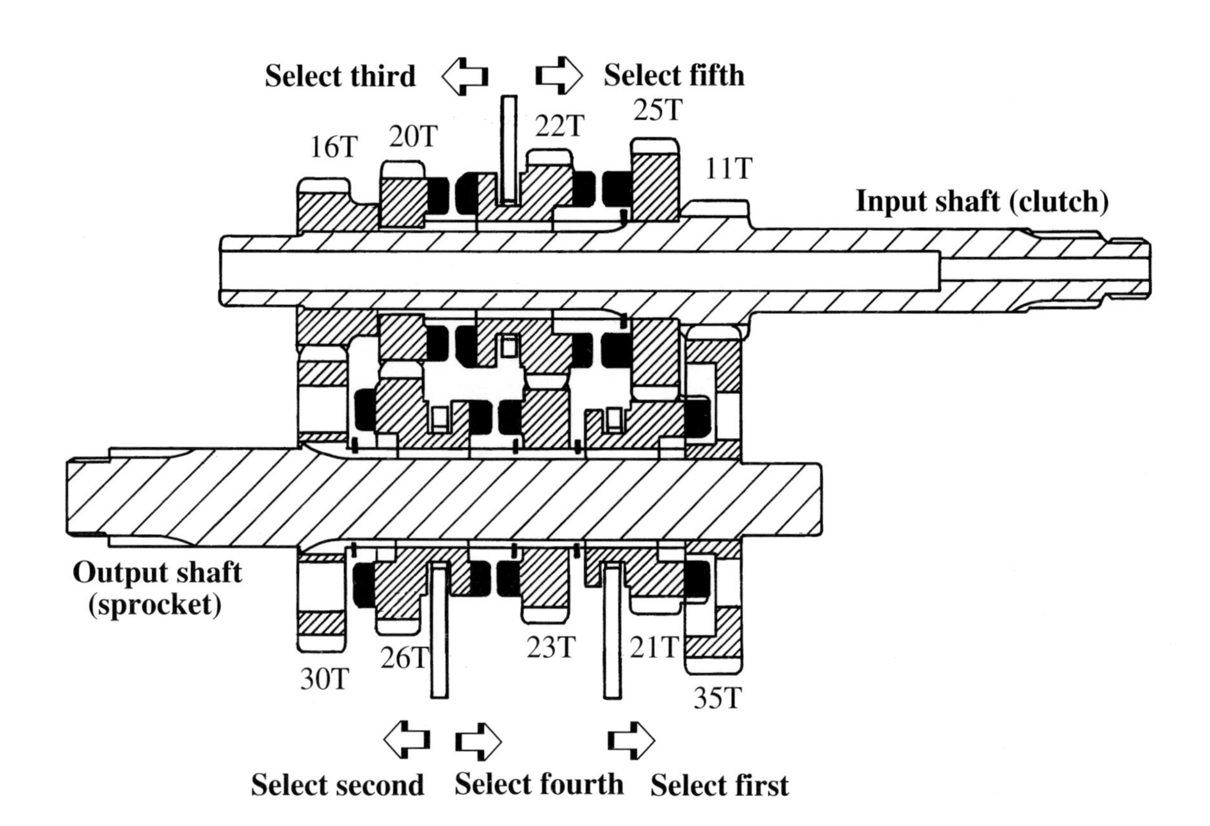

Gear	Driver	Driven	Ratio
1	11	35	3.182
2	16	30	1.875
3	20	26	1.3
4	22	23	1.045
5	25	21	0.840

Fig 2.15 *Calculation of internal ratios for a modern all indirect gearbox. The drive moves through only one pair of meshing gears at a time.*

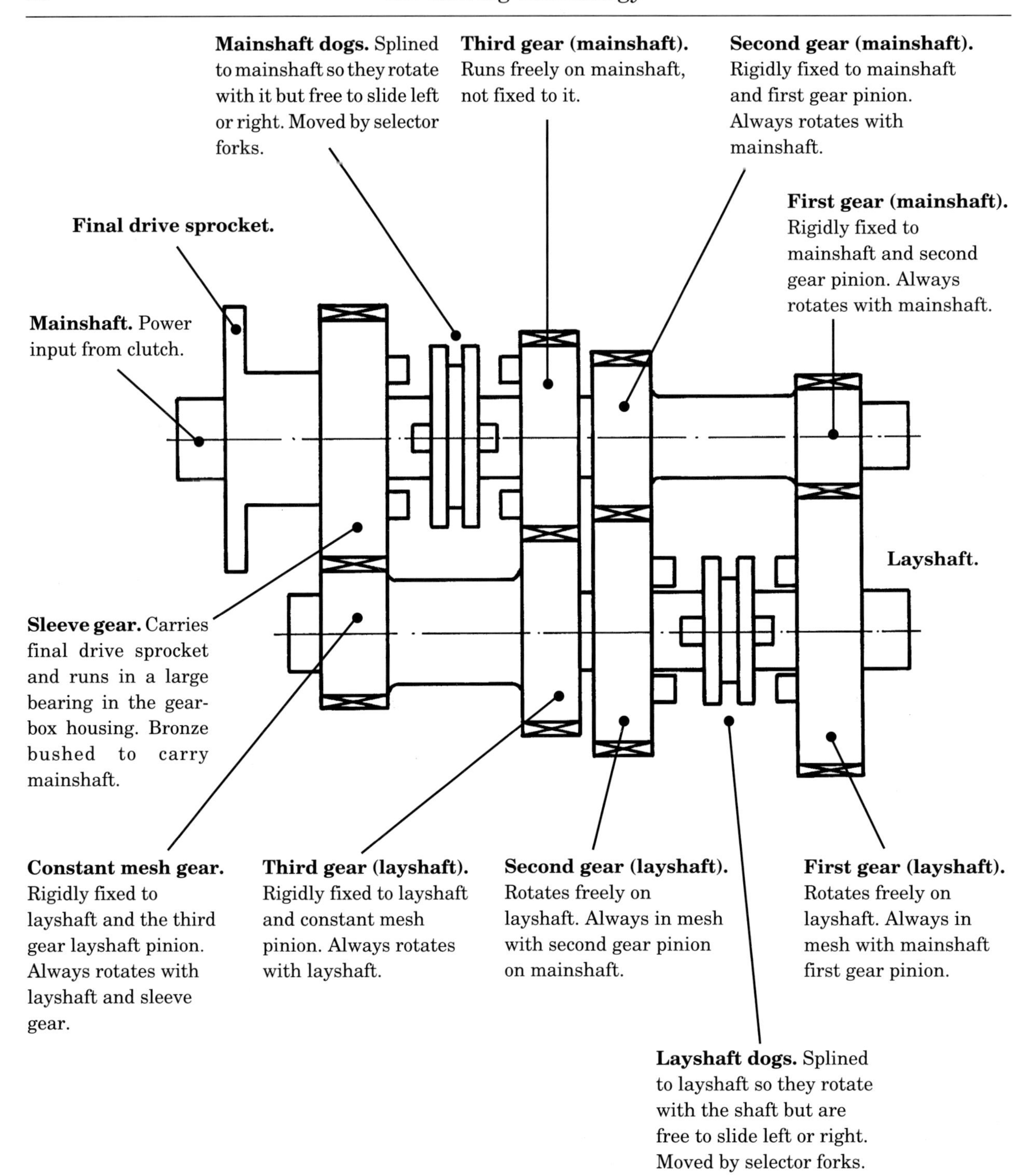

Fig 2.16 (two pages) *Simplified schematic of a typical four speed classic gearbox. On this page the gearbox is shown in neutral. Power comes in via the mainshaft at the left. This causes the first and second gear pinions to rotate. Both pinions mesh with mating gears on the layshaft but these gears run freely and therefore no drive is transmitted to the layshaft. Selection of other gears is detailed opposite.*

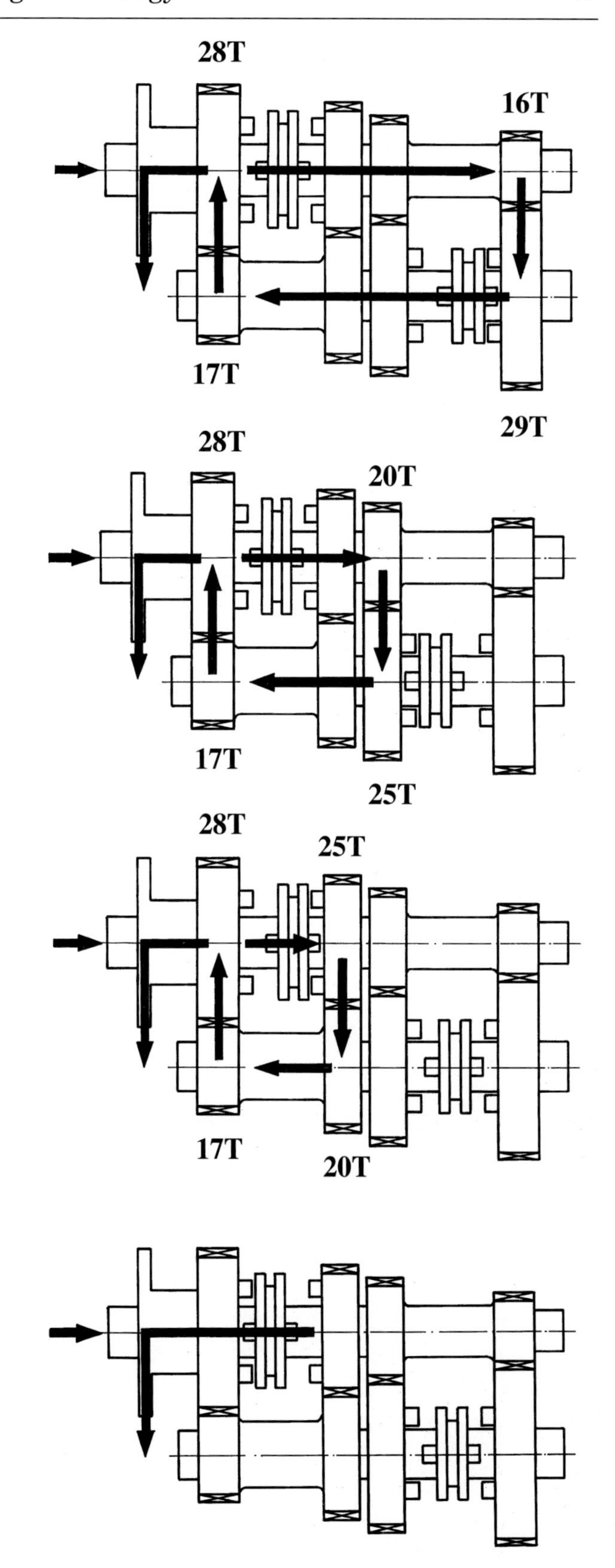

Selecting first gear. To select first gear the layshaft dogs move to the right and engage the 29T gear. This makes the layshaft rotate because the dogs are splined to the layshaft . The 17T constant mesh pinion rotates with the layshaft. This pinion drives the 28T sleeve gear and hence the final drive sprocket. The transmission path is shown on the right and there are two stages of gearing. Going from mainshaft to layshaft gives a ratio equal to (driven teeth / driver teeth), ie 29/16 or 1.8125:1. Going from the layshaft to the sleeve gear the ratio is 28/17 = 1.6470588. The total internal ratio from both stages is 1.8125 x 1.6470588 = 2.985:1.

Selecting second gear. The layshaft dogs move left engaging the 25T gear to the layshaft. The two stage ratios are now 25/20 and 28/17 which gives a combined ratio of 2.059:1.

Selecting third gear. The layshaft dogs are in their neutral position. The mainshaft dogs move right which engages the 25T gear to the mainshaft. This drives the 20T layshaft gear to give a first stage ratio of 20/25 = 0.8:1. Power then transfers back to the sleeve gear by the usual 28/17 ratio. The combined result is a ratio of 1.3176:1.

Selecting fourth gear. The layshaft dogs are in the neutral position. The mainshaft dogs move left and engage the sleeve gear directly to the mainshaft. The layshaft is not involved and top gear has a 1:1 ratio.

Summary. To determine the internal ratio in a particular gear (except top). a) Multiply the number of teeth on both the driven gears together. b) Multiply the number of teeth on both the driving gears together. c) Divide a) by b).

Torque transmission

Now that the drive system for the whole transmission has been discussed we can look at the way in which the torque and speed change throughout the whole process. Fig 2.17 gives an example.

The engine produces 60kW (nominally 80 hp) at the crankshaft and does so at 10000 revs/min. The torque associated with these values is 57.32N-m or 42lbf-ft, calculated using the formulae given in the last chapter.

Power is first transmitted via the two primary gears which, with a ratio of 2.6:1, cause the speed to be reduced and the torque to increase. The speed drops to 3846 revs/min and the torque rises in proportion to 149 N-m (109 lbf-ft) assuming 100% efficiency.

The internal gearbox now provides a further speed reduction because there are more teeth on the final drive shaft than the clutch shaft. In the gear shown the ratio is 2:1 and so the speed halves again, this time to 1923 revs/min. The torque therefore doubles to 298 N-m or 218lbf-ft. Again, all the power is being assumed to arrive at the output shaft. Finally, with a 15 tooth gearbox sprocket and 36 tooth rear wheel sprocket, there is a futher reduction of 2.4:1 giving a final rear wheel speed of 801 revs/min and a torque of 715.2 N-m (which is 523 lbf-ft in imperial units).

In reality some power will be converted to noise and some of it will be used to drag the gears, shafts and bearings around in the oil. This appears as a rise in oil temperature and is eventually transferred to the atmosphere where, as far as you are concerned, it is 'lost' forever.

With two pairs of meshing gears carrying load, together with a chain drive and the oil drag on other gears, you might get perhaps 92% of the 715N-m you expected, ie 658 N-m (513 lbf-ft). Not suprisingly, 658N-m at 801 revs/min gives a power delivery to the rear wheel of 55kW which is 92% of what the engine delivered at the crankshaft!

Below. ***Fig 2.17*** *Transmission of speed, torque and power through to the back wheel assuming 100% efficiency.*

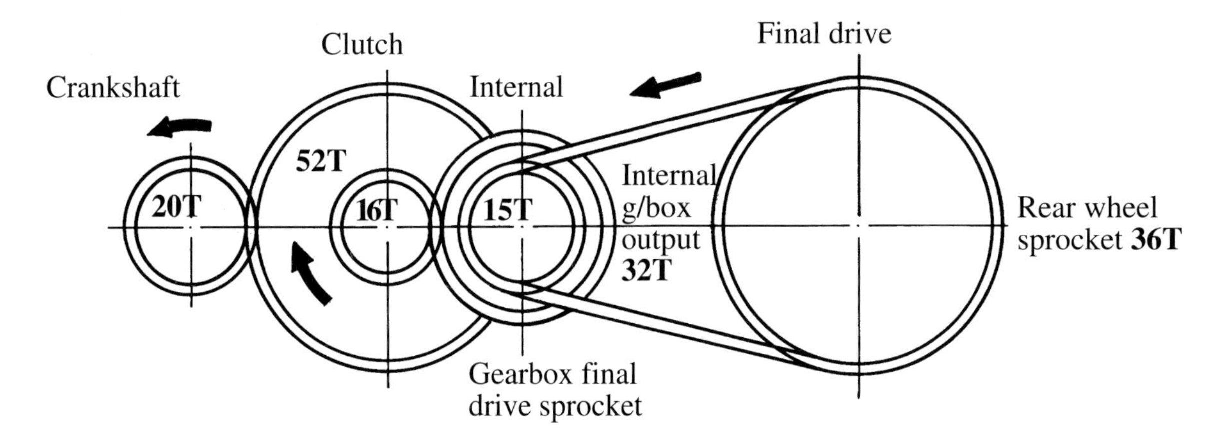

Value	Crankshaft	Clutch	Gearbox Output	Rear Wheel
Speed revs/min	10000	3846	1923	801
Power kW	60	60	60	60
Torque N - m	57.32	149	298	715.2

2.3 Engine/gearbox selection

Introduction

Engine/gearbox selection is usually based on six things.

- Eligibility.
- Availability.
- Suitability.
- Cost.
- Performance.
- Potential.

Within each area there are numerous aspects to consider and practical constraints will dominate the whole issue. For most people, cost and availability will play a major role. Very few competitive engines are available off the shelf and those that are will not be cheap so one is invariably forced to buy a secondhand unit or perhaps even a complete bike in order to extract the engine from it.

Although this is a basic fact of life, a warning about trying to do things on the cheap is necessary. The performance of the bike will be heavily dependent on the engine and no amount of work on the rolling chassis will hide this fact. While it is perfectly possible to build a bike that performs much better than most with the same engine, you will eventually have to face up to people with the same flair and enthusiasm as you for bike development but who have, for one reason or another, got more competitive engines. At this point you will start to lose out, assuming equal riding ability. Because of this it is essential to select the engine carefully and buy the best you can afford. If the engine fails to be competitive, and the bike does not perform reasonably, then its resale value will not be as high as it might have been.

Another reason for buying something decent in the first place is that the amount of work involved in building a bike is such that there will not be a great deal of time left over for working on engines initially and so you really need something that is in good condition to get started with. The last thing you want is to be rebuilding engines every five minutes when you are still trying to get the bike sorted out.

In fact at this stage of the project it is probably much more important to have an engine that is mechanically sound and reliable than it is to have something that is immediately competitive. This approach will allow you to sort out the bike as quickly as possible and it provides you with a baseline from which to work in terms of performance. Once this is done, serious engine development can begin and you will then know whether you have made things better or worse!

The general concept of engine characteristics has already been covered but it is interesting to note the way in which performance has evolved. Fifteen years ago a typical 125cc racing two stroke cylinder produced about 24kW (32hp), yet today we are looking at around 33kW (45hp) from GP bikes that are, in mechanical terms, the same basic two stroke.

The increase is substantial (38%) yet gradual in the sense that it did not happen overnight. Perhaps you could say it has risen by about 0.6kW per year but it did not actually happen that way either. Each small advance along the way has come about from meticulous attention to detail and great refinement in terms of cylinder scavenging, exhaust system design, ignition optimisation, materials, thermal stability and so on. Quantum leaps in output are no longer possible for any engine that is moderately competitive and you have to work at it in very small increments.

Generally speaking, this situation has made dynamometer testing essential and has moved eveything on from the 'garden shed' era so beloved by many of us.

What is the relevance of all this? Well, many bikes evolve around engines that were not originally intended for the final application. Frequently they are road bike engines or those from another sphere of competition and a great deal of work and expense may be necessary to make them competitive in their new environment.

Only you can make the decision as to whether it is all going to work out and whether the costs involved will be acceptable. One thing is certain. Going down this route and getting a result from something that proves to be relatively inexpensive is the ultimate turn-on, well nearly, and no amount of throwing money at things will be able to match it. The problems occur when it all fails!

General considerations

Some of the basic things you should consider when selecting an engine are shown in Fig 2.18. This assumes that the engine is eligible for the class concerned, you can afford it, it is available, and it is going to prove competitive either now or later on after suitable development.

It is simply not practical to work through this list in a book because every application is different and builder priorities vary. Instead, what I propose to do is to leave the tuning aspects to someone else and concentrate on the area that may well impose the greatest constraints in the long term, gearing. There are three gearing related aspects that are important to consider before you actually part with too much money.

- Chain lines.
- Overall gearing requirements.
- Internal ratios.

These aspects are important in all cases but they are particularly important if you intend to use a motocross engine in a roadracer or get involved in any other project where the engine experiences a major change of use.

Chain lines

For any motorcycle to run safely and reliably two things are vital. Firstly the wheels must line up down the centre of the tyres and secondly the gearbox and rear wheel sprockets must line up and sit in the same plane. The chain line in plan view (from above) is something that must be considered early in the design process. Within reason you will know the size of wheels and tyres

Engine Selection

- **Engine availability**
- **Availability of spares**
- **Cost of engine**
- **Cost of spares**
- **General Layout**
- **Weight**
- **Bulk (lack of)**
- **Internal gear ratios**
- **Chain line**
- **Primary ratios**
- **Performance**
- **Vibration characteristics**
- **Development potential**
- **Casting limits**
- **Engine mountings**
- **Ease of access**
- **Exhaust length**
- **Potential reliability**
- **Access to information**
- **Cooling requirements**
- **Interchangeability**
- **Track record if any**
- **Ignition requirements**
- **Overall quality**

Fig 2.18 *Some of the technical and practical aspects that should be considered when selecting an engine and gearbox for a special.*

you intend to use. The front and rear must line up along a centreline, ideally the centreline of the whole bike, and the chain must clear the rear tyre, preferably by about 10mm. This means that one extreme of chain position is immediately fixed.

This aspect needs to be considered when buying the engine and back wheel. If the wheel hub is too narrow then the rear sprocket will have to be spaced out accordingly. Small amounts of spacing are no problem but anything more than perhaps 20mm may involve some serious engineering to avoid the sprocket bolts being subjected to high bending loads. A wider hub is a better option.

There is normally much less scope to shift the gearbox final drive sprocket relative to the crankcases or gearbox housing and this means that the engine cannot move any further to the right of the bike than chain clearance at the rear tyre allows, unless of course you want to get involved in making serious shaft extensions and outrigger bearing mounts.

The relationship between the centreline of the engine and the position of its final drive sprocket varies enormously so it is perfectly possible for you to finish up with the engine hanging out from one side of the bike when the chain line is correct.

How much this matters depends on the type of engine and the amount of work you are prepared to do in order to solve the problem. One thing is certain, the sprockets must line up.

A wide bulky engine is going to ground more easily on one side if it is significantly offset from centre and it may have to be mounted somewhat higher up in the bike than you would otherwise like in order to solve the problem (Chapter 3.2). There will also be an unbalanced feel to the bike when stationary though it is suprising just how much offset can go un-noticed once the bike is on the move unless the flywheels are large and heavy. In this case, gyroscopic effects can make the bike behave differently when it turns in different directions and power is applied. It will tend to lift up when going one way and lie down when going the other. The basic message is simply to think about it before spending money.

Fig 2.19 shows the ideal situation that you could achieve but in practice most specials involve a degree of compromise in terms of engine positioning. Personally, I would consider the choice of engine to be more important than the choice of wheel and usually proceed on the following basis using a pencil and paper (this being cheaper than

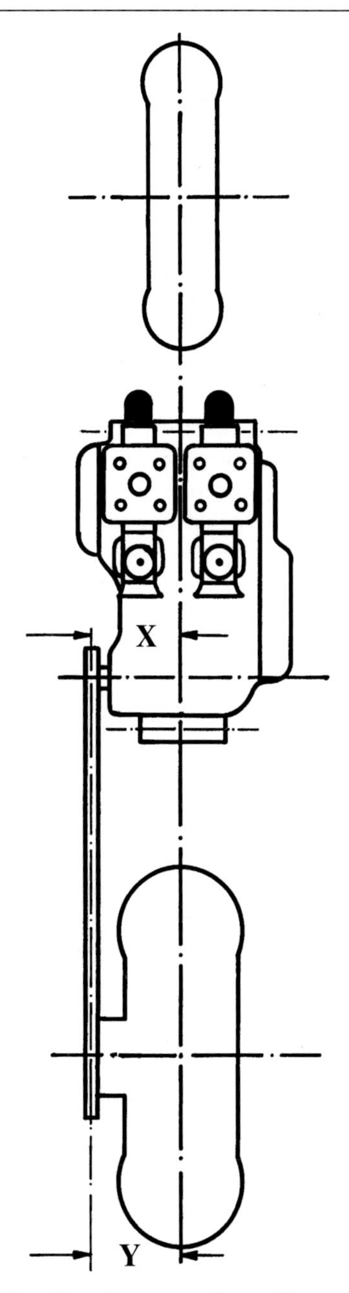

X = Gearbox sprocket offset
Y = Half tyre width + clearance

Fig 2.19 *One extreme of chain line is immediately fixed by the tyre width and engine offset to comply with this may be a problem. This diagram shows the ideal situation you might achieve.*

metal and less depressing to throw in the bin).

- Measure from the gearbox sprocket to the centreline of the engine. Go by the physical centreline, ie where it balances, or where the cylinders are equispaced about a centreline, rather than any crankcase joint lines.
- Draw a centreline on paper and mark the rear tyre width on it.
- Mark where the gearbox sprocket will come with the engine 'on centre'.

If the chain will clear the tyre acceptably with the engine on centre then life is great and all you need to do is to find a suitable wheel or hub.

Alternatively, if the chain does not clear the tyre look at the possibility of spacing out the gearbox sprocket. This will only work for small amounts unless you want to get serious about it and include outrigger bearings.

If none of this leads to a solution you will have to fit the engine off centre unless you are prepared to use narrower tyres. Small engine offsets, eg 10mm, are neither here nor there and most bikes have some element of this but if you look like finishing up with the engine underneath one of your feet then it is time to think again. Fig 2.20 summarises the possibilities that can occur.

The other important aspect of rear chain alignment is that the wheel spindle and gearbox output shaft are parallel and lie in the same plane. If they are not then the chain will, at best, wear rapidly and at worst it will break repeatedly. This aspect has nothing to do with initial selection but I mention it as a reminder of the need to check this during construction. Also note that it is easy to build a bike where everything lines up with the swinging arm at full droop but is a long way out with the swinging arm at full lift!

Fig 2.20 *Checking out chainline problems before finally purchasing components.*

Dimensions	Condition	Possible options
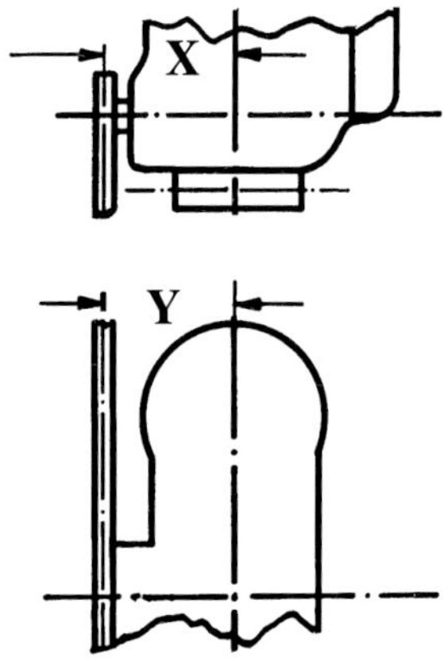 X	X = Y	Fit engine on centre Fit rear sprocket to suit
Y	X greater than Y	Move engine to right Space wheel sprocket left
X = Gearbox sprocket offset Y = Half tyre width + clearance	Y greater than X	Move engine to left Use gearbox outrigger Use narrower tyres

Overall gear ratios

Overall gear ratio was defined in the last chapter and you may feel that this is not the sort of thing to be considering at this stage where a new bike may be but a figment of your imagination. This could be a big mistake as many people have discovered, even though final assessment has to be undertaken at the track.

Problems are most likely to arise when you are changing the application of an engine. The overall gear ratios are the product of three stages; primary, internal and final drive, and you should not assume that it will be possible to sort everything out just by changing sprockets.

The first thing to note is the great range of primary reduction ratios in use. The Honda RC45 goes very quickly and as such has to have high overall gearing. The primary contribution is a ratio of 1.939:1 which is considerably different to the 4 or 5:1 you might find on a motocross bike.

What the manufacturer is doing is building in suitable gearing at this stage so that the range of rear sprockets will be sensible in the chosen application. There will always be practical limits on the size of sprockets you can use both at the gearbox and rear wheel so it is essential that you have some idea of what is required early on. This will save the misery of producing a bike that needs a rear sprocket with four teeth or requires a big hole drilling through the frame for the chain to pass through!

The classic problem area is the transfer of a motocross engine to tarmac. The gearing will be low at all three stages because the bike does not have to run at roadrace speeds. Put it on tarmac and you may find that 120km/hr (75 miles/hr) is top whack with the original rear sprocket. Changing this to the smallest sprocket that allows the chain to clear the hub and fitting the largest gearbox sprocket possible may still only yield a road speed that is much less than you need and is also much less than the power available would allow. There is nothing you can do about it except re-develop the engine to run at higher revs (may not be appropriate) or fit new gearbox/primary internals which will be expensive. The following method of estimating sprocket sizes may save any such disasters.

Road speed

The overall gear ratio required in top gear will depend on the engine characteristics, the road speed and the size of tyres employed. Assuming that you have decided on the size of tyres involved and have a reasonable idea of the engine speed at which maximum power is, or will be, produced, then the main thing missing is an estimate of possible road speeds.

Given some of the information that appears later in the book, you will be able to estimate the true top speed fairly accurately but what you need here is not the ultimate top speed but the sort of speeds you might attain at each circuit. These will normally be lower and the best way to get values is by taking revcounter readings from a similar bike. This is one of many examples where it pays to write things down. Other options include using a bike fitted with a speedometer or making a guess based on experience. The main requirement of such a guess is to be realistic and not assume more power than is likely to be the case. Try to make estimates for the fastest and slowest circuits you know of. Once this is done, the speed at which the rear wheel rotates can be found using either of the following formulae,

$$\textbf{Wheel speed revs/min} = \frac{2652.6V}{r}$$

where V = road speed in km/hr
r = rolling radius of rear tyre in mm

or

$$\textbf{Wheel speed revs/min} = \frac{168.1V}{r}$$

where V = road speed in miles/hr
r = rolling radius of rear tyre in inches.

The true rolling radius of the tyre is a bit tricky. It can be obtained from the tyre manufacturers though you can get started simply by measuring from the wheel spindle to the ground on a laden bike fitted with the same tyres. A more accurate option is to roll a laden bike along and measure the road distance corresponding to say ten revolutions of the wheel. Divide this distance in mm by 62.84 to get the radius in mm or divide the distance in inches by 62.84 to get a radius in inches.

If you feel happy about drawing graphs then it is only necessary to do this calculation once for a given size of tyre. You can then produce a graph like that in Fig 2.21 from which any other value of wheel speed is easily obtained.

Fig 2.21 *Using a graph to relate all wheel and road speeds from one calculation. The graph is only valid for one rolling tyre radius.*

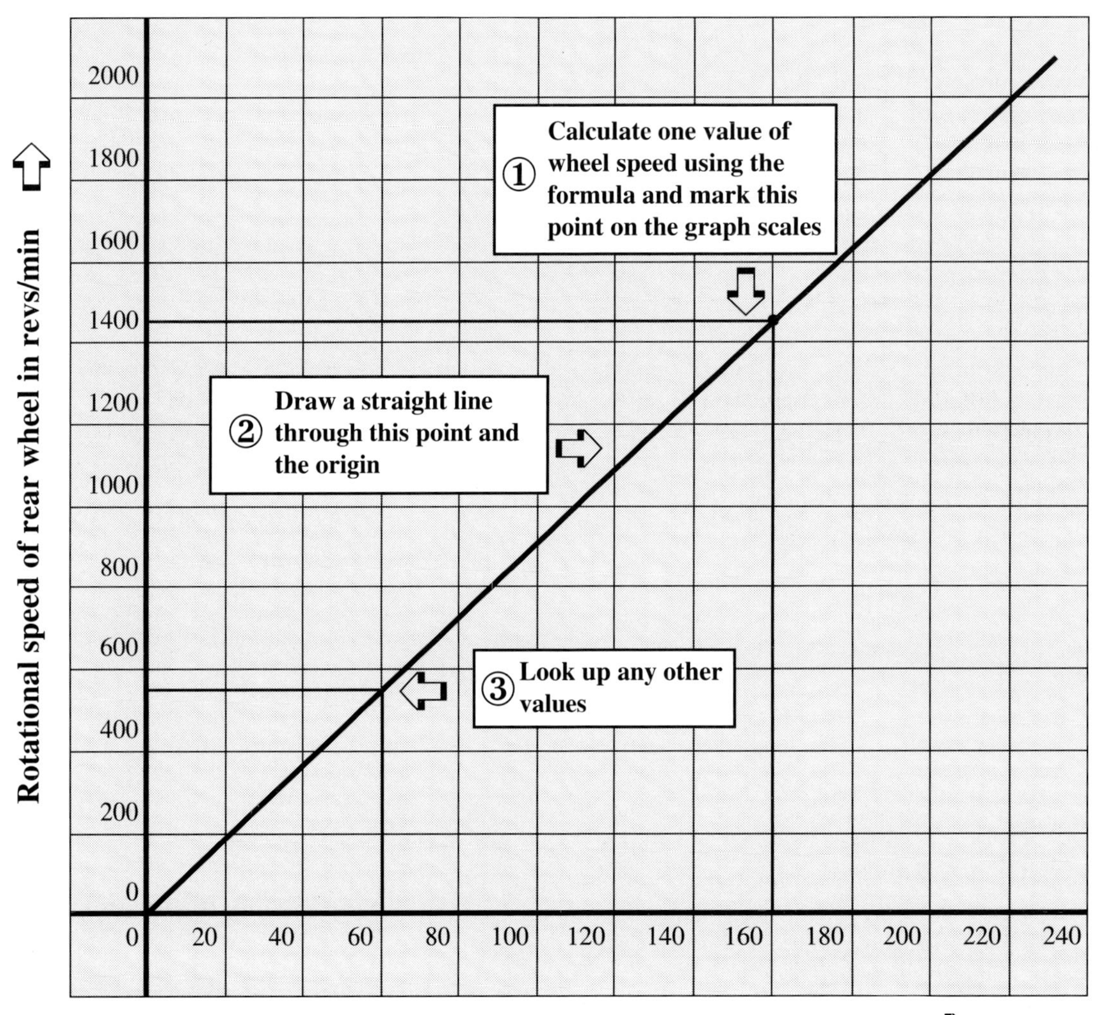

The overall top gear ratio required can now be found from,

$$\text{Overall Top Gear Ratio} = \frac{\text{Max Engine Speed}}{\text{Rear Wheel Speed}}$$

Once the overall top gear ratio is known then the final drive ratio required to achieve it is given by,

$$\text{Final Drive Ratio} = \frac{\text{Overall Top Gear}}{\text{Primary x Internal Top}}$$

This is all much harder to describe than it is to do and Fig 2.22 provides an example for you to follow using metric units. Fig 2.23 overleaf does a similar example using imperial units.

Once you have arrived at the overall ratio then suitable sprocket pairings can be estimated. The range of gearbox sprockets that can be fitted is usually fairly small and it is sensible to avoid anything with thirteen teeth or less because the substantial 'polygon action' they create gives the chain a very hard time. If you had a totally free choice of sprocket size then 17 teeth would be a reasonable minimum to ensure longevity. Unfortunately, such ideals are rarely possible.

Fig 2.22 *This example estimates the range of rear sprockets that will be required using known and estimated data. Remember that the result can only be as good as the data you use to obtain it.*

A top speed range of 160km/hr (100miles/hr) to 208km/hr (130miles/hr) is estimated for a 125cc bike producing 27kW (36bhp) at the back wheel. Data is as follows, rolling radius = 300mm, maximum useful engine speed = 12500revs/min, primary ratio = 3.28:1, internal top gear = 1:1, gearbox sprockets available = 15,16 and 17T.

Value	Formula	Data for 160km/hr	Answer for 160km/hr	Data for 208km/hr	Answer for 208km/hr
1. Max wheel speed	2652.6V / r	2652.6 x 160 / 300	= 1414.7revs/min	2652.6 x 208 / 300	= 1839revs/min
2. Overall top gear ratio	Max eng speed / Rear wheel speed	12500 / 1414.7	= 8.836:1	12500 / 1839	= 6.80:1
3. Final drive ratio	Overall top gear / Prim. x internal	8.836 / 3.28 x 1	= 2.694:1	6.80 / 3.28 x 1	= 2.07:1
4. Nearest sprockets	ratio x teeth on gearbox	ratio = 2.694 15x2.694 = 40.4 16x2.694 = 43.1 17x2.694 = 45.8	Nearest values 40T/15T = 2.667 43T/16T = 2.688 46T/17T = 2.706	ratio = 2.07 15x2.07 = 31.1 16x2.07 = 33.1 17x2.07 = 35.2	Nearest values 31T/15T = 2.067 33T/16T = 2.063 35T/17T = 2.059

Virtually all gearboxes use something in the range 14 - 17 teeth but you need to check that large sprockets will allow the chain to clear the gearbox castings. Multiplying the number of teeth on each gearbox sprocket by the final drive ratio just calculated will give you the number of teeth required on the rear wheel as shown in the example. You should really confine the calculation to the largest gearbox sprockets available because we are trying to estimate the highest gearing required on different circuits.

In the first example given, we see that it is likely to be necessary to accommodate rear wheel sprockets from 30T to 46T. These are typical sizes found on road or race bikes but it might have been the case that we needed much larger or much smaller sizes than it was physically possible to fit. The example in Fig 2.23 is also straightforward. To highlight the sort of problems that can occur, Fig 2.24 gives a further example. In this case, a serious problem with the gearing was highlighted very early on (before the engine was paid for!) indicating that the standard engine could not be used without significant modification. However, in this particular case the engine had so many other advantages that they far outweighed the overall gearing problem and it was decided to continue with the project and do what was necessary to develop the engine. The bike eventually proved to be very successful with numerous wins and several lap records but it could easily have been a very different story.

Below. Fig 2.23 *Another example of estimating sprocket sizes, this time in imperial units.*

Right. Fig 2.24 *Example of an overall gearing problem associated with using a motocross engine in a roadracer.*

A top speed range of 130miles/hr to 150miles/hr is estimated for a 250cc bike producing 80bhp at the back wheel. Data is as follows, rolling radius = 12inches, maximum useful engine speed = 13000revs/min, primary ratio = 2.9:1, internal top gear = 0.909:1, gearbox sprockets available = 14,15 and 16T.

Value	Formula	Data for 130miles/hr	Answer for 130miles/hr	Data for 150miles/hr	Answer for 150miles/hr
1. Max wheel speed	168.1V / r	168.1 x 130 / 12	= 1821.1revs/min	168.1 x 150 / 12	= 2101.3revs/min
2. Overall top gear ratio	Max eng speed / Rear wheel speed	13000 / 1821.1	= 7.139	13000 / 2101.3	= 6.187
3. Final drive ratio	Overall top gear / Prim. x internal	7.139 / 2.9 x 0.909	= 2.708:1	6.187 / 2.9 x 0.909	= 2.347
4. Nearest sprockets	ratio x teeth on gearbox	ratio = 2.708 14x2.708 = 37.9 15x2.708 = 40.6 16x2.708 = 43.3	38T/14T = 2.714 41T/15T = 2.733 43T/16T = 2.688	ratio = 2.347 14x2.347 = 32.9 15x2.347 = 35.2 16x2.347 = 37.6	33T/14T = 2.357 35T/15T = 2.333 38T/16T = 2.375

This example is for a 250cc single cylinder roadracer based on a Honda CR250R motocross engine. A top speed estimation of 190km/hr (118miles/hr) was used at the time. This was based on the power available from the standard engine (see Section 4) and was typical of 125's running in the same races. When developed, a higher top speed would be assumed. Standard gearbox sprockets were 14T and 15T, other data is as follows.

Rolling Radius = 295mm, Max Engine Speed = 7800revs/min, Primary Ratio = 3.25:1, Internal Top = 0.839:1

1. $$\text{Max Wheel Speed} = \frac{2652.6V}{r} = \frac{2652.6 \times 190}{295} = 1708.5\text{revs/min}$$

2. $$\text{Overall Top Gear Ratio} = \frac{\text{Max Engine Speed}}{\text{Rear Wheel Speed}} = \frac{7800}{1708.5} = 4.565:1$$

3. $$\text{Final Drive Ratio} = \frac{\text{Overall Top Gear}}{\text{Primary} \times \text{Internal}} = \frac{4.565}{3.25 \times 0.839} = 1.674:1$$

With the largest standard gearbox sprocket (15T) the rear sprocket requires 15 x 1.674 = 25T (nearest whole)

A 25T rear sprocket is very small and was actually smaller than the pitch circle of the bolts required to hold it to the rear hub. A 16T gearbox sprocket was the largest that would allow the chain to clear the engine castings and such a sprocket was specially made. However, this only changes the rear sprocket requirement to 16 x 1.674 = 27T which was still too small to fit. It was therefore evident that the standard engine could not be used effectively. For this reason the engine was redeveloped and repiped to produce maximum power around 9000revs/min. Using this,

$$\text{Overall Top Gear Ratio} = \frac{\text{Max Engine Speed}}{\text{Rear Wheel Speed}} = \frac{9000}{1708.5} = 5.268:1$$

$$\text{Final Drive Ratio} = \frac{\text{Overall Top Gear}}{\text{Primary} \times \text{Internal}} = \frac{5.268}{3.25 \times 0.839} = 1.932:1$$

The smallest rear sprocket required now is 16 x 1.932 = 31T (nearest) and this would fit. When the bike was finally built and raced 30T was the smallest sprocket ever used but the motor needed to rev to 9500revs/min at Snetterton or it was undergeared. The only other options were (1) Change tyre size (2) Fit new primary gears (3) Make a new internal top gear pair.

More speed estimates

If you are a bit unsure of the road speed figures you are using then one way of obtaining a fairly accurate result is to work back from a friend's revcounter readings. By combining the formulae given earlier we can obtain the road speed using either of the following,

Road Speed km/hr $= \dfrac{Nr}{2652.6G}$

where N = engine speed in revs/min

G = overall gear ratio used

r = rolling radius of tyre in mm

or

Road Speed miles/hr $= \dfrac{Nr}{168.1G}$

where r is now in inches.

Fig 2.25 gives an example. Obviously, the bike you take this data from should be as similar as possible to what you intend to create, at least in terms of power and overall bulk. It must be stressed that any figures you obtain for sprocket sizes using the methods in this chapter will only be as good as the data on which they are based. If you have seriously underestimated the road speeds involved then the calculations will imply a lower overall ratio than that actually required and, unless a smaller rear sprocket or larger gearbox sprocket can subsequently be fitted, you will find yourself flat out in top gear before the end of the straights. Although gearing can only be set up at the circuit, the methods described here should avoid any serious blunders at the early stages.

Example of Road Speed Estimation

Data: Primary Ratio = 3.28:1

Internal Top Gear Ratio = 1.0:1

Rolling Radius = 300mm

Rear Wheel Sprocket = 36T

Gearbox Sprocket = 16T

The revcounter reads 12500revs/min at the end of the straight in top gear.

Overall Ratio $= \dfrac{3.28 \times 1 \times 36}{16}$

$= 7.38:1$

Road Speed $= \dfrac{12500 \times 300}{2652.6 \times 7.38}$

$= 192$km/hr (119 miles/hr)

Fig 2.25 *Example of road speed estimation based on a revcounter reading and known gearing.*

Changes in overall ratio

Chapter 2.4 looks at this in more detail but the general ideas are as follows. The overall gearing is normally set so that the engine reaches peak power revs in top gear at the fastest part of the circuit and it therefore has to be altered to suit each track. The estimates just discussed are based on this principle.

Alterations are generally done by changing the final drive sprockets to suit. Similar changes can of course be achieved by changing the primary ratio or a combination of both though this takes longer to carry out.

The finesse with which you can fine tune the overall gearing depends on the variety of sprockets you have available and one of the first things you should do is to compile a table of final drive ratios like that shown in Table 2.3. To construct such a table you need to divide the number of teeth on each rear wheel sprocket you have by the number of teeth on every gearbox sprocket you have. This gives a mass of ratios which you can then place in order, trying not to leave any out!

Even if you do not actually have a full set of sprockets it is worth producing a table that covers every combination that is within the useable range. The deficiencies of your current sprocket set will then stand out.

The table shows the smallest ratio changes available to you. For example, the table given indicates that current gearing of 40T/17T can be lowered very slightly by using 38T/16T or raised slightly with 35T/15T. Note that a 'lower' gear corresponds to a larger ratio value.

If you only change the rear wheel sprocket then the table shows that a one tooth change to 39T/17T or 41T/17T gives a much greater alteration than the combined changes just suggested. A one tooth alteration at the gearbox sprocket is coarser still and is typically equivalent to two or three teeth at the back wheel. Such tables are therefore a great aid when it comes to gearing optimisation at the race track.

Setting the overall gearing so that the engine just peaks in top is only the begining. If the gearing can be slightly lower then acceleration will benefit. Whether this is possible depends to a large extent on the shape of the power curve after peak power has been reached and your willingness to push the limits of mechanical reliability.

Even then the problems have only just begun because you will almost certainly find a corner for which none of the internal ratios is suitable. With a cassette type gearbox and a box of bits costing thousands you can try to optimise the gearing for every corner but most people don't have this level of sophistication. Because of this, you are now forced to compromise somewhere.

The ability to accelerate out of corners is crucial to lap times so the overall gearing has to change slightly. This is where a flexible motor starts to pay dividends. Slight changes in overall ratio, up or down, may solve the problems and reduce lap times but you will only find out by experiment.

This does of course assume that you have a reasonable set of internal ratios. Two strokes with narrow powerbands are particularly sensitive to their internal ratios. If the spacing of the gears is too large, especially in fourth, fifth and sixth, then no amount of adjusting the overall gearing will solve the problems that occur. We therefore need to look at the internal ratios as well.

Final Drive Ratios		
Rear	**Gearbox**	**Ratio**
42	15	2.800
41	15	2.733
40	15	2.667
42	16	2.625
39	15	2.600
41	16	2.563
38	15	2.533
40	16	2.500
42	17	2.471
37	15	2.467
39	16	2.438
41	17	2.412
36	15	2.400
38	16	2.375
40	17	2.353
35	15	2.333
37	16	2.313
39	17	2.294
36	16	2.250
38	17	2.235
35	16	2.188
37	17	2.176
36	17	2.118
35	17	2.059

Table 2.3 *A final drive ratio chart. This one is compiled for 15,16 and 17 tooth gearbox sprockets combined with 35 - 42 tooth rear wheel sprockets.*

Internal ratios

Selecting a gearbox with suitable internal ratios is extremely important. As with overall gearing, problems are most likely to occur when the original application of the engine is changed or it is developed in such a way that the range of useful engine speeds is reduced.

This situation can occur when using motocross engines on tarmac. The original torque curve is usually relatively flat in roadrace terms with more midrange torque to aid flexibility. Peak power is unlikely to be developed close to the mechanical limits of engine speed and is also restricted by the need for flexibility.

Subsequent development to obtain more power is almost certain to lower the mid-range torque and will move everything up the speed range of the engine. Suddenly, the original internal ratios may become totally unacceptable.

Similar problems also occur with engine/gearbox units that were originally intended for road bikes though these days the symptoms are unlikely to be as bad as they used to be.

Further pressure to check out the internal ratios before you commit yourself comes from the fact that the majority of engines are now of unit construction. Unless the gearbox is a GP style sideloading unit, it may be necessary to strip everything in order to change ratios and this normally precludes making any changes to the internal ratios while actually at the circuit.

Furthermore, if the engine you select has no prior record of success on the track then it is also unlikely that any alternative ratios will already be in production. This problem is rarely insurmountable, but if you are faced with obtaining 'one-off' internals of the required quality, then the cost may come as something of a shock and cancel out all hope of producing a relatively inexpensive competitive unit.

Ratio spacing

Selecting internal gear ratios is always a compromise, even for manufacturers. Top gear is easy to deal with since it can be based on the bike's maximum road speed potential but first gear is more of a problem and is always, to some extent, an arbitrary decision. For example, on a road bike the designer may decide that first gear should be such that it is possible to start off on a one in three gradient with minimal clutch slip but the choice of ratio will still vary because a small engine with less torque is going to need lower gearing to comply with this requirement than something larger with masses of low speed torque.

When first gear is low, as it is on just about all bikes except roadracers, then a lot more head scratching will be required to sort out suitable ratios for everything in-between. Mathematics can provide a starting point with the use of geometric progressions etc but such simplistic ideas are inadequate given the range of conditions. There are other practical problems as well, for example you cannot have a gear with half a tooth! Despite these problems the manufacturers will do their best to arrive at suitable ratios for the specific application. If you change that application then you may well have to change the internal gears as well. The gaps between some of the gears may be too great once the engine is developed for use on tarmac and unfortunately raising first gear may not prove to be the only requirement.

We can divide the seriousness of potential problems into two categories. Firstly, if the internal ratios are particularly unsuitable for the characteristics of the developed engine, then it will drop out of the powerband after you change up to the next gear. For example, if we assume that a race engine only produces useful power down to 10000revs/min, then if you change up from third gear at say 12500revs/min, the road speed must be such that it corresponds to an engine speed that is greater than 10000revs/min in fourth gear.

If this is not the case then the engine will have to be coaxed through the change on the clutch and even this might prove difficult if the ratios are particularly poor. A situation like this is totally unacceptable, except perhaps in first gear, and therefore the most elementary aspect of selecting internal ratios is to make sure that this does not happen. The second stage of ratio assessment is more subtle and, as you might expect, requires more work to check out. Different internal ratios will produce different amounts of torque at the back wheel and will therefore influence acceleration. To get the best acceleration you will need to select the ratios very carefully and change gear at specific engine speeds in some cases. Even this is not the end of the story because you must have a gear that is suitable for each corner even though this may compromise what could be achieved at a straight test track. The more detailed discussion associated with this aspect is covered in the next chapter. The purpose of what follows is to enable you to make a quick assessment of whether the gearbox you have chosen will be tolerable or a total disaster.

Initial ratio assessment

The first thing to do is to find out what all the internal ratios are and then 'normalise' them for convenience. What this involves is making top gear equal to 1:1 (on paper!) and adjusting all the other ratios so that the original gear spacing is retained. This will make all subsequent comparisons easier because every cluster you look at will have a 1:1 top gear.

Tabulate the data as per Table 2.4. To obtain the values in the last column proceed as follows.

- Take the internal top gear ratio and divide it by itself to obtain 1:1.

- Now divide all the other ratios by the top gear value.

In the example given, top gear is 0.963:1 so we divide all values by 0.963. Fourth gear becomes 1.120/0.963 = 1.163 and so on.

You now need to know the useful powerband of the engine. Often, this is not known at the outset because there is development work to do, however it should be possible to make some sort of reasonable estimate. It is particularly important to estimate the maximum engine speed you will use. The lower engine speed you can use may be severely restricted by the gear ratios you have, thus implying a limitation on any proposed development.

As an example, I will assume a 125cc engine that produces useful power between 10000 and 12500revs/min. Once these figures are known it is easy to see if the engine will be able to make the jump to the next gear and remain within the powerband. Table 2.5 shows what the engine speed will drop to each time a gearchange is made at 12500revs/min. This calculation is based on the fact that, at the instant you change gear, the road speed has to be the same in adjacent gears.It may well be that this peak engine speed is not the one to change up at for maximum acceleration but at this stage you have little choice but to use it.

The figures in Table 2.5 are obtained as follows.

- Multiply the engine speed at which you change gear by the normalised ratio you are changing up to.

- Divide this result by the normalised ratio you have changed up from.

Below. Table 2.4 *Normalising a set of internal ratios to give 1:1 top gear.*

Gear	Teeth	Ratio	Normalised Ratio
1	35/19	1.842	1.913
2	32/22	1.455	1.511
3	30/24	1.250	1.298
4	28/25	1.120	1.163
5	27/26	1.038	1.078
6	26/27	0.963	1.000

Below. Table 2.5 *Determining the new engine speed after changing up to the next gear.*

Gear Number	Normalised Gear Ratio	Engine Speed with 12500 rpm change up
1	1.913	-------
2	1.511	9873
3	1.298	10738
4	1.163	11200
5	1.078	11586
6	1.000	11596

In the example, the change from first to second gear gives,

- 12500 x 1.511 = 18887.5
- 18887.5/1.913 = 9873revs/min

Similarly, when going from fifth to sixth we get,

- 12500 x 1 = 12500
- 12500/1.078 = 11596revs/min

The spacing of these ratios therefore seems to be quite good for the proposed engine. The only real problem area is the change from first to second gear which drops the engine just out of the powerband, however this will occur at relatively low road speeds where there is a large amount of surplus torque (even with a 125) and very little resistance to motion. Unless there is an almost total cut off at 10000revs/min, the engine should be able to cope.

It is the way things progress as we work up through the gearbox that is much more important. Road speeds, and therefore resistance to motion, are increasing. In fifth or sixth gear the bike may be working close to the limits of available power if the overall gearing is relatively high and so it is essential that the engine speed keeps well up in the powerband, preferably close to the point at which peak torque is produced.

It would seem reasonable to assume that the speed range calculated, ie from 10738 (change to third) to 11596 (change to sixth) complies with this for the engine concerned so we could be reasonably satisfied with this gearbox. In particular, note how the engine speed after changing gear rises as you work up through the gearbox so that the motor is further up in the powerband the faster you go. This aspect is important and will be discussed in a moment.

Now consider the same engine with the gear ratios in Table 2.6. This five speed set is from a motocross application and it is immediately obvious that they are not suitable. The engine speed drops below the powerband when changing up to second or third and it barely makes it when moving into fourth or fifth either. Although the engine speed is moving up the powerband as we go faster it is nowhere near high enough. Even when travelling in a straight line, it is likely that the engine will have to be coaxed through all but the first low speed change on the clutch. When cornering, or in traffic, the slightest hesitation would cause the engine to bog down immediately following the gearchanges. This gearbox is useless for its new application. In general for an engine with this sort of characteristic, a powerband from 10000 to 12500revs/min, the engine speed after changing up should always be above 11000revs/min in the last two gears. The TZ250(94) data in Table 2.7 is typical of what you are looking for.

Gear Number	Normalised Gear Ratio	Engine Speed after change at 12500 rpm
1	2.462	-------
2	1.893	9611
3	1.476	9746
4	1.190	10078
5	1.000	10504

Table 2.6 *Modified engine speeds after changing gear when an unsuitable five speed cluster is used.*

Table 2.7 *These gearbox ratios for a TZ250 are typical of the type required in the application described. Good as they are, they cannot cover all conditions and options are available on the first three gears as standard.*

Gear Number	Normalised Gear Ratio	Engine Speed after change at 12500 rpm
1	2.200	-------
2	1.624	9227
3	1.362	10483
4	1.188	10903
5	1.059	11143
6	1.000	11804

Gear Number	Teeth	Ratio	Normalised Ratio	Engine Speed with 12500rpm change
1	32/13	2.462	2.462	-------------------
2	30/16	1.875	1.875	9520
3	28/18	1.556	1.556	10373
4	26/20	1.300	1.300	10443
5	24/22	1.091	1.091	10490
6	23/23	1.000	1.000	11457

Table 2.8 *This gearset is reasonable for the engine considered but not particularly good because the engine is too low down in the powerband following changes to third, fourth and fifth.*

Tables 2.6 and 2.7 represent two extreme cases. Table 2.8 bridges these by identifying an example of a more subtle nature that lies somewhere in-between. This six speed gearbox obviously covers things rather better than the five speed type used previously but the engine is still sitting too close to the bottom of the powerband when changing up to third, fourth or fifth.

When riding in a straight line and clear of traffic this gearbox should be acceptable but again we have to consider the consequences of any hesitation when cornering at speed. If you have just changed up to fifth, then any momentary slowing down will kill the engine and either force a change back to fourth where the engine screams or the use of some clutch slip. Neither option is desirable when you have your knee on the floor.

We could thus conclude our rough investigation of these ratios by saying that those in Tables 2.5 and 2.7 seem good, those in Table 2.8 seem tolerable, and those in Table 2.6 are useless for the engine characteristics quoted.

The implication of this on engine development is obvious. If we could spread the powerband down to 8000revs/min then even the five speed box could be used, albeit with relatively poor acceleration. If on the other hand development moves the lower powerband limit up to 10500revs/min then only the gearsets in Tables 2.5 and 2.7 have any chance of coping.

Some readers might find a slight extension of this approach useful. It will not reveal anything new, but presents the information in a road speed related form. Table 2.9 overleaf sets out the original ratios from Table 2.5 but it has three columns added. Column four shows the actual road speed of the bike at 12500revs/min in the gear concerned as a percentage of the maximum road speed in top gear. Thus the road speed in top gear is listed as 100%. The values in this column are obtained as follows.

- Divide '1' by the normalised ratio.
- Multiply the answer by 100.

Thus third gear gives,

- 1/1.298 = 0.77
- 0.77 x 100 = 77%

This means that if the overall gearing was such that the bike did 208km/hr at 12500revs/min in top gear then it would do 160km/hr when running at 12500revs/min in third gear, 160km/hr being 77% of 208km/hr.

The next column produces the same type of figures but at 10000revs/min, ie at the bottom of the powerband. To obtain these,

- Divide the lower engine speed limit by the upper engine speed limit.
- Multiply all the road speed percentage figures already calculated by the figure obtained above.

Considering third gear in the example,

- 10000/12,500 = 0.8
- Road speed at 10000revs/min in third = 0.8 x 77% = 62%

These two columns map out the range of road speeds covered by each gear and in the last column I have listed the overlap between the gears. A negative value means there isn't any. We might conclude the following.

- The coverage is generally reasonable with increasing overlap as speeds rise. This is how it should be.
- Clutch slip is required up to about 42% of top speed. This is due to the fairly high first gear. A lower option is available for this particular cluster but it further compromises the change from first to second and so the best option could only be decided with a much closer examination in relation to a specific track.
- Corners taken at around 64% of top speed would require a lot of skill. The engine would be screaming in second but if you let the roadspeed drop below 62% of maximum then the engine would drop out of the powerband in third.

I hope that these examples give some idea of how to roughly assess the internal ratios available to you. It does require experience and is obviously more critical for small bikes because the surplus torque available is much less.

The best thing to do initially is to put together data for bikes you have already ridden. That way you will be able to get a feel for how the figures translate onto the track.

It would be nice to be able to suggest some magic mathematical progression for the ratios but this is not realistic given the range of uses, track configurations and engine characteristics possible. One 'text book' approach is to select the ratios so that after changing up to the next gear, the engine speed drops to that at which maximum torque is produced. This is an excellent idea and is something to aim for in the higher gears but, if you try to apply it to all the ratios, the gearbox will not produce a wide enough range of road speeds when the powerband is narrow.

As usual, anything that yields realistic results requires a lot more work and I will outline a suitable method in the next chapter. Internal ratios are always a compromise when you are limited to six speeds or less.

Table 2.9 *Determining the range of road speeds, as a percentage of top speed, that are covered by the gear set.*

Gear Number	Normalised Ratio	Engine Speed After Change at 12500rpm	Max Road Speed % at 12500rpm	Max Road Speed % at 10000rpm	Road Speed covered by adjacent gears
1	1.913	----------------	52	42	--------------
2	1.511	9873	66	53	-1
3	1.298	10738	77	62	4
4	1.163	11200	86	69	8
5	1.078	11586	93	74	12
6	1.000	11596	100	80	13

2.4 Driving force

Introduction

The information given in the last three chapters should help you to make a general assessment of engine/gearbox suitability. Unfortunately, to obtain a clear picture of how the engine characteristics and gearbox ratios really interact we need to do some more calculations. These will allow us to predict the actual driving force available at the back wheel. At the begining of Chapter 2.1 I listed the main aspects that influence acceleration and as far as the engine/gearbox is concerned we obviously want to maximise the driving force delivered to the rear wheel at all road speeds.

You may of course be in the fortunate position of having so much driving force available that you cannot control the bike or the wheelspin but that is unlikely. For the majority, every minuscule increase in driving force that can be obtained will translate into improved performance, except perhaps at relatively low road speeds in first gear.

The object of this chapter is therefore to look at the driving force produced in more detail and suggest ways of comparing different engine/gearbox combinations.

There are several methods of doing this and I have chosen the method which I find the most straightforward. It is somewhat tedious (as are all the methods) and if you have access to a computer with a spreadsheet program then the task can be changed from something rather time consuming into something fairly trivial.

To do what is proposed you will need to know details of the engine's power curve (or torque) and the internal ratios in the gearbox. If the engine is standard then you can usually prise this data out of the manufacturers fairly easily and do the work before parting with any money. For a non standard engine there is no alternative to conducting suitable dyno tests in order to get the data.

It pays to find out if any alternative gearsets exist and be warned that they will not be cheap. An aftermarket cluster that is produced in small batches for popular engines is likely to set you back about £1000 and individual gear pairings, eg a higher first gear, can also be several hundred pounds. For one-offs, to your own spec for an untried engine, the cost will be very high indeed so it certainly pays to give this aspect some of your time before making decisions. I will have more to say about gears in the next chapter but what you must not do is cut corners on quality. Gearbox failures are nearly always both painful and expensive!

Peak power and gearing

The driving force at the rear wheel is proportional to the torque produced so to obtain the maximum force we need to deliver the highest torque possible. It may therefore seem that we are primarily concerned with the engine's torque curve and can begin by selecting the one that indicates the greatest torque delivery. Unfortunately it is not quite as simple as this and so I shall begin by considering the way we perceive power and torque.

Firstly, we think of a powerful bike as having the potential to travel at high road speeds. This is technically correct and there is a relationship between the ultimate top speed that a bike can achieve and the power it produces. Just how fast it can go will depend on the resistance to motion and this varies dramatically from one bike to another. However, if we stick to the same bike then more power gives more top speed provided you can optimise the gearing to suit.

Also note that we are only concerned with peak power here. If we fit two totally different engines, eg a four stroke single and a two stroke twin, then, if the peak power they produce is identical, the top speed achieved in each case will be similar though the overall gearing requirements to do this may be totally different.

Although the top speed attainable will depend on resistance to motion (which has not been considered yet), we can get a rough idea of what is involved by studying the mass of test data available for road bikes. Obviously there are limitations to this approach. You cannot believe everything that you read; there is no guarantee that the overall gearing is optimised and not everyone can get the best out of a bike. Nevertheless, there is so much data available that a fairly clear picture of the power-road speed relationship emerges.

Figs 2.26 and 2.27 are based on the mass of road test data available. Because the resistance to motion varies considerably there is a zone to consider rather than just a line. Obviously a racing bike should err on the low power-high speed side of this data. Ideally it should be a lot better (lower resistance to motion) but many are not, indeed some are worse than road bikes. More of this later. As an example, consider Fig 2.26. To achieve a top speed of 160km/hr takes between 17 and 29kW according to how 'slippery' the bike is. In Fig 2.27, the imperial equivalent, 100miles/hr involves 23-40bhp. These are of course wide variations and serve to show how important resistance to motion can be. Even so, these graphs do provide a starting point. It is also worth pointing out the vast increase in power that is required to raise top speed significantly. This is something that I will cover in detail later on. Returning to the subject in hand, it is clear that peak power will

Below. Fig 2.26 *This graph shows the relationship between power at the rear wheel and the maximum road speed attainable. It is based on a large number of road bike tests published in the motorcycle press.*

Right. Fig 2.27 *This graph holds the same data as Fig 2.26 but is given in imperial units for those who prefer to use them.*

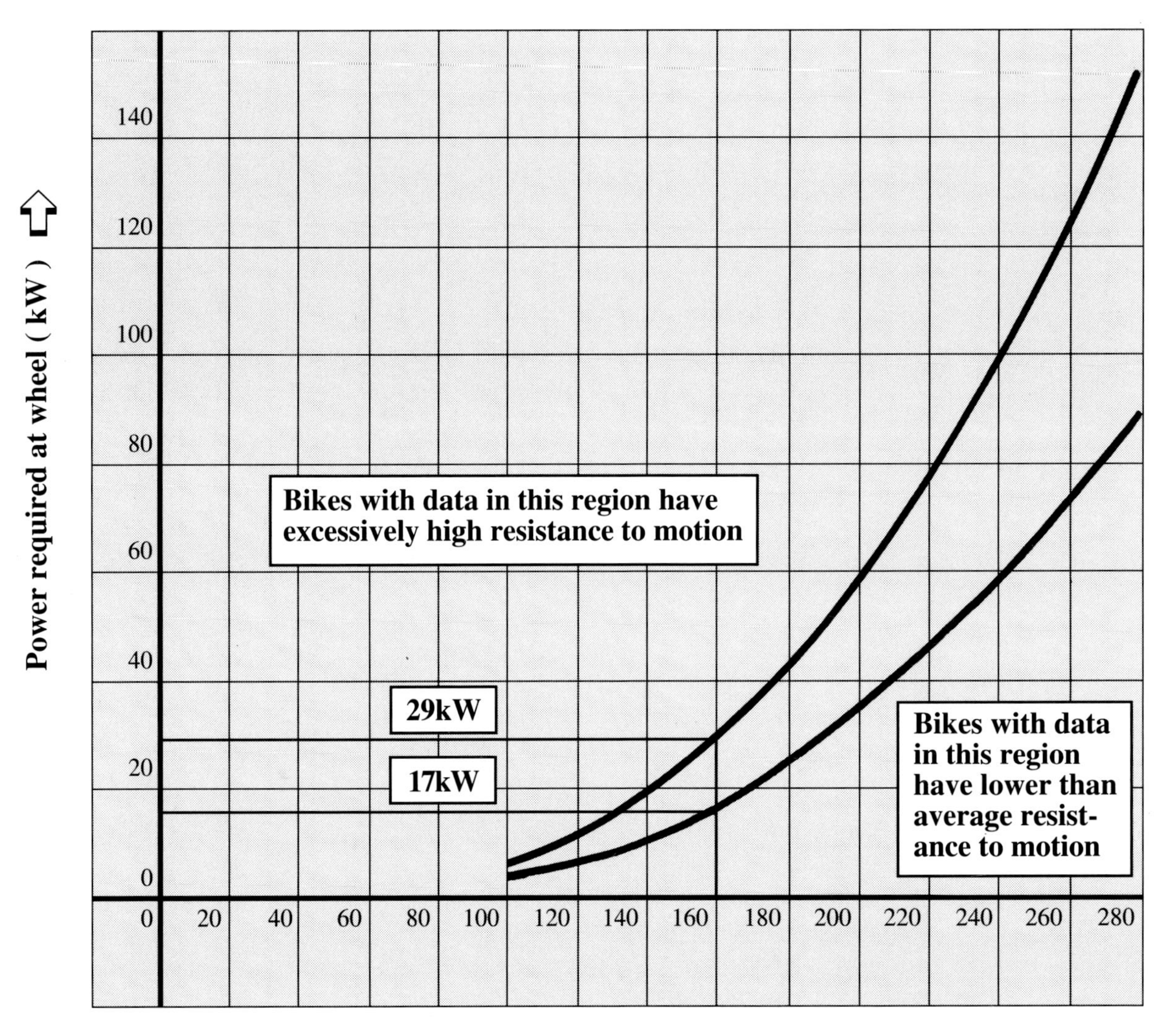

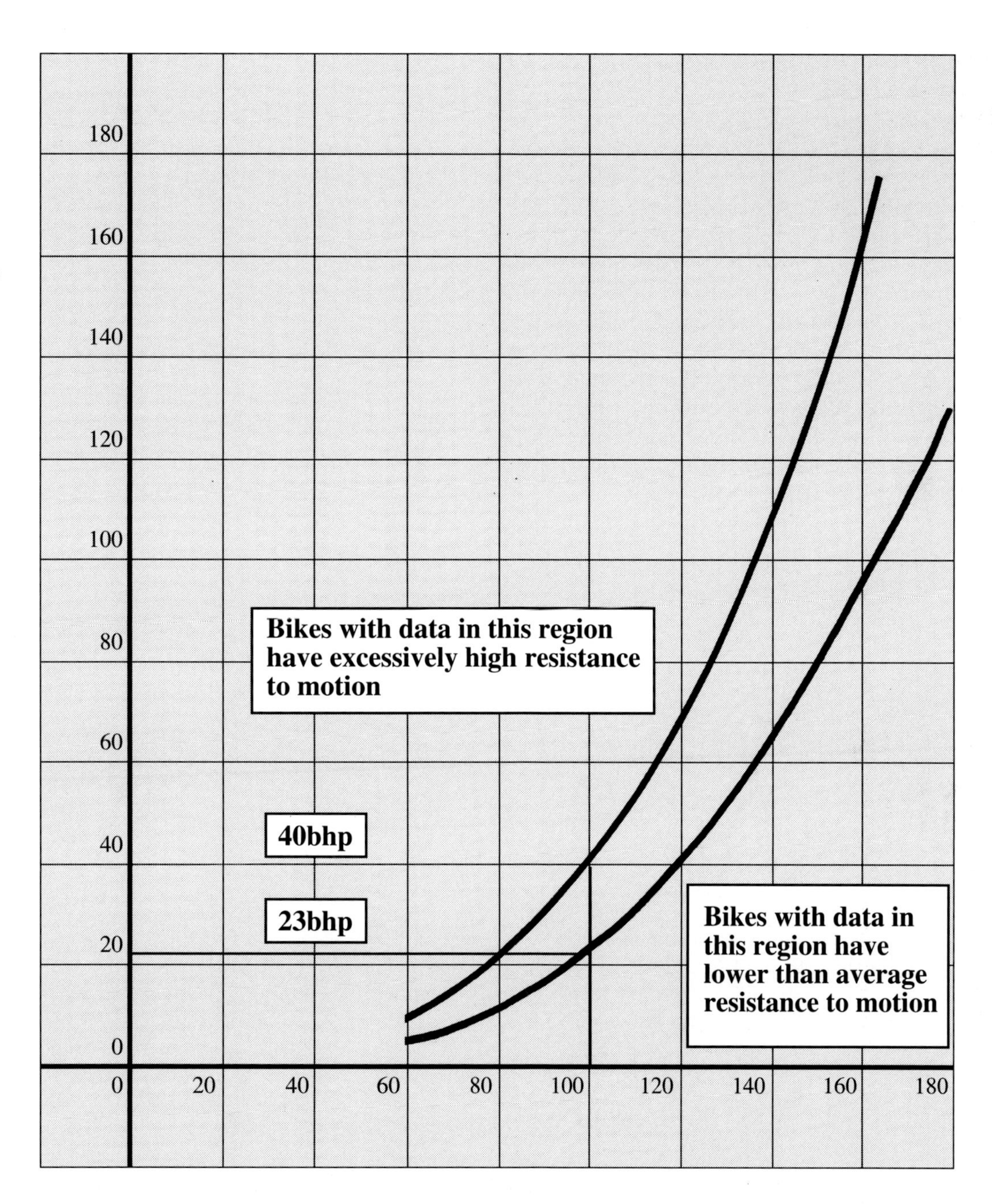

Power required at wheel (bhp)
180
160
140
120
100
80
60
40
20
0
0
20
40
60
80
100
120
140
160
180
Bikes with data in this region have excessively high resistance to motion
40bhp
23bhp
Bikes with data in this region have lower than average resistance to motion
Desired road speed (miles/hr)

determine the ultimate top speed that the bike is capable of. The engine speed at which this peak is produced will therefore determine the overall gearing required when speed is the ultimate goal. This can have interesting effects on the torque delivery to the back wheel.

Fig 2.28 depicts the same bike using two engines **A** and **B** which both produce the same peak power. Apart from this, the engines are very different because **A** gives peak power at 6000revs/min while **B** does so at 12000revs/min. Because of this, engine **A** will produce twice as much torque as **B** under these conditions and the diagram attaches some specific figures for illustration. With 60kW at the engine, the torque figures are 95.5N-m and 47.75N-m respectively. It may therefore seem that **A** has a substantial torque advantage and will generate more driving force at the wheel. The problem with this is that we have not yet considered gearing.

If we assume that 60kW can run the bike up to 225km/hr (140miles/hr) and gear the bike to achieve this then with engine **A** fitted an overall top gear ratio of around 3:1 will be required, the exact value depending on tyre size.

Engine **B** is different. It peaks at twice the speed of **A** and therefore this engine will need much lower gearing, a ratio of around 6:1.

As a result of these gearing requirements the rear wheel torque with engine **A** is nominally three times what the engine produces (ignoring transmission inefficiency) while that produced by engine **B** is magnified six times. The final result is that both engines give the same torque at the wheel under peak power conditions.

Fig 2.28 Effect of gearing requirements on torque delivery to the wheel at peak power engine speed. The transmission efficiency is taken as 100%.

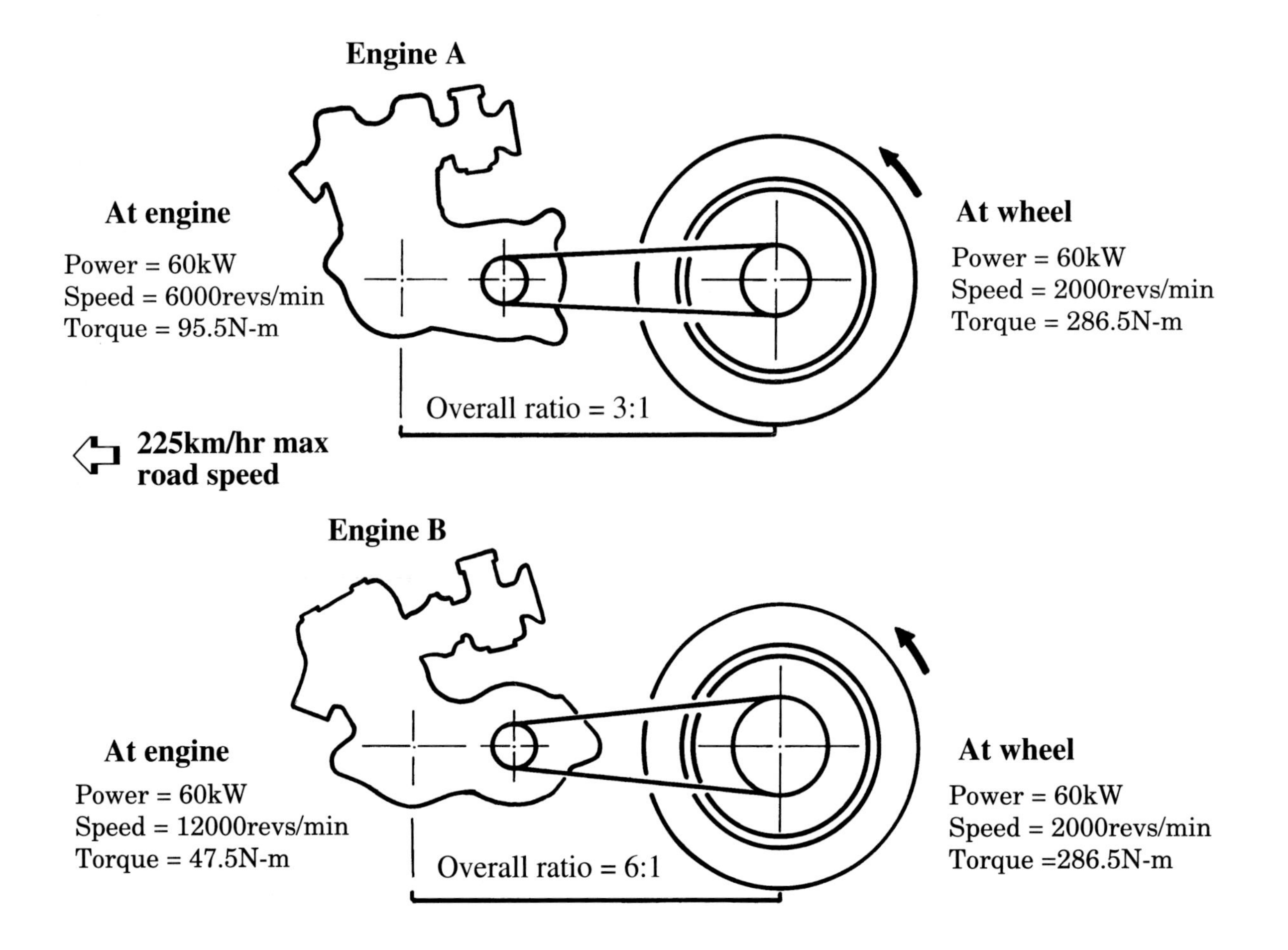

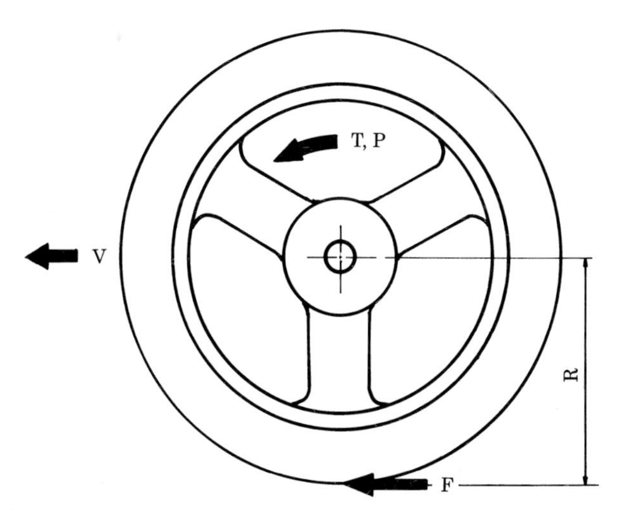

V = roadspeed, F = driving force, T = torque, P = power, R = rolling radius of wheel

$$F(N) = \frac{T(N\text{-}m)}{R(m)}$$

$$F(lbf) = \frac{T(lbf\text{-}ft)}{R(ft)}$$

or

$$F(N) = \frac{3600P(kW)}{V(km/hr)}$$

$$F(lbf) = \frac{375P(bhp)}{V(miles/hr)}$$

Fig 2.29 *Driving force can be related to rear wheel power or torque. The need to accelerate rotating parts is being neglected at this stage.*

This is a rather longwinded way of proving something simple but it does make the point that gearing is crucial to what arrives at the back wheel and you cannot jump to conclusions on the basis of engine torque values alone.

The next question is of course what happens when we are not at peak power? What happens when we set the overall gearing much lower than that required for true top speed? These are the realities of the race track and what follows will allow you to investigate as many possibilities as you wish, thereby providing a useful means of comparing different engine/gearbox combinations.

Driving force

The thing that really matters is the driving force at the rear wheel. This can be related to either the torque available at the rear wheel or the power available at the rear wheel as shown in Fig 2.29. Dealing with torque first, the torque available actually has to do two things. It has to accelerate the rotating parts and what is left over appears as a driving force to accelerate the bike. If we include the first aspect at this stage things are going to get complicated and it is much easier to ignore it for now. It can be introduced later on much more easily and in any event if you are using the best components you can afford there is probably not much that can be done to reduce the torque required to accelerate rotating parts.

Accepting this, and assuming there is no tyre slip, the torque appears as a driving force between the road surface and the tyre. This is then imparted to the wheel spindle and pushes the bike forward. The maximum driving force available at the back wheel is given by, driving force = torque/wheel radius. This immediately raises the question of wheel size. Will different sizes of tyres give more or less driving force? The general answer is no but there are exceptions which I will mention in a moment. Taking the usual case, a small wheel will have to rotate at higher speed in order to move the bike at a given road speed. This means that the overall gearing has to be higher (small ratio) and the torque delivered is therefore less, thus cancelling out the effect.

If the tyre can slip then things are different. Grass track racing is a good example and any experienced rider will tell you that a 22inch rear wheel gives more drive than a 19inch wheel when fitted to a 500cc bike. This is the complete opposite to what was implied but the reason lies with the lack of grip. The 500cc bike can spin the rear tyre almost continuously and this limits the driving force that can be generated. When a larger rear tyre is used the increased radius gives a lower driving force and that allows the tyre to bite more effectively thus picking up more drive. Although the gearing requirement is altered, the bike is invariably geared well below that required for true top speed because the tracks are short and an element of wheelspin is essential for cornering in a powerslide. Under these conditions simple sums do not apply.

We can, alternatively, relate driving force to power and road speed. Note how wheel radius does not present itself here, it is actually buried in the calculation of road speed. I prefer to use power as a means of calculating driving force simply because power curves are more common than torque curves and a lot of dyno tests are carried out at the rear wheel. These are the figures we need and the ones I shall now use.

Ultimate driving force

Since the driving force is ultimately determined by the power available we can begin our assessment of engine suitability by looking at the peak power produced.

If we had an infinitely variable gearbox so that the engine could be kept running at full power engine speed, irrespective of road conditions, then the force available at the rear wheel would vary with road speed along the lines of Fig 2.30. A graph like this is easily constructed using either of the following formulae.

$$\text{Driving force (N)} = \frac{3600P}{V}$$

where P = power at wheel in kW
V = road speed in km/hr

or

$$\text{Driving force (lbf)} = \frac{375P}{V}$$

where P = power at wheel in hp
V = road speed in miles/hr

This decline in force with speed is most upsetting but it is a fact of life. Power = force x linear velocity so if we go faster the force will reduce, assuming constant power. The engine with the greatest peak power output will produce the largest force values on such a graph but this does not mean that it will produce the greatest acceleration, even if the bikes are otherwise identical. The reason for this is that we do not have an infinitely variable gearbox and the engine cannot be kept running at its point of maximum power.

What Fig 2.30 effectively represents is the 'ultimate' driving force we could hope for from the peak power available and the object is therefore to get as close to this as we can, given the problems of power band, gear ratios, and the need to run the bike at any possible road speed that is attainable on the circuit. A racing bike has a maximum of six gears and for each gear there will be a limited range of road speeds that allow the engine to remain in the power band. First gear will produce the greatest torque delivery to the wheel because the gear ratio has the largest numerical value, but it also covers only the lowest range of road speeds. As we select higher gears the ratio value is smaller so the torque gets less while the road speeds corresponding to the power band get higher, assuming of course that there is sufficient power to overcome the resistance acting on the bike.

If we calculate the driving force available in each gear and plot this against the corresponding road speeds then something like Fig 2.31 overleaf results in which our nice smooth 'ultimate' force curve has been replaced by a set of curves, one for each gear. These are commonly called 'cascades' and may be produced for torque or driving force. I have chosen to work with force since this is what will be required if you want to quantify the speed -time history that the motorcycle might achieve.

The area between these curves and the 'ultimate' force line is the shortfall in driving force due to having a limited number of gears and an infinitely variable road speed that forces the engine to operate over a range of crankshaft speeds. In this particular example, which I will work through

Right. Fig 2.30 *Example of the force available at the wheel when the power output is constant. In practice this would require an infinitely variable gearbox and straight track but it does provide something to aspire to.*

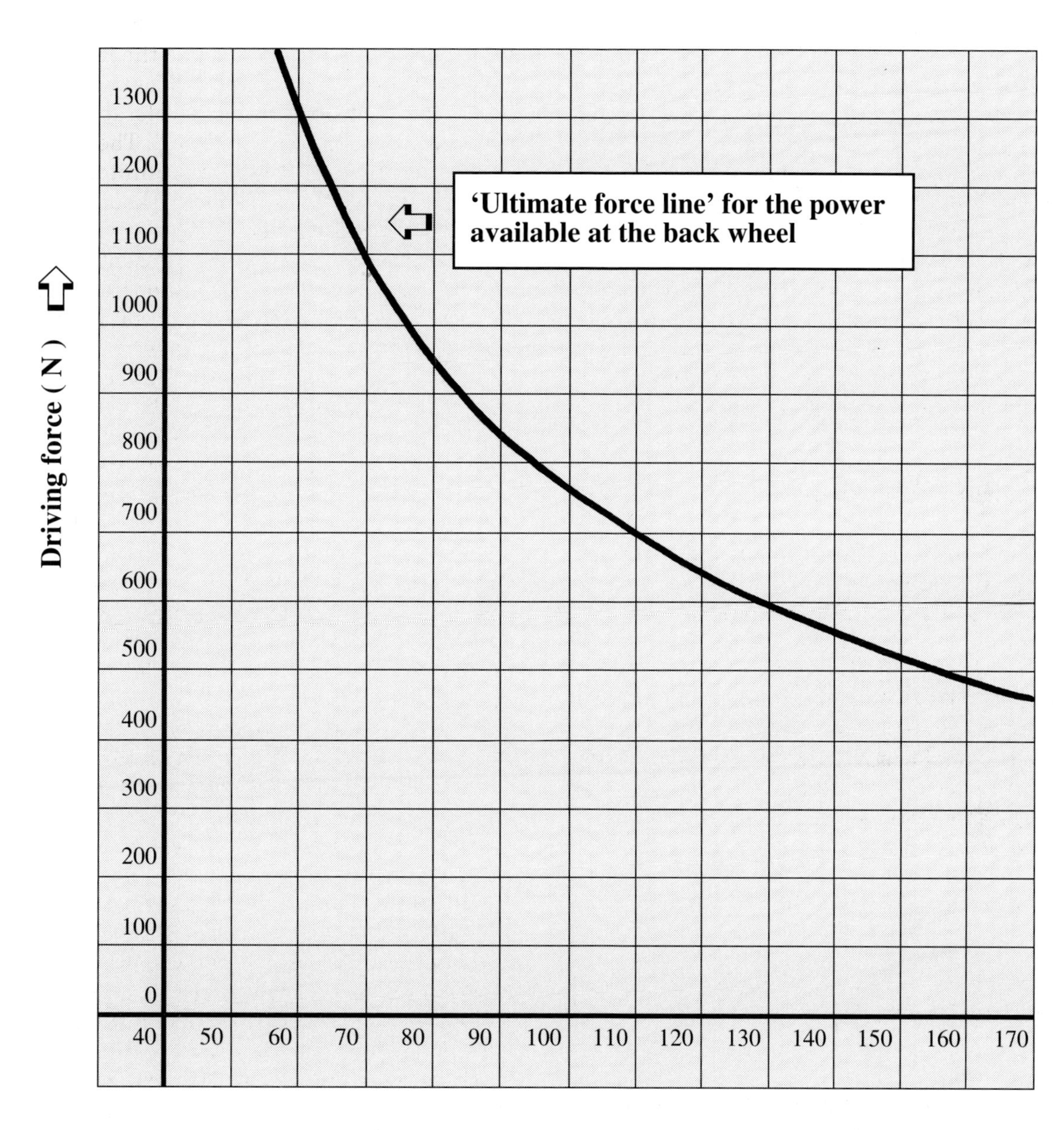
'Ultimate force line' for the power available at the back wheel
Driving force (N)
1300
1200
1100
1000
900
800
700
600
500
400
300
200
100
0
40
50
60
70
80
90
100
110
120
130
140
150
160
170
Road speed (km/hr)

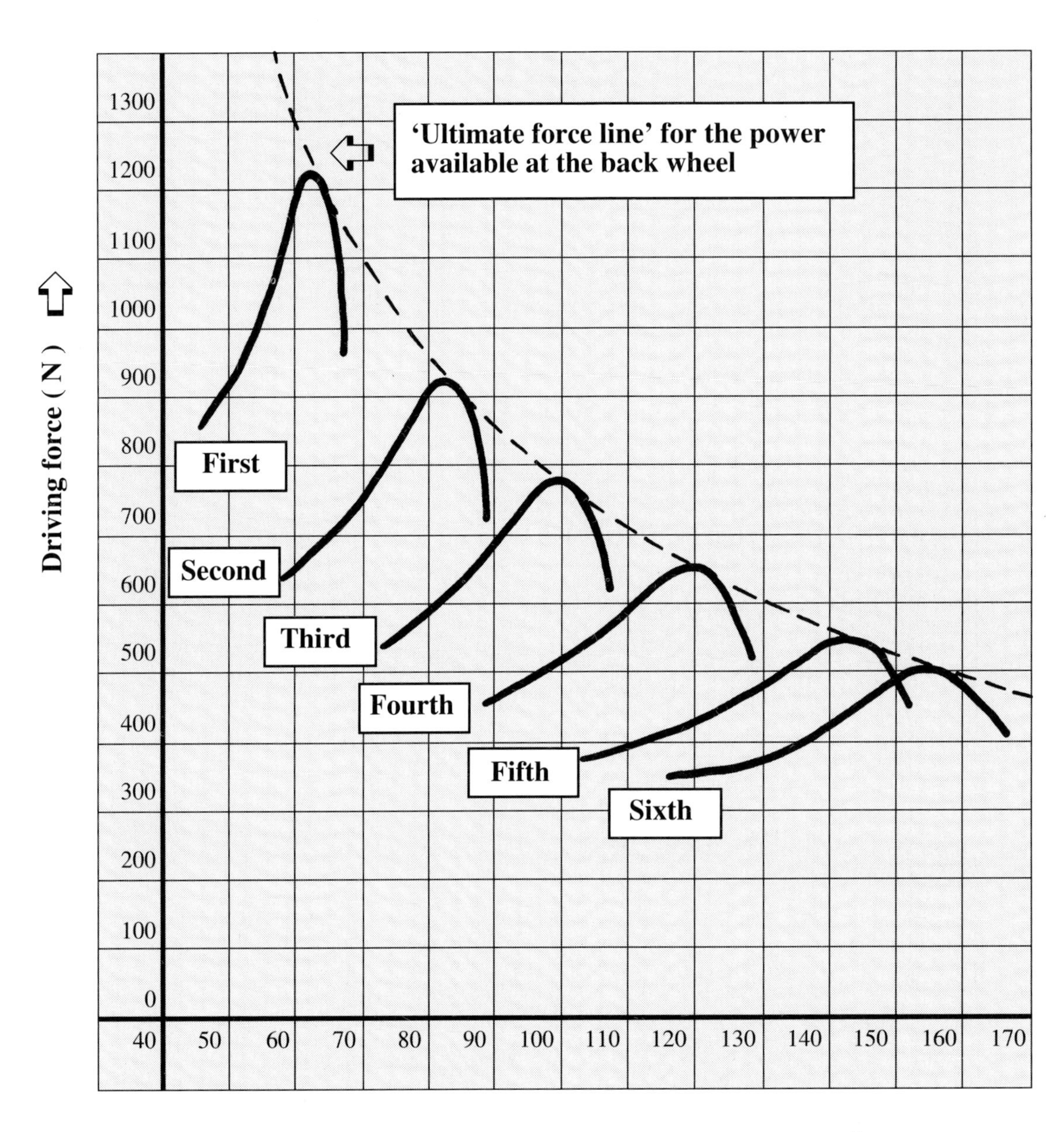

Fig 2.31 *Example of the driving force at the wheel for an engine fitted with a six speed gearbox. The individual curves for each gear only touch the 'ultimate' force curve produced by constant power at one point and the area between the two graphs represents the shortfall in force delivery due to gearbox and power band restrictions.*

step by step in a moment, a number of problems are evident. The shape of the power curve is typical of a small two stroke racing engine but the gear ratios being used are not really suitable for it.

Starting with first gear it is clear that the ratio is relatively low with clutch slip only being required up to about 45km/hr (28miles/hr). This makes starting easy but the consequences are evident as we approach second gear. The two gears are so far apart that even if the engine is revved right out to its mechanical limit there is a drop in driving force of around 230N (52lbf) when we change up to second gear. This may not sound much but the example is only 125cc and the drop is 33% of what the engine provides when second gear is first selected. Changing gear any sooner makes the situation even worse. When the change is made, at about 67km/hr (42miles/hr), the engine drops well down the powerband in second and is clearly delivering a lot less driving force than it is capable of. A similar situation continues right through into fifth gear.

The transition from fifth to sixth is rather better and it certainly needs to be. With the curves overlapping it is necessary to change gear at the crossover point in order to maximise the force delivered to the wheel. At present all these changes relate to road speed but I will show how they can be related to engine speed shortly.

If the suggested gearchange points are adopted then we achieve the best driving force 'envelope' we can hope for. This is shown in Fig 2.32 and the shaded area represents the shortfall in force delivery, relative to the 'ultimate' force line discussed initially. This particular example is fairly clear cut. To get any real improvement a higher first

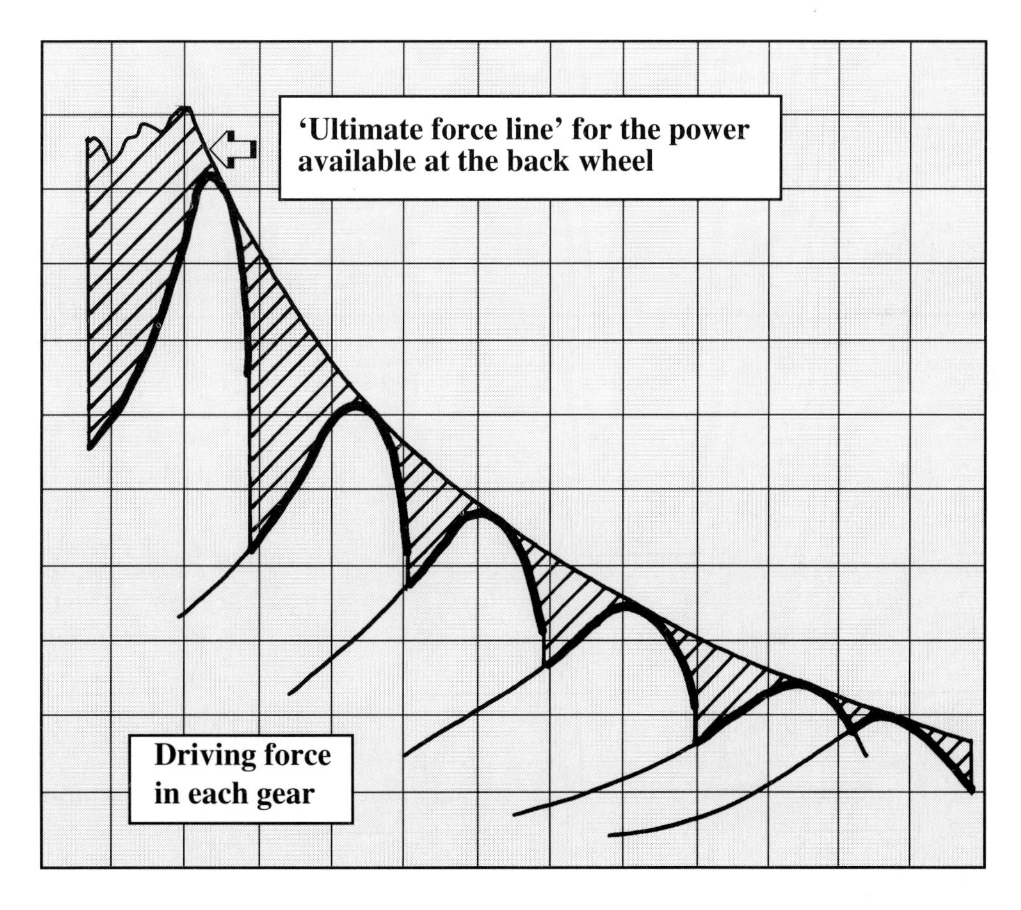

Fig 2.32 *This diagram shows the maximum driving force we can obtain from the data in Fig 2.31. To achieve this it is necessary to change gear at specific points. The shortfall, as represented by the shaded area, will increase if gearchanges are made at any other point.*

gear is essential and if this is done the four intermediate gears will need to change as well. Every case is an individual one but for the moment we could make the following general observations.

- The engine with the greatest peak power will produce the highest 'ultimate' driving force graph.

- The engine with the greatest peak power will produce the highest top speed from the bike if it is correctly geared.

- It is possible that the engine with the greatest peak power will not always produce the best acceleration because the driving force may be inferior at all speeds other than those at which peak power is produced. Since it is acceleration that usually wins races, this is important.

- The shape of the power curve and the suitability of the gear ratios is extremely influential. Two engines having identical power curves will produce different acceleration if the internal ratios are different. An engine that is slightly down on peak power compared to another may well give better acceleration if its power curve and gears are better matched.

- Gearchange points are critical to the whole matter and I shall look at this in detail. The good news is that once you have a fixed set of internal ratios and have determined the engine speeds to change up at, these speeds will not change when the overall gearing is altered.

Given the dramatic influence that these factors can have on acceleration there is really no alternative to plotting out such a graph for each case you want to consider. This will not only account for peak power, it will include the shape of the power curve, the width of the powerband and the influence of the gear ratios all in one go. Even this will not tell you everything you want to know but it is as good as you are going to get without being circuit specific.

Calculating driving force

The procedure that follows is simple but tedious. Nevertheless, it is well worth the effort considering the cost of the components involved. The general method is as follows and I will discuss each step by working through an example.

- Decide on an overall top gear ratio and calculate the final drive ratio involved.

- Determine the overall ratio for each of the gears.

- Find the road speeds corresponding to a range of engine speeds in each gear.

- Calculate the driving force at the wheel corresponding to each road speed and, ideally, plot the values of force and road speed on a graph.

- Find the optimum gearchange points.

- Compare graphs for different gearsets or engine/gearbox combinations.

There are several formulae involved, some of which have appeared before. These are listed in Fig 2.33 with both metric and imperial options.

Right. Fig 2.33 *Formulae used to determine the variation of rear wheel force with road speed. These can easily be programmed into a spreadsheet application making the calculations much less tedious.*

<table>
<tr><th>Reference in text</th><th>Formula</th><th>Metric version</th><th>Imperial version</th></tr>
<tr><td>1</td><td>Overall top gear =</td><td>$\frac{Nr}{2652.6V}$</td><td>$\frac{Nr}{168.1V}$</td></tr>
<tr><td>2</td><td>Final drive ratio =</td><td colspan="2">$\frac{\text{overall ratio}}{\text{primary ratio x internal top}}$</td></tr>
<tr><td>3</td><td colspan="3">Overall ratio = primary x internal x final drive ratio</td></tr>
<tr><td>4</td><td>Road speed =</td><td>$\frac{Nr}{2652.6G}$ (km/hr)</td><td>$\frac{Nr}{168.1G}$ (mph)</td></tr>
<tr><td>5</td><td>Driving force =</td><td>$\frac{3600P}{V}$ (N)</td><td>$\frac{375P}{V}$ (lbf)</td></tr>
<tr><td colspan="2">N = engine speed revs/min
r = rolling tyre radius
P = net power at back wheel
G = overall gear ratio</td><td>V in km/hr
r in mm
P in kW</td><td>V in miles/hr
r in inches
P in bhp</td></tr>
</table>

Example. The following example is based on the data given in Table 2.10.

Step 1. Select an overall top gear.

The results we get are determined directly by the gearing since lower overall gearing would give more torque delivery. We can in fact do what is required by picking any arbitrary ratio, 1:1 if you like, but the results, though perfectly good for comparison, will not relate to real track road speeds and most people seem to prefer this.

The gearing could be calculated to obtain maximum top speed using the data already given for power vs road speed. Alternatively, for an existing bike you can use whatever gearing is currently fitted for a particular circuit. In general I simply gear the bike for a top speed that I know it will be capable of. Since my interest lies with small capacity bikes, a figure of 160km/hr (100miles/hr) seems appropriate. If you are dealing with larger capacity bikes then a proportionally higher figure could be chosen.

To find the overall top gear ratio required for this or any other road speed, use equation 1 in Fig 2.33. I generally assume the engine is running at maximum power but you could just as easily use the maximum safe engine speed. It does not matter, provided you are consistent.

Taking the data given in Table 2.10, and using a maximum speed of 160km/hr,

$$\text{Overall top gear} = \frac{Nr}{2652.6V}$$

$$= \frac{12500 \times 300}{2652.6 \times 160}$$

$$= 8.84:1$$

Step 2. Find the final drive ratio.

Using equation 2 in Fig 2.33,

$$\text{Final drive ratio} = \frac{\text{overall ratio}}{\text{primary} \times \text{int. top}}$$

$$= \frac{8.84}{3.28 \times 1}$$

$$= 2.694:1$$

Step 3. Find the overall ratio in each gear.

Using equation 3 in Fig 2.33,

Overall ratio = primary x internal x final

eg first gear = 3.28 x 2.462 x 2.694

= 21.76:1

Table 2.10 *Data used for the worked example.*

Constants: primary ratio = 3.28:1, rolling radius = 300mm				
Internal ratios		Engine data		
		Speed (revs/min)	Power (kW)	Power (hp)
		9000	11.2	15.0
First	2.462	10000	13.4	18.0
Second	1.875	11000	17.2	23.0
Third	1.556	12000	21.3	28.5
Fourth	1.300	12500	21.7	29.1
Fifth	1.091	12750	20.2	27.1
Sixth	1.000	13000	18.0	24.1

Engine Speed (revs/min)	Road Speeds (km/hr) in each gear					
	First	Second	Third	Fourth	Fifth	Sixth
9000	46.8	61.4	74.0	88.6	105.6	115.2
10000	52.0	68.3	82.3	98.5	117.4	128.0
11000	57.2	75.1	90.5	108.3	129.1	140.8
12000	62.4	81.9	98.7	118.2	140.9	153.6
12500	65.0	85.3	102.8	123.1	146.7	160.0
12750	66.3	87.0	104.9	125.5	149.7	163.2
13000	67.6	88.7	107.0	128.0	152.6	166.4

Table 2.11 *Road speeds in each gear at different engine speeds.*

Repeating for all gears we get,

Gear	Overall ratio
First	21.76
Second	16.56
Third	13.75
Fourth	11.49
Fifth	9.64
Sixth	8.84

Step 4. Find the road speeds.

This was done previously in Chapter 2.3. Use equation 4 in Fig 2.33, thus in first gear at 12500revs/min,

$$\text{Road speed km/hr} = \frac{Nr}{2652.6G}$$

$$\text{Road speed km/hr} = \frac{12500 \times 300}{2652.6 \times 21.74}$$

$$= 65\text{km/hr}$$

You can do this for all the engine speeds listed in each gear but it is easier to do it by proportion or plot a graph. If the speed of the bike is 65km/hr at 12500revs/min in first gear then in the same gear at 12000revs/min it will do,

$$65\text{km/hr} \times \frac{12000}{12500} = 62.4\text{km/hr}$$

Similarly, at 10000revs/min in first we get,

$$65\text{km/hr} \times \frac{10000}{12500} = 52.0\text{km/hr}$$

It is usually more than adequate to calculate the road speeds at 1000rev/min intervals and the results of this are shown in Table 2.11.

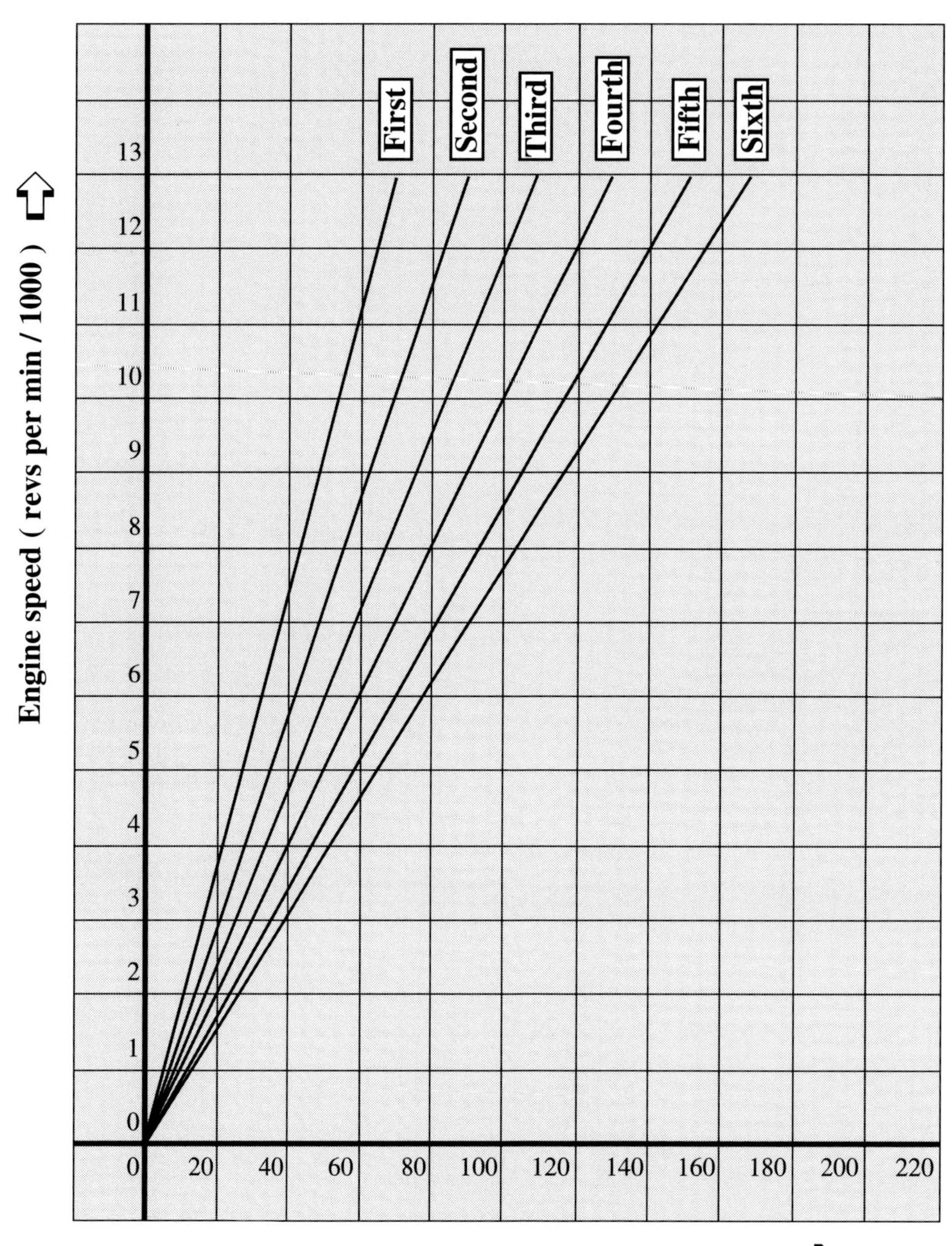
First
Second
Third
Fourth
Fifth
Sixth
Engine speed (revs per min / 1000)
0
1
2
3
4
5
6
7
8
9
10
11
12
13
0
20
40
60
80
100
120
140
160
180
200
220
Road speed (km/hr)

Alternatively, you can calculate just one road speed for each gear and draw up a set of graphs like those in Fig 2.34.

Step 5. Find the driving force

The driving force is calculated using equation 5 in Fig 2.33. To do this, select an engine speed and determine the corresponding road speed as shown in step 4. The driving force available at this road speed can then be calculated using this figure and the corresponding power output. For example, in first gear at 12000revs/min.

Road speed = 62.4km/hr (step 4)

Power = 21.3kW (Table 2.10)

$$\text{Driving force} = \frac{3600P}{V}$$

hence,

$$\text{Driving force} = \frac{3600 \times 21.3}{62.4}$$

$$= 1228.9\text{N}$$

Similarly, in sixth gear at 10000revs/min,

Road speed = 128km/hr (step 4)

Power = 13.4kW (Table 2.10)

$$\text{Driving force} = \frac{3600P}{V}$$

hence,

$$\text{Driving force} = \frac{3600 \times 13.4}{128}$$

$$= 376.8\text{N}$$

Doing this for a range of engine speeds in each gear gives Table 2.12.

Left. Fig 2.34 *Graphs plotted using the data written in Table 2.12. You only need one pair of values for each gear since all the graphs will pass through the origin.*

Below. Table 2.12 *Final data giving driving force and road speed values in each gear.*

Engine Speed (revs/min)	First Gear		Second Gear		Third Gear		Fourth Gear		Fifth Gear		Sixth Gear	
	Force N	Speed km/hr	Force N	Speed km/hr	Force N	Speed km/hr	Force N	Speed km/hr	Force N	Speed km/hr	Force N	Speed km/hr
9000	861.6	46.8	656.3	61.4	544.4	74.0	455.0	88.6	381.7	105.6	350.0	115.2
10000	927.8	52.0	706.7	68.3	586.4	82.3	490.0	98.5	411.0	117.4	376.8	128.0
11000	1082.6	57.2	824.6	75.1	684.2	90.5	571.7	108.3	479.5	129.1	439.7	140.8
12000	1228.9	62.4	936.1	81.9	776.7	98.7	648.9	118.2	544.4	140.9	499.1	153.6
12500	1201.9	65.0	915.5	85.3	759.6	102.8	634.7	123.1	532.4	146.7	488.2	160.0
12750	1096.9	66.3	835.5	87.0	693.3	104.9	579.2	125.5	485.9	149.7	445.5	163.2
13000	958.6	67.6	730.2	88.7	605.9	107.0	506.2	128.0	424.6	152.6	389.4	166.4

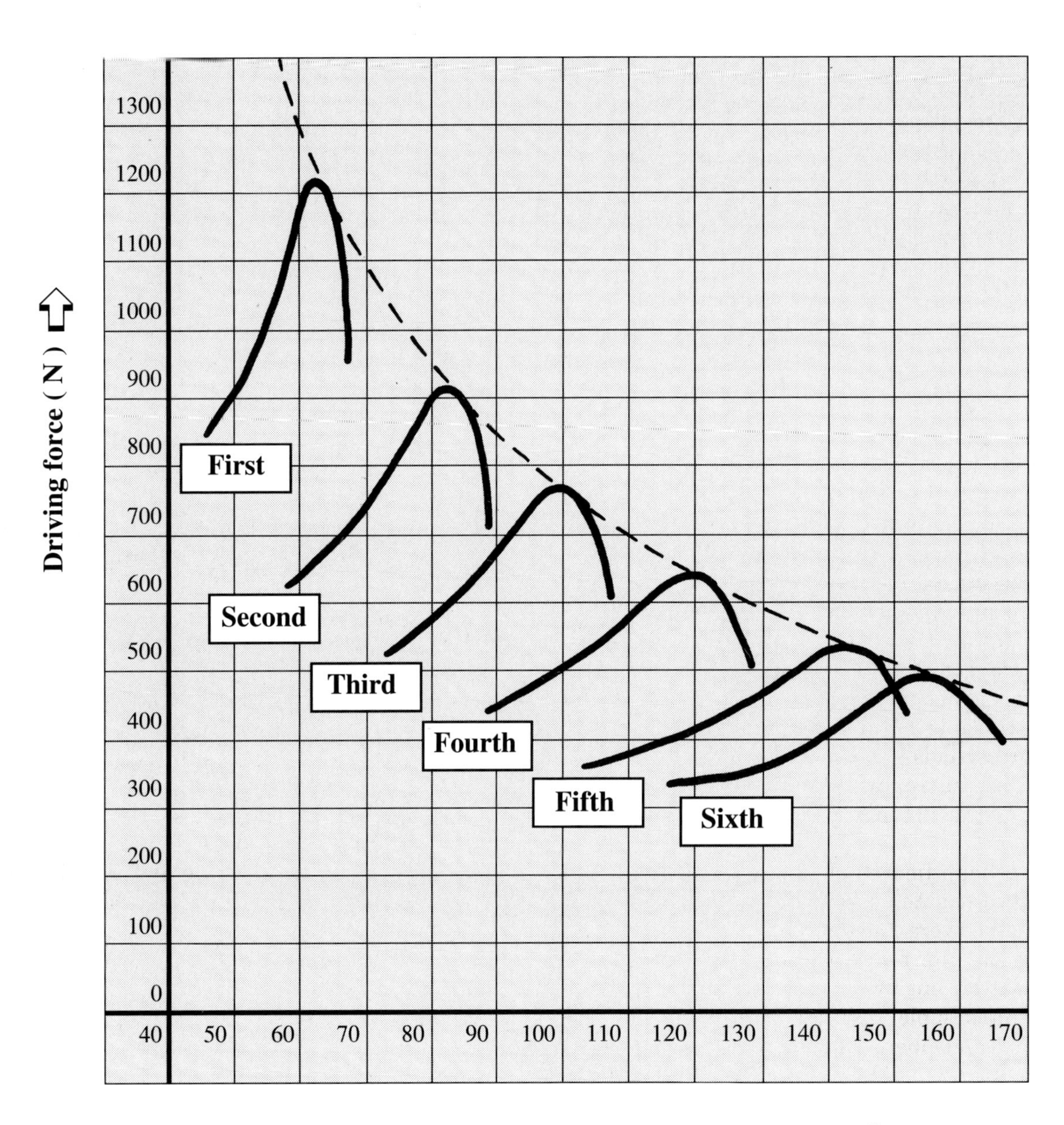
1300
1200
1100
1000
900
800
700
600
500
400
300
200
100
0
40
50
60
70
80
90
100
110
120
130
140
150
160
170
First
Second
Third
Fourth
Fifth
Sixth
Driving force (N)
Road speed (km/hr)

It is possible to get most of what you need from this table but it is much better to plot out this data in the form of a graph - Fig 2.35. It is common practice to superimpose the cascades over the top of the engine speed vs road speed graph so that it is easy to relate the two but some people find this a bit overwhelming. There is nothing wrong with owning two graphs!

Although this may all seem rather tedious it is definitely worth the effort. Once you get used to the idea it is quite easy to do the work longhand in an evening and if you have access to a spreadsheet program (which many people do these days) then it can all be churned out very quickly.

Gearchange points

The example I have worked through is the one originally discussed in relation to Fig 2.31 and therefore all the initial observations about the gearing apply. In this particular case it is necessary to change gear at the red line limit (13000revs/min) in all gears except fifth.

In fifth gear, you need to change into sixth where the two graphs intersect and this corresponds to around 150km/hr on the chosen gearing. By refering back to your table of speed data (the values in Table 2.11 or 2.12 will do) it is clear that this corresponds to about 12750revs/min in fifth. If you took the trouble to produce a graph like that shown in Fig 2.34 then you can read any required values off it.

Once the optimum gearchange points have been related to engine speed they do not alter if you change the overall gearing. They will alter if you change the internal ratios so it is best to thrash such matters out first.

In this example the best point to change gear at is easily remembered, 13000revs/min in the first four gears and 12750revs/min in fifth. Some examples will yield a different speed for every gear and the effect of ignoring this is significant in terms of acceleration.

Left. Fig 2.35 *These are the final cascades produced from the example given. The shortfall in driving force is very evident.*

There are obviously practical limits to how many figures you can keep in your head and the practicalities of racing will prevent your doing it correctly every time. Nevertheless, it is important to look into the general requirements and, if the data says you need to change up at 10000revs/min, you will lose a lot of time by taking the engine up to its red line at perhaps 13000revs/min

Revcounter problems

Discussing this does of course raise the question 'how good is your revcounter?' Answers vary widely but most riders assume that what the revcounter says is gospel. In reality many revcounters are very poor. With some, the steady state calibration is a long way out so that if, for example, you excite the instrument with a signal representing a true input of 10000revs/min it may well read 10500revs/min.

Even worse, it may read 9500 on cold days and 10500 on hot days! Problems like this are easily spotted by routine calibration but their significance should not be underestimated. Differences of a few hundred revs/min can be crucial to maximising the driving force.

More difficult to deal with are linearity and damping problems. What I mean by linearity is the way the readings tie up through the whole range. For example, if the instrument is calibrated correctly at 10000revs/min is it then correct at say 5000revs/min? If the error is unacceptable then re-calibration at this lower speed can produce more error at the higher speed. How well you can solve this depends on the design of the instrument and the calibration facilities available. Whatever the case it will be a compromise and it needs to be done in such a way that the errors are smallest in the normal working range, ie that corresponding to the powerband.

The matters discussed so far only address the static calibration problems. In reality the revcounter has to try and track speed variations that take place extremely rapidly and, since it does not know a change of speed is about to occur, it cannot anticipate it and therefore lags behind the true engine speed. There is some inevitability about this. The revcounter has a moving pointer which has to be accelerated but it is also fragile and has to be controlled. Damping can be applied both mechanically and/or electronically to limit overshoot and protect the mechanism from damage but this automatically restricts its speed of response. Provided the overshoot is not excessive there is little you can do about this because if the needle moves any faster you will not be able to follow it! I have only discussed these aspects so that you cease to think of the revcounter as some sort of god and appreciate that routine checks and calibration by the manufacturer are an important aspect of performance.

Modified ratios

Returning to the example given, a number of gearbox deficiencies have been noted and the need to come up with new ratios is paramount. Table 2.13 lists an alternative set of ratios for this engine and we can look at the effect they produce on the driving force. First gear has been raised (lower ratio figure) and the rest of the set improved considerably, subject to practical constraints that I will discuss in the next chapter.

Note that the final drive ratio remains unchanged because the new gearset also has a 1:1 internal top gear but if this was not the case then it would have to be altered to retain the 8.83:1 overall gearing before doing all the calculations. All initial comparisons should be done using the same overall top gear ratio and again it is useful to work with normalised ratios when making initial comparisons. Note however that the 'real' ratios will have to be used if you take this work further and seek to predict the speed-time history of the bike..

The results are given in Fig 2.36 and there is a significant improvement in potential force delivery over a wide range of road speeds. I say potential force delivery because certain things are required to achieve it. The rider must change gear at the right engine speed and limiting factors must not cause too many problems. Limiting factors include the amount of grip available and the tendency to wheelie.

In the example, the engine only produces a peak output of 21.4kW (29bhp) so wheelspin and wheelie problems are unlikely given a sensible layout. With larger bikes this aspect becomes more important and you can frequently raise first gear to close up the ratios and still get more driving force than you can control. Wheelspin depends on tyre adhesion which in turn depends on a whole range of things mainly outside your control. However, as a useful guide in these early stages you might expect wheelspin to take place once the driving force exceeds the total laden weight of the motorcycle and rider. This assumes dry road conditions and moderately warm race tyres. It does not apply to dragsters or wet tracks! In the example given, the small bike and rider might weigh 1500N (153kgf, 338lbf) so wheelspin is unlikely to be a problem in the dry. Even with the original low first gear, a maximum driving force of only 1230N was produced. More powerful bikes can present serious wheelspin problems and where this is the case it may be acceptable to use relatively high first gears, subject to track layout.

Provided the new higher gear still gives enough force to spin the wheel then any excess is going to be squandered. First gear will also cover a much higher range of road speeds and this can save on gearchanges at some tracks in addition to allowing better ratios all round.

Below. Table 2.13 *Modified gearset used to improve the driving force from the same engine.*

Right. Fig 2.36 *Cascades produced by the new gearset which has a higher first gear and better spacing of the intermediate gears.*

Gear	Original Ratio	New Ratio
First	2.462	1.913
Second	1.875	1.511
Third	1.556	1.298
Fourth	1.300	1.163
Fifth	1.091	1.078
Sixth	1.000	1.000

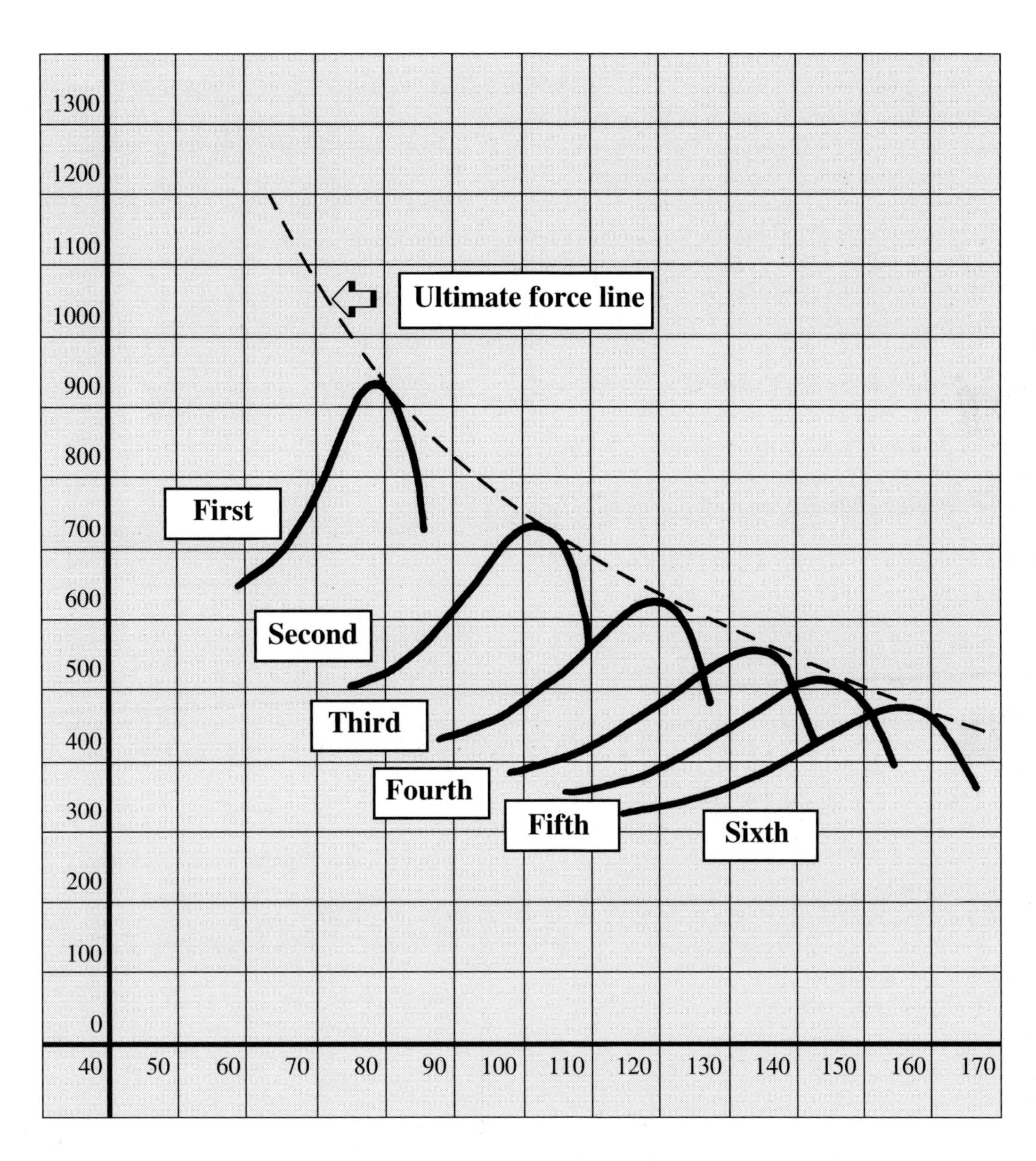
Ultimate force line
First
Second
Third
Fourth
Fifth
Sixth
Driving force (N)
Road speed (km/hr)
1300
1200
1100
1000
900
800
700
600
500
400
300
200
100
0
40
50
60
70
80
90
100
110
120
130
140
150
160
170

Example. As a second example I am going to look at something completely different and have chosen this one because it is a total contrast to what was covered previously. In addition, I shall work in imperial units so that there is one example for each system.

The following analysis is based on a Suzuki GSX - R1100WP engine/gearbox. It has five gears, produces a peak power output of 112bhp at 9750revs/min and has strong, flat torque output which is above 70lbf - ft most of the time. All the relevant data is given in Table 2.14 below.

In this particular example, steps 1 and 2 are not required because the final drive ratio is specified. The bike was fitted with a 15T gearbox sprocket and a 42T rear wheel sprocket giving 2.8:1 for the final drive.

Step 3. Find the overall ratios

Overall ratio = primary x internal x final

For example, in first gear,

Overall ratio = 1.565 x 2.714 x 2.8

= 11.892:1

Repeating this for the other gears gives,

Gear	Overall ratio
First	11.892
Second	7.927
Third	6.174
Fourth	5.175
Fifth	4.549

Step 4. Find the road speeds.

This is done using the imperial version of equation 4 in Fig 2.33,

$$\text{Road speed miles/hr} = \frac{Nr}{168.1G}$$

For example, in first gear at 3500revs/min,

$$\text{Road speed miles/hr} = \frac{3500 \times 11.8}{168.1 \times 11.892}$$

$$= 20.66\text{miles/hr}$$

Table 2.14 *Data used for GSX - R1100WP driving force example.*

Constants: primary ratio = 1.565:1, final drive ratio = 2.8:1, rolling radius = 11.8inches			
Internal Ratios		**Engine Data**	
		Speed (revs/min)	**Power (bhp)**
First	2.714	3500	40
Second	1.809	4000	50
		5000	63
Third	1.409	6000	75
		7000	93
Fourth	1.181	8000	106
		9000	110
Fifth	1.038	10000	110
		10750	102

Engine Speed (revs/min)	First Gear		Second Gear		Third Gear		Fourth Gear		Fifth Gear	
	Force lbf	Speed miles/hr	Force lbf	Speed miles/hr	Force lbf	Speed miles/hr	Force lbf	Speed miles/hr	Force lbf	Speed miles/hr
3500	726	20.7	484	31.0	377	39.8	316	47.5	278	54.0
4000	794	23.6	530	35.4	412	45.5	346	54.3	304	61.7
5000	801	29.5	534	44.3	416	56.8	348	67.8	306	77.1
6000	794	35.4	530	53.1	412	68.2	346	81.4	304	92.6
7000	844	41.3	563	62.0	438	80.0	367	94.9	323	108.0
8000	842	47.2	561	70.8	437	90.9	366	108.5	322	123.4
9000	777	53.1	518	79.7	403	102.3	338	122.0	297	138.9
10000	699	59.0	466	88.5	363	113.7	304	135.6	267	154.3
10750	603	63.4	402	95.2	313	122.2	262	145.8	231	165.8

Table 2.15 *Driving force and road speed data calculated as shown in the text.*

All such values, for each gear and each engine speed given, are listed in Table 2.15. These have been rounded up to one decimal place.

Step 5. Calculate the driving force.

The driving force is found using the imperial version of equation 5 in Fig 2.33. Power figures come from Table 2.14 and speed data from step 4. Using first gear at 3500revs/min,

Road speed = 20.66miles/hr (step 4)

Power = 40bhp (Table 2.14)

$$\text{Driving force} = \frac{375P}{V}$$

hence,

$$\text{Driving force} = \frac{375 \times 40}{20.66}$$

$$= 726\text{lbf}$$

This calculation is repeated for each engine speed listed using all of the gears and the values are given in Table 2.15 alongside the corresponding road speeds.

As you might expect this engine yields vastly higher driving forces than the previous example. In first gear there is almost 850lbf available and the gear is not particularly low. On the race track a lower overall ratio could easily produce 1000lbf at the back wheel and with a laden weight of perhaps 650lbf this is serious wheelspin and/or wheelie machinery.

Another obvious feature is just how flat the torque curve is. In top gear the driving force shows less than 10% variation between 4000 and 9000revs/min. No razor sharp powerbands here! However, to get a clear picture of what we are dealing with it is best to plot out this data as shown in Fig 2.37 overleaf.

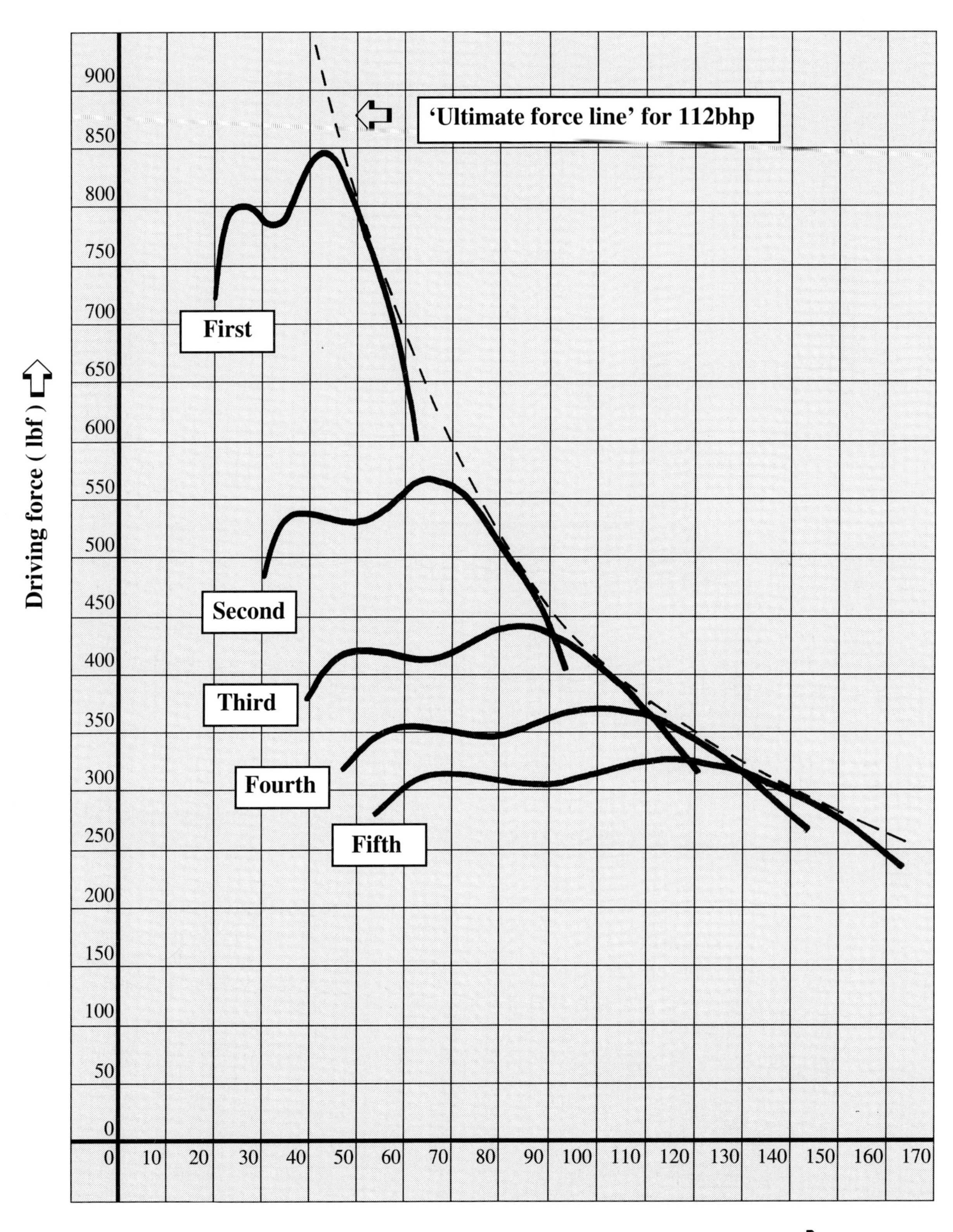
'Ultimate force line' for 112bhp
First
Second
Third
Fourth
Fifth
Driving force (lbf)
900
850
800
750
700
650
600
550
500
450
400
350
300
250
200
150
100
50
0
0 10 20 30 40 50 60 70 80 90 100 110 120 130 140 150 160 170
Road speed (miles/hr)

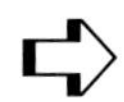

Fig 2.37 shows that the interaction between the engine characteristic and the gear ratios is very different to the previous example. You may recall that the previous example exhibited a 33% drop in driving force when changing from first gear up to second (original ratios) whereas in this case the drop is only 7%. The only thing in common is that the engine needs taking to the limit in first.

The situation with the remaining gears is very different. All curves overlap and do so beyond the point of peak torque. The curves track the ultimate force line so well that fourth gear serves almost no purpose. One could argue that the ratios need to be altered but with so much power available the rider of this bike finds he can short shift into fifth without really sacrificing anything.

Although one might stick out for something different on theoretical grounds the rider has a lot of flexibility in where he changes gear. This can gain valuable time on certain tracks because changing gear in mid-corner can be difficult and roadracing conditions never match those found on the drag strip.

For pure racing, first gear could be raised and the bike would still pull like a train from even the slowest corners. Bear in mind that geared as it is overall this bike is capable of around 165miles/hr and on most racetracks it will not get there due to lack of straights. Geared down overall to suit it is a fearsome beast but that is what people like!

The optimal points for gearchanging are easily calculated. Fig 2.37 shows that they correspond to road speeds of approximately 63miles/hr in first, 92miles/hr in second, 110miles/hr in third and 132miles/hr in fourth. The approximate engine speeds can be found from the tabulated data or, better still, by producing a graph like that shown previously in Fig 2.34. Failing this use,

$$\textbf{Eng. spd.(revs/min)} = \frac{168.1GV}{r}$$

where V = roadspeed at intersection in miles/hr
G = overall ratio in gear concerned
r = rolling radius in ins

For second gear the overall ratio is 7.927, the speed at intersection is 92miles/hr and the rolling radius is 11.8inches thus,

$$\text{Eng. speed} = \frac{168.1 \times 7.927 \times 92}{11.8}$$

$$= 10389\text{revs/min.}$$

By a similar process the figures are,

First to second at 10750revs/min
Second to third at 10389revs/min
Third to fourth at 9675revs/min
Fourth to fifth at 9731revs/min

Taking the engine to its rev limit in every gear is detrimental to the driving force though not dramatically so. In any event, why thrash the motor if changing up at a lower crankshaft speed actually gives better results. The last couple of thousand revs/min has a big influence on wear and reliability.

I do hope that these two contrasting examples have provided a basic insight into what this is all about and have highlighted the sort of things to look for. It is impossible to cover all the options in a book but what I have done should be sufficient to get you started.

At the circuit

Getting the best out of this is basically all work and the general ideas on gearing have already been discussed. Sort out the overall gearing at the circuits concerned using the ratios you already have and identify the corners where the gearing is not ideal. Determine whether the bike is undergeared or overgeared for these corners. If overgeared, note the engine speed and how far out of the powerband it is.

At this stage you have two options. The first is to try and go faster! Ironically, slight overgearing on a corner can be useful because it forces you to

Left. Fig 2.37 *Driving force cascades for the Suzuki GSX - R1100WP example. The main points to note are the flexibility, the way the curves track the constant power line and the fact that fourth gear is almost redundant.*

try harder. Keep pushing things and you may find that you can actually go a bit faster. This may well make the gearing suitable and if this happens on the corner that leads to the longest straight you can then find yourself undergeared when flat out in top. Raising the overall gearing to compensate will put you back where you started!

There are no short cuts to this process. You have to go through it repeatedly and practice is never long enough. Once you believe you have the best set-up write down the final drive ratio and note engine speed at the point where you start to accelerate from each corner.

Based on what you have found you can now go through the driving force routine again using just one or two internal ratio changes to suit the circuit concerned. Your choice of internal ratios is limited by the practical constraints of gear manufacture and what you can afford but it is worth doing the work, especially if other circuits produce similar requirements.

Once you have done this, compare the driving force cascades against those obtained with the original ratios. Ratio selection is never simple because altering any intermediate ratio does more than change that specific gear. It also determines what happens when you change up to it and what happens when you change up from it! If the shortfall from the ultimate power line is similar or reduced slightly then it is worth pursuing the new internal ratios. If there is an obvious increase in shortfall then you have the problem of trying to assess the consequences.

For example, suppose you have two first gear hairpins, a third gear corner and three long straights. Furthermore, assume that third gear is a bit too low so you are considering raising it. This will solve the problem on that corner but there are three 'dragster mode' straights to consider. If the cascades show an obvious loss in straight line performance then any gain on the third gear corner may well be cancelled out. Lap times may well increase and track tests are essential.

Split time data will assist you in sorting out these situations but I'm afraid there are no short cuts. Even a full blown computer simulation requires a great deal of experiment to make it do the job for you. For a start, you need to measure up the whole circuit fairly accurately and then calibrate the software against a specific rider. For the majority, a stop watch and full set of sprockets will do the job more effectively!

Performance summary

At this stage, a logical sequence requires that I look into the performance of a motorcycle in detail. This would yield the relative merits of all the various features and thus assign priorities for the design that follows.

Up to about the tenth rewrite this was what I did but it leads to another thirty pages of sums which some readers may not find very inspiring. Accordingly, I have moved this subject to the end of the book where you can easily ignore it if you wish. No sums are required to summarise the basic requirements and these are as follows.

- Weight is one of the most influential factors and considerable effort should be put into reducing it within the limits of safety. This includes the weight of the rider! Weight reductions improve just about everything.

- Things that rotate with the wheels need special attention. In particular, try to keep the heavy bits at a small radius. Most people will simply use the best components they can afford. Most spoked rims can be lightened but I didn't say so.

- Maximise the driving force as described in this chapter. This will keep you busy for years with engine development and gear ratios.

- Minimise the forces resisting motion. These are dominated by aerodynamic drag which is discussed later. Reducing resistance to motion should be considered as important as developing the engine.

- The centre of gravity location must allow a good balance of braking, cornering and acceleration performance.

- Use good quality suspension, brakes and tyres. Set them up to suit you.

- Open the throttle!

2.5 Chains, sprockets and gears

Introduction

In the previous chapters I have made a number of suggestions concerning gearing. To implement any of the changes discussed it will be necessary to alter sprockets and gears as required and it therefore seems appropriate to discuss at least some of the practicalities involved.

As standard components I intend to cover these items in the second volume of this book, particularly in relation to materials and heat treatment, but I do feel that some basic ideas need to be included here so that you do not try to seek the impossible. You cannot buy gears with half a tooth, at least not ones that work!

Chains

The conventional roller chain was invented in the UK by Renolds and is widely used in all sorts of power transmission systems, not just motorcycles. Industrial drive chains are governed by British and other standards which seek to tie up certain features so that everything works in harmony. The basic sizes which are standardised are those known as the gearing dimensions: pitch, roller diameter and inside width - Fig 2.38. These measurements are vital since sprockets have to be made to suit.

All these dimensions are, historically, Imperial and I am told that there is no legislation currently afoot which will change this. Basic designation comes in the form pitch x inside width, eg 1/2in x 1/4in. Chains are commonly sold with a three digit size code, eg 420 and this system is related to the imperial dimensions as follows. The first digit gives the pitch of the chain in 1/8in increments, ie a 420 chain has a pitch of 4 x 1/8 = 1/2in. 520 chain has a pitch of 5/8in and so on.

The other two digits generally give the inside width of the chain in 1/80ths of an inch so a 415 chain has an inside width of 15/80, ie 3/16in. 420 size chain is 1/2in x 1/4in, 530 chain is 5/8in x 3/8in and so on as detailed in Table 2.16 overleaf. There are one or two exceptions to this general rule. A type 428 chain does not actually have an inside width of 28/80 but in fact has thicker sideplates. Type 428 chain is still 5/16in inside width and will run on the same sprockets as 425 chain. Type 532 chain is another example of the manufacturer using the last digit to indicate something different. In this case it is still a 5/8in x 3/8in chain but the rollers are of a larger diameter. This is important because roller diameter is a fundamental gearing dimension and this chain will not mate correctly with a sprocket machined to the normal 530 dimensions.

You may also find some variation in the sizes quoted for the same chain. The chains are made to Imperial sizes and that normally quoted, eg 1/2in x 1/4in, is the nominal size. Pitch and roller diameter are precisely controlled and any metric equivalents will be exact. However, inside width is not as crucial and specifications often give the maximum value allowed. This can be confusing because there may appear to be errors, eg a nominal 1/4in inside width may appear as 6.7mm even though 1/4in = 6.35mm. 6.7mm is actually the maximum inside width, 6.35mm is the nominal width.

Fig 2.38 *Basic chain dimensions.*

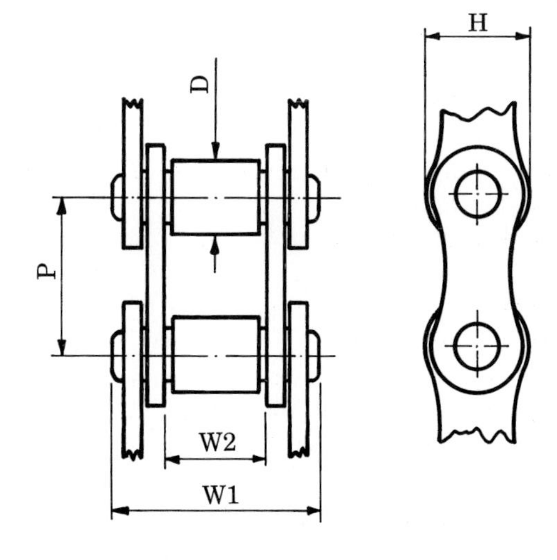

D = roller diameter
P = pitch
W1 = outside width (over rivets)
W2 = inside width
H = maximum depth

Motorcycle chains, as you have probably gathered, do not conform to the industrial drive standards but for obvious reasons they are based on them. The modifications are necessary to provide you with the best performance. Chain performance is conveniently considered under three headings.

- Ability to resist tensile (pulling) loads.
- Fatigue life.
- Wear resistance.

The chain can fail under any of these headings but it should be designed and selected to fail through wear. The chains specified under British Standards will generally have larger rollers than motorcycle chains and a better wear life but they are likely to fail under fatigue, ie the chain breaks due to the repeated application of loads and can do so even if the load is substantially less than that required to break the chain in one application. This is a disaster for motorcycles because the engine characteristics are impulsive and sudden load reversals can take place according to what the wheel and engine are trying to do at a given time. These are exactly the conditions that cause fatigue failure. Resistance to fatigue is highly dependent on the most detailed aspects of chain design. Some aspects, such as changes in sideplate thickness and profile are easy to see but others, such as the tolerances used on interference fits, are hidden. Obtaining the basic tensile strength is never a problem for normal bikes and once it is adequate the other factors are much more important. Selecting the best chain purely by looking at tables of breaking load is not satisfactory. Incidentally, the safe working load of the chain should not exceed 65% of the breaking load specified.

With industrial drives there are standard design procedures that allow you to select chain size on the basis of the power to be transmitted. This is not generally the case with motorcycle chain and indeed is rarely necessary. Standard practice is adequate for all but the most demanding applications, eg drag racers, and if you have any doubts the manufacturers are normally very willing to help you. As I have already said, the detail design and manufacturing quality of the chain is crucial to both wear life and the avoidance of fatigue failure. High surface finishes reduce wear and tolerances are critical, however it is easy to forget that the chain roller is a primitive journal bearing. It needs to be kept clean and cool or it will fail, just

Table 2.16 *Common chain designations together with the corresponding pitch and width. These particular examples are the figures quoted by Reynold Chains. The metric inside width is a maximum, the Imperial value is a nominal figure.*

Chain designation	Pitch (ins)	Nominal width (ins)	Pitch (mm)	Maximum width (mm)
415	1/2	3/16	12.7	4.7
420	1/2	1/4	12.7	6.25
425	1/2	5/16	12.7	7.75
428	1/2	5/16	12.7	7.75
520	5/8	1/4	15.875	6.7
525	5/8	5/16	15.875	7.95
530	5/8	3/8	15.875	9.53
532	5/8	3/8	15.875	9.53
630	3/4	3/8	19.05	9.53

as a similar big end bearing would. This brings us to cleaning and lubrication. Chains are supplied pre-stretched (raises yield point) and pre-lubricated but for non 0-ring chains there is no way of retaining this lubricant in use and further lubrication is essential. It is my view, and that of the major manufacturers I have dealt with, that the application of cold lubricants is not ideal. Penetration is limited no matter how much resistance to being flung off there may be and the only real answer is to cook the chain periodically in one of the specialised hot lubricants that are available.

With 0-ring chains the manufacturer's lubricant is sealed in but now the main enemy is corrosion. Even slight corrosion of the plates will damage the 0-rings and promote wear. The use of a specialised spray-on oil is thus required. Both types of chain should be cleaned in paraffin. Petrol can damage some O-rings.

Chains will always be something that some riders cherish and others tolerate. Those who cherish them have usually suffered the misfortune of a chain failure in the past and some still carry the scars on their backs and legs. Scrap them when the free length has extended by 2%, less if you can afford it.

Sprockets

The prime function of the sprocket is to gear with the chain and as such it has to be machined to suit. From the constructor's point of view the most important consideration is pitch circle diameter (PCD) as shown in Fig 2.39. The pitch of the chain used and the number of teeth required automatically determine the pitch circle and hence the physical size of the sprockets. Knowing this size is

$$\mathbf{PCD = P.Cosec\left[\frac{180}{N}\right]}$$

where P = pitch of the chain
N = number of teeth

Note that the value of 180/N is in degrees.

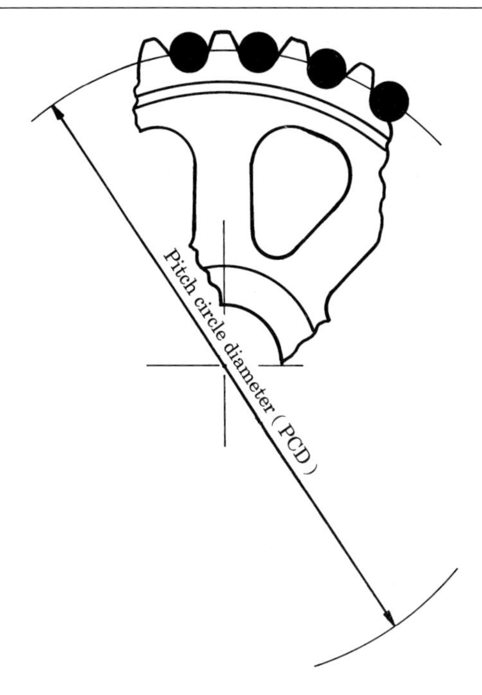

Fig 2.39 *Pitch circle dimension of sprockets.*

very useful because it allows you to determine where the chain will pass given any particular sprocket pairing. You would not be the first person to design a bike and then find that there are problems with the chain run!

The formula given is used to determine PCD. When using this formula the pitch circle diameter will have the same units as the pitch and this is normally given in inches. If you want the result in millimetres multiply the answer by 25.4.

To save you work I have calculated the values of Cosec(180/N) for N = 13 teeth to 57 teeth and present them in Table 2.17 overleaf as value K. With this range of sprockets you simply multiply the pitch of the chain involved by the value of K to obtain the PCD.

Example. What is the PCD of a 42 tooth rear sprocket to suit type 420 chain?

The chain is 1/2in pitch.

For 42T, K = 13.381 (overleaf)

hence PCD = 1/2in x 13.381

= 6.69in (169.94mm)

If you need to go outside this range then proceed as follows on a calculator.

- Divide 180 by the number of teeth.
- Look up the Sine of this answer, ensuring the calculator is set to degrees.
- Divide 1 by the Sine value.
- Multiply the result by the pitch to get the required PCD.

Example. What is the pitch circle diameter of a 72T sprocket for 5/8in pitch chain?

This sprocket has too many teeth for you to use the data in Table 2.17. Using the method just outlined,

- (180/72) = 2.5 degrees
- Sine(2.5 degrees) = 0.043619
- 1/0.043619 = 22.9256
- 5/8in x 22.9256 = 14.328ins

ie PCD = 14.328ins or 363.94mm

Pitch circle diameter is about the only aspect of sprockets that is universal and different manufacturers employ various tooth forms, though these are generally based on involutes (see gears). The outside diameter of the sprocket is nominally equal to the PCD plus one roller diameter but this does vary slightly with tooth design. Note that in order to lift the chain clear of the teeth during removal you will need to allow some extra space.

Readers who really like sums and never seem to have any spare bits around them can use the formula opposite to determine the length of chain required to match a sprocket pair at a given centre distance. I have left everything in imperial units because chain data is normally given in this form. When you obtain an answer, divide it by the pitch to find the number of links, rounding up to the nearest whole number. If this number is odd you will have to use a cranked half link. This should be avoided. When applying this formula to the final drive, ensure that you account for the variations in centre distance that occur under different circumstances.

Table 2.17 *This table contains values of constant K where K = Cosec(180/N). N is the number of sprocket teeth. For sprockets in the range 13 - 57 teeth multiply the appropriate K value by the pitch to get PCD.*

Teeth	K	Teeth	K	Teeth	K	Teeth	K	Teeth	K
13	4.178	22	7.027	31	9.885	40	12.745	49	15.610
14	4.494	23	7.344	32	10.202	41	13.063	50	15.926
15	4.810	24	7.661	33	10.520	42	13.381	51	16.244
16	5.126	25	7.980	34	10.838	43	13.700	52	16.562
17	5.442	26	8.296	35	11.156	44	14.018	53	16.880
18	5.759	27	8.614	36	11.474	45	14.336	54	17.198
19	6.076	28	8.931	37	11.792	46	14.654	55	17.517
20	6.392	29	9.249	38	12.110	47	14.972	56	17.835
21	6.710	30	9.567	39	12.428	48	15.290	57	18.153
To calculate the sprocket PCD multiply the K value above by the pitch of the chain									

$$L = 2C + \frac{(N1 + N2)P}{2} + \frac{P^2(N1 - N2)^2}{39.4C}$$

where L = length of chain in inches
N1 = teeth on large sprocket
N2 = teeth on small sprocket
P = chain pitch in inches
C = centre distance in inches

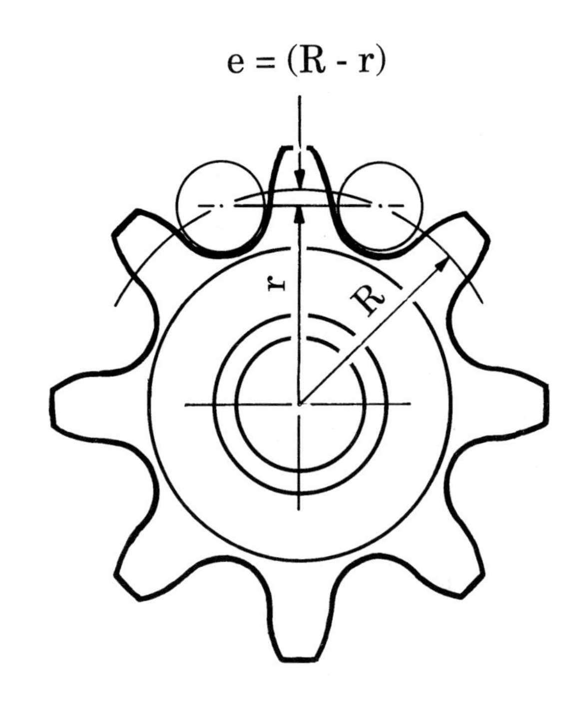

Polygon action

One aspect already mentioned but worthy of some further discussion is the polygon action of chain and sprocket drives. When you calculate a ratio using the number of teeth it is only an average value. In reality, the torque is transmitted via a radius which is constantly changing and this causes the chain's linear speed to fluctuate. To minimise such variations, the dimension 'e' in Fig 2.40 should be as small as possible and the value of e/R is a measure of the speed fluctuations that will occur. If you calculate the speed variations produced by different sprockets then Fig 2.41 results and it is clear that small sprockets are a real problem in this respect. Using them will bring on both wear and fatigue problems very rapidly. Industrial designers try to avoid anything less than 17T and, if you are having chain problems, you should try to find ways of increasing the gearbox sprocket sizes, assuming that basic aspects such as alignment are correct.

As with chains, talking to reputable manufacturers is the way forward. Many offer all sorts of lightening patterns and clearance grooves to suit personal preference. Some sprockets, eg Sidewinder, are dynamically balanced and this is particularly desirable on very large sizes.

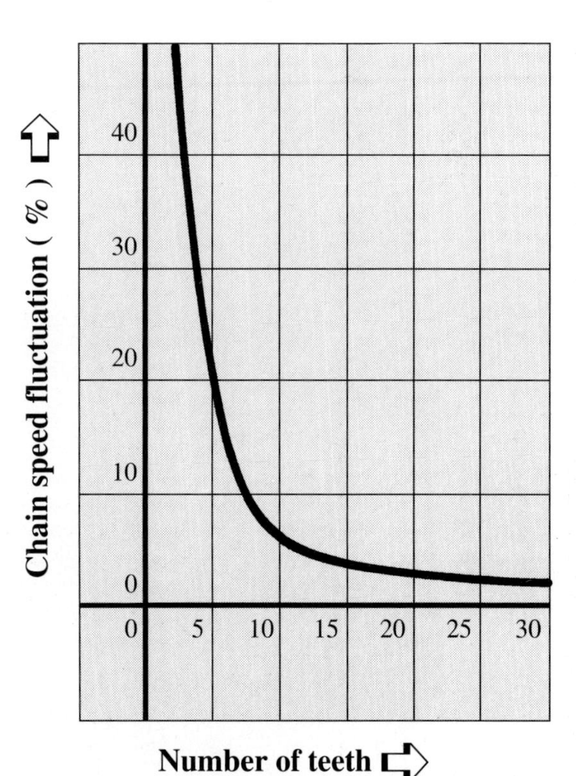

Top right. Fig 2.40 *The effective radius of sprockets changes as they rotate. This produces fluctuating chain speeds.*

Bottom right. Fig 2.41 *This graph shows how the percentage speed variation alters with the number of teeth. In industrial applications, 17 teeth is regarded as a sensible minimum to avoid fatigue problems.*

Gears

The subject of gears is vastly more complex than sprockets and it is only possible to touch lightly on the basic ideas. If you need to modify stock gears or make new ones then discussion with a reputable manufacturer is not desirable, it is essential.

The big thing that separates gears from sprockets is the fact that pairs of gears have to mesh together very precisely and the shaft centres are fixed. New gear pairs have to comply with the existing shaft centres (unless you want to alter every gear in the engine) and any imperfection in the gears that tries to force the shafts apart is likely to lead to failure. This means that everything about gears involves high precision and even then only gears produced from the best materials with the best heat treatment will survive. Perhaps the biggest problem facing the non-specialist trying to understand gears is the fact that manufacturers 'fiddle' with the basic ideas to achieve acceptable ratios. This can completely throw even experienced engineers who are not gear specialists so I repeat the need for talking to a reputable manufacturer. It is clearly impractical for me to attempt to cover all the relevant aspects of gear technology in this book but what I will try to convey are the basic ideas and the variations from these that manufacturers commonly utilise. This should at least provide a feel for what you are dealing with and make discussions with a specialist easier.

The terminology I am going to use reflects current thinking in gear design (which moves ever closer to ISO standards) and this may not be the same as you read in other books or encounter during discussions. This is unfortunate but eventually it will come to everyone involved. What follows is assumed to apply only to straight cut spur gears and covers 99% of racing requirements. Helical cut primary gears are often found on road bikes since they make less noise but I shall not consider them.

Fig 2.42 *A typical motorcycle gear cluster.*

Fig 2.43 *State-of-the-art gear cutting. This is a Pfauter Shobber at work, ie a combined hobbing and shaping machine. The hob cutter on the left and the two shaping cutters on the right work simultaneously to machine this complex gear from a blank in less than a minute (photograph courtesy of Gear Technology, Rotherham).*

Manufacture

To help understand the problems associated with gear design it is necessary to provide some insight into their manufacture. Spur gears are produced in a variety of ways but for machined gears there are two major sub-divisions, forming and generating. Forming implies that the gear teeth take on the exact form of the cutting tool. The gear is produced by cutting one 'gap' between the teeth and then rotating the blank and cutting another 'gap', the bit between the gaps forming the tooth.

Forming gears in this way is reasonably straightforward but it is not as accurate as the alternative about to be described, nor is it as efficient for production items. You also need more cutters than you might expect. For example, one standard cutter will only produce gears with 12 or 13 teeth. Another covers 14 to 16 teeth and so on. These then have to be duplicated for every 'size' of tooth.

The alternative to forming is generating and the design of gears is, to a large extent, based on the fact that most teeth will be generated. When a shape is generated it results from the combined movements of work and cutter. An obvious example is the generation of a cylindrical shape in a lathe. This results from the combination of a rotating workpiece and a single point tool moving in a straight line. On this basis, the shape of a gear tooth has to satisfy two main requirements. Firstly it has to do the job required of it and secondly it must be possible to generate it using combinations of simple work/cutter movements.

The generation of gear teeth is based on the idea of a rack type cutter (see Fig 2.44 overleaf) that moves in synchronism with the rotating gear blank while cutting across the blank width. In practice this method is only used for very large gears. For motorcycle gears, two variations on this theme are used. The processes are called hobbing and shaping and, though the principle is exactly the same, these methods allow the cutter and work to move more efficiently. This is more productive. You really need to see these operations being carried out to appreciate what is going on but the idea of a rack type cutter is adequate for this discussion of the basic ideas. The shape that best satisfies both these requirements, ie suitability and ease of manufacture, is called an involute and it is used for the majority of gears (and sprockets). Great details of involute geometry are not necessary here but note that the appearance of the involute changes with the number of teeth involved and gear tooth geometry is based on what you get for an infinitely large number of teeth.

Gear proportions

As the number of teeth increases the involute curve straightens out. For an infinite number of teeth the 'curve' becomes a straight line and the radius of such a gear is so large that the gear circumference also becomes a straight line. The result is a rack. The proportions of all involute gear teeth are based on such a rack, Fig 2.44 showing that specified in BS436 Part 2 1970.

The numbers on this rack (top diagram) are not measurements, they are proportions. For example, if the depth given as 2.25 happened to be 22.5mm then the depth given as 1.25 would be 12.5mm. Because these figures are simply proportions, they have to be scaled by some measurement to represent an actual gear tooth.

Module

Gear teeth come in different 'sizes', each based on the proportions given. The scaling factor is called the module (mod) and it is specified in millimetres. I will discuss older gears made to entirely Imperial dimensions at the end.

The bigger the module the bigger the teeth. A small size of tooth allows more teeth to occupy a given diameter of gear but the teeth also have to be strong enough. Using bigger teeth, ie those with a larger module, increases tooth strength but obviously requires larger diameter gears for a given number of teeth.

BS436 lists 18 preferred modules but only a small range of these are relevant, in particular 2.0, 2.5 and 3.0 module. In practice, the requirements of motorcycle gears leads to the use of several intermediate modules and 99% of all bike applications are covered by 1.75, 2.0, 2.25, 2.5, 2.75 and 3.0 module. Table 2.18 gives application examples and Fig 2.44 also shows the standard

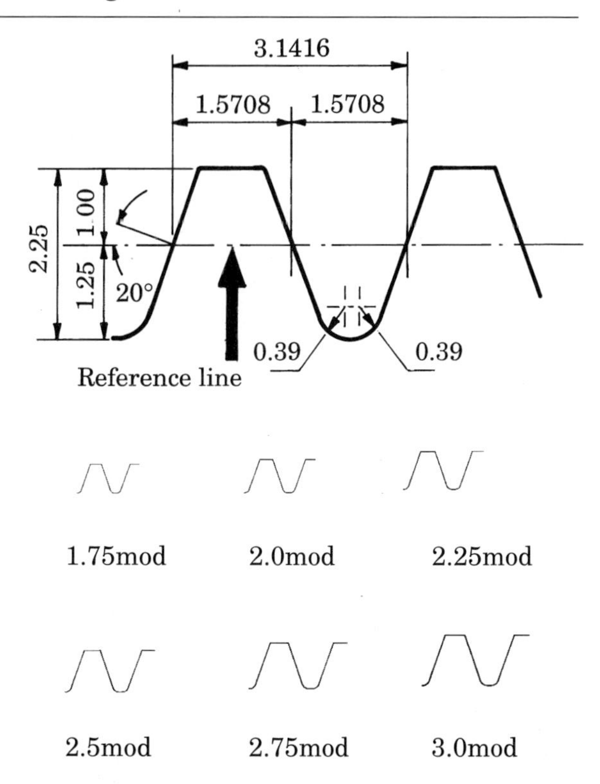

Above. Fig 2.44 *Standard rack proportions and examples of racks using modules common to motorcycle gearboxes.*

Below. Table 2.18 *Examples of module usage in motorcycle gearboxes (data courtesy of Graham Dyson).*

Module	Applications
1.75	200cc road bikes, Ducati singles
2.0	very common on 125/250cc
2.25	favoured by Suzuki eg RG500
2.5	big bikes, Yamaha 500/750
2.5 - 3.0	Yamaha 500 V4 GP bike

rack form in each of these module sizes. A cutter having the same basic shape as these racks can be used to generate the tooth form on gears. Any gear so produced will mesh with the rack or with other gears that have the same module.

Gear geometry

Teeth are generated as the cutter and work move relative to each other but there are many constraints on what we can achieve, notably the fact that we need to have a whole number of teeth! On the standard rack you will observe a reference line. Note that the rack defines the proportion of the tooth outside this line and inside it.

The gear blank has to have what is termed a reference diameter and this is chosen so that a whole number of teeth (of the desired module) will fit around it. The diameter is given by,

Reference dia = module x N° teeth

where the module and dia are in mm

The portion of each tooth that lies outside this diameter is called the addendum while that lying inside the reference circle is called the dedendum - Fig 2.45. This reference diameter is frequently called the pitch circle diameter but you would be unwise to do this. The reason is that pitch circles are not actually a property of the gear itself, they (two of them) are properties of a pair of meshing gears. The actual reference diameter of the gears, and the pitch circles of the gear pair, will only coincide for a very small number of 'unmodified' gears. I will explain this in more detail shortly.

Fig 2.45 *Some elements and dimensions of gear teeth. The reference circle is commonly called the pitch circle but, in current ISO terminology, pitch circles (a pair of them) are properties of meshing gears, not individual gears. For simple gears the reference circle touches the reference line on the cutter. When this is not the case the gears are said to have addendum modification.*

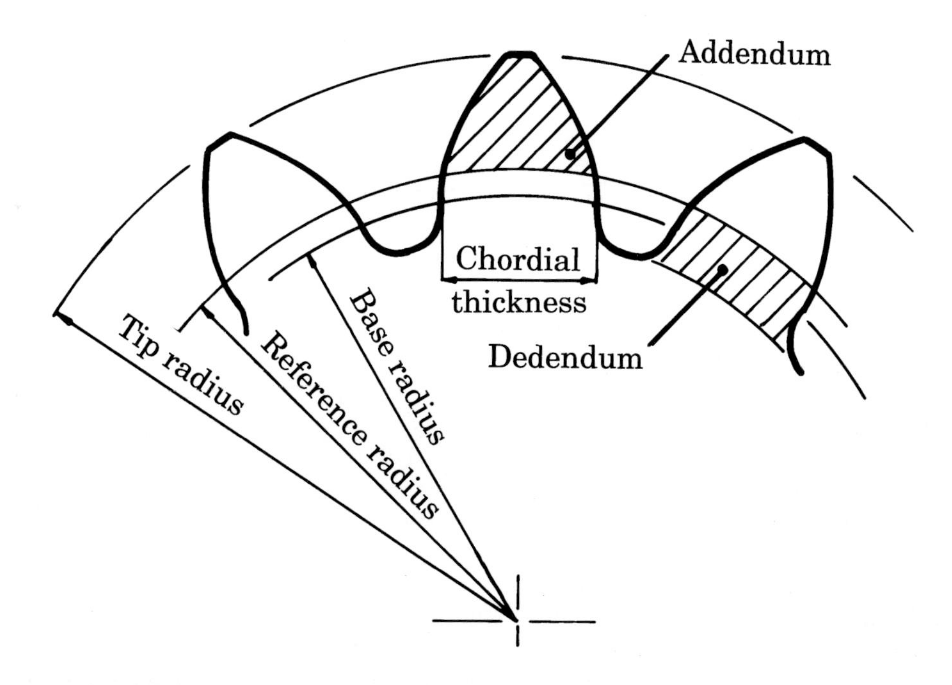

Base diameter defines the starting point for generation of the involute tooth form.

Reference diameter has a value equal to module x number of teeth. For unmodified gears the cutter's reference line is set to form a tangent to this.

Centre distance of unmodified gears

When an unmodified gear is cut, the reference line on the cutter is set to touch the reference circle on the gear blank. For two such gears in mesh, the reference circles will touch and the centre distance between them is given by the sum of the two reference radii. Each radius is half the value of (module x number of teeth) and, since the module of meshing gears is equal we get,

$$\textbf{Ctr distance} = \frac{\textbf{mod x Sum of teeth}}{\textbf{2}}$$

This value is what is termed a 'tight mesh centre distance'. At this value there is no backlash between the gears, nor do they interfere with each other. In practice there must be some backlash to account for changes in centre distance due to temperature rises and also to allow for tooth errors and gear eccentricity. Accordingly, real gears are produced as if they operated on slightly shorter centres. The amount of 'drop back' employed in motorcycle gearboxes is typically 0.127mm - 0.203mm (5 - 8thou).

Example. Two uncorrected gears with a module of 2mm are in mesh. If one has 20 teeth and the other 36 teeth then the tight mesh centre distance is,

$$\text{Ctr dist.} = \frac{2\text{mm}(20 + 36)}{2}$$

$$= 56\text{mm}$$

Example. Two uncorrected gears with a module of 2.5mm are in mesh. If one has17 teeth and the other 18 teeth then the tight mesh centre distance is,

$$\text{Ctr dist.} = \frac{2.5\text{mm}(17 + 18)}{2}$$

$$= 43.75\text{mm}$$

Following on from this, if gears in mesh must have the same module, and if several gear pairs occupy the same shafts as they do in a motorcycle gearbox, then it follows that the sum of teeth in mesh must be the same for each pairing. For example, if first gear has a 35 tooth gear meshing with an 11 tooth gear then the tooth sum is 46. The next available pairings (of the same module) that will run on the same centres are 34T/12T, 33T/13T, 32T/14T and so on. In the early days this was adhered to. Taking post 1953 BSA's as an example, all gear cluster pairs for the Goldstar, 500cc twins and 650cc twins added up to 43 teeth. Prior to this they all added up to 45 teeth.

Tip diameter

Sticking with the basic ideas for a moment, the tip (outside) diameter of an uncorrected gear is determined by the reference diameter and the addendum. Since the standard proportions produce an addendum that is 1.0 times the module the tip diameter is equal to the reference diameter (module x number of teeth) plus 2 x module. Hence,

$$\textbf{Tip dia.} = \textbf{module(N}^{\circ}\textbf{ teeth + 2)}$$

Because tip diameter can be measured relatively easily (unlike the reference diameter) this formula can be useful in identifying gears that have been modified in some way. If you have a 30 tooth gear that is clearly 2module (by comparison with the standard racks) then if it has not been modified the tip diameter should be 2(30 + 2) = 64mm. You can measure this diameter directly though note that placing a vernier across the teeth is not really good enough. The job needs to be done properly with the gear mounted on a mandrel between centres. In some cases everything will tally but, especially for motorcycle gears, the chances are rather slim!

Intermediate ratios

The information I have given so far covers the basic ideas but motorcycles impose other constraints. Not only do we have to fit up to six gear pairs on the same shaft centres but we also want to obtain ratios that are best suited to performance. There has to be some compromise here because you must have whole numbers of teeth but even so the manufacturers have found ways of improving on what has already been outlined. In an ideal world we would seek any ratio that we desire for performance. As an example, assume that one simple unmodified gear pair comprises a 20 tooth gear and a 16 tooth gear, both of 2.0 module. We can immediately identify all the simple gear pairs of 2.0 module that will fit the centre distance since they must have a total of 36 teeth.

Table 2.19 gives some of these combinations and the corresponding ratios they produce. Obviously the choice is limited and if performance dictates that something in-between is required what do you do?

The first option is to use gear pairs that are not the same module as the rest. Apparently, the Kawasaki KR1 used gear pairs with 1.75, 2.0, 2.25, and 2.5 module all in the same gearbox. Even this idea has serious problems because unless the existing tooth sum is divisible by the new module (whole number answer) it will not be possible to achieve the required centre distance.

I have deliberately chosen a 36 tooth sum for illustration because it divides by 2.25 as well as 2.0. This means we could use a gear pair of 2.25 module to achieve an intermediate ratio.

Right. Table 2.19 *In this example the tooth sum is always 36 teeth and as such all these gear pairs can use the same centre distance without modification. However, the choice of ratios is limited and is unlikely to be compatible with best performance.*

Example. A ratio in-between the 0.800 and 0.895 values of Table 2.19 is required. Find suitable unmodified gears.

The original gear tooth sum is 36 and the module is 2.0. This gives a tight mesh centre distance of 36mm.

The new 2.25 module gears must also have a 36mm centre distance so,

$$36\text{mm} = \frac{\text{module(Sum of teeth)}}{2}$$

$$36\text{mm} = \frac{2.25\text{(Sum of teeth)}}{2}$$

$$\text{Sum of teeth} = 32$$

Using a 15 tooth driven gear and a 17 tooth driver provides a ratio of 0.882 which, possibly, meets your requirements. This looks easy but nine times out of ten it cannot be done at the required centre distance.

Addendum modification

The final option in our search for the best ratios is to introduce what is called 'addendum modification' . Alternative terms include 'rack displacement' and 'corrected gears'. The good news about addendum modification is that it can often provide a means of adding or subtracting one or two

Driver Teeth	Driven Teeth	Ratio
16	20	1.250
17	19	1.118
18	18	1.000
19	17	0.895
20	16	0.800
21	15	0.714

teeth on a particular gear whilst still allowing it to mesh correctly. There are strict limits on what can be done because the technique alters the tooth shape while maintaining the module, and hence the ability to mesh. Fig 2.46 gives some examples of modified tooth shapes. These are achieved by moving the cutter reference line inside or outside the reference circle on the gear blank. Moving it inside is generally very limited because the gear tooth starts to undercut as shown. This can destroy the involute forms that move across each other as well as weakening the root.

Moving the cutter away has more scope but eventually the tip of the gear is thinned out and it becomes too weak. Despite these limits there is a lot of scope here. The technique is used extensively in motorcycle gearboxes because it gives the best choice of ratios. For example, Table 2.19 provided ratios of 0.800 and 0.895 using 2.0 module gears that have a 36 tooth sum. We achieved 0.882 by changing module but, sticking with 2.0 module a combination of 20 teeth and 17 teeth would yield 0.850 giving yet another option. The tooth sum of the gear pair is now 37 so simple unmodified gears could not do this at the required centre distance. Modified gears can.

Almost every motorcycle gearbox utilises this technique. RG500 gears were 2.25 module but drastically modified. Honda 750/4 were 2.0 module but again heavily modified. The amount of modification employed is indicated by an 'addendum modification factor' (x) and this system gives the ultimate in ratio flexibility. The snag, and it is a very big snag for the non-specialist, is that most of the relationships given for simple gears go out of the window. The tip diameter changes to,

tip dia. = mod(N° of teeth + 2(1 + x))

Fig 2.46 *When addendum modification is applied to the gear the cutter's reference line is not tangential to the blank's reference diameter and the tooth shape generated is different. Although this provides flexibility in the relationship between diameter and number of teeth, there are strict limits imposed by undercutting or weakening of the tooth tip.*

Gear blank
Cutter
No offset
Blank reference radius
Cutter reference line
Normal tooth shape

a) Cutting an unmodified gear

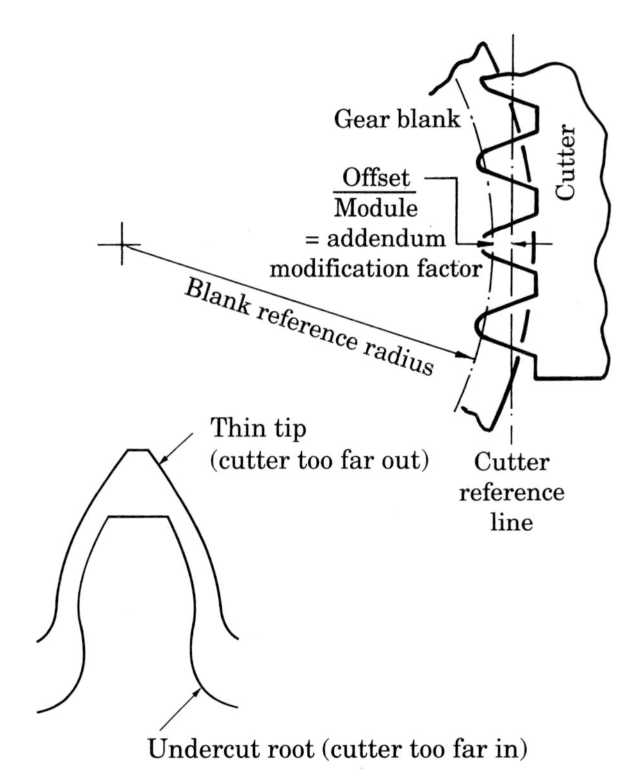

b) Cutting a modified gear

but alas there is no longer a simple formula for centre distance. Another problem you will encounter is that heavy modification distorts the tooth shape so much that you will become unsure of the module. Fig 2.47 demonstrates this very clearly. Both gears have 28 teeth, they are the same module and they mesh, but look at the difference in diameter and tooth shape. The only reliable check is a rolling test against a master gear. This is why you really need to work with a specialist from the outset when contemplating new ratios. There is no point in working away for hours based on performance and then find that the required gear pairing is unrealisable. I hope the discussion has not put you off. Knowing these basic ideas should at least help you understand what the specialist will try to tell you.

Fig 2.47 *An extreme example of addendum modification. These gears have the same number of teeth and the same module but they are of different diameters. The gears will mesh correctly but you can see the potential weakening of root and tip very clearly here.*

Diametral pitch

Before the metric module concept came into being, British gearboxes used a related but different concept, that of diametral pitch (dp). The basic rack proportions are not changed but all measurements are now in inches and the diametral pitch is equal to,

$$\text{d.p.} = \frac{1}{\text{module in inches}}$$

Example. Since 2.0mm is equal to 0.07874ins, a 2.0 module gear is equivalent to 1/0.07874 = 12.7dp.

Example. A 14dp gear has a module of 1/14 = 0.0714in which is a metric module of 1.81mm.

As with metric module there were preferred values of diametral pitch. 9, 10, 11, 12, and 14dp covers almost everything you will encounter. Addendum modification was less common on early gears so the Imperial equivalents of the formulae given can be useful. These are,

$$\textbf{Tip dia.(ins)} = \frac{\textbf{(No teeth + 2)}}{\textbf{dp}}$$

$$\textbf{Ctr dist. (ins)} = \frac{\textbf{Sum of teeth on pair}}{\textbf{2dp}}$$

(unmodified gears only)

Sadly, any addendum modification will again invalidate these relationships and you are back to the specialist. There are many other relationships for gears, particularly in relation to tooth thickness and depth but you do need specialised equipment to make measurements. If you have such equipment, I am sure you do not need me to tell you how to use it! Going beyond this point is not worthwhile unless you really appreciate the practical realities of gear manufacture. What you should do is to see what tooth combinations come closest to your desired ratios and then take the whole bundle of paper and parts to your chosen gear manufacturer. Previous warnings on costs will not be repeated here! The following people are always very helpful.

Graham Dyson, Nova Racing Transmission. 8 Horseshoe Yard, Crowland, Lincs PE6 0BJ. Tel 01733 - 210082. Graham specialises in motorcycle gears and has close ratio clusters available for many different bikes, especially classic racers. His products are widely used and have a good reputation for reliability.

Gear Technology Ltd., PO Box 49, Rotherham, South Yorks, S60 1JR. Telephone 01709 - 703707. Gear Technology do not make gears but they import Pfauter gear cutting and grinding machines into the UK. They also know a lot more about gears than most companies and are involved with manufacturers producing gears for the most arduous conditions, including Formula 1 cars. If you have a particularly demanding requirement they can suggest which manufacturers to use.

3.1 Front end geometry and wheelbase

Introduction

The information given in the previous chapters will, hopefully, assist you in selecting engine/ gearbox units and also focus attention on the factors that determine straight-line performance. There is of course a lot more to it than any performance predictions you might make on the basis of simple calculations. The bike has to be rideable and it has to stay in one piece. It has to go round corners at an acceptable pace and it has to inspire confidence in the rider. Last but far from least, you have to build it. This is always much more hassle than sitting by the fire with a calculator and dreaming of what might be!

For most people the first major requirement is to sort out the geometry of the bike, ie the fixed relationships, lengths and angles that contribute to performance and feel. I have broken this area down into several sections. Wheelbase is first, followed by front end (steering) geometry. This gives a 'space' into which all major components can be fitted with due regard for centre of gravity location, rider positioning and mechanical constraints - Fig 3.1. Once the engine location is known the rear end can be sorted and the basic geometry is well on the way to completion. Although these aspects are straightforward it pays to think about them carefully before welding bits together because they are usually rather time consuming to alter once the bike is finished.

Fig 3.1 Basic motorcycle geometry requires that you decide on a) wheelbase b) castor angle c) trail and d) swinging arm location. The conditions under which the measurements are taken, eg laden or unladen, need to be standardised.

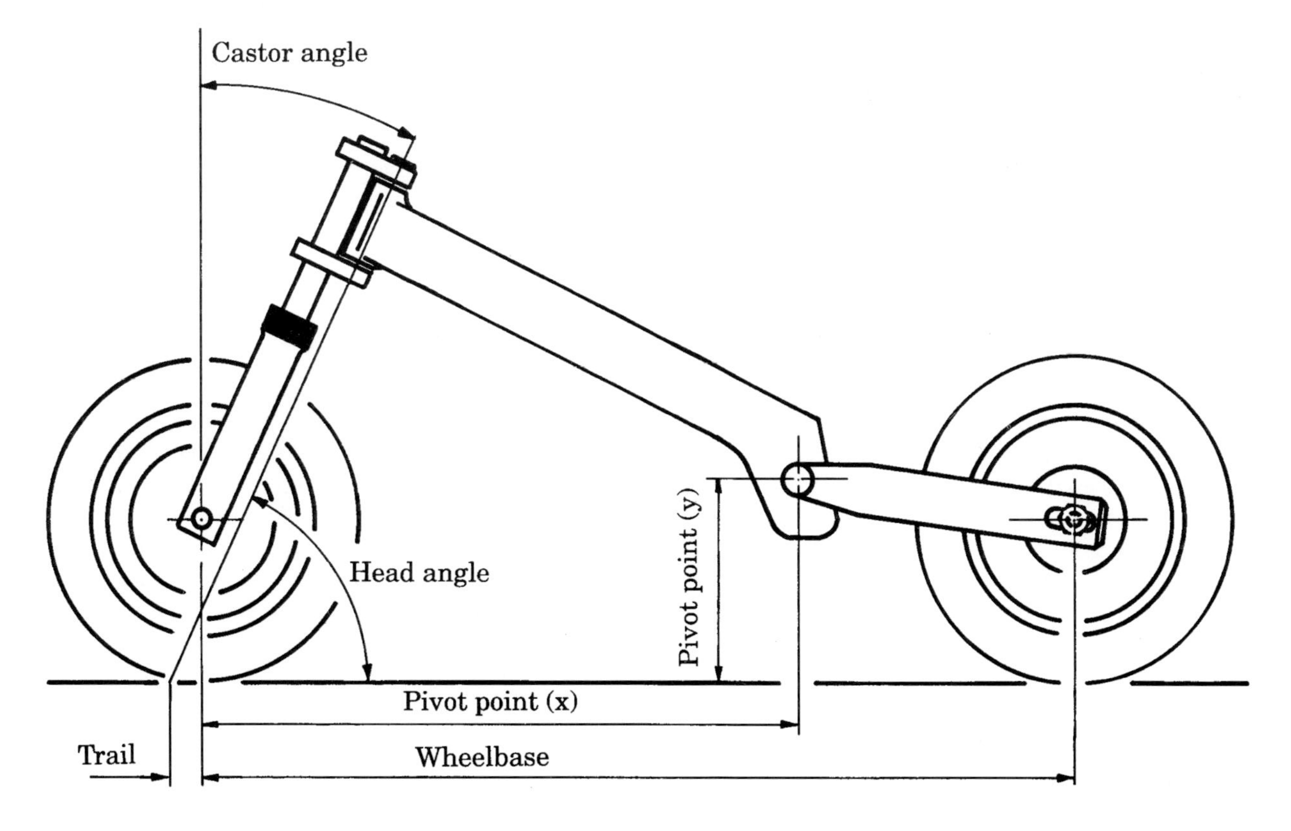

Roadholding

Roadholding is the ability of the bike to stay in contact with the road on a specific path. There is nothing subjective about roadholding, the bike either sticks or it does not. Under severe conditions a good design will hold the road better than a bad design but the result is a matter of fact rather than a matter of personal interpretation.

The three most important factors influencing roadholding on a given surface are the torsional stiffness of the bike, the suspension, and the suitability of the tyres. Torsional stiffness is the bike's resistance to being twisted and recent years have seen a massive increase in torsional stiffness, mainly to accommodate increasing power and tyre grip. The more easily the wheels can be twisted out of line the worse the roadholding will be. The general trends in frame and swinging arm design have all been led by the need to increase stiffness and the use of materials like carbon fibre has enabled the desired stiffness to be achieved without an excessive weight penalty.

The need for stiffness is clearly demonstrated when you watch GP bikes flicking left then right. During this process they can tie themselves in knots and the roadholding obviously suffers. Nevertheless, it has to be said that some of this has gone a bit far for the majority. You frequently hear experienced GP riders in the 250 class saying that the bikes are now so stiff that it is difficult to get feedback from them, yet at the same time you hear lesser mortals complaining that the only thing between them and a world title is a stiffer chassis!

The geometry of the motorcycle is not a prime consideration in terms of roadholding. There are obviously limits and a long wheelbase will, in general, make the bike easier to twist but, if the geometry resembles any normal set-up, then it does not have a great influence on the actual roadholding ability. What it does influence is the characteristic we know as handling.

Handling

Handling is different from roadholding. It means the way that the bike behaves from the rider's point of view. Clearly there is a human factor involved. There are bikes that feel peculiar to one rider while other riders win races on them so we could argue continually about whether there is anything actually wrong with these bikes. Handling is influenced heavily by torsional stiffness and tyres just like roadholding but, assuming these aspects are satisfactory, the geometry then plays a significant part in the way the bike actually 'feels' and that has a lot to do with psychology, previous experience, and the expectation of the rider. Oversteer to one rider is simply a nimble machine to another.

Since a change of tyres or track conditions will alter the feel that the geometry imparts, there is a strong case for having a degree of adjustability to cope with this. Unfortunately, with anything that is adjustable there is always a danger of becoming paranoid about the set-up. There is a lot to be said for riding the wheels off whatever you have built before making any adjustments, assuming the design is sensible.

This makes the whole subject of geometry one with two levels. The first level involves selecting a layout that, based on the experience of others, should feel acceptable. The second level involves experimenting with it until it feels right to you and the psychological influence of this cannot be overstated. If it feels right you go faster.

There is nothing that can tell you about refining the geometry other than experience and experiment. This chapter is about the first level, basic geometry, how it is defined, what it influences, and how to set it up.

Wheelbase

In general it is not possible to isolate one aspect of motorcycle geometry and discuss it. Every aspect interacts and it is the effect of the combination that is important. However we have to start somewhere and wheelbase is the best place.

Wheelbase is the distance between the wheel spindle centres when the steering is straight. On most motorcycles the wheelbase adjusts by 20-40mm to accommodate sprocket variations and adjust chain tension. In addition, the wheelbase of small bikes is shorter than that of large bikes. These rather obvious statements are actually important because they indicate that there is no magic wheelbase for a motorcycle. With a conventional motorcycle the wheelbase cannot be less than one tyre diameter plus the length of the engine and gearbox, thus for adult machines anything less than 890mm (35ins) is unlikely to be

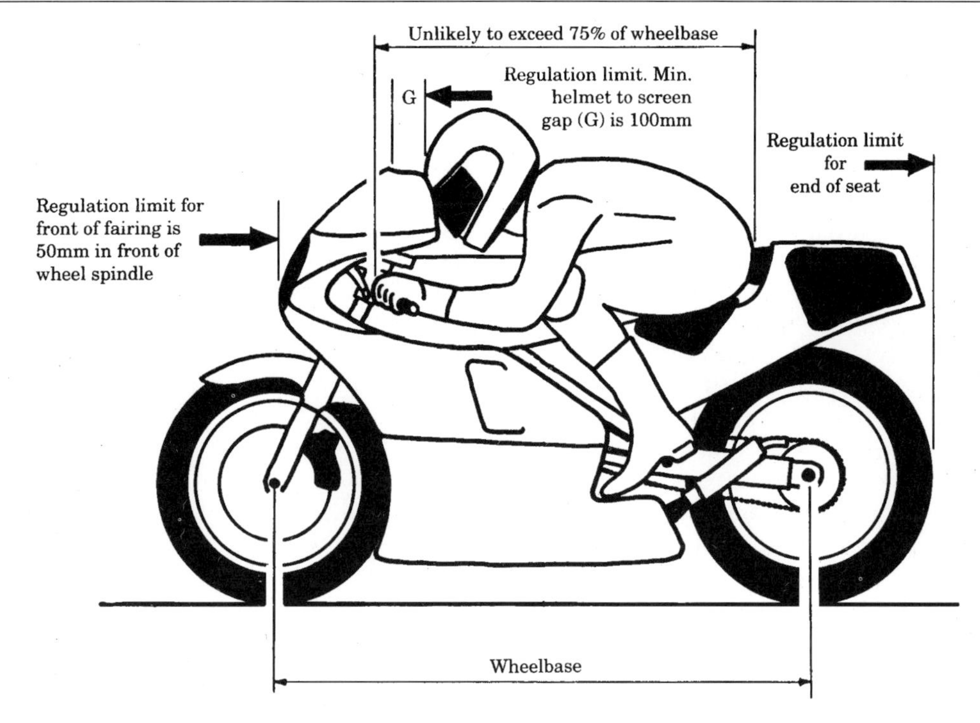

practical. You then have two more practical aspects that will extend it even more. The first question is, can the rider fit on the bike and where will the rider fit? Your position on the bike will determine the centre of gravity but, ignoring anything technical and using common sense, your backside should not lie to the rear of the back wheel spindle - Fig 3.2. Unless the rider is particularly small, this criterion will make it difficult to fit on any bike in a fully prone position if the wheelbase is shorter than about 1250mm (49ins). This is a typical 'short' wheelbase for a 125, the majority of bikes being in the range 1300 - 1400mm (51 - 55in) and if you are of average build things can be a bit tight on a short bike. Some extra space can be found if the forks are particularly upright or extended clipons are used but we are only talking about small amounts. If you are going to ride the bike this is a very important consideration. If you are not the rider then you can of course look round for a suitable candidate to fit the available space.

The next practical requirement concerns accommodating the exhaust system. Regulations stipulate that no part of the exhaust must lie beyond any part of the motorcycle or its bodywork. They also state that 'no part of the machine shall project to the rear of a vertical line drawn through the exterior edge of the rear wheel', so the exhaust limit is defined as per Fig 3.3.

Above. Fig 3.2 *The first consideration for wheelbase is the ability of the rider to fit on the bike in a prone position. Riders of average build are likely to struggle with wheelbases below 1250mmm(49.2ins).*

Below. Fig 3.3 *A second consideration is the exhaust length, especially for single cylinder engines with rear exit exhausts.*

Exhausts need to be as straight as possible but the worst restrictions on length occur with the straightest pipes, ie rear exit exhausts. The problem can be particularly serious on large capacity single cylinder engines. Sensible bends in the pipe do not normally affect peak power much but they can take some of the area out of the torque curve, hence reducing acceleration.

Other things being equal, engines which produce power at lower engine speeds will require longer exhaust systems for best performance. Four strokes have all sorts of exhausts so it is impossible to generalise here. The optimum overall exhaust length will depend on the type of system fitted and the way multiple cylinders are covered, eg individual pipes, two into one, four into one and so on. You will have to sort this one out from tuning books or experience.

$$L\,(mm) = \frac{46612KE}{N}$$

where

L = length of exhaust from piston skirt to start of tailpipe

E = total exhaust period in degrees

N = engine speed at which maximum torque is produced

Use the following values of K

Max torque speed	K
below 7000revs/min	1.00
7000 - 9000revs/min	1.05
9000 - 11000revs/min	1.15
11000 - 13000revs/min	1.20

If you prefer inches, divide the answer given in mm by 25.4

For two strokes, with multi-stage expansion chambers, the situation is more straightforward in that one exhaust is used per cylinder and the general concept of the exhausts is common. Although the detail design will vary considerably according to how many individual stages there are, the formula shown on the left gives a good idea of the overall length from piston skirt to the start of the tailpipe. Don't forget that it is also necessary to accommodate a silencer and they are getting bigger every year to meet the noise regulations. Some designs require very long tailpipes indeed.

This formula is a simplistic one based on a mean gas temperature of 520°C. In reality the gas temperature varies very substantially throughout the system and this in turn varies the speed at which the pressure waves move about the pipe. They can travel three times as fast in the header as they do in the reverse cone so simple expressions like this, which work on average figures, are never going to give you a superfast engine. They will however give a decent ball-park figure to help decide if you can fit the exhaust on the bike!

The length calculated using this formula is deliberately slightly on the long side which usually makes it easier to get the pipe working properly. Short pipes require excellent matching of all stages if torque is to be maintained. Final lengths, after much development, usually come out about 10-15% shorter than these initial values.

To illustrate the problems that the exhaust might cause, Fig 3.4 gives an example. It estimates the length for a 250cc single cylinder two stroke with an exhaust period of 198 degrees and peak torque at 8500 revs/min. The length of 1140mm (44.9ins) is almost as long as the wheelbase of a small bike and, if this involves a rear exit exhaust port, there is a serious problem even without a silencer. These aspects are going to impose a practical minimum for the wheelbase and are worthy of consideration before going any further.

Right. Fig 3.4 *Estimating an exhaust length for a 250cc single cylinder two-stroke. The relatively low peak torque engine speed leads to a long pipe, possibly longer than you can accommodate from a rear exit exhaust port. If the engine could be re-ported for peak torque at 10000revs/min (and will stay together!) then a much shorter pipe (around 970mm, 38.15in) could be used.*

Example. A 250cc two stroke single produces peak torque at 8500revs/min. The exhaust port opens at 81° after top dead centre. Estimate the maximum length of pipe required from piston skirt to tailpipe entry.

If the exhaust port opens at 81° after top dead centre then the total exhaust period will be equal to,

$$2(180 - 81) = 198°$$

This is shown graphically in the timing diagram below.

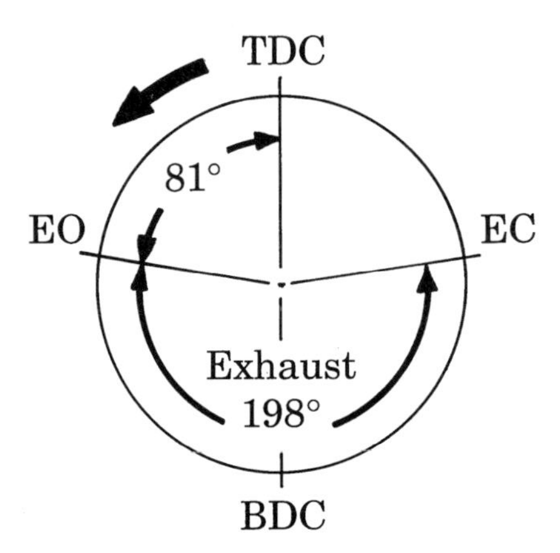

Using the formula given the required length is,

$$\text{Length} = \frac{46612 \times 1.05 \times 198}{8500}$$

$$= 1140\text{mm from skirt to tailpipe}$$

$$= 1140/25.4 = 44.9\text{in}$$

Wheelbase selection

The previous discussion should help you to estimate the minimum wheelbase that you can use in practice. As you increase the wheelbase beyond any practical minimum several things will happen. How good or bad this will be depends on the application of the bike, your style of riding etc.

- The minimum turning circle will increase. Within limits, this is not normally a problem for roadracing but if you were balanced feet up in a tight corner on a trials bike a short wheelbase would be appreciated.
- Pitching movements, ie a rise or fall at either end of the bike, produce a smaller angle of tilt for the rider when the wheelbase is long. The bike therefore feels more stable when a relatively long wheelbase is employed.
- To follow a particular cornering path, a longer wheelbase requires more steering effort to set the bike in the corner. Again, the bike feels more stable but steering is slower.
- When accelerating or braking, a longer wheelbase gives less weight transfer for a given acceleration or retardation. This is important and will influence the minimum wheelbase you finally use.
- The wheels, which are relatively heavy things, sit at the ends of the wheelbase. Increasing the wheelbase therefore increases the bike's reluctance to change direction.
- A long wheelbase increases the bending effects on the frame but, unless we are talking about choppers, the effect is small.

Road bikes

Make and model	mm	in
Kawasaki ZZ-R1100	1495	58.8
Suzuki GSX-R750(96)	1400	55.1
Honda Fireblade(96)	1345	53.0
Kawasaki ZX-7R(96)	1435	56.5
Yamaha YZF750 (96)	1420	55.9
Honda RC45	1410	55.5
Triumph Trophy 900 (96)	1490	58.7
BMW R1100RS (96)	1473	58.0
Honda RC30	1410	55.5
Suzuki Bandit 1200 (96)	1440	56.7
Yamaha 600 Thundercat	1415	55.7
Honda TRX (96)	1435	56.5
Honda CBR600 (96)	1405	55.3
Tigcraft Honda600 (95)	1375	54.1
Kawasaki ZXR400 (96)	1385	54.5
Honda RVF400 (96)	1345	53.0
Suzuki RGV250 (96)	1330	52.4
Aprilia RS250 (96)	1370	53.9
Honda Hornet 250 (96)	1340	52.8
Suzuki RG250	1380	54.3
Aprilia Sport Pro 125	1365	53.2
Yamaha TZR125 (95)	1370	53.9

Roadrace

Make and model	mm	in
Honda NSR500 (95)	1400	55.1
Honda NSR500 (92)	1410	55.5
Honda NSR500 (88)	1375	54.1
Honda NSR500 (86)	1370	53.9
Honda NSR250 (95)	1345	53.0
Honda NSR250 (93)	1340	52.8
Honda RS125 (96)	1215	47.8
Honda RS125 (95)	1215	47.8
Honda RS125 (88)	1280	50.4
Harley VR1000 (96)	1410	55.5
Muzzy Kawasaki 750 (95)	1395	54.9
Yamaha YZF750race (95)	1410	55.5
Baines Ducati 907SP (95)	1390	54.7
Honda NSR500 (Doohan 95)	1405	55.3
Aprilia RSV250 (Biaggi 95)	1340	52.8
Ducati 916 (Foggarty 95)	1428	56.2
Aprilia RSV400 (96)	1345	53.0
Tigcraft Yamaha single	1455	57.3
Dr John Moto Guzzi (94)	1460	57.5
Britten (95)	1420	55.9
Cobas 125 (89)	1270	50.0
Derbi 125 (90)	1310	51.6

Roadrace

Make and model	mm	in
Gagiva 500	1390	54.7
Crighton Duckhams Norton	1375	54.1
Yamaha TZ250 (93)	1328	52.3
Yamaha TZ125 (94)	1220	48.0
Aprilia RSR125 (95)	1270	50.0

Motocross/Enduro

Make and model	mm	in
Yamaha YZ125 (95)MX	1436	56.5
Kawasaki KX125 (95)MX	1455	57.3
Yamaha YZ250 (95)MX	1489	58.6
Honda XR250R (96)END	1400	55.1
Yamaha TT250R (96)END	1415	55.7

Grasstrack/Speedway

Make and model	mm	in
Typical speedway	1295	51.0
Typical grasstrack	1448	57.0

Trials

Make and Model	mm	in
Gas Gas 325	1320	52.0
Scorpa (96)	1320	52.0
Fantic (96)	1334	52.5
Yamaha TY250 (93)	1340	52.8

Considering these factors, the general result of increasing the wheelbase is to make a bike feel more secure or stable. It also allows greater acceleration and braking without standing the bike on end. Unfortunately, it is also more reluctant to make sudden changes in direction. Such directional changes will take longer and need more track space when a long wheelbase is employed. As usual you are going to have to compromise.

Standard practice is generally representative of these observations. Although wheelbase is not critical in the sense that it has to be exact, the general order of wheelbase is extremely influential in determining the handling and general feel of the bike. There are points where the bike starts to feel distinctly different and going past them puts you into a different category. Once a 125 exceeds about 1310mm (51.6ins) it gets a bit like a 250. Beyond perhaps 1350mm (53.15ins) the 250 starts to become noticeably less nimble and feels more like a 500. Beyond 1450mm (57.1ins) that sharp manoeuvrable feeling is lost and using radical steering geometry will not bring it back.

Table 3.1 gives a wide range of data and the general trend is fairly clear. Small capacity roadracers, trials bikes and speedway bikes have short wheelbases. In the case of trials and speedway such wheelbases do not produce the problems that they do on roadracers because there is less requirement for the rider to tuck in and minimise resistance to motion, nor do they have to brake from high speeds. Some 125cc racers have very short wheelbases, eg 1195mm (47in) and are really only suitable for very small riders. Current bikes are somewhat longer but they are still very short for riders of average build. Note that these figures are generally standard published data and in most cases will relate to an unladen bike. With conventional telescopic forks at the front, the wheelbase will shorten as the forks compress and it is worth taking note of this if you propose to have a lot of suspension travel. At the rear, the wheelbase will also change slightly as the swinging arm moves up or down from the position of maximum chain tension.

In addition, I have no idea where within the range of adjustment the rear wheels will be for most of the figures given. Generally speaking, wheelbase is not one of the most critical factors on the bike until it starts to get excessively long or short. If you have no real reason to do otherwise you might just as well pick a value straight out of the table as a starting point.

Existing bikes

If you increase the wheelbase on an existing bike there are two ways of doing it. When the swinging arm is extended the weight carried by the front tyre will increase. Alternatively, if the front wheel is moved forward instead, the weight carried by the rear tyre increases.

Both these changes will affect weight distribution and that can have a very significant effect on many aspects of behaviour. The implications of this are discussed in Chapter 3.2.

My own preference has always been to err on the short side as a starting point for wheelbase selection. The bike always seems to work best if you can tame the short wheelbase, rather than chicken out and go straight for the longer one. Typically, the short wheelbase can cause problems with wheelies. The situation can be improved, within limits, by slightly increasing the front end weight bias but you can easily overdo this and other aspects of handling will suffer. As I said earlier, you cannot isolate just one thing and it may help if you read all of Section 3 before jumping to conclusions.

Left. Table 3.1 *Wheelbase data for a variety of road and competition motorcycles.*

Steering geometry variables

Conventional steering geometry involves setting up two measurements known as castor angle (or rake) and trail. Both of these values are indicated in Fig 3.5.

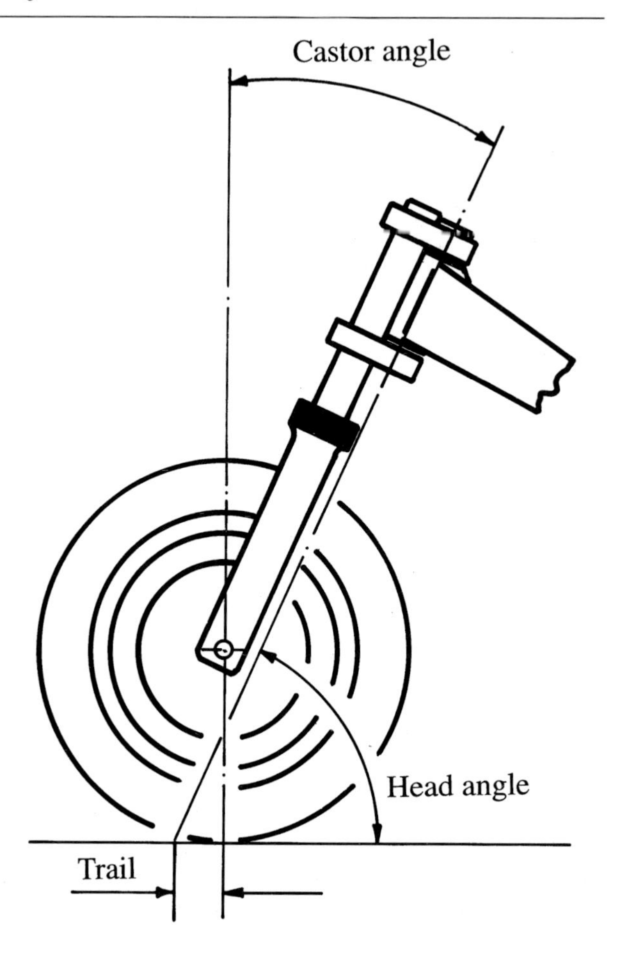

Above. Fig 3.5 *Castor angle and trail.*

Castor angle

This is the angle that the steering head is raked back from the vertical and for this reason it is also commonly termed the rake angle.

For conventional road or race machines used on tarmac the castor angle is typically between 22 and 29 degrees but values outside this range are used in specialised applications, particularly speedway, grasstrack and custom 'choppers'.

The inclination of the steering axis may also be quoted as an angle from the horizontal in which case the term head angle is often used.

- Head angle = 90° - castor angle
- Castor angle = 90° - head angle

This makes the common range of head angles between 61 and 68 degrees. In virtually all cases the fork legs run parallel to the steering axis. I have never seen any that do not do this but I am told that Harley Davidson sometimes adopt such an approach. I can see no reason to do this on a racing bike.

Trail

This is the horizontal distance from the point where the tyre contacts the road to the point where a line drawn through the steering axis would contact the road. Under normal static conditions the tyre contact point lies vertically below the wheel spindle as indicated in the diagram. From this description it is clear that trail is not something that can be measured easily or directly with a ruler, however it is the most influential value as far as steering behaviour is concerned. Typical trail values for roadracers lie in the range 80 to 120mm but small changes within this range can have large effects. Both castor angle and trail alter when the bike is in use. If the front tyre hits a bump the contact point moves forward substantially. If this point coincides with the point where a line through the steering axis touches the road then the trail is momentarily reduced to zero. If the contact point is even further to the front of the wheel then the trail is considered to be negative or, alternatively, is termed lead.

The castor angle will also change. When the front suspension is compressed under braking the castor angle will reduce and so, for that matter, will the trail and wheelbase. This makes it important to adopt a fixed set of conditions when making measurements and stick to them. Because castor angle and trail alter when the bike is in use, the selection of both values is a compromise which must take account of what the bike is going to experience. One would hope that the variation in conditions for a roadracer is somewhat less than it would be for a motocross bike but even so there is a strong case for building in some adjustment, especially for trail. This can be accomplished by

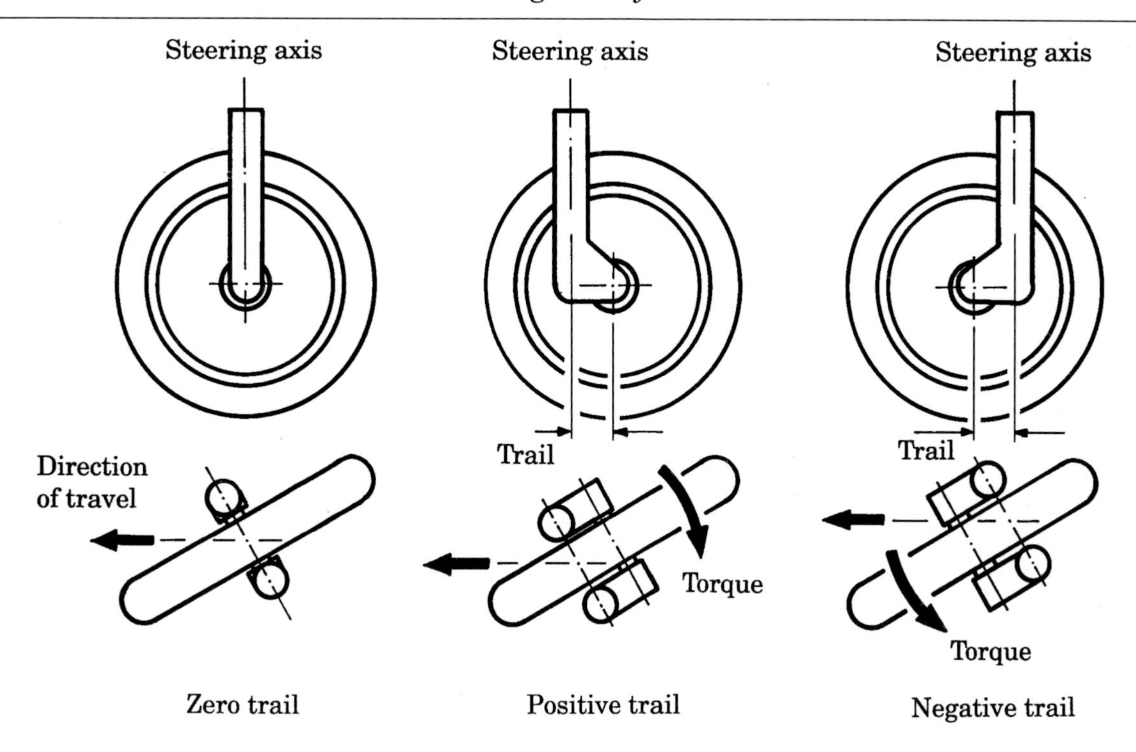

using adjustable fork yokes like those in Fig 3.6. Setting up the castor and trail on a new bike is a relatively straightforward task involving some other dimensions but first it is necessary to consider what is required.

Above. Fig 3.7 *Torque produced by trail. The upper diagrams show the steering straight and the lower diagrams are a plan view with the steering turned. With no trail there is no torque. With positive (normal) trail the contact patch is behind the steering axis and it produces a restoring torque. With negative trail the torque tries to force the steering further out of line.*

Fig 3.6 *Adjustable fork yokes provide a simple means of adapting trail to varying conditions. You can either use an eccentric bush (top diagram) or make the yoke in two parts and insert suitable spacers (lower diagram).*

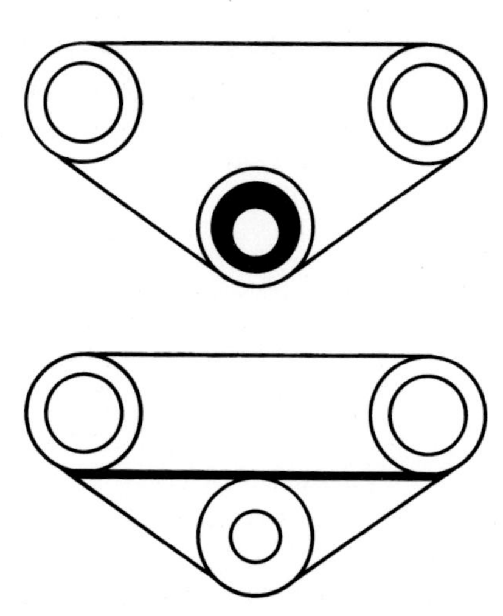

The need for trail

The main purpose of trail is to give the bike some straight line stability, ie the steering tends to self-centre if it is momentarily deflected when travelling in a straight line. Fig 3.7 shows three different trail situations combined with zero castor angle, a convenient place to start.

If the trail is negative then any deflection of the front wheel sets up a turning effect that tries to make the situation worse. This condition is frequently encountered off road and if you are not holding on firmly at the time the consequences are obvious. When the trail is positive, as it should be, the situation is completely different. If the wheel is at an angle to the actual direction of motion (this is called the slip angle) then the friction between the tyre and road again produces a turning effect but this time it is one which has a tendency to move the wheel back in line with the direction of travel. The amount of restoring torque that is set up in this situation will depend on the tyre characteristics, the road surface, the steering angle and the amount of trail. Other things being equal, more trail will produce a higher restoring torque.

At this stage it therefore appears that a large amount of trail is a good thing since it will restore wheel alignment more easily. However, when we actually want to turn the wheel out of line using the handlebars then the job will be more difficult. Large amounts of trail will tend to make the steering feel very heavy and the bike will not be as agile as one with less trail. A summary of the straight line situation is therefore as follows.

- Under normal conditions the trail must be positive to give any self-centring effect.

- Small amounts of positive trail give a small restoring torque, other things being equal. The steering is light but easily deflected by bumps.

- Larger amounts of positive trail give a greater restoring torque, other things being equal. The bike feels very stable but needs significant physical effort to change direction.

Although I did not discuss it in such terms, wheelbase is also a form of trail, the trail of the rear wheel. Both trails produce similar effects and the combination of the two is important, especially when the wheelbase is very short.

This is of course far from the end of the story. When we lean the bike over the contact patch rolls round to the side of the tyre and the torque exerted by the trail then contributes to the cornering characteristics. This effect is particularly influenced by the tyres and therefore in strict engineering terms the whole of the steering geometry should be designed around the tyres. In general we cannot do this since the data is not easily acquired or applied and in any event we are back up against the human factor. We could assume that factory GP bikes are designed in this way but put any two different riders on them and they will finish up using totally different steering geometry at every circuit. It is all a question of feel. Because of this there is no possible way that the normal bike builder can calculate an optimum trail value from first principles and it is much better to examine current practice which takes on board both tyre technology and general rider reaction. Table 3.2 gives numerous examples of castor angle and trail for you to choose from. Remember that the wheelbase will influence the feel that the trail produces.

Care should be taken not to select values that are too lively for your ability. Some 250GP bikes are deemed to be extremely twitchy when ridden by normal mortals and they would certainly be a handful on airfield gravel patches! Once the bike is built using such data you can then experiment to get a final feel you prefer. Changing tyres will almost certainly demand geometry modifications if you are sensitive to these aspects.

Steering oscillation

There is one more aspect of trail that needs to be appreciated and that is the fact that in seeking a self-centring tendency for the steering we are potentially setting up one requirement of an oscillatory sytem, ie one which is likely to shake or wobble at the slightest disturbance.

If you put any conventional motorcycle on a stand with the front wheel in the air and then hold the handlebars tightly while someone else tries to turn the wheel to one side the result will often be a noticeable twisting of the front end.

A similar test could be carried out on the wheel itself revealing even more twist and there is then the sidewall distortion of the tyre. Continuing through the machine you would soon conclude that the whole motorcycle is far from rigid and is in fact held together by components that behave more like springs than rigid elements, albeit much stiffer ones than we use for suspension.

Right. Table 3.2 *Castor angle and trail values as published for a variety of motorcycles. The castor and trail values are only a starting point which will need to be refined according to tyres, track conditions and personal preference. Experiment is the only way forward.*

Road bikes			
Make of Machine	**Castor**	**Trail**	
	deg	**mm**	**ins**
Honda Fireblade (96)	24	90	3.54
Kawasaki ZX-7R (96)	25	99	3.90
Yamaha YZF750 (96)	24	97	3.82
Suzuki GSX-R1100M	25.8	91	3.58
Triumph Trophy 1200	27	105	4.13
BMW K1100LT	27	101	3.98
Ducati 916 (96)	24-25	94-100	3.90-3.94
Suzuki GSX-R750 (96)	24	96	3.78
Bimota Furano FZR	24	95	3.74
Yamaha FZ750	26	94	3.70
Honda VFR750	28	108	4.25
Kawasaki GPX750	27	97	3.82
Honda CBR600F-M	25	94	3.70
Ducati 750SS (95)	25	103	4.06
Yamaha FZR600	25	94	3.70
Suzuki GSX600F-M	25	98	3.86
Honda CBR400RR	25	91	3.58
Kawasaki ZXR400 (96)	23.5	82	3.23
Yamaha RVF400 (96)	25	92	3.62
Aprilia RS250 (96)	25.5	102	4.02
Yamaha TZR250	24	90	3.54
Suzuki RGV250SP (96)	24	89	3.5

Road race			
Make of Machine	**Castor**	**Trail**	
	deg	**mm**	**ins**
Honda NSR500 (92)	23	95	3.74
Honda RC45	24.5	92	3.62
Harley VR1000 (95)	23	96	3.78
Cagiva V592 500 (92)	24/25	n/a	n/a
Suzuki RGV500XR78 (92)	23	95	3.74
Honda NSR500 (95 Doohan)	22.5	95	3.74
Muzzy Kawasaki 750 (95)	24.5	100	3.94
Ducati 916 (95 Foggarty)	24.5	100	3.94
Honda RS125 (96)	23.5	84	3.31
Aprilia RSV400 (95)	21	76	2.99
Aprilia RSV250 (95 Biaggi)	21	76	2.99
Honda RS250 (93)	22.5	86	3.39
Yamaha TZ250 (93)	22.5	82	3.23
Yamaha TZ125 (94)	22.2	81	3.19
Trials/Motocross/Enduro			
Fantic (96)Trials	23	n/a	n/a
Kawasaki KX250 (93) MX	26	108	4.25
Honda XR250R (96) Enduro	24.75	92	3.62
Kawasaki KX125 (93) MX	26	106	4.13
Grasstrack/Speedway			
Typical Speedway	19	73	2.88
Typical Grasstrack	21	79	3.10

No matter how stiff you try to make everything this situation will still apply to a greater or lesser extent. When a momentary side force is exerted at the tyre during use it is very likely that the whole front end will oscillate for a short time. This oscillation results from three things. Firstly, the structure is not rigid as I have just discussed and neither are your arms! Secondly, the components have inertia and finally, there are a number of reaction forces which are trying to restore alignment to the original position. These will usually succeed as soon as the external force is removed and in fact they will often overdo things somewhat given the inertia of the components. This actually helps the oscillation to continue.

Some of the restoring torque is generated by you and some is produced internally by component materials. However, there is also a big external reaction, that due to trail. The irony of this is that it is quite possible to get a trail-induced oscillation for which one cure may actually be a reduction in trail if straight line stability is still acceptable! Things can get even worse. Forces can also be generated by virtue of wheel imbalance due to a variety of causes and these forces are repetitive. In any system that has an inherent tendency to oscillate, persistent 'nudging' with external forces can, if the timing is right, lead to a build up in the severity of any oscillation. This phenomenon is called resonance and it presents itself as a wobble or shake at the front end which will occur at a road speed where the timing of external forces is synchronised to the inherent oscillation frequency of the front end. These effects are familiar to most riders.

The frequency at which the front end would like to oscillate depends on many things but notably the stiffness of the structure and the moment of inertia about the steering head. The moment of inertia about the steering head is a measure of the reluctance of the complete front end to go in any direction other than the one it is currently going in. If it is swinging right and trying to tear your arms off then the greater the moment of inertia the more chance it will have of succeeding! Also, when the moment of inertia is high, the steering feels heavy for a given amount of trail.

Moment of inertia is discussed in more detail in Section 6. It does not just depend on how heavy the components are but is in fact made up from individual masses and the square of their distance from the steering axis. As such, something relatively light, but far away, can make a significant contribution. What you need to aspire to is infinite stiffness and no inertia! Most medium sized bikes will show up any resonance problems between 50 and 70km/hr (30 - 44miles/hr) but the effect often repeats at a higher speed as well. In general such wobbles are stable and will die away if you go faster or slower. If you accelerate quickly through the critical range you may never even notice them.

Unfortunately, the true situation is much more complex than the one I have described and it is possible that such oscillations will die away if they are small but increase substantially if they manage to get large enough in the first place. This constitutes the dreaded tank slapper over which a rider has limited control. Further complication arises as soon as the bike is leaned over because several other modes of oscillatory behaviour can occur and these then cross couple with everthing else, not a good situation.

I have only discussed these aspects here because of the important role played by trail and to emphasise the need to ensure that the front end is compact, light and very stiff. We cannot hope to analyse the bike's oscillatory behaviour mathematically. It can be done, and a lot of work has been published on such topics, notably by Robin Sharp at Cranfield, but the analysis is far too involved to form the basis of a general guide.

It is important to note that fitting a steering damper is not a sensible solution to any such problems and it could well make the situation worse. Damping is indeed the transfer of energy away from a system so that oscillation dies down but by fitting a steering damper the feel and precision of the steering is lost. The damper serves an excellent role in steadying the steering when it is airborne over high speed ripples or bumps but to do so it only needs to be at a light setting. If you have to set the damper so that you can hardly turn the bars in order to subdue steering oscillation then something else needs to be done based on the factors just outlined.

The need for castor angle

The need for castor angle is very different to the need for trail and from one point of view it could be argued that you don't need any! Perhaps one of the most dominant needs for castor angle is structural. If the forks are upright then applying the brakes will lead to considerable 'chatter' as the forks flex back and forth. Many hub centre designs, which are much stiffer than telescopic forks, only have between about 5 and 12 degrees of castor instead of the usual 22 - 29 degrees so clearly our normal angles are not essential for effective steering.

However, if we accept a conventional motorcycle, and that is all this book covers, then the castor angle has a major role to play in the way we feel the effect of the trail. It causes the front wheel to lean when it turns and if you are used to riding conventional motorcycles you have come to accept all this. We are back to the human element and the abstract concept of 'feel'. Generally speaking, more castor angle requires more trail to give the same feel but it is uneconomical to try and attach formulae to all of this.

Setting up steering geometry

For a given castor angle the desired trail is achieved via two other measurements, the rolling radius of the tyre and the offset of the front wheel spindle from the steering axis - Fig 3.8.

Rolling radius

The rolling radius used is determined by the tyres being employed. Given the need to use the best tyres you can afford the only decision concerns wheel size and again this is predominantly influenced by cost and tyre availability. There is no point in arguing the case for 17in wheels over 18in if you cannot buy tyres so the decision is often made for you.

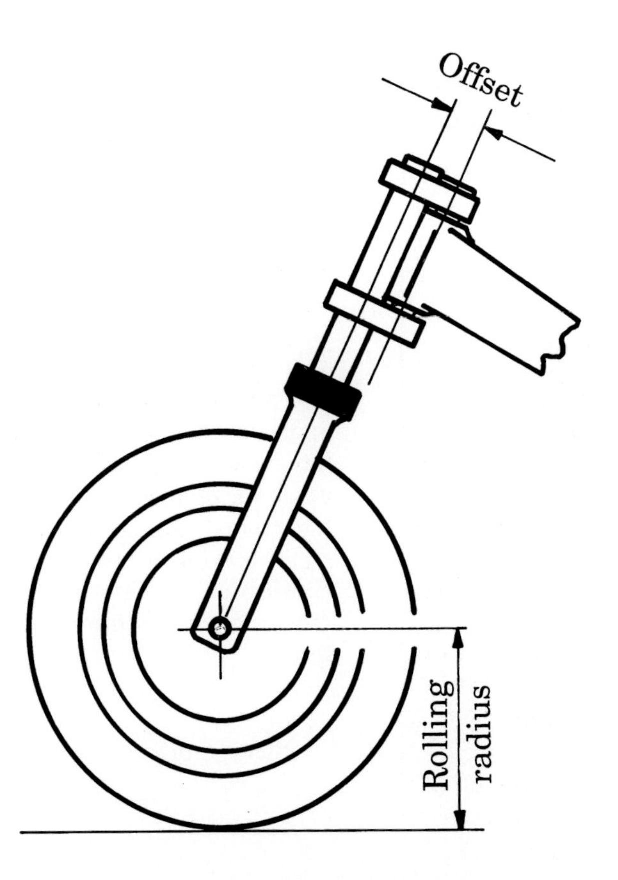

Fig 3.8 *For a given castor angle the trail is determined by the combination of rolling radius and wheel spindle offset.*

Most builders will know exactly what they are using at the outset. Obviously the rolling radius changes according to tyre pressures and riding conditions, especially when braking. Do not lose any sleep over this. It is really just a case of deciding the conditions under which you will make measurements and sticking to them. If you have trail problems under heavy braking then you will have to modify the basic unladen values. No doubt we will arrive at the stage where the geometry varies automatically to suit conditions but for the moment you have to live with this.

Wheel offset

This is the distance between a line passing through the steering axis and a parallel line passing through the wheel spindle. If the fork legs are parallel to the steering axis and the wheel spindle lies on the axis of the fork legs, then the wheel offset is produced solely by the fork yokes.

With some forks, particularly motocross, the wheel mounts on lugs that are in front of the legs. This arrangement increases the torsional stiffness of the forks and allows the bulk of the forks to be close to the steering axis. When forks like this are used the offset is made up of two elements, the contribution of the yokes and that due to the forward mounted wheel lugs - Fig 3.9.

Castor angle, trail, rolling radius and wheel offset are related to each other as follows.

Required Wheel Offset = RSinØ - TCosØ

where R = rolling radius
T = trail
Ø = castor angle

Values of R and T must have the same units eg both mm, both inches etc.

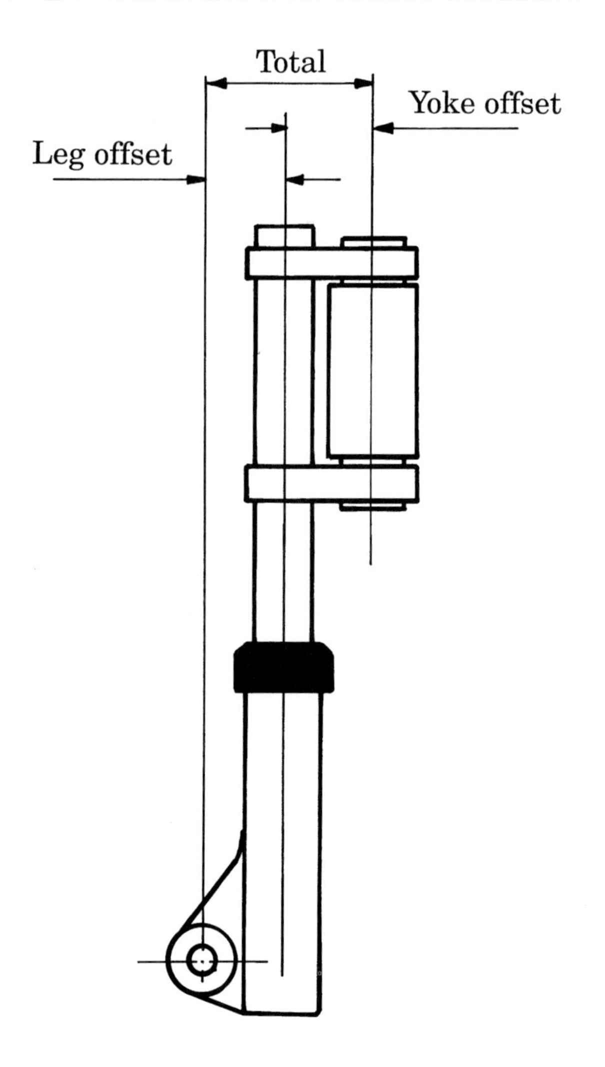

Fig 3.9 *Forks with the wheel spindle mounted in front of the fork legs provide two stages of offset.*

Table 3.3 gives values of SinØ and CosØ for castor angles in the range 20 - 30 degrees at half degree intervals. Values outside this range can be looked up on most calculators.

Example. If the rolling radius is 300mm, the required trail 95mm and the castor angle 24° then,

Offset (mm) = 300Sin24° - 95Cos24°
= (300 x 0.407) - (95 x 0.914)
= 122.1 - 86.8
= 35.3mm

Example. If the rolling radius is 11.4ins, the required trail 4.2ins and the head angle is 64° then,

Castor angle = 90° - 64° = 26°

Offset (ins) = 11.4Sin26° - 4.2Cos26°
= (11.4 x 0.438) - (4.2 x 0.899)
= 4.99 - 3.76
= 1.23 ins

There are basically three situations to be dealt with as far as sorting out steering geometry goes.

- Designing a new bike.
- Using an existing pair of forks or yokes on a new frame.
- Modifying an existing motorcycle.

Designing a new bike

This assumes that you are prepared to make or find ideal fork yokes. Proceed as follows,

- Select front tyre size and determine the rolling radius. This must be in mm if the trail will be in mm.
- Select the desired castor angle (deg) and the required trail (mm).
- Calculate the required wheel offset (mm) using the formula given.
- If the wheel is offset from the fork leg axis subtract this amount from the total calculated offset to get the yoke offset dimension.

On a new bike it will pay you to draw this out full size for use later on. If the maximum fork movement is known, allow that plus mudguard clearance etc and you can see where the yokes and headstock are going to be.

Angle Ø°	Sin Ø°	Cos Ø°
20	0.342	0.940
20.5	0.350	0.937
21	0.358	0.934
21.5	0.367	0.930
22	0.375	0.927
22.5	0.383	0.924
23	0.391	0.921
23.5	0.399	0.917
24	0.407	0.914
24.5	0.415	0.910
25	0.423	0.906
25.5	0.431	0.903
26	0.438	0.899
26.5	0.446	0.895
27	0.454	0.891
27.5	0.462	0.887
28	0.469	0.883
28.5	0.477	0.879
29	0.485	0.875
29.5	0.492	0.870
30	0.500	0.866

Table 3.3 *Values of Sin Ø and Cos Ø.*

Using existing yokes

A common situation is one in which you have a pair of forks and would like to use the standard yokes on a new frame that is being made to give a specific castor angle. You know what trail you would like and need to see if the standard yokes will be suitable. Proceed as follows,

- Determine the wheel offset (mm) by measurement. It is best to take this direct from the yokes - Fig 3.10. Don't forget any spindle offset.
- Determine the rolling radius (mm)
- Select the ideal castor angle.
- Calculate the actual trail from,

$$\textbf{Trail} = \frac{\textbf{RSin}Ø \ \textbf{- O}}{\textbf{Cos}Ø}$$

where O is the offset in mm
R is the rolling rad in mm
Ø is the castor angle

If you use inches or any other units make sure that the offset and radius are in the same units. The answer will also be in these units

The trail that you obtain may not be what you want. If this is the case you will need to reconsider your specification or make new yokes as the following example demonstrates.

Example. Existing forks have a total wheel offset of 30mm all provided by the yokes. The tyres have a rolling radius of 300mm and the desired trail/castor are 92mm and 22° respectively. Using the formula given,

$$\text{Actual trail} = \frac{300\text{Sin}22° - 30}{\text{Cos}22°}$$

$$= \frac{300 \times 0.375 - 30}{0.927}$$

$$= \frac{82.5}{0.927}$$

$$= 89\text{mm}$$

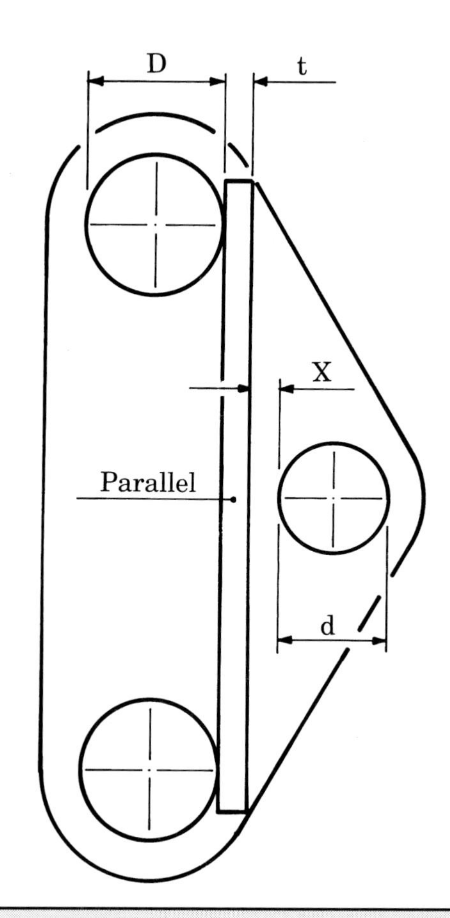

$$\textbf{Offset} = \textbf{X + t +} \frac{\textbf{(D + d)}}{\textbf{2}}$$

Fig 3.10 *Determining yoke offset when the legs and stem are still fitted. Measure the stanchions (D) and the headstock collar (d). Place a parallel of thickness t as shown and measure gap X.*

This may or may not be acceptable since it is clearly 4mm less than you hoped for. When the calculated trail is less than you would like, as in this example, try increasing the castor angle by 0.5°. In this case it would produce 91.8mm of trail and the compromise values of 22.5° castor and 91.8mm trail may be preferable to making new yokes. In any event, you would need to be very good to build to an accuracy better than 0.25° and a practical person would probably try out this set-up before making new yokes.

If the actual trail is more than you would like, investigate the effect of slightly reducing the castor angle. If you cannot get a combination that is acceptable you will just have to make your own yokes.

Using a drawing

Some readers will much prefer to use a drawing for things like this. This is perfectly acceptable but it does need to be at least half size, preferably full size, and it does need to be done very accurately. An error of one degree in the head angle will typically produce a trail value that is 5 - 8mm different to that with the correct angle. This is something to note if you intend making your own frame. The general method of drawing is,

- Draw a horizontal line and a vertical one as shown in Fig 3.11a).
- Mark the rolling radius on the vertical line and from this point draw a line upwards at the castor angle, diagram b).
- If you know the trail you want and need to find offset, mark the trail on the horizontal line and draw another line up at the castor angle. Measure the gap between the lines to find the required offset, c).
- If you have yokes of a certain offset, draw a line parallel to the first castor line, separated from it by the offset. Measure the trail along the horizontal line as shown, c).

Fig 3.11 *Using a drawing to determine trail or offset as described in the text.*

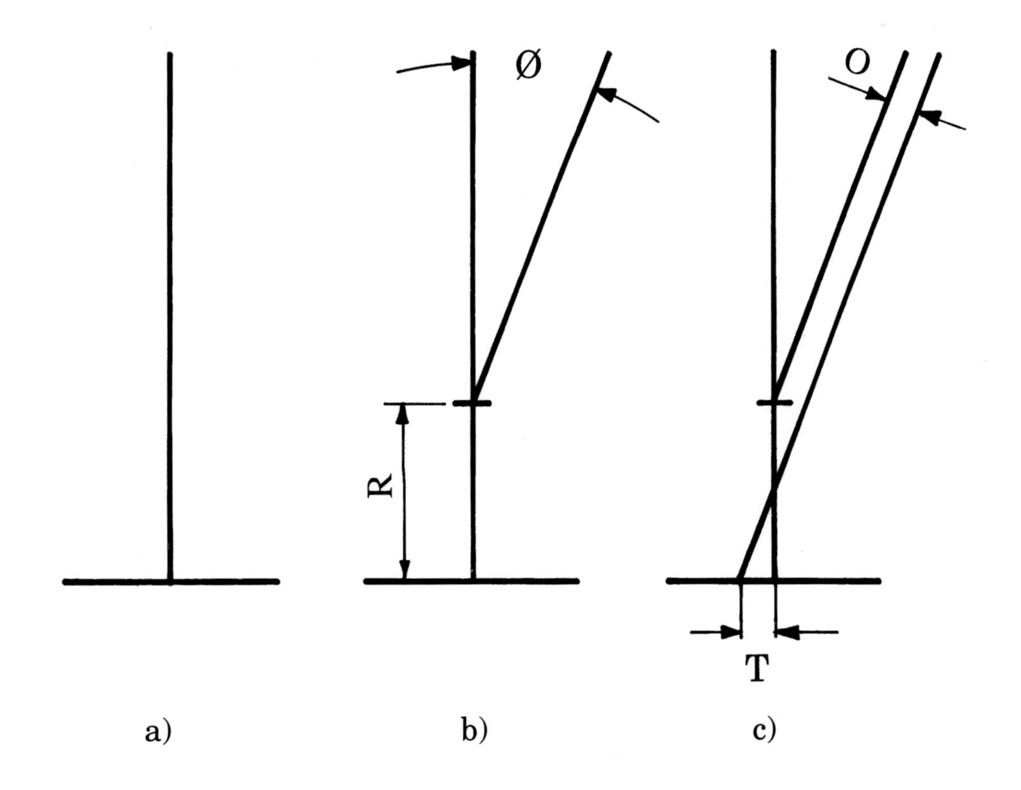

Modifying an existing machine

This is slightly different and it raises the problem of measuring an existing set-up. For small changes you can slide the fork stanchions up or down in the yokes and/or raise/lower the back end of the bike.

All such changes will affect several things at once including ground clearance, centre of gravity location, castor angle, trail and wheelbase. This is not ideal but it may be acceptable. The following will occur.

- Moving the stanchions up through the yokes will reduce the castor angle, trail and wheelbase.
- Moving the stanchions down through the yokes will increase the castor angle, trail and wheelbase.
- Raising the back end of the bike reduces the castor angle, trail and, usually, the wheelbase. Lowering it increases them.

Measuring up requires some decent equipment to do the job really well but you can usually get by with a variety of home-made items. To check castor angle, or any other angles on the frame, the best tool is a clinometer as shown in Fig 3.12. When you look through the eyepiece you see a high resolution protractor scale that is set to zero on a suitable datum, in this case the ground. The clinometer is then placed on the fork stanchions and readjusted until the spirit level centres again. Looking through the eyepiece then gives the angle very accurately relative to the ground.

Accepting that such items are expensive, there are several low cost alternatives. The first option for obtaining castor angle is to use a plumb line and square as shown in Fig 3.13. A convenient point to fix the plumb line is at the top yoke.

Measure the distance from this point to the wheel spindle (L) and also the distance shown as X. The castor angle is then the angle that has a Sine value equal to X/L. Table 3.3 given previously can be used to find the nearest angle in 0.5° increments or you can use a suitable calculator to find the angle exactly. Note that the measured values of X and L must be in the same units, eg both mm or both ins. To measure the trail on existing bikes I sometimes use the method shown in Fig 3.14. A steel rod (a broom handle would do if it was straight) has a taper turned on one end and is lightly clamped to the stanchions as shown, the spacer being such that the axis of the rod is in the same plane as the steering axis. With the rod just touching the floor the trail is easily measured. If you don't want to mess about with plumb lines and Sines you can also use the rod to mark the castor angle onto a suitable piece of ply and then measure the angle with an ordinary 'drawing' protractor. Yoke offset, which needs to be known before the rod spacer can be made, is best measured using a vernier caliper and a parallel. This was shown earlier in Fig 3.10.

Fig 3.12 *A clinometer is what you really need for checking castor angle.*

Top right. Fig 3.13 *A tape measure, plumb line and square provide a low cost means of checking the castor angle.*

Bottom right. Fig 3.14 *Using a suitable pointer parallel to the fork legs for determining trail and / or castor angle. Yoke offset is straightforward to measure with a vernier caliper and parallel.*

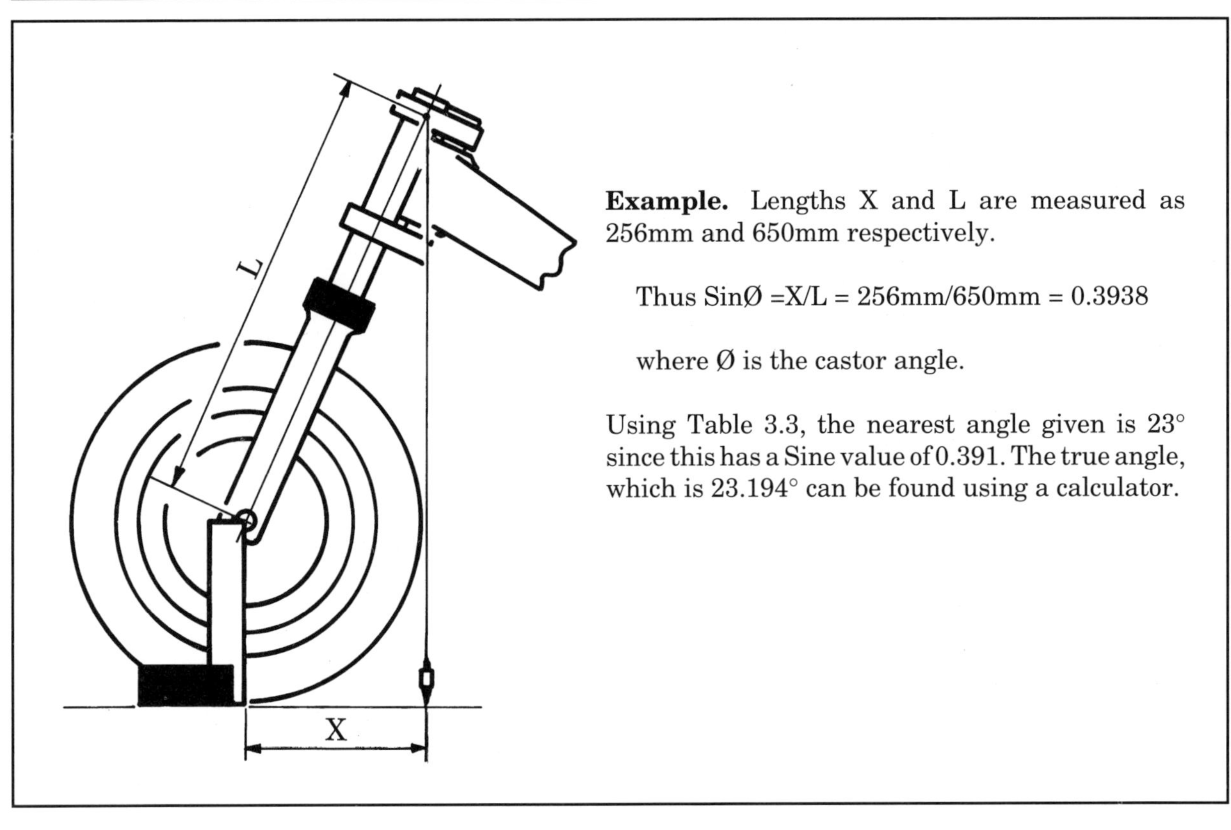

Example. Lengths X and L are measured as 256mm and 650mm respectively.

Thus SinØ =X/L = 256mm/650mm = 0.3938

where Ø is the castor angle.

Using Table 3.3, the nearest angle given is 23° since this has a Sine value of 0.391. The true angle, which is 23.194° can be found using a calculator.

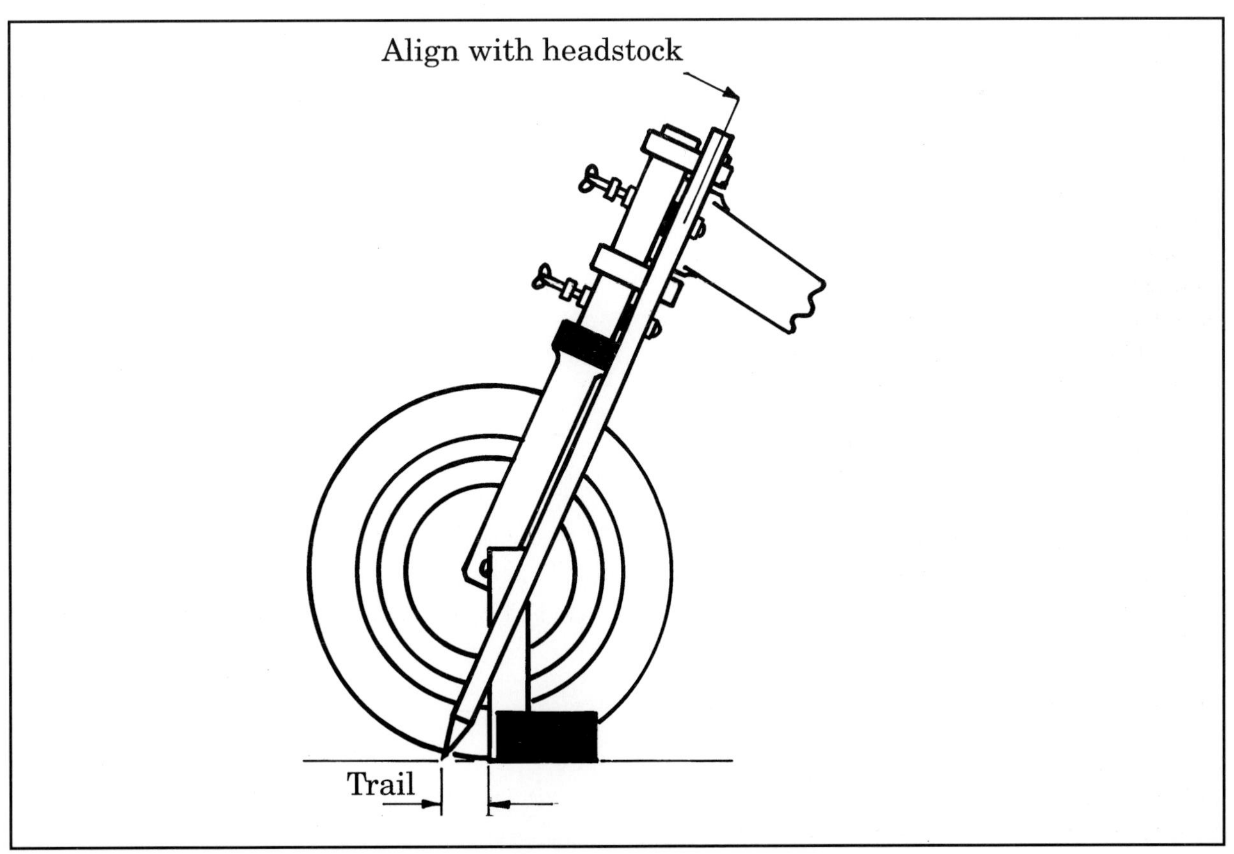

3.2 Centre of gravity and rider positioning

Introduction

One of the most important design features of any motorcycle is the manner in which weight is distributed throughout the machine. This controls so many aspects of performance that it should be 'designed in' and not left to chance.

Weight distribution (in all three dimensions) is determined by where we choose to locate parts, particularly the very heavy ones such as the engine, fuel tank, forks, wheels and rider. The overall result is defined by the location of something called the centre of gravity. This is the point at which the whole weight of the motorcycle and rider can be assumed to act for the purpose of assessing the response to accelerations.

To some extent the layout of a conventional motorcycle limits the scale of errors you can make here. Most motorcycles that look 'normal' will have a centre of gravity location that is 'reasonable' but this is far from adequate when you are seeking race-winning performance. Small changes in the centre of gravity location can often yield significant improvements in handling, traction, acceleration and general feel so we need to explore this area in some detail.

There are of course numerous practical constraints on where you can physically locate things. The engine has to have sufficient ground clearance. It has to clear the front tyre when the suspension is fully compressed and so on. Even with such restrictions there is still a great deal of scope and engine position is one of the things most frequently experimented with at GP level. Because the engine is invariably the heaviest component, small changes in its position can be crucial.

There are other factors involved. In selecting an engine position you do, to some extent, define the swinging arm geometry. Will this be suitable? Does it matter anyway? These are some of the aspects I want to explore in this chapter and the one that follows it. Like gearing, centre of gravity location is not something you want to be stuck with simply because it turned out that way. It needs to be planned in advance to the best of your ability. If you fail to manage this aspect, and the centre of gravity location is poor, it might be possible to correct it only by starting again!

There are four basic requirements.

- All components have to fit in physically acceptable locations.
- The rider has to fit comfortably on the bike in a position that minimises aerodynamic drag.
- The centre of gravity must be in a suitable position. If it is not, the bike will experience artificially low limits on its acceleration and braking as well as various handling problems.
- The swinging arm geometry must be acceptable. It must allow a sensible chain run without excessive changes in centre distance and it must not induce excessive pro-squat or anti-squat tendencies.

In my opinion, if a bike has steering geometry that suits you and the centre of gravity is sensibly located, you are well on the way to having a motorcycle that is a pleasure to race.

Centre of gravity

The centre of gravity of an object is defined as the point at which the entire weight of the object may be assumed to act. Clearly this is an idealisation, since the weight of a motorcycle is distributed throughout the space that it occupies, however it is not a 'poor approximation' but a method of working and it will give useful practical results. The term 'centre of gravity' is frequently shortened to cg and its location is generally denoted by the symbol ⊕.

In all cases it is the centre of gravity of the combined bike and rider that is of interest since we have not yet reached the stage of racing by remote control. Clearly this will be altered by rider movement and that fact is greatly exploited in all off-road applications. The same applies on tarmac but

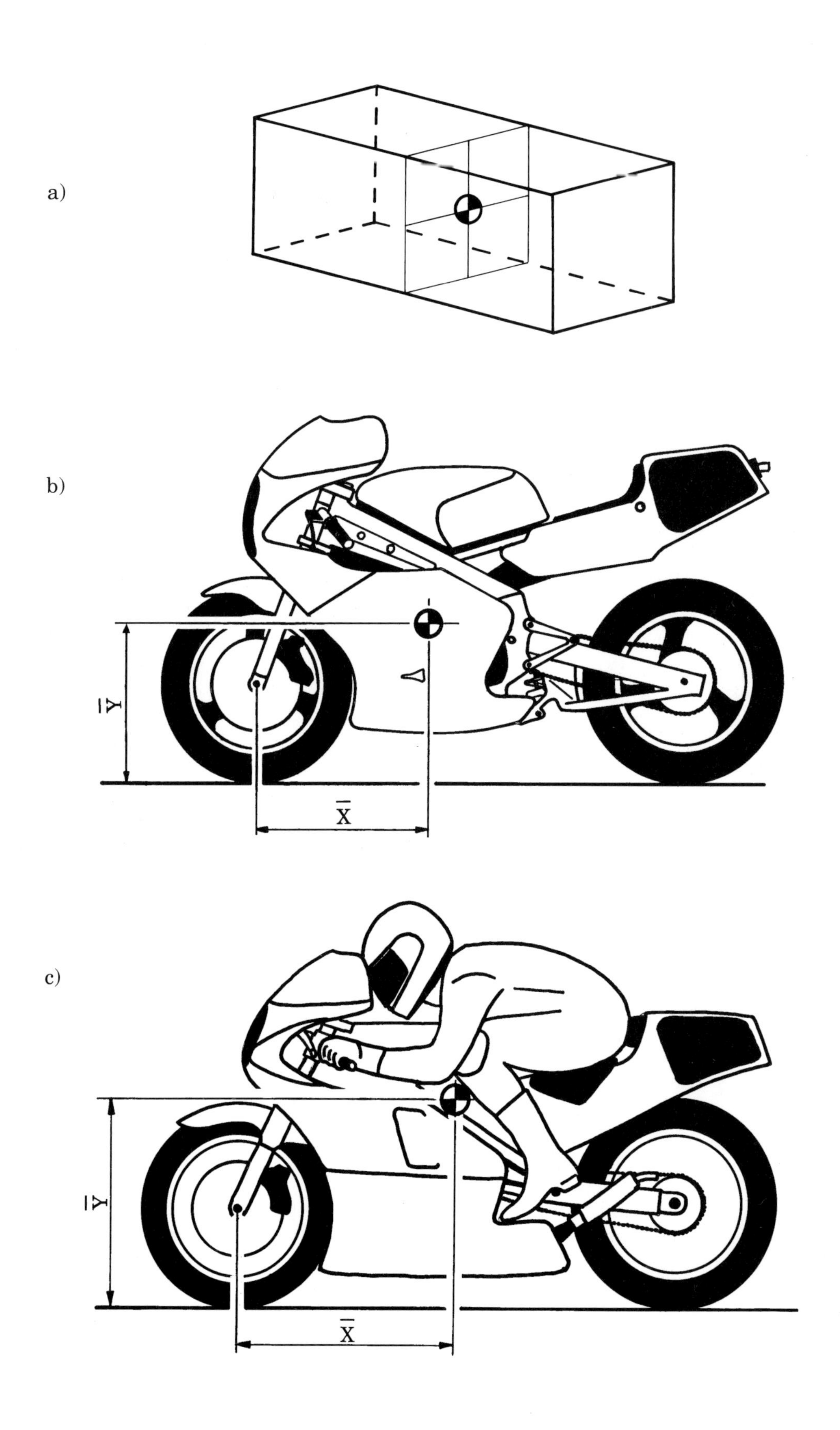
a)
b)
$\bar{Y}$
$\bar{X}$
c)
$\bar{Y}$
$\bar{X}$

the rider movements are more restricted, thus increasing the need to think about it before you start welding bits together.

Even though we are interested in the centre of gravity of the combined bike and rider it is useful to keep data for both the unladen and laden conditions. This allows you to compare bikes very easily but you must then take account of the riding position and weight of the rider before you can establish what is likely to happen on the track.

Centre of gravity location

With simple objects, a rectangular strip of metal for example, it is easy to see where the centre of gravity is located by trying to balance it. By balancing the strip on each of its edges in turn we can decide how far along that edge the centre of gravity must lie. Using the metal strip as an example, if we try to balance it on a knife edge then the balance point will lie halfway along any edge that we choose, provided the strip does not have any holes in it!

From this we deduce that the centre of gravity actually lies at a point which is right in the centre of the metal, somewhere we cannot actually touch as shown in Fig 3.15a). This arises because we are dealing with a three-dimensional object. A motorcycle is a three-dimensional object and so it too will have its centre of gravity at a point which we possibly cannot see or touch. However, like the strip of metal, most motorcycles are reasonably symmetrical either side of a centreline when viewed from above and are therefore sensibly balanced about a central plane. Because of this there is usually little concern for how far into the side of the motorcycle the cg lies (it is near the middle) and attention is focused on just two measurements, one to define how far along the length of the bike the cg lies and another to indicate how high up it is as shown in Fig 3.15b). These distances can be measured from any convenient datum of your choice and it is therefore absolutely essential to know where that datum is. The vertical distance, usually denoted by $\overline{y}$, is nearly always taken from ground level but the horizontal dimension, denoted by $\overline{x}$, may be from the front wheel spindle, the rear wheel spindle, or even the edge of a tyre. This does not cause any problems at all provided you know exactly where!

Left. Fig 3.15 *a) The centre of gravity of a simple strip of metal is located half way along each side and as such is at a point inside the metal. b) For a motorcycle the situation is similar. Because a bike is, or should be, reasonably balanced about its centreline, the cg location is normally only specified in two dimensions. c) In the laden condition the cg will move to a new position that is generally higher up, and further back, than the unladen position.*

The cg location of a complete motorcycle and rider combination will be determined by the weight of each individual component and the location of the cg for each individual component. As we gradually decide where things will go the overall cg location moves about according to how heavy the parts are and where we put them.

Finally, when the rider gets on the bike, the overall cg location shifts yet again to some point between the unladen bike's cg and that of the individual rider - Fig 3.15c). In general the cg will move backwards and upwards.

All of this can be worked out relatively easily as you go along and the implications of cg location can be followed. For example, if you have decided to position the engine as close to the front wheel as possible, and calculation shows that the overall cg is still too far back, then you will have to make every effort to get other heavy parts, including the rider, as far forward as possible until the problem is solved. Similarly, if the proposed engine location has plenty of ground clearance but calculation shows the cg location to be high, you can look at lowering the engine. We now have three things to consider.

- Where should the overall cg be located?
- How can we determine where the overall cg is while we are actually designing the bike?
- How can we determine the cg location of existing bikes so that we can check out something we know works well?

I will consider each of these aspects in turn. It is a fairly lengthy discussion but at the end of it you will be in a much better position to make something work reasonably well 'straight from the drawing board'. If you ignore all this and start building, then there is often nothing that can be done to correct a poor cg location without resorting to very serious metal surgery.

Overview

The ability of the bike to accelerate and brake is highly dependent on the location of the cg. All riders recognise four situations that impose a limit on what can be achieved under such conditions. When braking a limit will eventually be found either in the form of the front wheel locking up or when the back wheel leaves the ground. During acceleration, either the rear wheel will spin or the front wheel will lift.

All these conditions impose a very definite limit and no amount of power or brake performance can overcome them. If the wheels lift then they will only go down again if the acceleration or retardation is reduced. Note that retardation is the term used to describe the rate at which you slow down, negative acceleration if you like. Each limit is related to both the horizontal and vertical cg location. Unfortunately, it is only possible to improve one condition at the expense of another so as usual we are attempting to seek a compromise. This is made worse by the fact that the optimal cg location varies with the amount of tyre grip available and therefore what is ideal in the dry will not be ideal in the wet. Despite these frustrations cg location remains one of the more important aspects of motorcycle design and needs to be addressed.

Horizontal cg location ($\bar{x}$)

The general influence of horizontal cg location is outlined in Table 3.4. The four limits are not affected equally by cg movements but this will do as a starting point. Horizontal cg location is much easier to deal with than the vertical location. Data is more readily available and measurements are easier to carry out.

The horizontal location of the overall cg will determine the static weight distribution of the bike, ie how much of the total weight is carried by the front wheel and how much is carried by the rear wheel. The vertical cg location plays no part in this which is very useful because it allows us to determine $\bar{x}$ on an existing bike simply by placing scales under the wheels. If the cg lies mid-way along the wheelbase then each wheel will support half the total weight when the bike is stationary (or travelling at a constant speed in a straight line, ie no acceleration or braking). When this is the case the bike is said to have a 50/50 weight distribution. If the cg is nearer to the front wheel than the rear, then the front wheel carries more than the rear, eg 55% front, 45% rear and vice-versa. The actual static weight distribution is related to the horizontal cg location as follows.

Table 3.4 *General influence of horizontal cg location on the four conditions that limit acceleration and braking. Note that not all conditions are influenced equally. In this table the cg location is being measured from the front wheel spindle.*

Event	Limiting condition	$\bar{x}$ reduced (move cg location forward)	$\bar{x}$ increased (move cg location rearwards)
acceleration	front wheel lift	less likely	more likely
acceleration	rear wheel spin	more likely	less likely
braking	rear wheel lift	more likely	less likely
braking	front wheel locking	less likely	more likely

$$\text{\% Weight on rear} = \frac{100\bar{x}}{L}$$

$$\text{\% Weight on front} = \frac{100(L - \bar{x})}{L}$$

where L = wheelbase

and $\bar{x}$ = horizontal distance from front wheel spindle to cg

The values of $\bar{x}$ and L that you use can be in any units but they must be in the same units, eg both mm or both ins.

Example. If the wheelbase is 1400mm and $\bar{x}$ is 800mm then,

$$\text{\% Weight on rear} = \frac{100 \times 800}{1400}$$

$$= 57\% \text{ approx.}$$

$$\text{\% Weight on front} = \frac{100(1400 - 800)}{1400}$$

$$= \frac{100 \times 600}{1400}$$

$$= 43\% \text{ approx.}$$

Example. If the wheelbase is 56ins and $\bar{x}$ is 27ins then,

$$\text{\% Weight on rear} = \frac{100 \times 27}{56}$$

$$= 48\% \text{ approx.}$$

$$\text{\% Weight on front} = \frac{100(56 - 27)}{56}$$

$$= \frac{100 \times 29}{56}$$

$$= 52\% \text{ approx.}$$

Note that in general both the cg location and the weight distribution will change when the bike is laden. Quoted weight distributions are invariably for the unladen bike and serve as an excellent basis for comparison. It is however the laden values that are most important.

In practice you are unlikely to know the horizontal cg location and are more concerned with finding it. If you have an existing bike that handles particularly well then the horizontal cg location can be found as follows. Put the bike on two sets of scales and note the reading under each wheel. It makes no difference what units the scales read in provided both figures are in the same units. Having done this, measure the wheelbase in your chosen units and the value of $\bar{x}$, in the same units as the wheelbase, is given by,

$$\bar{x} = \frac{W_r L}{W_r + W_f}$$

where W_r = the scale reading at the rear wheel

W_f = the scale reading at the front wheel

L = the wheelbase

$\bar{x}$ = horizontal distance from front wheel spindle to cg

Example. When placed on scales the readings obtained are 120kg at the front and 105kg at the rear. If the wheelbase is 1400mm then,

$$\bar{x} = \frac{105 \times 1400}{(105 + 120)}$$

$$= 653\text{mm}$$

Example. When placed on scales the readings obtained are 250lb at the front and 200lb at the rear. If the wheelbase is 56ins then,

$$\bar{x} = \frac{200 \times 56}{(250 + 200)}$$

$$= 24.9\text{ins}$$

Do this for both the laden and unladen conditions. You can then see how much the presence of the rider alters the horizontal cg location. On most bikes the rider is likely to move the cg backwards slightly and the unladen values need to account for this when the bike is built.

Using two sets of scales always seems to give the best results but if you only have one set then you will have to put a block under the wheel without the scales in order to keep the bike level. Two sets are particularly beneficial when taking laden values because small rider movements can make a noticeable difference. It is important to note the exact rider position so that reliable comparisons can be made.

The final possibility is that you have been given figures for the weight distribution. These are not published that often but Table 3.5 opposite lists one or two that I have noticed over the years. The value of $\bar{x}$ can be obtained from these using,

$$\bar{x} = \frac{W_r\%.L}{100}$$

where $\bar{x}$ = the horizontal distance from the front wheel spindle to the cg

$W_r\%$ = the percentage of the total weight carried by the rear wheel

L = wheelbase

Machine	% front	% rear
Muzzy Kawasaki(95)	54	46
Ducati 916(95)	51.5	48.5
Honda NSR250(95)	53	47
Honda NSR250(88)	56	44
Honda NSR500(90)	53	47
Honda NSR500(87)	54	46
Honda RC45(95)	54	46
Suzuki RGV500(92)	53	47
Suzuki RGV500(88)	55	45
Cagiva 500(88)	53	47
Gilera 250(93)	54	46
Aprilia 400(95)	54	46
Aprilia 250(95)	53	47
Aprilia 250(88)	55	45
Ducati(Polen 93)	52	48
Yamaha 250(90)	55	45
Yamaha 250(89)	53	47
Bimota YB4EIR 750	54	46
EMC 250	53	47
Derbi 125	55	45
Cobas 125	57	43

Table 3.5 *Examples of published weight distribution figures.*

The value of $\overline{x}$ so calculated will have the same units as the wheelbase.

Example. The weight distribution of a bike is 52% front, 48% rear. How far is the cg from the front spindle if the wheelbase is 1400mm.

$$\overline{x} = \frac{48 \times 1400}{100}$$

$$= 672\text{mm}$$

Example. The weight distribution of a bike is given as 55% front, 45% rear. How far is the cg from the front spindle if the wheelbase is 52ins.

$$\overline{x} = \frac{45 \times 52}{100}$$

$$= 23.4\text{ins}$$

Published data is always a bit dubious because it never seems to give full details. In general, published figures will be unladen but details are rarely given for fuel/oil/water load and this can make a significant difference on some bikes.

Optimum horizontal location

I will look at the more mathematical aspects of this at the end of the chapter. For the moment we can go a long way using common sense. When the bike is in motion, the load carried by each tyre will determine the grip that is available under any specific conditions and this alone seems to suggest that a 50/50 weight distribution when laden would be a very good starting point on tarmac. In other words, the horizontal cg location is half way along the wheelbase in the laden condition. When cornering at a constant speed we could suggest, quite reasonably, that if the front carries substantially more than 50% of the total load then the rear is in danger of losing grip. Similarly, if the rear carries substantially more than 50%, then the front end is likely to 'push' into the turns or simply go away from you.

Despite the simplicity of this argument you would not be far out and any classic bike should perform more than adequately on this basis. There are however many other things to consider. Power is only applied at the rear and tyre technology has advanced considerably along with suspension in recent years. As a result of this a slightly greater forward weight bias is now often appropriate, up to around 53% front, 47% rear when laden. How this relates to the unladen value can only be determined by the individual rider and riding position but in general the cg will move back towards the rear wheel slightly when the rider is on board. This means that the unladen weight distribution will show a greater front wheel bias and 54% front/ 46% rear is a common choice.

A weight distribution of between 45%/55% and 55%/45% front to rear when laden covers most bikes raced on tarmac. The figures with a greater rear end bias are found on early classic racers and these can often benefit from a bit more even distribution if modern tyres are being used and the engine is somewhat more powerful than that originally fitted.

On modern bikes, a 50%/50% distribution seems to suit average tyres, average suspension and conservative steering geometry, typically 26° castor and 90 - 100mm trail. Slightly greater front end bias seems to suit modern (wide) race tyres, good suspension, good riders and more radical steering geometry with less castor and less trail, say 22 - 23° castor and 75 - 90mm trail. You will need plenty of room to move about on the bike in order to get the best from this set-up.

If you are a tall, relatively heavy rider on a small bike then it is most unlikely that you will be able to reach a 50%/50% laden weight distribution. The light engine means that it may even be difficult to exceed 50%/50% when unladen and adding a heavy rider could produce laden figures between 35%/65% and 45%/55% front to rear. Fortunately, the tendency for the front end to lift is somewhat compensated for by the relative lack of power in a small engine but the bike will not handle as well as it could with a lightweight rider and a more central cg location. Obviously the laden values will depend on where and how the rider is positioned but, if you can achieve it, I think 54%/46% is a good unladen limit.The tendency for the front end to 'push' is reduced and modern rear tyres can maintain a great deal of traction, suspension permitting. Considerably more front end bias than this has been used but I doubt if it works. Next year's bike always seems to revert back to more conservative values! Unless you have the best riders, tyres, and suspension you are likely to go too far. It may look trick in the paddock but it is likely to finish up on the floor. The discussion so far has been relatively simple, mainly because the vertical cg location plays no part in the static load carried by each tyre. However, to investigate the influence of vertical cg location we need to take account of accelerations as well.

Vertical cg location ($\bar{y}$)

The centre of gravity of a motorcycle and rider is located at some considerable height above the ground. This height, which we define by the distance $\bar{y}$, has no effect on the static weight distribution but it immediately shows its influence when the bike accelerates or brakes.

As before we can start with some elementary observations as per Table 3.6. Again, these are purely general statements and the conditions are not equally affected by cg movements.

When any change in speed takes place, we get an effect that is commonly known as weight transfer. This occurs because the driving and braking forces are actually generated at ground level, significantly below the centre of gravity. This means that both these forces will, in addition to simply trying to speed the bike up or slow it down, cause a turning effect that is determined by both the force and the distance $\bar{y}$ - Fig 3.16.

The greater the acceleration, the more weight we transfer from the front wheel to the rear wheel and it is easy, with a racing motorcycle, to reach the point where the whole weight of the bike is carried at the rear wheel. Any increase in the acceleration value beyond this point will cause the front wheel to lift and eventually you fall off the back if the acceleration is not reduced.

Similarly, the greater the retardation caused by braking, the greater the transfer of weight from the rear wheel to the front wheel, and again a point can be reached where all the weight is on the front wheel and further increases in retardation cause the rear wheel to lift. All racers are familiar with these events which are exciting but increase lap times. Also note that once a wheel leaves the ground the cg height is increasing and this actually makes the problem worse.

It is important to realise that weight transfer has nothing to do with suspension, ie having suspension does not cause weight transfer. The weight transfer would be exactly the same with no suspension, though obviously if springs are provided they will respond to it by compressing further in order to transmit the extra load. The root cause of the problem is the displacement of the centre of gravity from the point at which the forces are applied and as long as this situation exists, weight transfer will occur. If we could apply these forces actually through the cg location then the weight transfer would be zero. The frustrating thing about weight transfer is that half of it works in our favour and half of it works against us. Increased load on one wheel gives more grip on the road but at the same time load is always taken off the other wheel and the grip at that end reduces, a no win situation. This is why selecting a vertical cg location is always a compromise.

Below. Table 3.6 *General influence of vertical cg location. The limiting conditions are not equally affected by changes in cg height. The cg height is measured from the ground.*

Event	Limiting condition	$\bar{y}$ reduced (cg location lowered)	$\bar{y}$ increased (cg location raised)
acceleration	front wheel lift	less likely	more likely
acceleration	rear wheel spin	more likely	less likely
braking	rear wheel lift	less likely	more likely
braking	front wheel locking	more likely	less likely

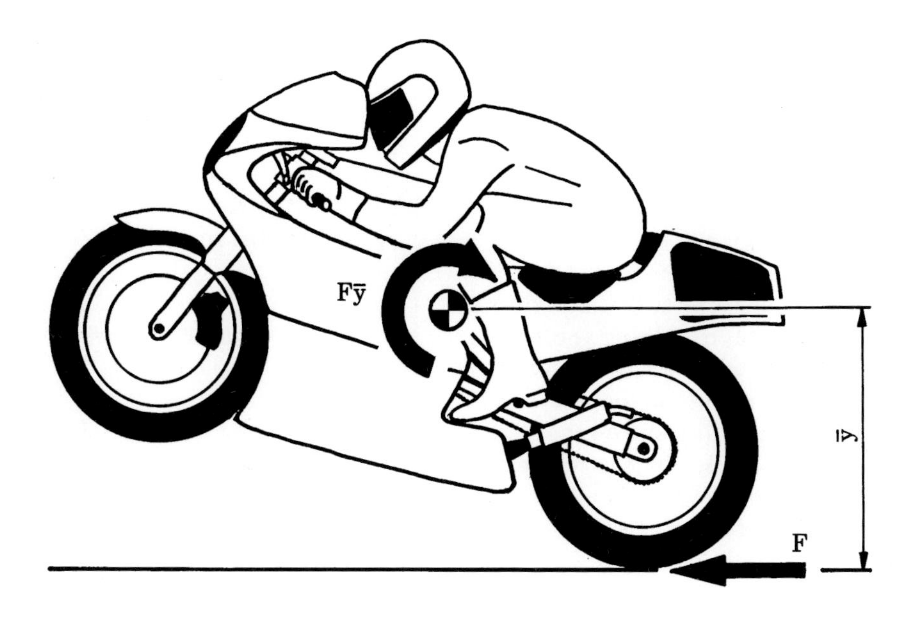

Above. Fig 3.16 *The forces that produce acceleration and braking are applied at road level, remote from the centre of gravity. This means that in addition to producing an acceleration or retardation, they also give a turning effect about the cg which causes the bike to rotate if the acceleration / retardation is great enough.*

Optimum vertical location

Sorting this out properly requires a reasonable amount of arithmetic which I will leave until later. For those who prefer quick rules of thumb the following will provide a starting point.

Vertical cg location is always a problem for a variety of reasons. Firstly, the best height is related to the coefficient of friction between the tyres and the road. Given that this can easily reduce by 70% in the wet the required cg height is totally dependent on the conditions. The two values given on the right are typical but, assuming you build close to the 'dry' value, you will not be able to raise it sufficiently to give best results in the wet, even by sitting up. The rear tyre will spin and the front will lock up a lot more easily. It is possible to compensate somewhat by building in considerable ride height adjustment and raising the whole bike in the wet but as I said earlier you cannot really cover the range of adjustment required.

Given the British climate it seems sensible to build the bike with the cg somewhat higher than the dry optimum. If you have the scope to raise the cg even further when the bike is completed, eg by lifting the engine, then try it. You can continue to raise the cg until it clearly causes problems in the dry and then drop back. The bike eventually gets hard to flick about, apart from the problems already mentioned. Do not forget that the cg height which really matters is that actually present when braking or accelerating, ie suspension travel needs to be accounted for.

You may wish to pursue this further, particularly the way in which the four limits are traded off. In arriving at the values given it is assumed that the front wheel starts sliding when the rear starts lifting. It is also assumed that the laden weight distribution is 50/50 and so on. This may not be what you want and a lot depends on how powerful the bike is and your style of riding. Many riders will always prefer the back end to lift before the front locks up on braking.

Because all the limits are inextricably linked you cannot pick and choose as you might like. For example, if the horizontal cg location is at the centre of the wheelbase then the acceleration that lifts the front will have the same magnitude as the retardation which lifts the rear. The cg height will only determine what the value is. Similar observations apply to sliding the front and spinning the rear. This is covered at the end of the chapter.

Compromise cg height for the dry

$$\bar{y} = \frac{\text{wheelbase}}{2}$$

Compromise value for the wet

$$\bar{y} = \text{wheelbase}$$

In the wet the requirement could be even greater, up to about 1.5 x wheelbase, if grip is very poor

Measuring cg height

Determining the cg height on an existing bike is not easy and this is one of the reasons values are not commonly quoted. It is possible, in some cases, for two or three people to carefully lower the bike, side down, onto a long narrow support and see where it balances but this is rarely convenient and only suited to very light bikes with certain layouts. A more general method of finding cg height involves hanging the bike up, usually from the wheel rim. Referring to Fig 3.17,

- Having found $\bar{x}$ by measuring the weight distribution, put a piece of masking tape vertically up the side of the bike at this point.
- Hang the bike up at the wheel rim from a beam, hoist etc by using suitable straps. You are on your own with this. Make sure everything is safe and don't expect me to vouch for cast wheels holding up your 300kg monster. If the wheels are strong enough to race on there should be no problems.
- Using a plumb bob, mark where it crosses the tape and that gives the cg location.

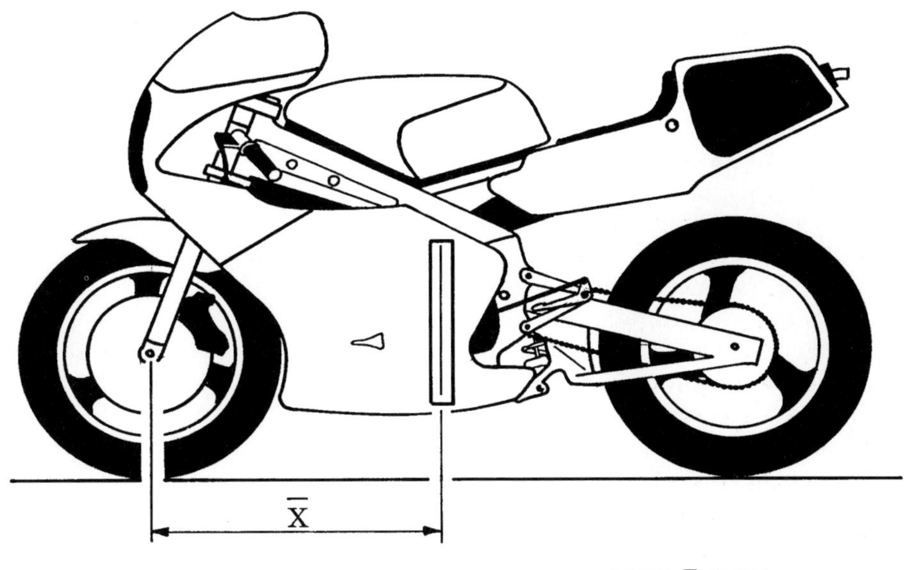

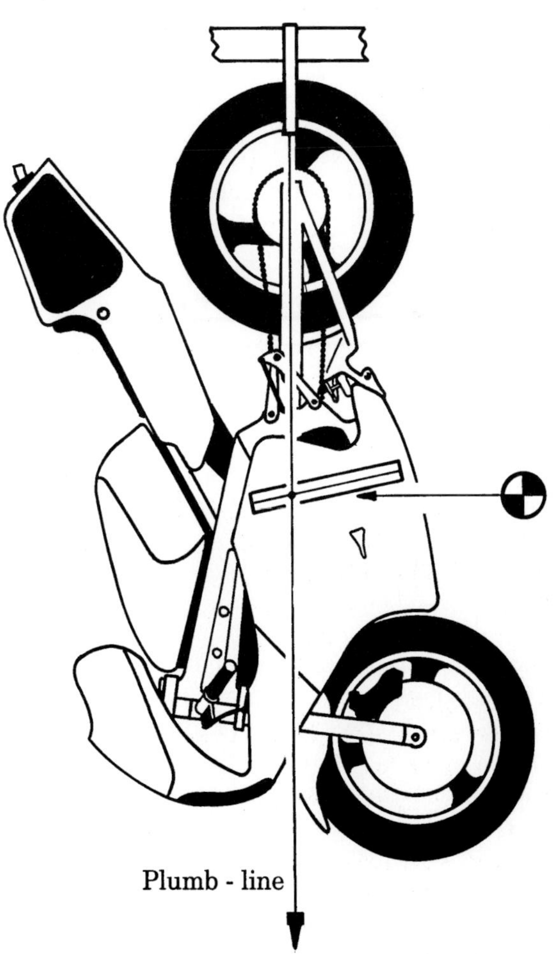

Fig 3.17 *Finding the cg location. Begin by finding the horizontal cg location using the methods described previously. Once the position is known place a length of masking tape vertically up the bike as shown above and mark a line on it. Now hang the bike up as shown on the right. A plumb-line attached to the suspension point will also pass through the cg so the point where the line crosses the mark on the tape gives the actual cg location. Mark it and then measure the cg height when the bike is placed back on the ground.*

This method will give you the point where the unladen cg actually is. With this point suitably marked you can put the bike back on the ground and measure values of $\bar{x}$ and $\bar{y}$ (unladen). I will deal with the effect of the rider shortly.

The final method of finding the cg height involves a reasonable amount of working out. To do this, you need to record the rear tyre load with the bike inclined. It needs to be tilted enough to give distinctly different scale readings to when the bike is level. Raising the front 600 - 700mm should be enough (23 - 28ins). It is possible to do this laden as well as unladen but it can be difficult to hold a normal riding position. If this proves difficult you can deal with the rider separately as described later. The calculation opposite is not absolutely exact but it is close enough for all practical purposes, as long as the bike is of a conventional layout and the tyre rolling radii are not dramatically different at front and rear. Proceed as follows referring to Fig 3.18

- Find the total weight (W), the weight distribution when level, the wheelbase (L) and the horizontal distance from the front wheel spindle to the cg first.
- Put the rear wheel on a set of scales.
- Raise the front wheel by at least 400mm.
- If the scale reading does not change significantly from that obtained when level, raise the front even more.
- Measure the supporting radius of the front tyre(r_f) and the rear tyre (r_r). Calculate the average of these.
- Measure the amount by which the front tyre contact point is above that of the rear tyre and call it ' h'.
- Divide h by L (both in the same units). Use a calculator to find out what angle (Ø) has this as its Sine value, eg, if h/L = 0.5, Ø = 30° because Sin30° = 0.5.
- Now use the calculator to find CotØ. To do this, look up TanØ directly and then divide one by that value eg if Ø = 30°, TanØ = 0.5774 and hence CotØ = 1/0.5774 = 1.732.

The cg height above ground when the bike is level can now be calculated from,

$$\bar{y} = \text{Cot}\varnothing\left[\frac{RL}{W} - \bar{x}\right] + r_{av}$$

where

$\bar{y}$ = height of the cg above ground when the bike is level

R = weight reading under rear tyre, laden or unladen as required when inclined

W = total weight of the bike, laden or unladen as required

$\bar{x}$ = horizontal cg location from front wheel spindle

r_{av} = mean tyre radius

L = wheelbase

Ø = the angle for which SinØ = h/L (see text)

Be consistent with the units you use, eg all lengths in mm, all weights in kgf. Imperial values would typically be inches and lbf. The calculated value will have the same units of length. Here is an example.

Right. Fig 3.18 *Determining the cg height by measuring weight shift when the bike is inclined.*

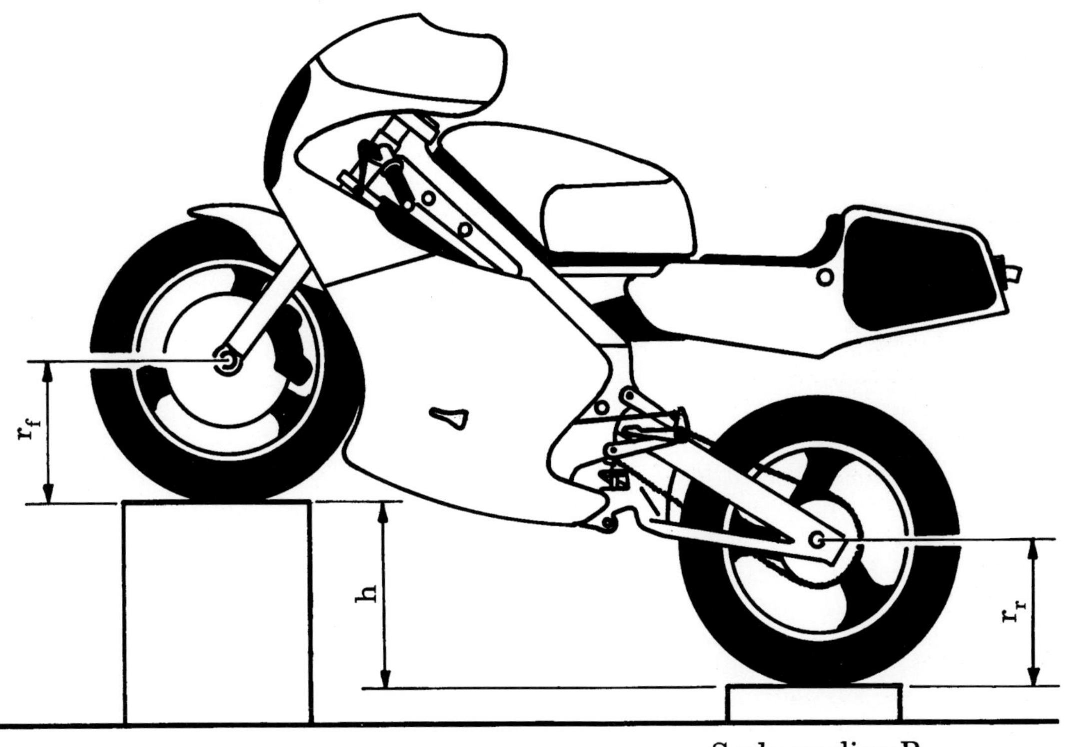

r_f
h
r_r
Scale reading R

Example. The following data was determined when the bike was level. Total weight unladen = 72kgf, weight on front = 35kgf, weight on rear = 37kgf, and the wheelbase is 1254mm. $\bar{x}$ is thus equal to 37 x 1254/72 which is 645mm from the front spindle (using the method described for horizontal cg location).

- The rear wheel is put on the scales.
- The front was raised such that value h = 685mm.
- The scales now show 42kg so the weight on here is 42kgf. When the bike was level it was 37kgf. (Refer to Appendix 1 for a detailed explanation).
- The support radii are measured as follows, front r_f = 290mm, rear r_r = 296mm. The average is 293mm.
- Divide h by L ie 685mm/1254mm to obtain h/L = 0.5462.
- Use arcsin on calculator to get Ø = 33.11°.
- From calculator, Tan33.11° =0.652 hence Cot33.11°= 1/0.652 = 1.5333.
- Using the formula,

$$\bar{y} = 1.5333\left(\left(\frac{42 \times 1254}{72}\right) - 645\right) + 293$$

$$\bar{y} = 1.5333((731.5) - 645) + 293$$

$$\bar{y} = 1.5333(86.5) + 293$$

$$\bar{y} = 132.63 + 293$$

$\bar{y}$ = 426mm approx. from the ground unladen.

At only 34% of the wheelbase this sounds low but this is the unladen value of a 125cc bike. When the rider is added the cg height rises considerably.

Example. The following data was determined when the bike was level. Total weight unladen = 159lbf, weight on front = 77lbf, weight on rear = 82lbf, and the wheelbase is 50ins. $\bar{x}$ is thus equal to 82 x 50/159 which is 25.78ins from the front spindle (using the method described for horizontal cg location).

- The rear wheel is put on the scales.
- The front was raised such that value h = 27ins.
- The scales now show 93lb so the weight on here is 93lbf. When the bike was level it was 82lbf.
- The support radii are measured as follows, front r_f = 11.4ins, rear r_r = 11.7ins. The average is 11.55ins.
- Divide h by L ie27ins/50ins to obtain h/L = 0.54.
- Use arcsin on calculator to get Ø = 32.68°.
- From calculator, Tan32.68° =0.6416 hence Cot32.68°= 1/0.6416 = 1.559.
- Using the formula,

$$\bar{y} = 1.559\left(\left(\frac{93 \times 50}{159}\right) - 25.78\right) + 11.55$$

$$\bar{y} = 1.559((29.245) - 25.78) + 11.55$$

$$\bar{y} = 1.559(3.465) + 11.55$$

$$\bar{y} = 5.4 + 11.55$$

$\bar{y}$ = 16.95ins from the ground unladen.

Practical optimisation

The methods described will allow you to determine the cg location of existing bikes as well as giving some idea of where the cg should be. If you are building a new bike then the more data you can collect from bikes that work well the better. This is even more use if you can recognise any deficiencies in the bike and correct them before utilising the data for another bike.

Table 3.7 may help in this respect. It is effectively a combination of the tables given earlier in relation to cg locations. You have to be careful when doing this sort of thing to ensure you are not seeking the impossible. Modern brakes will allow you to lock up wheels very easily and powerful bikes can always spin the rear tyre or lift the front. What you are looking for are obvious imbalances which, because of the interlinking of the four limits, will occur in pairs if they are very poor. Experiments can be carried out by moving engines, raising or lowering the bike, or by adding large lumps of lead. Beware that under acceleration and braking heavy lumps of lead can exert considerable force on what holds them in place!

Other problem indicators include a tendency to oversteer (cg too far forward), to understeer (cg too far back) and difficulties when trying to flick the bike quickly from side to side (cg too high).

Moment of inertia

In seeking an optimum cg location you should note that although it is common to base the values used for a new bike on those of other bikes, the response of the new bike can still differ markedly due to other weight distribution aspects.

For example, if the total weight of the motorcycle could be concentrated at the wheels and equally shared between them, then the cg would lie half way along the wheelbase. It would still be at this point if the whole weight of the bike could be concentrated at the centre but the two bikes would behave very differently, the latter being much more manoeuvrable. The reason for this is the reduced moment of inertia of the second bike about its cg, achieved by keeping as much of the mass as possible close to the cg. This aspect is very important, but in practice you will be limited by the weight of the wheels, brakes and forks you can afford.

Table 3.7 *Suggestions for evolving the cg location of existing bikes.*

Problem	Modifications
1. Front end lifts too easily on acceleration and, 2. Rear end lifts too easily when braking.	Lower cg height
3. Rear wheel spins too easily on acceleration and, 4. Front end slides too easily on braking.	Raise cg height
If 1 or 2 are the problem, gradually lower the cg height until one of these aspects ceases to be a problem and then try moving the horizontal cg location nearer to the wheel that continues to lift too easily until the problem reduces to an acceptable level. If 3 or 4 are the problem, gradually raise the cg height until one of these aspects is cured, then move the horizontal cg location nearer to the wheel that still slips.	

Predicting cg location

Predicting cg location as you design the bike is very straightforward and well worth the effort. You will have a target location in mind based on the previous discussion but note that the ideal location is that which applies under the appropriate conditions. For example, if you decide that $\overline{y}$ is optimum at 700mm for braking then that is where it should be when actually braking and it will normally be higher when the bike is static and the forks are less compressed. Since there are so many variations, I would simply work to a normal unladen position and think about other changes later. In practice this means allowing for suspension compression from the unladen position so you have to make some decisions about suspension before you can finally sort this out.

Fig 3.19 shows the example I am going to work through. By starting with just the wheels and then gradually adding more components you will see how the cg location moves about as the bike evolves. The first thing to do is make up a table like the one used in Fig 3.20. If you have a computer and spreadsheet program this is an ideal application. Figs 3.20 and 3.21 show how the values of $\overline{x}$ and $\overline{y}$ evolve as we go from a pair of wheels towards a complete bike. Note how all $\overline{x}$ values are measured from the front tyre edge in these examples, not the wheel spindle. This ensures that nothing will lie to the left of the datum and simplifies the calculation. To get $\overline{x}$ from the front wheel spindle you will have to subtract half of the free tyre diameter at the end. The choice of the front tyre edge as a datum is arbitrary but the calculation is easier if all components lie to one side of the datum and I suggest you use the same point.

Each table is made up as follows. Starting at the left of the table, column 1 is the name of the component and column 2 is the weight of that individual component. In this example I have used kgf for weight which is the value you are likely to get from a set of scales. Although we should be using newtons, this would only mean multiplying all the figures by 9.81 and it serves no practical purpose to do so in this calculation. If you prefer to work in imperial units these values are likely to be in lbf.

Column 3 gives the distance from a line drawn vertically at the front edge of the front tyre to the cg location of the individual component. To get this distance you will have to know where the cg of each major component lies and I will deal with this aspect shortly.

Column 4 gives the height from the ground to the cg of each individual component. I have labelled these distances x and y so that you do not

Below. Fig 3.19 *Basic engine and wheel location for the example covered in Figs 3.20 and 3.21.*

Right Fig 3.20 *Estimating the cg location for just the wheels and engine. Fig 3.21 overleaf continues this process to include all major components.*

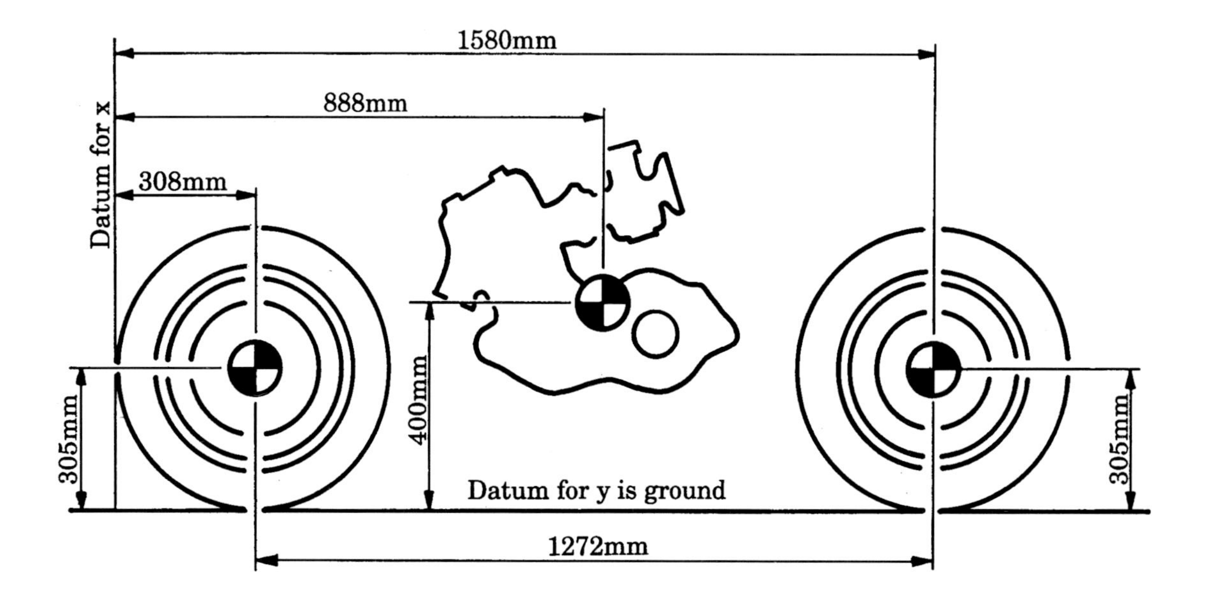

WHEELS ONLY

Component	Weight W(kgf)	cg distance from front tyre x (mm)	cg height from ground y (mm)	Wx	Wy
front wheel	9	308	305	2772	2745
rear wheel	11	1580	305	17380	3355
Totals	**20**			**20152**	**6100**

Distance from front tyre edge to cg $= \frac{\sum Wx}{\sum W} = \frac{20152\text{kgf.mm}}{20\text{kgf}} = 1008\text{mm}$

$\bar{x}$ value from front wheel spindle = 1008mm - 308mm = 700mm

Distance from ground to cg, $\bar{y} = \frac{\sum Wy}{\sum W} = \frac{6100\text{kgf.mm}}{20\text{kgf}} = 305\text{mm}$

WHEELS AND ENGINE

Component	Weight W(kgf)	cg distance from front tyre x (mm)	cg height from ground y (mm)	Wx	Wy
front wheel	9	308	305	2772	2745
rear wheel	11	1580	305	17380	3355
engine	20	888	400	17760	8000
Totals	**40**			**37912**	**14100**

Distance from front tyre edge to cg $= \frac{\sum Wx}{\sum W} = \frac{37912\text{kgf.mm}}{40\text{kgf}} = 948\text{mm}$

$\bar{x}$ value from front wheel spindle = 948mm - 308mm = 640mm

Distance from ground to cg, $\bar{y} = \frac{\sum Wy}{\sum W} = \frac{14100\text{kgf.mm}}{40\text{kgf}} = 353\text{mm}$

ALL MAJOR COMPONENTS

Component	Weight W(kgf)	cg distance from front tyre x (mm)	cg height from ground y (mm)	Wx	Wy
front wheel	9	308	305	2772	2745
rear wheel	11	1580	305	17380	3355
engine	20	888	400	17760	8000
forks etc	8	418	720	3344	5760
tank of fuel	12	888	800	10656	9600
full radiator	5	588	570	2940	2850
monoshock	3	1158	590	3474	1770
frame	7	1108	470	7756	3290
seat unit	3	1398	670	4194	2010
Totals	**78**			**70276**	**39380**

Distance from front tyre edge to cg $= \frac{\sum Wx}{\sum W} = \frac{70276\text{kgf.mm}}{78\text{kgf}} = 901\text{mm}$

$\bar{x}$ value from front wheel spindle = 901mm - 308mm = 593mm

Distance from ground to cg, $\bar{y} = \frac{\sum Wy}{\sum W} = \frac{39380\text{kgf.mm}}{78\text{kgf}} = 505\text{mm}$

WITH RIDER

Component	Weight W(kgf)	cg distance from front tyre x (mm)	cg height from ground y (mm)	Wx	Wy
front wheel	9	308	305	2772	2745
rear wheel	11	1580	305	17380	3355
engine	20	888	400	17760	8000
forks etc	8	418	720	3344	5760
tank of fuel	12	888	800	10656	9600
full radiator	5	588	570	2940	2850
monoshock	3	1158	590	3474	1770
frame	7	1108	470	7756	3290
seat unit	3	1398	670	4194	2010
rider	76	780	860	59280	65360
Totals	**154**			**129556**	**104740**

Distance from front tyre edge to cg $= \frac{\sum Wx}{\sum W} = \frac{142476\text{kgf.mm}}{154\text{kgf}} = 925\text{mm}$

$\bar{x}$ value from front wheel spindle = 925mm - 308mm = 617mm

Distance from ground to cg, $\bar{y} = \frac{\sum Wy}{\sum W} = \frac{104740\text{kgf.mm}}{154\text{kgf}} = 680\text{mm}$

get them confused with the overall cg location. Columns 5 and 6 are the key to all this. Column 5 is completed by multiplying together the individual component weights and the corresponding x value. Column 6 does the same job using the weight and the y values.

When you have entered all the components being considered total up columns 2,5 and 6. The total weight is labelled as ΣW (Σ is Sigma, it means sum of) while the totals of columns 5 and 6 are ΣWx and ΣWy respectively. To find the distance from the front tyre edge datum to the overall horizontal cg location divide ΣWx value by the ΣW value as shown. To get this as the standard $\overline{x}$ value from the front wheel spindle you will have to subtract the free radius of the front tyre, 308mm in the example.

To obtain the height of the overall cg from the ground (which is $\overline{y}$ directly) divide the ΣWy value by the ΣW value as shown. This is all much easier to do than it is to explain!

Fig 3.20 begins with only the wheels. The overall cg is at a height of 305mm (wheel spindle height) and 700mm back from the front spindle. It is therefore somewhat more than half way back along the wheelbase (the wheelbase is 1580mm - 308mm = 1272mm), simply because the rear wheel is heavier than the front.

Next in Fig 3.20, the engine is added where it seems to be OK from a purely physical point of view. The effect of this, as you might expect, is to pull the overall cg forward and upwards so that it is now 640mm from the front wheel and 353mm from ground level. In Fig 3.21 I have continued like this until, with all major lumps except the rider added, the estimated unladen values are $\overline{x}$ = 593mm from the front spindle and $\overline{y}$ = 505mm from the ground. As such, the unladen cg is 47% along the wheelbase from the front so the static weight distribution will be 53% front, 47% rear when unladen. The cg height is 40% of the wheelbase, very low but we are of course unladen.

Adding me as the rider in the proposed position gives a final overall location of $\overline{x}$ = 617mm and $\overline{y}$ = 680mm. The weight distribution will be 51.5% front, 48.5% rear and the cg height is 54% of the wheelbase, a perfectly reasonable value.

If you study this carefully you will see that it need not involve a lot of work. The things that make the greatest contribution are those with large Wx or Wy values and clearly the rider, engine, frame, wheels and fuel are the main ingredients in this example. You may not need to account for much more though in practice it is neither here nor there to add another bit to the table once you have made a decision.

Even a simple table can be an invaluable guide as you sit wondering exactly where you are going to position something. Without it, you will have to rely on luck or experience and it may not work out in the end, especially if you mount the engine directly to the frame and not via engine plates that could be modified fairly easily if it proves to be necessary later on. Whatever your methods, the overall cg must be in a reasonable position or the bike will definitely not perform well.

Left. Fig 3.21 *The idea shown in Fig 3.20 is continued here to yield the cg location for the proposed bike. All the significant components have been accounted for.*

Individual cg locations

To carry out the previous calculation we need the cg location of each major item. You can obtain these by a mixture of common sense, sums and experiment. Anything vaguely rectangular in side view that has an even distribution of weight should be taken as such with the cg location in the middle. With anything a bit odd, but manageable, try to balance it on the edge of a metal strip in the vice from two different sides and hence find the cg that way. Finally, with something like an engine (or any other component if you wish), follow the method given in Fig 3.22. Hang it up by a suitable corner, drop a plumb line over it and mark the path of the line on masking tape stuck to the component. Repeat this from a different corner and where the lines cross is the cg location.

If the object is such that it is not convenient to put tape on then attach a piece of card. If it does not have any suitable lugs to hang it up by then make some by bolting on brackets. If these fitments have insignificant weight compared to the actual component, they will not affect the actual cg enough to worry you.

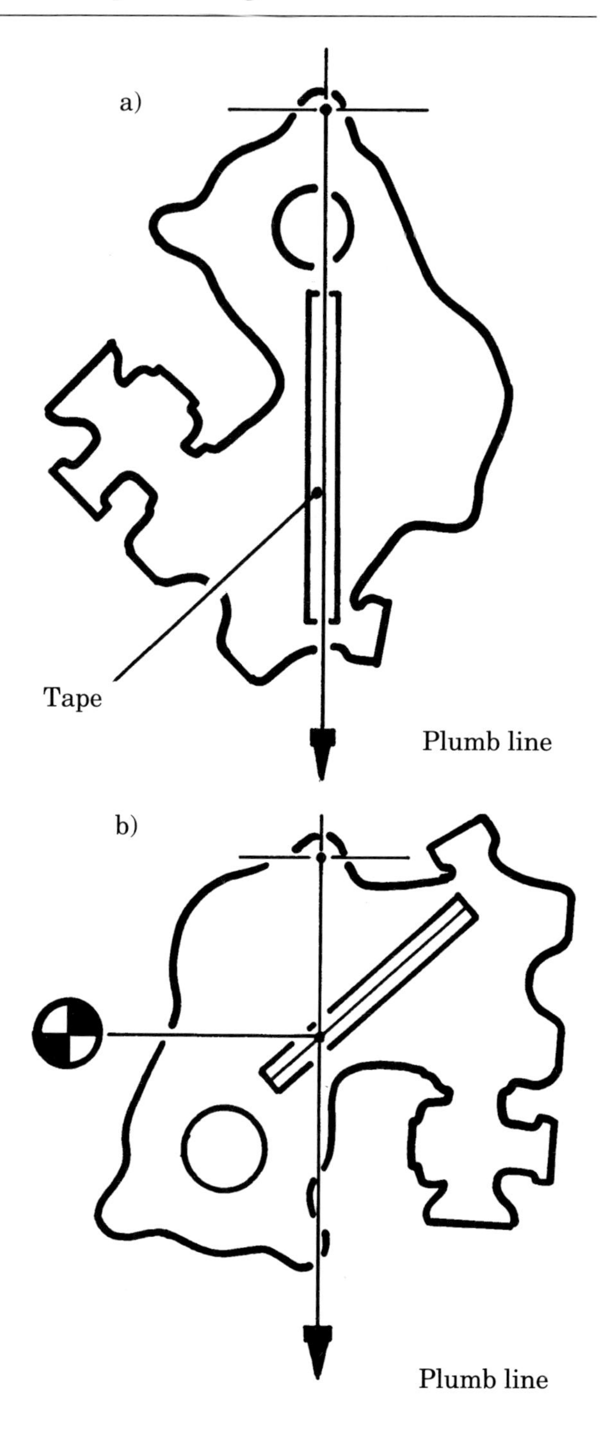

Fig 3.22 *Estimating the cg location for difficult shapes by suspending them from two different points. a) Hang the component up from a suitable point and attach a plumb line. Mark the line position on tape or card. b) Re-hang from another point. Where the lines cross locates the cg.*

Riding position

The riding position hits you as soon as you get on a motorcycle. Some you sit in, others you sit on. Some try to break your wrists and others wrap your legs up your backside. There are two distinct aspects of rider positioning to consider, firstly how it affects performance and secondly how comfortable it is. Although the former has priority you cannot race quickly when uncomfortable and getting cramp badly may stop you altogether. You must therefore adopt a practical position and to this end you should record suitable data showing how your hand, backside and feet positions relate when set comfortably on another bike - Fig 3.23. Within reason it will be possible to move these 'triangles' either forwards, backwards, up or down, and then rotate them, in order to comply with performance aspects.

It is essential that when establishing such data you do it with all your normal riding gear on since one is not as flexible when encased in leathers and body armour as one is when wearing normal clothes. Riding gear will impose serious restrictions. It is no good proposing a horizontal prone

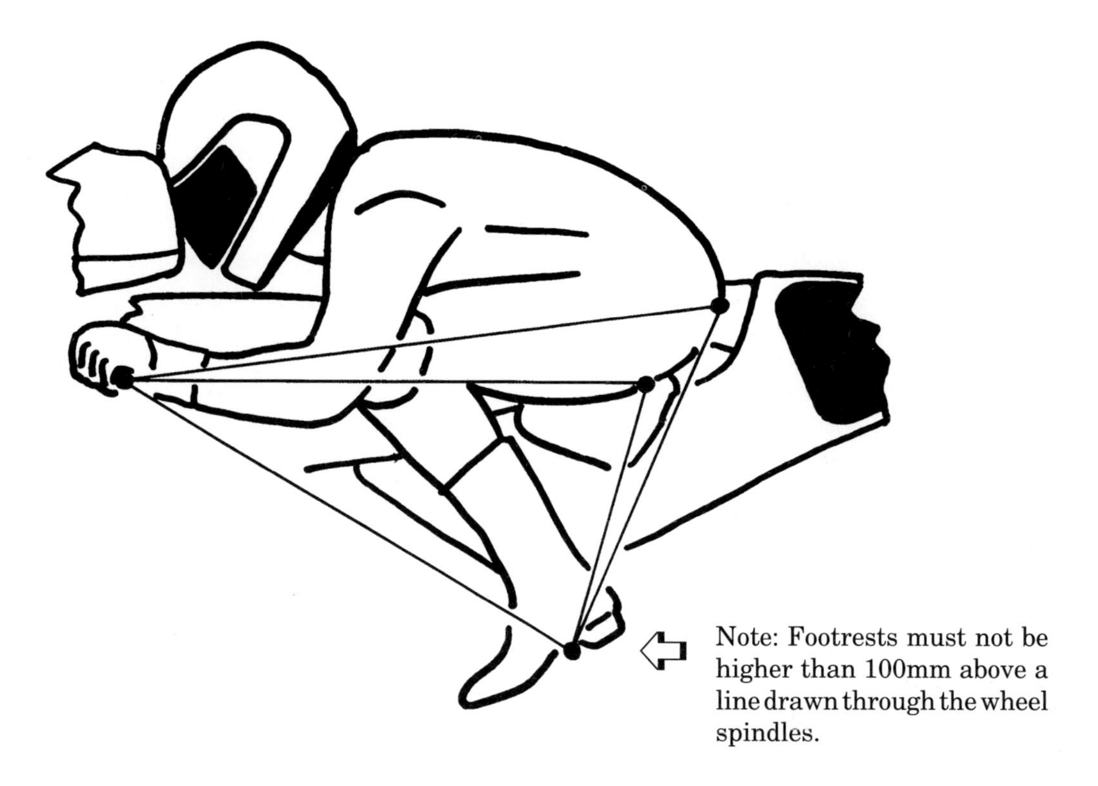

Fig 3.23 *Key dimensions required to define the riding position.*

position if your helmet prevents you lifting your neck back enough to see where you are going.

The second constraint on riding position comes from the regulations concerning footrests. Currently, they must not lie more than 100mm above a line passing through the wheel spindles when the bike is laden and they must be in front of the rear wheel spindle. Additionally, it must be possible to lean the bike over at least 50 degrees before anything grounds. This is unlikely to be a problem unless the footrests are very low and the bike is wide, in which case as soon as you corner and the suspension compresses the footrests will dig in and impede your progress. In practice the regulations virtually fix the footrest height because you will usually want them somewhere between spindle height and the 100mm limit.

Once footrest height is decided, the seat height lower limit is determined by tyre clearance at full suspension compression and the rider's own preferred body 'triangle'. Legs will only bend so far and the rear wheel should not hit the seat. Taking all this into account still leaves an infinite variety of positions and it is time to think about performance. Aerodynamics has a large section devoted to it later on but certain things are obvious. In general, the riding positions of the past (with some exceptions) were not always very good aerodynamically. The rider's back forms the upper aerodynamic surface and relatively upright positions cause virtually instant separation of the air flow at the shoulders creating massive wakes and associated drag. The currently favoured 'backside up' positions are better from this point of view, as well as contributing to the preferred front end bias. To adopt such positions, the whole body has to rotate around the footrests and the seat needs to be inclined, unlike earlier styles where the seat was horizontal. Such inclination must not be overdone and in any event the regulations restrict how much tilt can be used. Toes are lowered significantly and this can introduce problems such as brake pedals digging in on corners. Compensation via footrest height may test your limits of comfort. The resulting body tilt will put more weight on the wrists and I have actually seen people with so much tilt that they have a job to stay on the bike when braking. I think it is best to get the body tilt right based on a sensible footrest height and then look at moving everything forwards or backwards to suit cg location. The modern compacted riding positions with the rider well forward should allow you to achieve the desired cg location without too much trouble, though on small bikes, with light engines, it may be impossible to break the 50/50 weight distribution barrier and get your arms tucked in at the same time if you are of average build.

Rider influence on cg location

The presence of the rider raises the overall cg height and usually moves it horizontally as well, though not a great deal. If the bike is light and the rider is heavy, the laden cg will move significantly upwards from the unladen value and this fact needs to be taken into account when building small bikes. Conversely, a very light rider on a relatively heavy bike will have much less influence. Like other components, the cg location of a rider can be obtained by hanging them up by suitable appendages but it is not to be recommended. In any event, a rider is not a rigid object so their cg location alters when they adopt a different position. You may assume, with reasonable accuracy, that the rider's cg will lie about 60 - 70mm in front of their navel provided they are sitting down (when standing or prone it is nearer to the hip joint), and use the riding position to determine where this comes on the bike. The values can then be included in the table along with all the other components. If you wish to explore this aspect fully, the aircraft and automotive industries both have data on 'standard man' which they use for designing cockpits and other compartments. Some degree of cross checking can be carried out using the adjacent formula which will determine a value of $\bar{x}$ for the rider. To use it you must,

- Determine the value of $\bar{x}$ for the unladen bike using the methods described previously.

- Put scales under the rear wheel and a block under the front to set the bike level. Sit on it and record the scale reading under the rear wheel when laden.

$$\bar{x}_{rider} = \frac{W_{rl}L - W_{bike}\bar{x}_{bike}}{W_{rider}}$$

where

$\bar{x}_{rider}$ = the distance from the front wheel spindle to the rider's cg

W_{rl} = the weight carried by the rear wheel when the bike is laden

L = the wheelbase

W_{bike} = the total weight of the unladen bike

$\bar{x}_{bike}$ = the horizontal distance from the front wheel spindle to the cg when the bike is unladen

W_{rider} = the weight of the rider

Example. A bike weighs 120kgf and has a wheelbase of 1400mm. The unladen value of $\bar{x}$ is 650mm. The rider, who weighs 82kgf in riding gear, sits on the bike and scales under the rear wheel show a load of 100kgf.

$$\bar{x}_{rider} = \frac{100 \times 1400 - 120 \times 650}{82}$$

$$= \frac{140000 - 78000}{82}$$

= 756mm from the front spindle.

Example. A bike weighs 250lbf and has a wheelbase of 55ins The unladen value of $\overline{x}$ is 25.6ins. The rider, who weighs180lbf in riding gear, sits on the bike and scales under the rear wheel show a load of 220lbf.

$$\overline{x}_{rider} = \frac{220 \times 55 - 250 \times 25.6}{180}$$

$$= \frac{12100 - 6400}{180}$$

= 31.67ins from the front spindle.

This concludes my basic observations concerning cg location. For those who wish to pursue the idea further here are some additional notes. The main purpose of what follows is to allow you to estimate the accelerations and retardations that produce the various limits and adjust the cg location to suit personal preference.

Weight transfer

The aforementioned weight transfer is easily calculated. We can also derive equations that specify the accelerations and retardations at which the limits described will be experienced.

Although you are unlikely to know the actual values of acceleration and retardation experienced on the track (unless you have suitable data logging equipment) this is largely irrelevant to the formulae. What matters is the balance between the various conditions.

Acceleration is discussed in detail in Section 6 but the following brief summary may be useful for people who are unsure of the units involved.

Acceleration

Acceleration is defined as the rate of change of velocity and the bike is subjected to a variety of different accelerations during its journey round the racetrack. At this stage we are only interested in the bike's linear acceleration in the direction of travel and this is effectively the rate at which it increases its road speed. Acceleration is found by dividing the change in speed by the time taken so if the speed changed from 100km/hr to 150km/hr in two seconds the acceleration over this period would be (150 - 100)/2 = 25km/hr every second. These units are a bit unwieldy and acceleration is usually quoted in (metres per second) per second or (ft per second) per second. These are written as m/s^2 and ft/s^2 respectively.

Since road speed will normally be in km/hr or miles/hr and time is most conveniently measured in seconds, I have allowed for this in the formulae below.

$$\textbf{Acceleration} = 0.277 \frac{V - U}{t}$$

where **Acceleration is the average value in m/s^2 over the time period involved**

V = final road speed in km/hr

U = initial road speed in km/hr

t = time to change speed in seconds

or

$$\textbf{Acceleration} = 1.4667 \frac{V - U}{t}$$

where **Acceleration is the average value in ft/s^2 over the time period involved**

V = final road speed in miles/hr

U = initial road speed in miles/hr

t = time to change speed in seconds

Example. A bike reaches 100km/hr from rest in 3s. What is the average acceleration.

$$\text{Average acceleration} = 0.277 \times \frac{(100 - 0)}{3}$$

$$= 9.25\text{m/s}^2$$

Example. A bike accelerates from 40miles/hr to 70miles/hr in 2s. What is the average acceleration.

$$\text{Average acceleration} = 1.4667 \times \frac{(70 - 40)}{2}$$

$$= 22\text{ft/s}^2$$

It is important to note that these are average figures and you should restrict them to time periods of two or three seconds. In reality the acceleration changes continuously. It is a maximum just after starting from rest and eventually falls to zero. This is discussed in detail in Section 6.

For normal roadrace configurations a limiting acceleration of about 11m/s^2 (36ft/s^2) will be found due to either front wheel lift or wheelspin. It is easy enough to raise this limit but braking and cornering then suffer.

Use of 'g'

Another way of specifying acceleration figures is to do so in terms of some reference value and the one normally chosen is the acceleration that an object would experience if it fell to earth in a vacuum. This is called 'g'.

For objects near to sea level the value of 'g' is usually taken as 9.81m/s^2 or its imperial equivalent 32.2ft/s^2. Using this as a reference, if the bike was accelerating at 9.81m/s^2 then we could say that it has an acceleration of 1g. Similarly, if the acceleration happened to be 16.1ft/s^2 then this is equivalent to 0.5g and so on. In general, the acceleration is expressed in terms of 'g' using the formula on the right.

All of this applies to braking as well. If the final speed of the bike is less than its initial speed then the acceleration you calculate will be negative. You can leave it like this or remove the minus sign and call it retardation, eg an acceleration of -10m/s^2 is the same as a retardation of 10m/s^2. Top class 1996 250cc GP bikes can brake at a sustained value of about 12m/s^2 (39ft/s^2) which is 1.22g but remember that they have much better tyres, riders and suspension than most, see Section 5. Although these notes are very brief, and Section 6 looks at the subject in more detail, this basic coverage is all we need for the moment.

$$\textbf{Acceleration in 'g'} = \frac{\textbf{Actual Value}}{\textbf{Value of 'g'}}$$

where **Actual value is the acceleration in m/s^2 or ft/s^2**

Value of g is 9.81m/s^2 or 32.2ft/s^2 as appropriate

Weight transfer

Armed with some understanding of the units used for acceleration we can now look at weight transfer. Values are calculated using the formula on the right noting that the transfer is front to rear for acceleration and rear to front for braking.

Some readers may find the use of mass confusing and Appendix 1 should help. Provided you stick to kg or lb then the mass and weight figures are the same (on earth), the small 'f' distinguishing weight. All the formulae in this book are designed to take the numbers you read off bathroom scales directly. Newtons are different!

Example. A laden motorcycle weighs 250kgf and has a wheelbase of 1350mm. If the cg is 750mm from the ground what is the weight transfer at an acceleration of 8m/s^2?

If the bike weighs 250kgf then its mass is 250kg.

$$\text{Weight transfer from front to rear} = \frac{0.102ma\bar{y}}{L}$$

$$\text{Weight transfer} = \frac{0.102 \times 250 \times 8 \times 750}{1350}$$

$$= 113.3\text{kgf}$$

$$\textbf{Wt. transfer (kgf)} = \frac{0.102ma\bar{y}}{L}$$

where

m = laden mass in kg (reading on scales)

a = acceleration or retardation in m/s²

$\bar{y}$ = cg height above ground in mm

L = wheelbase in mm

or

$$\textbf{Wt. transfer (lbf)} = \frac{0.0311ma\bar{y}}{L}$$

where

m = laden mass in lb (reading on scales)

a = acceleration or retardation in ft/s²

$\bar{y}$ = cg height above ground in inches

L = wheelbase in inches

Example. A laden motorcycle weighs 400lbf and has a wheelbase of 54ins. If the cg is 30ins from the ground what is the weight transfer at an acceleration of 32ft/s²?

If the bike weighs 400lbf then its mass is 400lb.

$$\text{Weight transfer from front to rear} = \frac{0.0311ma\bar{y}}{L}$$

$$\text{Weight transfer} = \frac{0.0311 \times 400 \times 32 \times 30}{54}$$

$$= 221\text{lbf}$$

Now, as you can see from these examples, only the cg height is involved in the weight transfer but, and this is very important, you can only transfer weight that is already there. The static weight supported by each wheel is determined by the horizontal cg location and so the actual weight transfer that is possible depends on both co-ordinates of the cg location, even though $\bar{x}$ does not appear in the basic weight transfer formula.

Example. When placed on a set of scales, a motorcycle and rider produce a reading of 180kg. The cg location is such that $\bar{x}$ = 760mm from the front wheel and $\bar{y}$ = 750mm from the ground. The wheelbase is 1400mm. What is the static weight distribution and what will happen if there is sufficient power and traction available to accelerate at a) 4m/s² and b) 9m/s²?

The bike and rider have a total mass of 180kg and a total weight of 180kgf.

$$\text{Static weight on rear} = \frac{100\,\bar{x}}{L} \text{ \% of the total}$$

$$= \frac{100 \times 760\text{mm}}{1400\text{mm}}$$

$$= 54.3\% \text{ of total}$$

thus,

Weight on rear = 54.3% of 180kgf = 97.74kgf

Weight on front = 45.7% of 180kgf = 82.26kgf

a) For an acceleration of $4m/s^2$

$$\text{Weight transfer from front to rear} = \frac{0.102 m a \bar{y}}{L}$$

$$\text{Weight transfer} = \frac{0.102 \times 180 \times 4 \times 750}{1400}$$

$$= 39.3\text{kgf}$$

So this acceleration is possible and reduces the front wheel load to 82.26kgf - 39.3kgf = 42.96kgf.

b) For an acceleration of $9m/s^2$

$$\text{Weight transfer from front to rear} = \frac{0.102 \times 180 \times 9 \times 750}{1400}$$

$$= 88.52\text{kgf}$$

This is more than the static front wheel value of 82.26kgf so the front wheel is well in the air and, even though power and grip are available, the bike cannot accelerate at this value.

Example. A motorcycle and rider are placed on a set of scales and the scales indicate 397lb. The cg location is such that $\bar{x}$ = 27ins from the front wheel and $\bar{y}$ = 30ins from the ground. The wheelbase is 55ins. What is the static weight distribution and what will happen if there is sufficient power and traction available to accelerate at a) $13ft/s^2$ and b) $30ft/s^2$?

The reading of 397lb is the mass and the weight is therefore 397lbf.

$$\text{Weight on rear} = \frac{100\,\bar{x}}{L}\ \%\ \text{of the total}$$

$$= \frac{100 \times 27\text{ins}}{55\text{ins}}$$

$$= 49\%\ \text{of total}$$

$$\text{Weight on rear} = 49\%\ \text{of } 397\text{lbf}$$

$$= 194.53\text{lbf}$$

$$\text{Weight on front} = 51\%\ \text{of } 397\text{lbf}$$

$$= 202.47\text{lbf}$$

a) For an acceleration of $13ft/s^2$

$$\text{Weight transfer from front to rear} = \frac{0.0311 m a \bar{y}}{L}$$

$$\text{Weight transfer} = \frac{0.0311 \times 397 \times 13 \times 30}{55}$$

$$= 87.6\text{lbf}$$

So this acceleration is possible and reduces the front wheel load to 202.47lbf - 87.6lbf = 114.87lbf.

b) For an acceleration of $30ft/s^2$,

$$\text{Weight transfer} = \frac{0.0311 \times 397 \times 30 \times 30}{55}$$

$$= 202\text{lbf}$$

This acceleration is just possible. The front wheel is about to lift and no matter how much power you have this bike has reached an acceleration limit. From these examples it is clear that some of the aspects that determine weight transfer are under our control and others are not. Longer wheelbases will reduce the weight transfer and this is one reason why powerful bikes are generally a bit longer than less powerful ones but there is a limit to how long you can go before the bike gets difficult to turn. Mass will be the minimum you can achieve and so this only leaves the acceleration involved and $\bar{y}$. Reducing $\bar{y}$ will raise the value of acceleration that can be achieved before the front wheel lifts and similarly it will raise the retardation that can be achieved before the rear wheel lifts. Why not go for the lowest centre of gravity we can produce?

The four limiting values

If the only thing we had to worry about was wheels lifting off the ground then we would build bikes with long wheelbases and low centres of gravity, which is exactly what sprinters do.

We are assuming there is always grip at the rear and that the front end will not slide out from underneath us when braking. Such assumptions are clearly rather dubious and in practice we have identified four different limiting conditions that might occur in response to a change of speed.

- The acceleration that lifts the front wheel.
- The acceleration that causes the rear wheel to spin.
- The retardation that lifts the rear wheel.
- The retardation that causes the front wheel to slide.

If some assumptions are made about the available grip then the accelerations and retardations involved for each case can be estimated from the four equations given on the right. These equations do involve some approximations but nothing very dramatic. In any event, it is the balance between the conditions that really matters. Equation 4 assumes all the braking effort is applied to the front wheel since this is normally the case under heavy braking in the dry. In the wet, much shorter stopping conditions can be achieved when both brakes are used in the right balance. Since the best balance depends on cg location and since in practice you will not know what balance you actually use, I am only going to consider the limit given for front wheel braking.

The equations give a clear indication of the way $\bar{x}$ and $\bar{y}$ interact to control what happens. In each case you can work out the acceleration or retardation at which the limit will apply and then compare these with any previous performance predictions. When calculating straight-line speed-time history these limits need to be applied to obtain accurate results, hence the convenience of a computer. Alternatively, the centre of gravity location can be optimised according to need from the equations given. Starting on tarmac, suppose we decide that the rear should lift under the same magnitude of retardation as the magnitude of acceleration which lifts the front. By equating 1 and 3 and solving for $\bar{x}$ we get $\bar{x} = L/2$, which already found favour using common sense.

If we use $\bar{x} = L/2$ and decide that the rear should spin just as the front lifts then by equating 1 and 2 we find that $\bar{y} = L/2\mu$ where μ is the limiting friction coefficient between the tyres and the road. The same result is obtained if we decide that the rear wheel should lift at the point where the front slides. This indicates that the optimum cg height based on such a criterion varies with frictional conditions as stated earlier. On dry tarmac with race tyres μ usually has values around one so the cg should be located at a height equal to half the wheelbase. Off road, or in the wet on tarmac, μ will be less than one and optimum cg heights of around one wheelbase are then desirable (obtained using $\mu = 0.5$, a reasonable estimate in the wet). We reflect this when riding. Off road, when grip is

1. Acceleration to lift front $= \dfrac{g(L - \bar{x})}{\bar{y}}$

2. Acceleration to spin rear $= \dfrac{\mu g \bar{x}}{(L - \mu\bar{y})}$

3. Retardation to lift rear wheel $= \dfrac{g\bar{x}}{\bar{y}}$

4. Retardation to slide the front $= \dfrac{\mu g(L - \bar{x})}{(L - \mu\bar{y})}$

where

g = acceleration due to gravity ($9.81 m/s^2$ or $32.2 ft/s^2$)

L = wheelbase

$\bar{x}$ = horizontal distance from front wheel to cg location

$\bar{y}$ = distance from ground to cg location

μ = Limiting friction coefficient between tyre and road

Note that all lengths must be in the same units, eg all mm or all ins.

limited, everyone tends to stand on the footrests and so on. This shows that optimum cg height is very elusive and whatever value you choose it will be a compromise.

The basic fact is that you cannot have it both ways. Because our bikes have to accelerate and brake under conditions of variable grip you can only improve one aspect by penalising another. The secret is to get some sort of balance that reflects your equipment and style of riding.

Example. An existing bike has the following values when fully laden. Wheelbase = 1300mm, cg height from ground = 900mm, cg distance from front wheel = 800mm. How is it likely to behave on tarmac in the dry with $\mu = 1$?

We can use equations 1 - 4 to find the limiting accelerations and retardations as follows.

1. To lift front, acceleration = 5.45m/s^2
2. To spin rear, acceleration = 19.62m/s^2
3. To lift rear, retardation = 8.72m/s^2
4. To slide front, retardation = 12.26m/s^2

This bike obviously has a problem. The front end lifts at a very low acceleration value and the rear is not much better. The acceleration limit for spinning the rear is ridiculous. The first requirement would be to move the cg forward because at the moment there is more than 60% of the weight on the back wheel when static.

If we do this so that the static weight distribution is 50/50 ($\bar{x}$ = 650mm) then the acceleration and retardation figures change to,

1. To lift front, acceleration = 7.09m/s^2
2. To spin rear, acceleration = 15.94m/s^2
3. To lift rear, retardation = 7.09m/s^2
4. To slide front, retardation = 15.94m/s^2

This is getting better but there is still far too much imbalance between the limits. If we lower the cg to 700mm as well then we get,

1. To lift front, acceleration = 9.11m/s^2
2. To spin rear, acceleration = 10.63m/s^2
3. To lift rear, retardation = 9.11m/s^2
4. To slide front, retardation = 10.63m/s^2

This would suit most people. Unless you are a very skilled rider it is nice to keep a bit of a safety margin on the front end sliding under braking.

Example. A bike has a wheelbase of 1400mm and experience of tyres suggests that the front should carry 55% of the load while the rear carries 45%. It is the rider's opinion that the front should lift at an acceleration which is 80% of that required to spin the rear. How high should the cg be on a dry track if $\mu = 1$?

$$\% \text{ Weight on rear} = \frac{100\bar{x}}{L} = 45\%$$

Hence $\bar{x} = 0.45L = 0.45 \times 1400 = 630\text{mm}$

From the formulae given,

$$\frac{g(L - \bar{x})}{\bar{y}} = \frac{0.8\mu g\bar{x}}{(L - \mu\bar{y})}$$

ie acceleration for lift at front = 80% of that to spin rear.

g's cancel so,

$$\frac{(1400 - 630)}{\bar{y}} = \frac{0.8 \times 1 \times 630}{(1400 - (1 \times \bar{y}))}$$

$$\frac{770}{\bar{y}} = \frac{504}{(1400 - \bar{y})}$$

$$1078000 - 770\bar{y} = 504\bar{y}$$

$$1078000 = 1274\bar{y}$$

$$\bar{y} = 846\text{mm}$$

We can now check out the overall situation by substituting the $\bar{x}$, $\bar{y}$, μ and L values into equations 1 - 4. This gives,

1. To lift front, acceleration = $8.9m/s^2$

2. To spin rear, acceleration = $11.15m/s^2$

3. To lift rear, retardation = $7.3m/s^2$

4. To slide front, retardation = $13.6m/s^2$

I appreciate that such examples are not to everyone's taste but those with some numerical ability will find lots of avenues to explore.

What this discussion is demonstrating is that the centre of gravity location will have a limiting effect on any accelerations or retardations that you may estimate on the basis of engine output and braking power. Earlier, I suggested that acceleration values were likely to find a limit of somewhere close to 1g (ie $9.81m/s^2$ or $32.2ft/s^2$) if the bike can brake effectively and also go round corners. This will become very apparent if you do a few examples. Although I have not discussed going round corners this does not really change anything. A lower cg height will make the bike easier to flick about but if you go much below the L/2 baseline suggested then the front end will start to slide too easily. This is all right on the speedway but dubious on tarmac. The cg height also affects the required angle of lean but this will take second place to the limiting values that have already been outlined.

No more analysis can be justified since it will not lead to any new conclusions. Everything is a compromise and the important thing is to keep records so that you can evaluate modifications. No matter how much you like playing around with figures, only actual track testing will allow you to refine cg location, particularly $\overline{y}$, to its optimum value.

3.3 Swinging arm geometry

Introduction

The use of a swinging arm at the rear of the bike has been standard practice for many years now. It does have certain deficiencies but it represents a neat, simple, solution that rarely gives any insurmountable problems. It also has a certain aesthetic appeal and is likely to continue in use for a long time. For every line that is written about swinging arm geometry there are tens of pages written about steering geometry. This in itself is interesting and confirms the fact that most swinging arm layouts are produced on an 'if it looks right it is right' basis. It is possible to construct a bike with pretty awful steering geometry that still looks reasonable. When you ride it you realise that something is wrong, or not to your taste, but you have to actually measure it up to find the cause.

Swinging arms are not generally like this and if you ride only moderately powerful bikes on tarmac the swinging arm geometry does not have to be very precise. However, if you have experience of very powerful bikes on tarmac, or less powerful off-road machines, then you will know that swinging arm geometry can play a very significant role in how the bike behaves. What we are talking about here is the tendency of the bike to extend or compress the rear suspension when power is applied. These effects, commonly termed anti-squat and pro-squat, have a considerable influence on traction and they are the reason for the increasing use of swinging arm pivot adjustments. This means there are two things to consider initially as far as swinging arm layout is concerned.

- The basic practicalities, ie chain tension, chain clearance etc.

- The way the chosen geometry will affect the bike's behaviour.

General layout

Most people will recognise the 'standard' swinging arm layout. The pivot point is close to the back of the gearbox and the arm has a certain amount of 'droop' when the bike is unladen - Fig 3.24. The inclination of the arm alters according to suspen-

Fig 3.24 *Typical swinging arm layout when unladen. The arm is inclined down, usually at an angle of about 5-10 degrees to the horizontal and it pivots close to the gearbox. When laden the arm is usually just below the horizontal.*

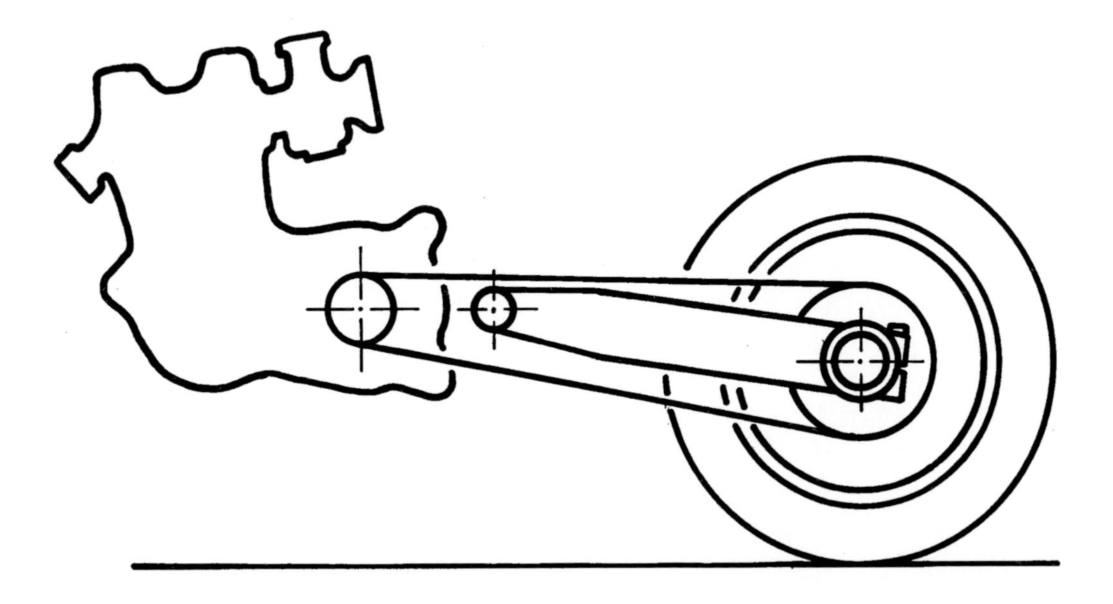

sion compression so you cannot really look at the layout without taking some account of how the suspension is set up. In general, when the bike is unladen, a light bike (125cc/250cc) is probably set up to just top out, ie the suspension just supports the sprung weight without any significant spring compression other than that imparted by preload. Larger, heavier bikes will have perhaps 7-15mm of compression under these conditions and this has to be considered when sketching the layout.

If, for simplicity, we assume the suspension is just topped out when unladen, then it is very clear that the 'standard' swinging arm appearance, with perhaps 5-10 degrees of sag below the horizontal, is a result of using conventional sized wheels and a conventional engine position because as we move the engine about the swinging arm geometry alters quite significantly - Fig 3.25. This is all rather convenient yet at the same time can be quite restricting if you want to alter it independently of engine position.

Fig 3.25 *Engine position is a key factor in swinging arm layout because the pivot point does, to a large extent, have to follow it. This alters the inclination of the arm.*

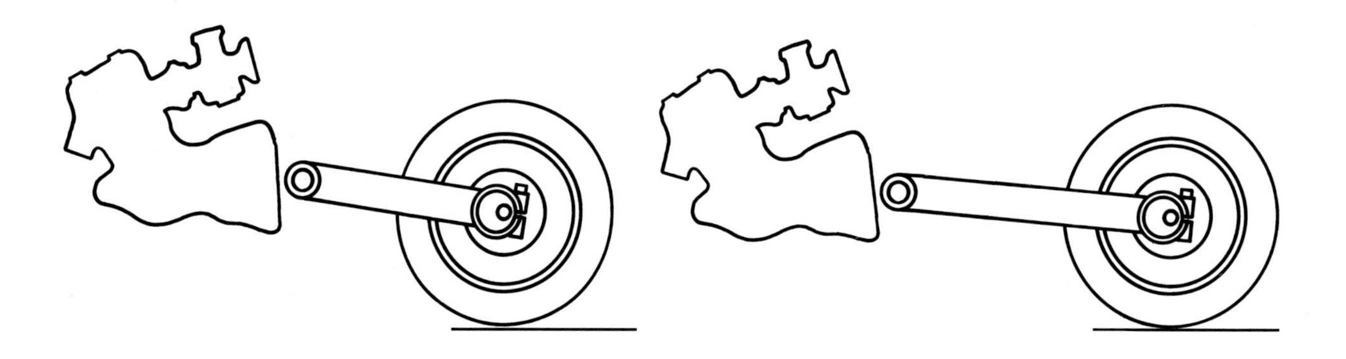

a) Original position.

c) Move engine forwards.

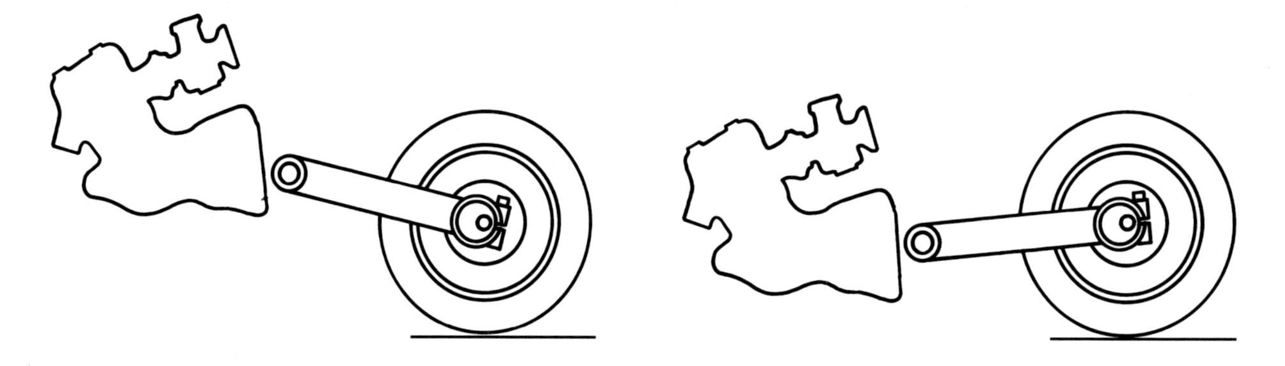

b) Move engine upwards.

d) Move engine downwards.

a) Swinging arm pivot on gearbox sprocket centre. AB = AC for any position. There is no variation in static chain tension.

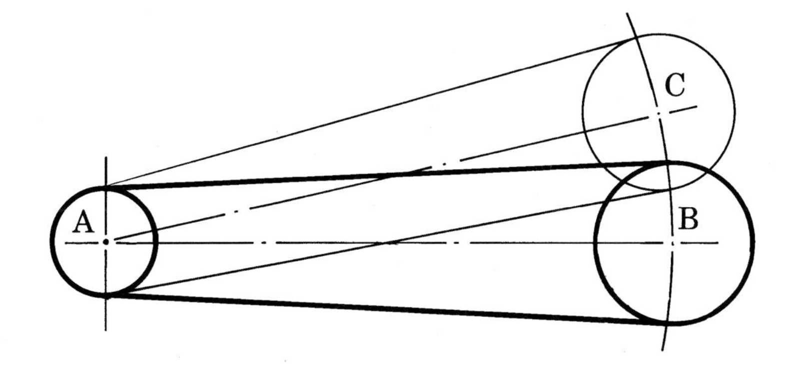

b) Normal layout. A and B are sprocket centres, D is the swinging arm pivot. AB is not equal to AC (AC is shorter) so the chain slackens on either side of the position where A,D and B are all in line.

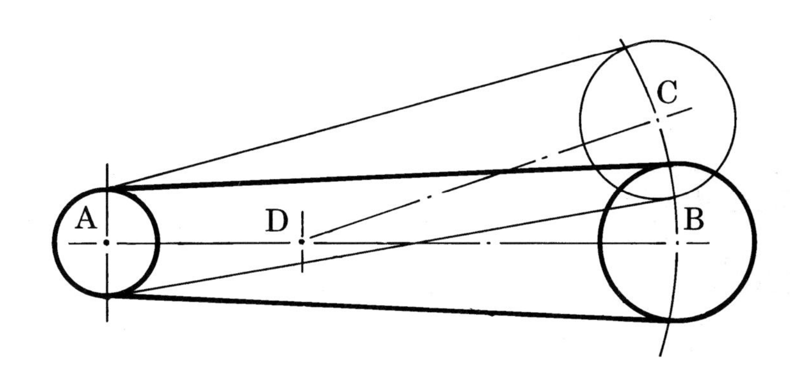

Fig 3.26 *Variations in chain tension. If the swinging arm pivot point is co-axial with the gearbox sprocket (diagram a), then there is no variation in the sprocket centre distance, however far the arm has to move. With a normal non co-axial pivot (diagram b) the static chain tension varies with travel.*

Pivot point

The choice of pivot point is fundamental to every aspect of swinging arm layout. The first consideration is the chain and it is well known that the conventional swinging arm system causes variations in chain tension. These variations become more problematic as greater suspension travel is sought. From this point of view the ideal swinging arm pivot point is co-axial with the gearbox sprocket as shown in Fig 3.26. This type of layout has been used by several special builders and has appeared on one or two factory bikes in the past. Because the rear wheel now swings about the gearbox sprocket axis there is no variation in the centre distance between the sprockets and therefore no variation in tension other than that associated with torque transmission. However, with conventional frames this type of system does complicate things somewhat and it needs to be done well if stiffness of the pivot area is to be maintained. Given the quality of modern chains the improvements possible do not seem to warrant the problems this layout creates. Accepting this, the next best thing is to locate the pivot as close behind the back of the gearbox as possible. Under these conditions there will be a change in the sprocket centre distance. The change is usually quite small for sensible suspension movements but since both chain runs have to accommodate every millimetre that the distance alters, the variation in tension is very noticeable when the travel is long and chains have to be adjusted to account for it.

Accepting that the pivot point should be close to the gearbox, we then have to decide how high up it is. Conventional wisdom is that the rear wheel spindle, the pivot point and the gearbox sprocket centre will all line up when the suspension has used up 40 - 50% of its total travel. On this basis, a first estimate of pivot point can be made as shown in Fig 3.27. Taking the unladen topped out case first,

- Draw out the rear spindle centre, and the gearbox sprocket centre based on the engine position you have chosen.
- Draw a vertical line where the pivot point can be located near to the gearbox.
- Mark full rear suspension travel above the rear wheel spindle and then 50% of it (or slightly less).
- Join the 50% point to the gearbox sprocket and where this line crosses the other vertical pivot line you have the pivot centre.

If the suspension is not topped out when unladen then this needs to be accounted for. For example, if there will be 10mm of sag then the suspension travel should be measured from a point 10mm below spindle level when seeking the 50% alignment point.

Once you have done this you can now begin to look at all the problems it creates for you! The greatest problems occur with small sprocket combinations so if you look like running a 14 tooth gearbox sprocket alongside a 30 tooth rear wheel sprocket you need to check things out carefully. With the arm deflected to give full suspension travel, see if the chain run will clear the pivot region. To do this the sprocket diameters need to be the appropriate pitch circles less one sideplate depth. If you are unlucky the chain will gouge into the pivot point before full travel and this can be difficult to sort out sometimes - Fig 3.28. There are various solutions.

Fig 3.27 *Making a first attempt at establishing pivot point based purely on chain clearance and tension requirements.*

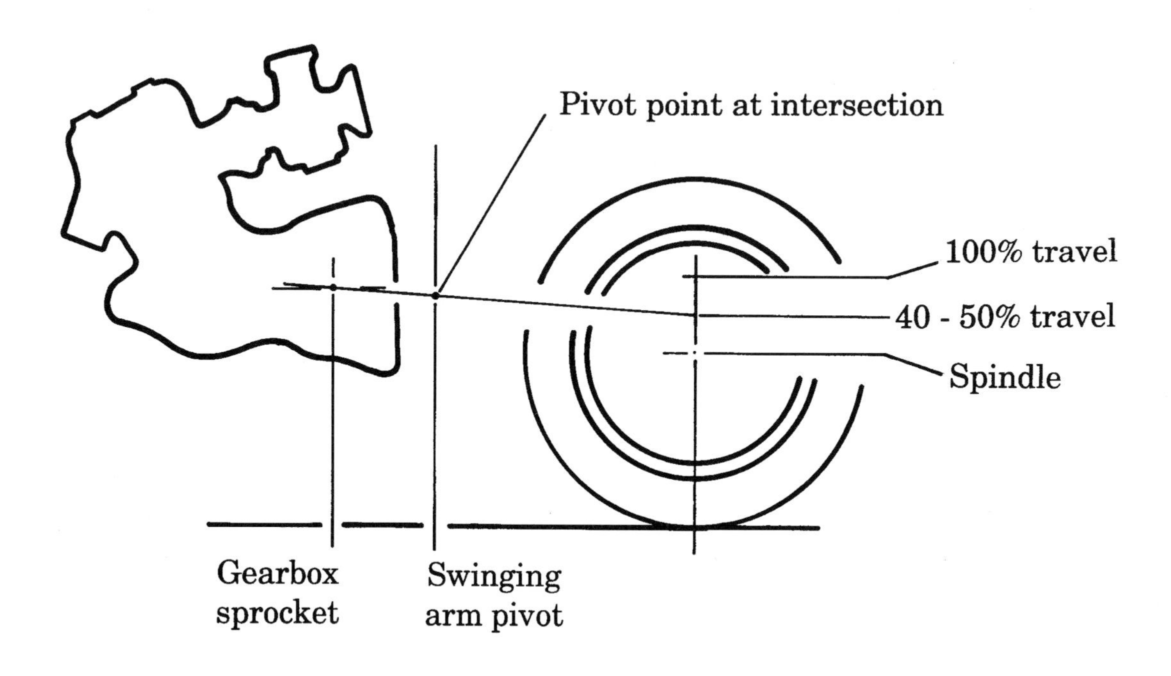

- Use larger sprocket combinations, eg instead of 15T/ 30T use 18T/36T. This has everything going for it, especially the reduction in chain fatigue mentioned earlier but it is not always possible. Some engines have castings that seriously limit gearbox sprocket size and you may not be willing, or able, to hack about the castings.

- Can a longer swinging arm be used? If it can, the degree of angularity will be less for the same suspension travel and this may solve the problem. However this usually implies either a longer wheelbase or a more forward engine location. Both options have implications covered in previous chapters and only you can decide what to do.

- If the swinging arm is relatively long you can consider moving the pivot point further away from the gearbox. Although this involves doing exactly the opposite of what I first suggested, it all depends on the relative sizes of arm, sprockets and suspension travel. As the pivot moves away, more space appears between the chain runs. If the arm is long you may find a solution fairly easily.

- A final 'solution', if the problem is slight, is to add plastic wear strips to the arm and ignore it! This technique became essential on motocross bikes as the suspension travel crept up. With typically 330mm (13ins) of travel it is impossible to avoid some problems and most motocross bikes have massive wear strips that always show plenty of evidence of use.

It is important to distinguish between the use of wear strips that prevent the whipping chain from cutting the arm to bits and those which act as an 'extra' sprocket for the chain to wrap round. The latter is a very bad situation that puts considerable load on everything and it must be avoided. It is tempting to move the pivot point up on the basis that the top chain run is tight and therefore less likely to flap about. In practice the top chain run flaps about quite dramatically and when you shut off quickly the back wheel drives the engine, hence the bottom chain run is tight and the top one clatters away at the arm. If you have positioned the pivot so that 40 - 50% of the suspension travel is required to line up the pivot, gearbox sprocket and rear spindle, then, at this mid-position, the chain clearance above and below the pivot will be approximately equal. Biasing it either up or down from this point will reduce the clearance available at one extreme of travel.

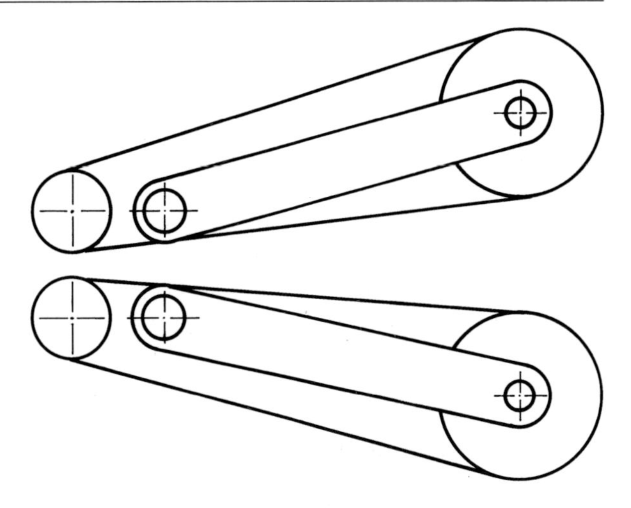

Fig 3.28 *At the extremes of suspension travel, the chain may come into contact with the swinging arm. Some contact has to be accepted with long travel and small gearbox sprockets so most off-road bikes use substantial wear strips. For roadracers it is best to avoid this if you can.*

The key to avoiding most of the problems associated with chain clearance is to use large enough sprocket pairings and I have only discussed all this because on some engines you may not be able to. Gearbox sprockets of a reasonable size remove most of these problems and ease the life of the chain considerably. They also create space for you to experiment further with the pivot point and this may well prove necessary in the case of very powerful roadracers. The reason for this is the behaviour known as anti-squat and/or pro-squat.

Swinging arms and squat

I first discovered the influence of swinging arm geometry when racing grass track bikes some thirty years ago and, as any experienced off-road rider will tell you, the effects can be quite dramatic. It is possible to change the characteristics of an off-road bike significantly by moving the swinging arm pivot, changing the length of the rear suspension units, or moving their mountings.

If you change the length of the suspension units or extend/reduce the mountings, then an awful lot of geometry changes occur at the same time. This is shown in the top diagram of Fig 3.29. The changes in behaviour you experience therefore come from many sources including altered steering geometry, centre of gravity and swinging arm inclination.

If you just move the swinging arm pivot up or down then the swinging arm geometry alters without too many other effects so this is the best way of experimenting with the layout. Examples of this are shown in the lower diagram of Fig 3.29.

When grip is intermittent, as it is in off-road applications, the influence of small changes in swinging arm pivot location can be surprising. It is possible to convert a bike that powerslides normally into a bike that does one of two things.

- It slides very easily but has no 'drive'. The lack of drive can be such that the bike can be ridden to a standstill, on full opposite lock, while the throttle is well open.

- It does not want to slide at all. When the bike is laid down and power is applied, it tries to pick itself up again and drive on in a straight line. This is very disturbing when the track has a steel fence around the outside of you!

Moving the swinging arm pivot up or down a bit on 'normal' roadrace bikes is unlikely to change anything dramatically, though if you alter the mountings/length of suspension units then very obvious changes will occur due to the new steering geometry and cg height.

However, at the more powerful end of the spectrum, where the power is sufficient to break traction easily, changes in pivot position can bring about similar effects to those found off-road. I have no personal experience of this and my desire to ride something that can light up the rear tyre like a speedway bike, only on tarmac, is about as close to zero as you can get! Nevertheless, if this sort of situation appeals to you then the influence of swinging arm geometry will be very important. At GP level even small capacity bikes can be improved by minor alterations to the swinging arm layout. It is no coincidence that the roadracers most adept at sorting these things out tend to be Americans with lots of flat (dirt) track experience because the problems are similar.

Swinging arm action

The source of the changes in traction described is the relative geometry of the swinging arm and chain run. This can produce a situation in which the forces involved exert a significant turning effect on the swinging arm.

The tendency of the arm to rotate when power is applied is determined by the forces and their moment arms about the pivot. The moment arms depend on the inclination of the swinging arm and the relative sizes of the front and rear sprockets.

If the arm rotates clockwise when viewed from the left of the bike then the suspension is forced to extend and the geometry is said to produce an anti-squat action. Note that it only does this when power is applied and grip is available.

Assuming this is the case, the application of power tries to rotate the arm. It cannot move down (unless the track is soft) so it raises the back of the bike. For most people, the benefits of this reaction will simply be a reduction in squat at the rear end

Right. Fig 3.29 *Diagrams like this need to be much larger than I can reproduce here, however the general idea should be evident. In each diagram the thick lines represent the initial starting point. The lines indicating the forks and frame are fixed in relation to each other so this combination effectively pivots about the front wheel spindle. When the length of the suspension units is changed, diagram a), the swinging arm angle is altered but there are quite major changes in everything else. In diagram b), the original frame is retained and the pivot point is moved up or down. This produces much less change in overall geometry for a given change in swinging arm inclination.*

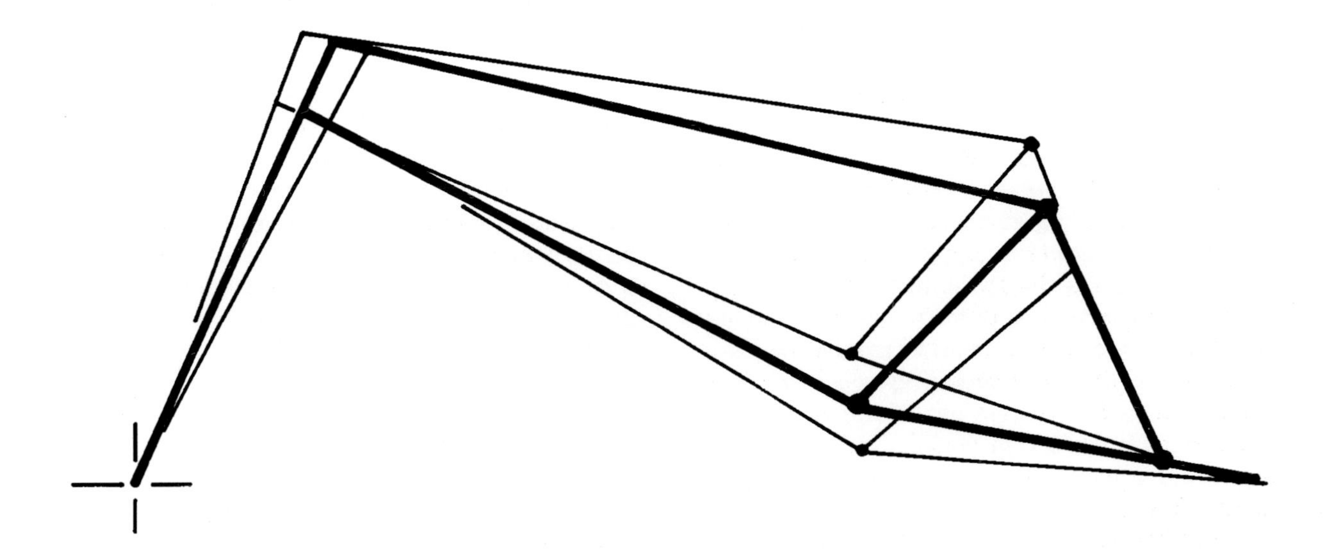

a) Changing the length of suspension units or their mountings.

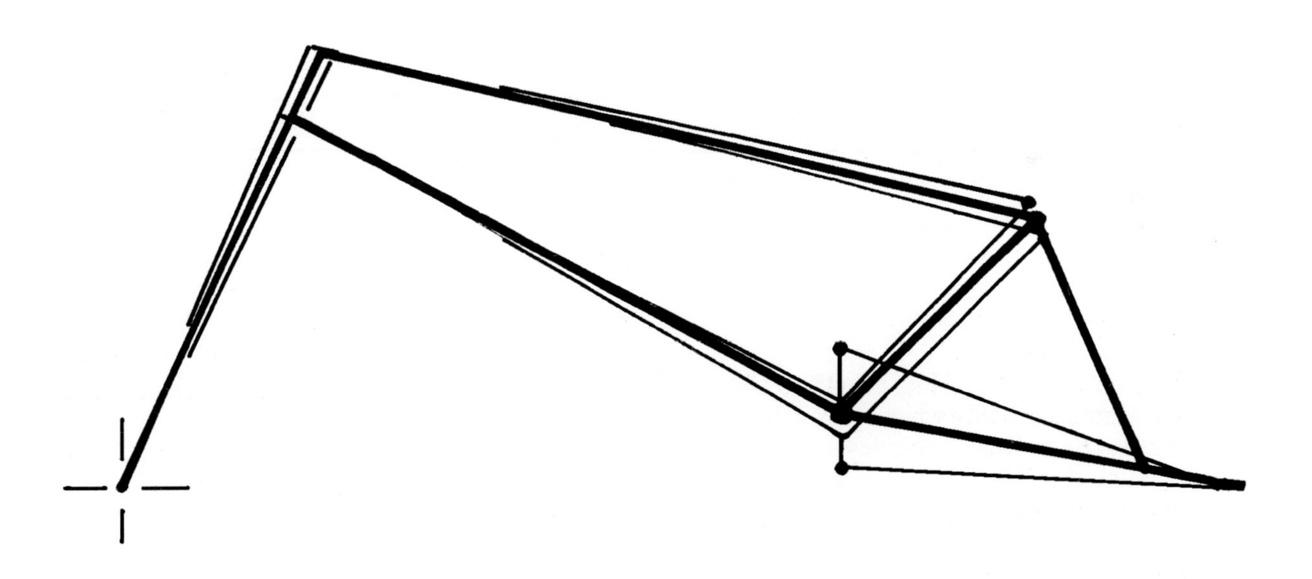

b) Altering the height of the swinging arm pivot.

during normal acceleration so once a sensible compromise has been achieved it will generally stay that way. GP riders need to adjust it to suit the specific circuit they are racing on and as usual it is the fast corners that have priority. For example, at Donnington Park, Craner Curves is a very fast downhill left hand corner where it is easy to either save time or crash! A touch more anti-squat than normal can help to keep the front end firmly planted when power is applied and one 250cc factory team sets the swinging arm pivot 3mm higher than normal at this circuit. The momentary effect of the anti-squat is to force the tyre hard onto the track thereby generating more grip. More grip gives better traction but, if the suspension extends too much, the suspension will top out and the reaction ceases. When the reaction ceases the back end sinks again, it finds grip and the whole process repeats itself. The result can be a sort of pogo-stick acceleration that is very obvious under off-road conditions.

On tarmac, where the grip is much greater, everything is smoother and more subtle. Because good grip is available the bike can accelerate at high values and consequently transfers most of its weight to the rear wheel. This compresses the suspension and causes the bike to squat significantly, lowering the cg height and encouraging wheelspin. Under these conditions, any tendency of the swinging arm to rotate as described will be a distinct advantage. Provided this is not too dramatic, it can be used to limit the squat produced and hence stabilise the cg and maintain traction. In suitable amounts, an anti-squat action serves an important function but when excessive it will jack up the back of the bike, raise the cg, and encourage wheelies.

The alternative action is for the swinging arm to rotate counter-clockwise when viewed from the left. This is the 'natural' response because of weight transfer but, if the swinging arm layout is such that it further encourages this tendency, then the back end will sink quickly and dramatically on acceleration. The swinging arm action is therefore one of pro-squat.

Excessive squat can often be observed when powerful bikes accelerate. Although it looks harmless enough in a straight line, the tyre is again encouraged to break traction and spin if the suspension bottoms-out, further helped by the now lower cg. In the milliseconds that separate excitement from disaster on the corners you might contemplate that the relatively light unsprung mass (swinging arm, wheel etc) is more inclined to move upwards than the sprung mass is inclined to move downwards. Grip is varied when you accelerate under these conditions and it is easy to lose the back end without realising the cause. It isn't that obvious, you just fall off!

These then are some of the general effects that can result from more radical swinging arm geometry in combination with either a lot of power (on tarmac) or a surface with relatively low grip, eg a grass track. Like many other things on a motorcycle they are difficult to quantify and the best option is to allow some scope for adjustments should the need arise.

Squat geometry

The swinging arm geometry is fairly simple. Predicting what it will do on the track is nothing like as simple because the geometry is changing all the time with suspension movement and the most important factor, the grip at the back wheel, is also variable.

Fig 3.30 *The swinging arm is acted on by both the chain force and driving force. Since these forces are remote from the swinging arm pivot they will cause the arm to rotate in some way when power is applied.*

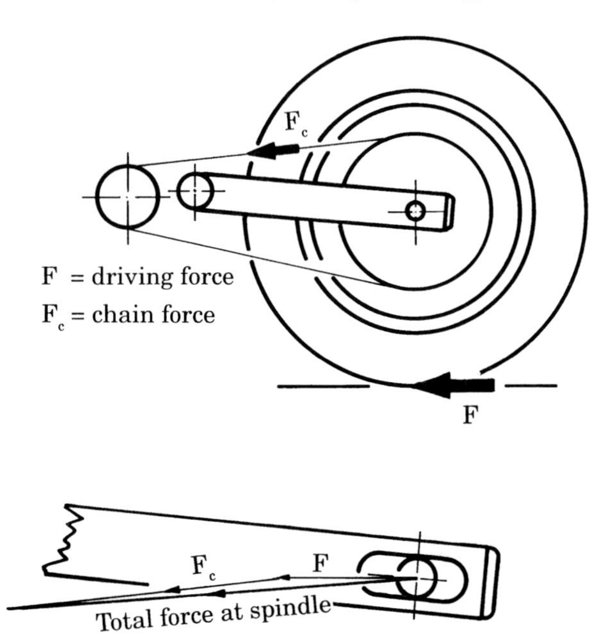

Fig 3.30 shows the situation we are dealing with. If we isolate the swinging arm then it can be shown that both the driving force at the ground and the chain pull on the sprocket get transmitted through the wheel spindle. The chain force is balanced by the force applied to the gearbox sprocket so it does not in any way add to the acceleration of the bike, it simply tries to crush and rotate the swinging arm.

We cannot analyse the behaviour in detail unless the moment of inertia of the wheel, swinging arm and sprung mass are known. Squat response is a highly dynamic phenomenon. What we can do is to determine whether the response will be anti-squat or pro-squat and establish some form of indicator that will show the degree of response we will get. Once you know this, you can modify the layout to either increase it or reduce it as required. To do this we need to add the forces acting at the spindle, taking account of their direction, and see how the direction of this force relates to the swinging arm. The direction can be established even though the actual forces remain unknown. It would be very foolish to try and accurately predict the forces involved since they vary with every tarmac marble you ride over!

Fig 3.31 gives the general method. Diagram a) shows the situation considered. In diagram b) a line is drawn to represent the swinging arm centreline. Use any convenient length, eg 200mm. In c) another line is drawn horizontally from the spindle. This line can also be any length, I would suggest 50mm, and it represents the driving force

Fig 3.31 *Determining the degree of anti-squat or pro-squat. a) Example details. b) Draw a line parallel to the swinging arm. c) Draw a horizontal line 50mm long to represent driving force. d) Draw another line to represent the chain force. The length is (50mm x D / d). Join the two lines as shown. The angle of the resultant indictes the degree of anti-squat.*

a) Layout considered.

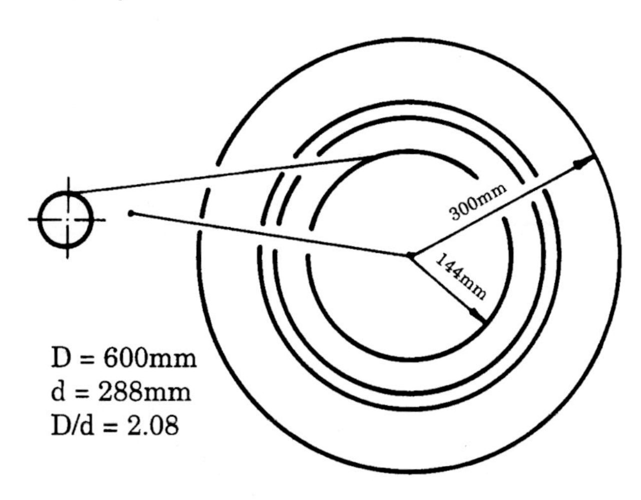

Line parallel to swinging arm

b) Line parallel to swinging arm, any convenient length.

c) Draw line L1 horizontally as shown to a known length, eg 50mm.

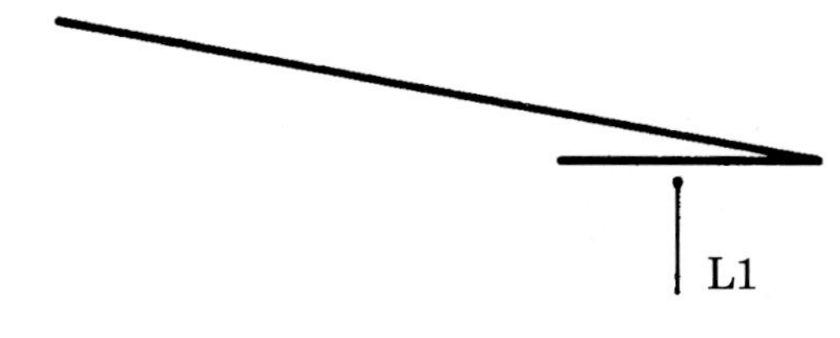

d) Line L2 starts at the end of L1.

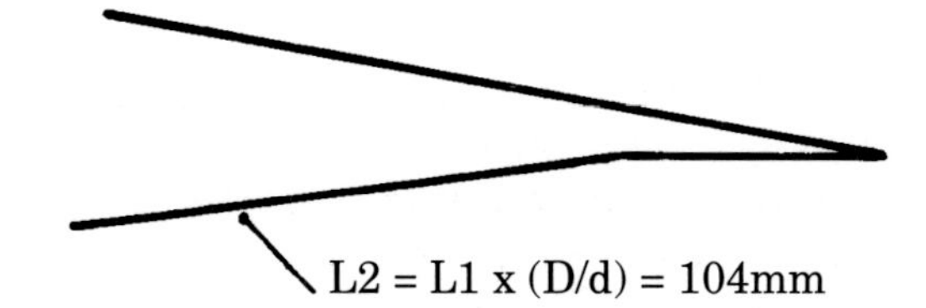

e) Join start of L1 to end of L2.

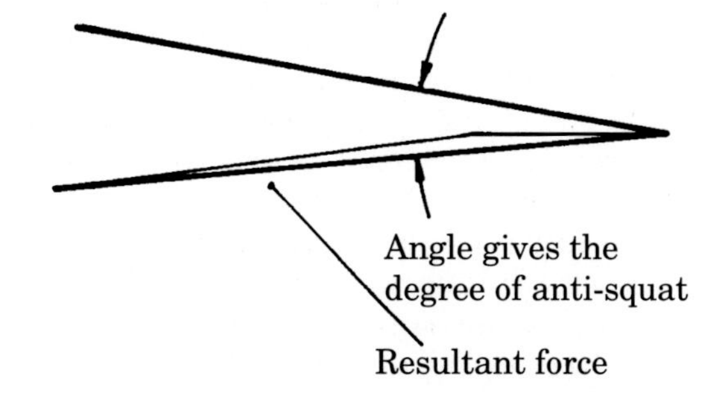

that is available on the road. The chain force and driving force are easily related if we neglect the moment of inertia of the wheel. In reality, some of the torque applied to the rear wheel will have to be used to accelerate the wheel itself so not all of it will translate into a driving force. Nevertheless, neglecting this aspect will not prevent you obtaining a useful guide. If the inertia of the wheel assembly is neglected then the chain force and driving force are related by the following.

$$\textbf{Chain force} = \frac{\textbf{Driving force x D}}{\textbf{d}}$$

where D = Rolling diameter of the rear tyre
d = pitch circle diameter of the rear sprocket

The chain force can thus be represented by a line, drawn in the correct direction, with a length equal to that used for driving force multiplied by D/d. In the example, D = 600mm and d = 288mm so the line will be 2.08 times as long, ie it is 2.08 x 50mm = 104mm. This is added in diagram d). It starts at the end of the horizontal line and is drawn at the same angle as the top chain run.

Finally, in diagram e), the two force lines are added by joining them as shown. The resultant does not have a known force value but the direction is clear and the angle to the swinging arm is indicative of the squat situation. In this example, the force acts below the arm and therefore generates anti-squat. The greater the angle shown, the more anti-squat there will be.

Doing this at several different swinging arm positions will usually show that the anti-squat reduces as the suspension compresses and it switches to pro-squat at some point near to full travel. In this case, the resultant force line will be above the swinging arm centreline. All changes are therefore a compromise over the whole range. Alterations to the swinging arm pivot point or the sprockets will change the degree of anti-squat you start off with, as will different tyre sizes. My practical suggestions are as follows. Firstly, when building powerful bikes, try to keep the size of the gearbox sprocket up so that there is room to move the swinging arm pivot. Secondly, provide some means of adjusting the pivot. It may also be possible to incorporate adjustment of engine position. This will change the angle of the chain run relative to the swinging arm but it will of course alter the centre of gravity as well. Table 3.8 gives details of how sprocket sizes and swinging arm pivot location will influence the tendency to produce an anti-squat reaction under power.

There is no doubt that the way the squat characteristic varies with suspension travel can make it difficult to get things right. For example, if there is too much anti-squat, and the back end tends to jack up too much, you can lower the swinging arm pivot point relative to the gearbox sprocket. This will reduce the anti-squat but it will reduce it throughout the suspension range.

If you had a small amount of anti-squat at say 70% suspension travel then that may have been turned into pro-squat and cause yet more problems under different conditions. As with most other aspects of the design, you are again forced to compromise or come up with a completely different system that eliminates these problems. What you cannot do is to ignore them.

Table 3.8 *Effect of changes to swinging arm pivot and sprocket combinations on squat tendency.*

Modification	Effect
smaller rear sprocket	less anti-squat
larger rear sprocket	more anti-squat
smaller g/box sprocket	more anti-squat
larger g/box sprocket	less anti-squat
lower s/a pivot	less anti-squat
raise s/a pivot	more anti-squat

4.1 Introduction to resistance

Overview

The straight-line performance of a motorcycle is described in terms of its top speed and the ability to accelerate. For a given engine, gearbox, weight and level of riding ability these performance indicators are determined almost entirely by the resistance to motion, though aspects such as cg location and tyres will have a big influence on what can be achieved at low speeds. Resistance to motion is therefore extremely important and does not always receive the attention it deserves.

Resistance to motion comes from a variety of sources but it is usual to consider it as just two components. Aerodynamic drag, which is the dominant form of resistance, is a result of moving you and the bike through the air. Rolling resistance is basically associated with the rolling friction of the tyres but it is usual to consider it as encompassing everything, other than aerodynamic drag, that has to be overcome by the driving force at the back wheel.

Both components of resistance generate forces that increase with road speed and the total is a figure that rises very rapidly once you reach the sort of speeds encountered on the race track. This is just the opposite of driving force which declines with increasing road speed - Fig 4.1.

As long as the driving force exceeds the total resistance the bike can accelerate. The acceleration possible is proportional to the difference between the two forces so the faster we go the less the acceleration will be. Once the two forces become equal the acceleration is zero and top speed has been reached. Because of this, reductions in resistance to motion will affect both speed and acceleration.

Fig 4.1 *While driving force falls with increasing road speed, the resistance to motion rises. Acceleration is only possible while the driving force is the greater of the two.*

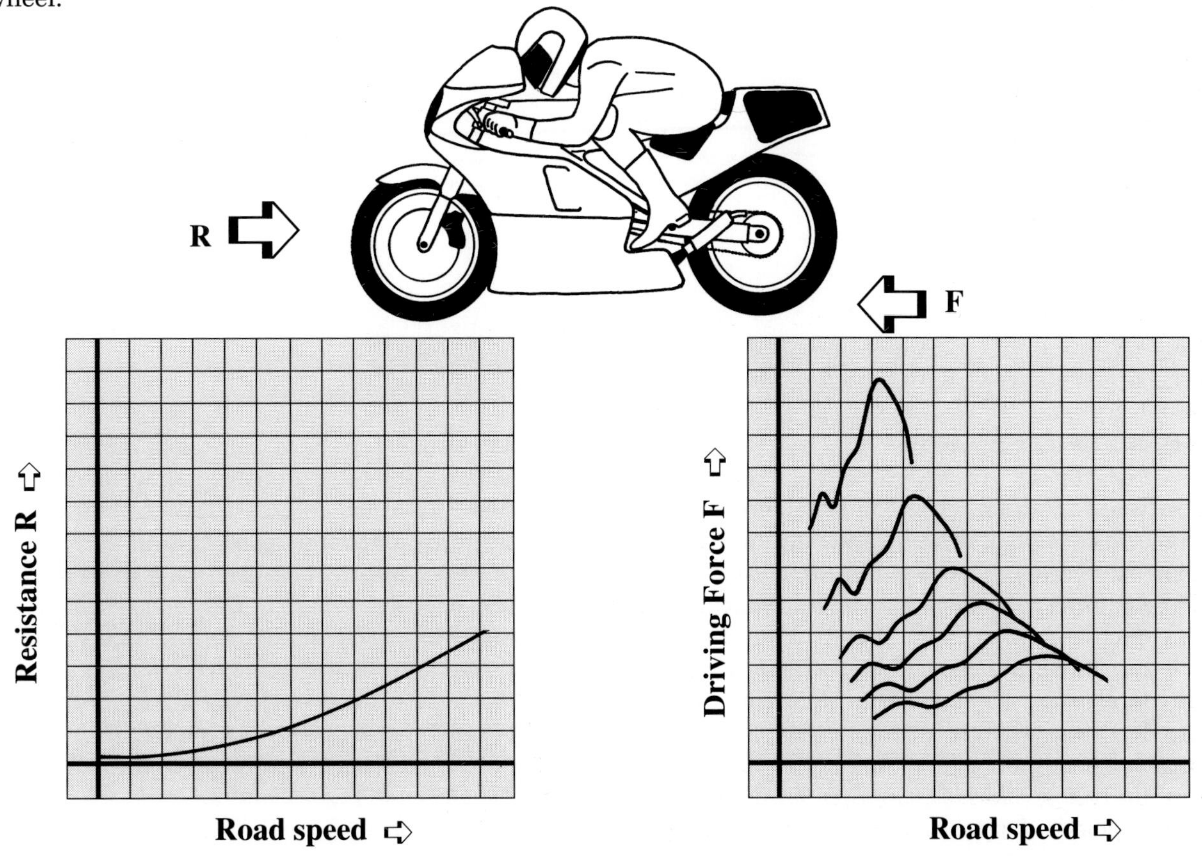

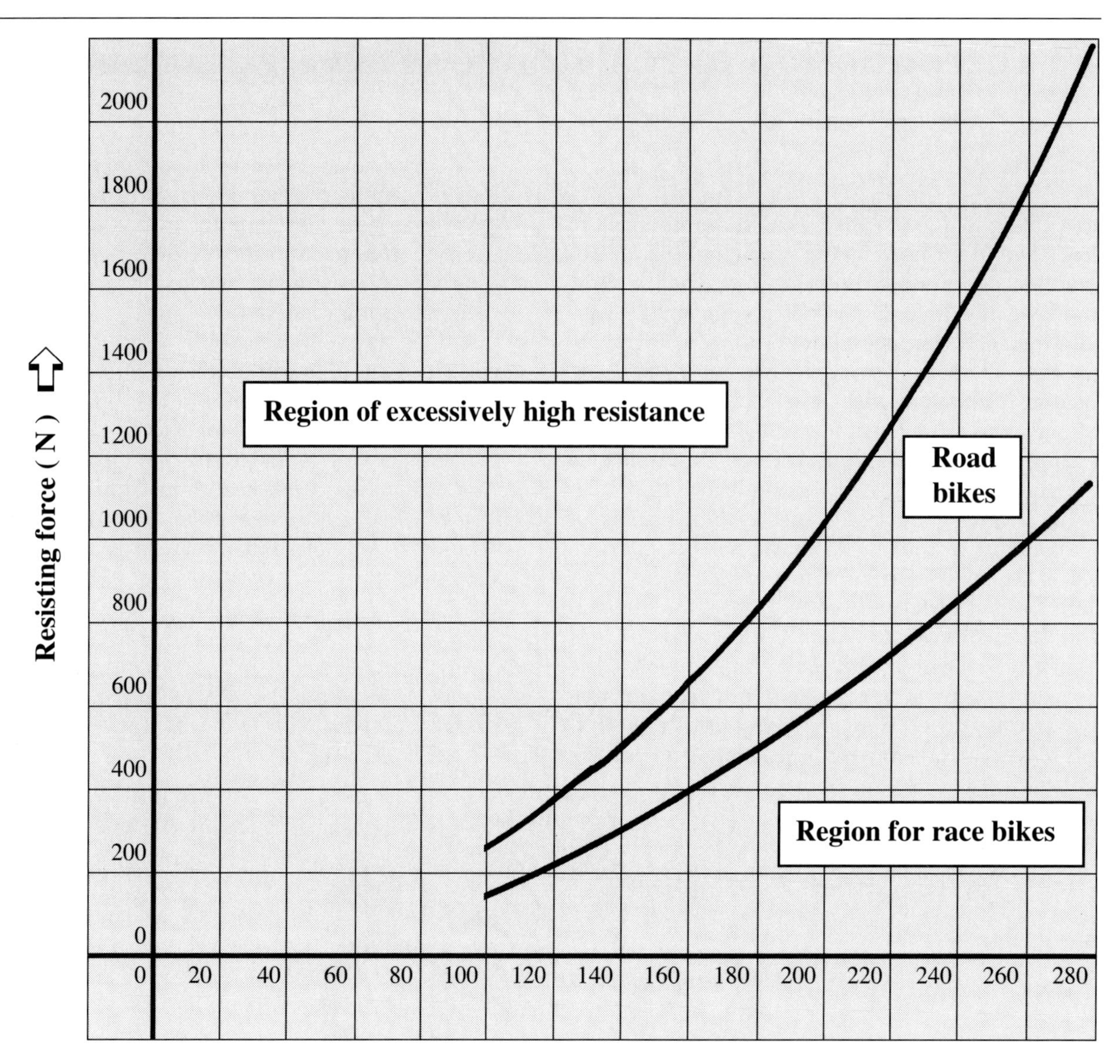

Resistance to motion

The total resistance to motion is heavily dependent on the design of the bike and obviously racing bikes should exhibit lower resistance than road bikes, though in some cases you might be rather disappointed.

To establish the basic ideas without any sums we can consider the resistance to motion experienced by a selection of road bikes. Later on you will be able to make more realistic estimations for specific racing bikes. In Chapter 2.4 I produced two graphs showing the amount of power required to reach a given top speed. Fig 2.26 gave figures in metric units and Fig 2.27 was in imperial units. It was also explained in this chapter that power, driving force and road speed can all be related. This means that the data originally presented in the form of power vs maximum road speed can be revamped into the form of driving force vs maximum road speed. Since this tells us the driving force we need to achieve these speeds, it also tells us the total resistance to motion experienced by these road bikes, the two values being equal under these conditions. Fig 4.2 and its imperial equivalent Fig 4.3 provide such data. As before, each

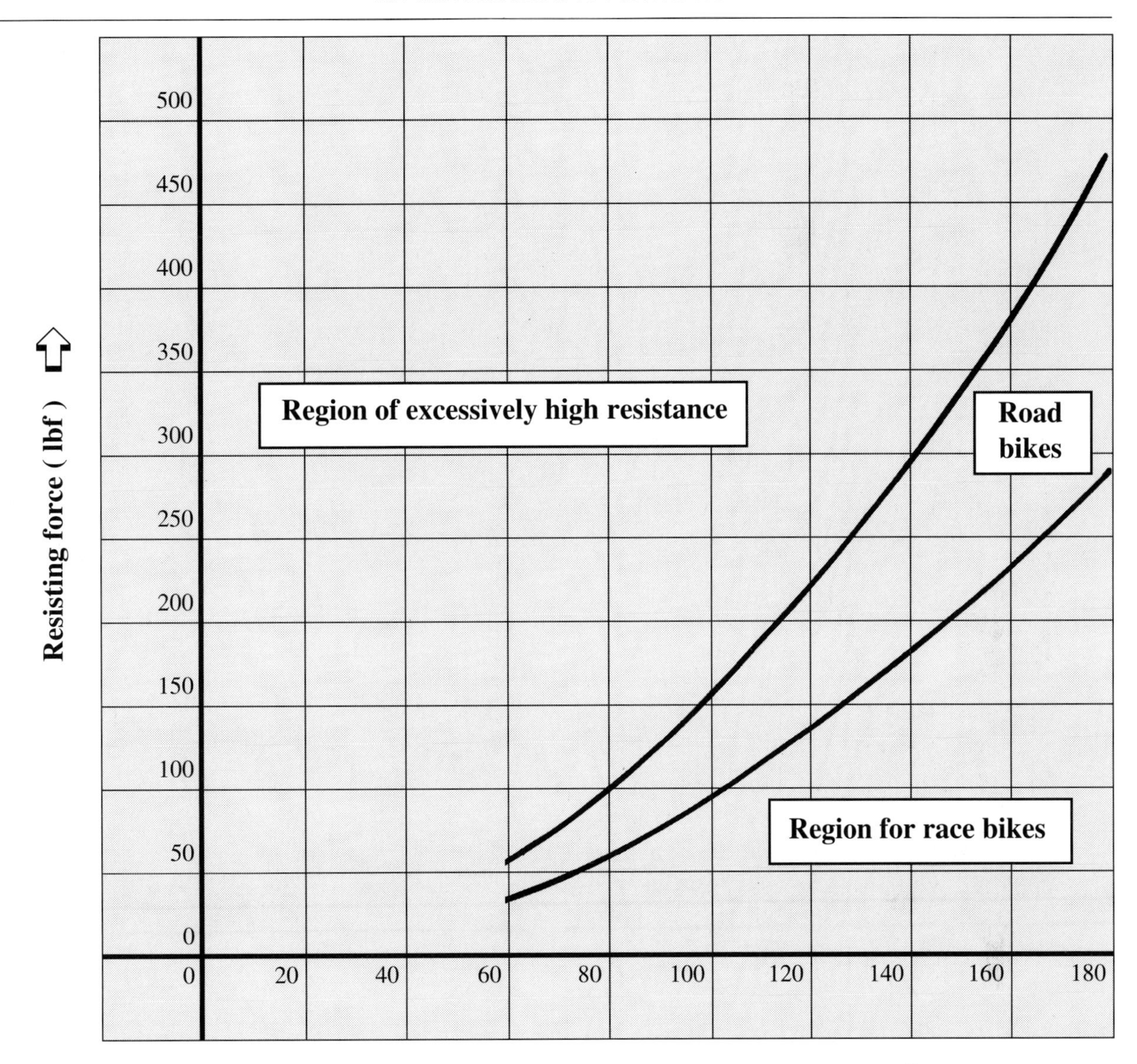

Left. Fig 4.2 *This graph gives the total resistance to motion experienced by a variety of road bikes at different speeds. It has been compiled from published road bike data and encompasses numerous configurations. In the absence of anything better, larger race bikes should be assumed to lie close to the lower of the two lines.*

Above. Fig 4.3 *Resistance to motion of road bikes using imperial values.*

graph has a zone of values to accommodate the variety of bikes tested and for racing you should be looking at the lower limits of this data, ie low resistance. Ideally you are well below these and I will discuss this shortly. There is no low speed data given on the graphs because motorcycles which do less than 100km/hr flat out are few and far between. What happens in this region depends largely on the tyres and tyre pressures used. This is discussed in the next chapter.

Taking the metric data first, we find that at 160km/hr the majority of road bikes will encounter a total resisting force of between 400N and

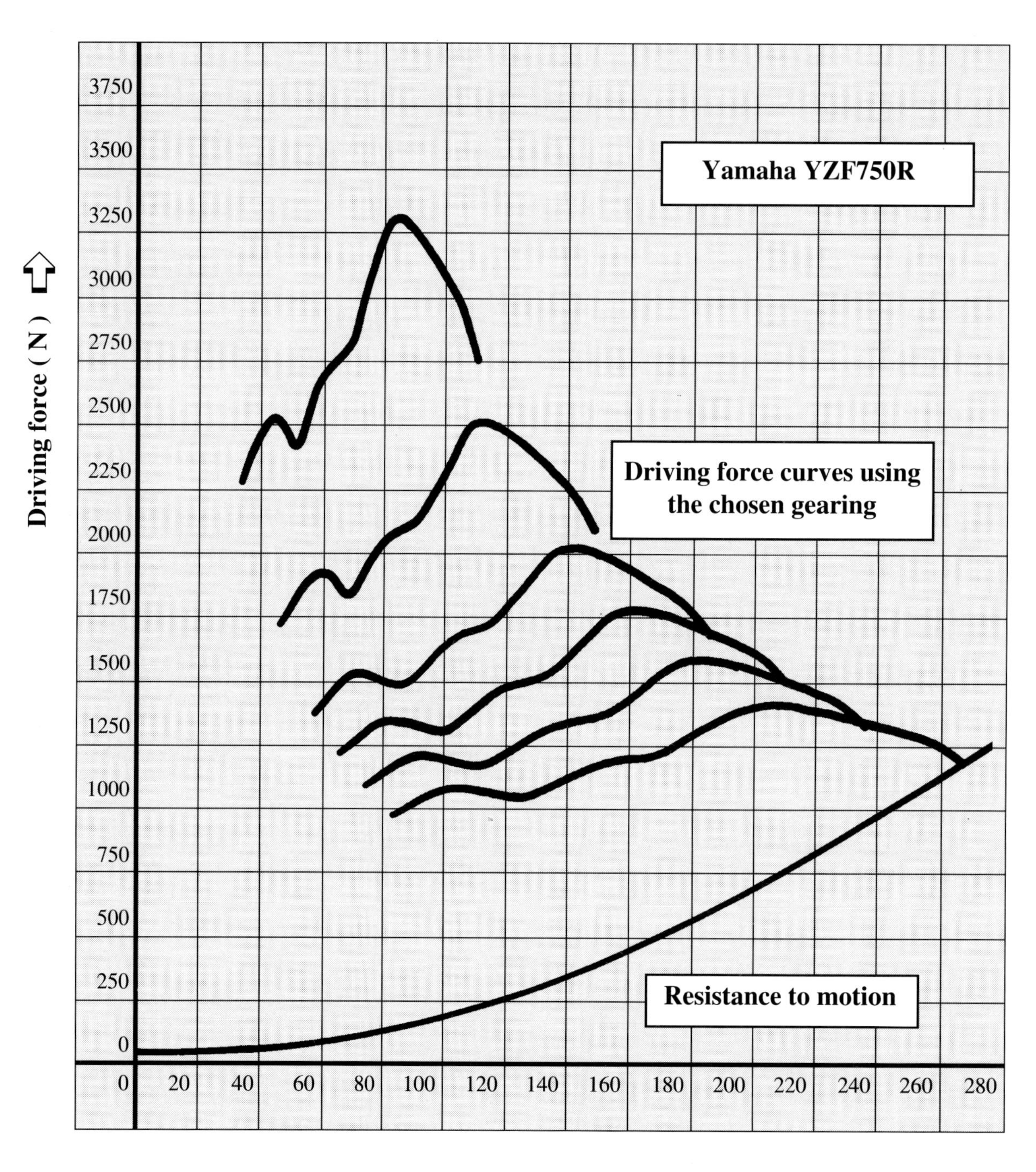
Yamaha YZF750R
Driving force curves using the chosen gearing
Resistance to motion
Driving force (N)
3750
3500
3250
3000
2750
2500
2250
2000
1750
1500
1250
1000
750
500
250
0
0 20 40 60 80 100 120 140 160 180 200 220 240 260 280
Road speed (km/hr)

668N (41-68kgf). The lower figure corresponds to a typical modern sports bike with the rider prone while the upper limit is a touring bike with the rider relatively upright. Using Fig 4.3 for the imperial data, an equivalent speed of 100miles/hr produces a resistance of between 90lbf and 150lbf for similar configurations. There is obviously a large variation here but once we start to include serious racing bikes the spread becomes even wider. For a 500cc GP bike the resistance at 160km/hr is around 320N whereas in the case of a 125cc GP bike a figure of 180N might be achieved with a very small rider. (Imperial equivalents 100miles/hr, 72lbf, 40lbf). Overall, vast differences in resistance to motion do exist, though you can never expect a 1000cc touring bike to slip through the air like a 125ccGP bike with a miniature rider on board.

Perhaps the most striking thing about these figures is that the difference is rarely obvious from a casual glance at the bikes concerned. Machines of apparently similar size and configuration can exhibit very large differences in resistance and later on I will be detailing exactly how the resistance of one particular racing bike was reduced by almost 55%. Gains like this are of course only possible if you are starting from something fairly poor but it is suprising how bad many bikes are in this respect.

Left. Fig 4.4 *Driving force and resistance plots for a Yamaha YZF750R. In this example the resistance to motion becomes equal to the driving force at about 265km / hr. Up to this point the bike is able to accelerate but the faster you go, the lower the acceleration possible. Section 6 looks at this in detail but the general idea is simple. Reducing resistance can improve both top speed and acceleration.*

To find out just how much excess force we have available for acceleration it is necessary to superimpose the appropriate resistance graph onto the one showing driving force at the rear wheel. Fig 4.4 is an example. The driving force is well in excess of the resistance at very low road speeds and so the acceleration will be relatively high.

With powerful bikes this difference is obviously greater than for low powered ones but the low speed acceleration will not necessarily increase in proportion because you can only transfer a certain amount of power to the road before wheelspin and wheelie problems occur.

The acceleration of this bike falls to zero at a speed of about 265km/hr (165miles/hr). This is the top speed figure for the data used. A more detailed discussion of these aspects is given in Section 6.

As far as this section is concerned I am going to look at resistance to motion in some detail and thereby suggest ways of reducing it. It is not easy, even if you happen to have a wind tunnel at the bottom of the garden, but once you are fully aware of the basic ideas it is surprising how much can be done without elaborate equipment. You will begin to see the bike in a different light and can identify features which are likely to increase the resistance to motion.

Whatever the case, the important thing is to consider resistance to motion right from the very beginning because this is the only way to achieve good results. There is more to it than just bolting on a standard fairing that is as small as you can find! Of the two areas mentioned, all useful gains will come from reductions in aerodynamic drag. Rolling resistance is normally of much less significance and it is very difficult to reduce. Nevertheless it would be rather narrow-minded for me to ignore it altogether.

4.2 Rolling resistance

Introduction

This short chapter has been included for the sake of completeness and readers with a purely practical interest in conventional racing motorcycles are unlikely to lose out by ignoring it.

The influence of rolling resistance on a conventional motorcycle is much less than the aerodynamic contribution. I don't think you can say that it is totally negligible, but the improvements you can make almost certainly are. For fully streamlined record breakers with low aerodynamic drag it is much more significant but again there is little that can be done other than to reduce the weight and increase the tyre pressures, both of which influence rolling resistance. If you are involved with anything like this, you need to talk to the tyre manufacturers at the outset.

Rolling resistance is difficult to deal with because most of the major factors involved, except weight, are fixed by other considerations. I am of course assuming that the bike is mechanically sound. If the wheel bearings squeak and the brake pads drag heavily on the disks then you may make some progress. Under normal circumstances I'm afraid that the possibility of improvement is small.

Rolling resistance

The best way to think about rolling resistance is as a term which lumps together everything the bike has to overcome except aerodynamic drag and transmission inefficiencies. If you tested the bike accurately in a wind tunnel and found the power required to overcome aerodynamic drag, and you also ran it on a dyno to find the net power available at the back wheel, then in track tests the figures would not add up, the bike not being able to perform as well as you thought.

The difference between the two sets of figures is due to what I am calling rolling resistance. Factors which influence rolling resistance include,

- Tyre wall construction.
- Road surface.
- Tyre temperature.
- Tyre pressures.
- Friction in wheel bearings.
- Windage at the wheels.
- Friction in suspension systems.
- Road speed.
- Laden weight.
- The amount of torque transmitted.

There are three basic areas within this list: the weight, properties of the tyres and aspects such as bearing friction which depend on mechanical quality. In general the mechanical aspects are less significant and firmly under your control.

The major contributor is the action of deforming the tyres. All aspects show some dependency on road speed and weight. The variation in tyre characteristics and construction is considerable and you may have noticed one leading car tyre manufacturer advertising tyres that can increase fuel economy by 5% compared with the standard construction but for racing the average rider has no influence on this area and has to use whatever is available in the right sizes. There is however a difference in the rolling characteristics of cross ply and radial tyres, the latter producing less resistance to motion in most cases. It is also important to ensure you have the correct rim width for the tyres concerned since incorrect widths can cause the tyres to produce more rolling resistance than normal.

For a given set of tyres on a particular surface the rolling resistance is most strongly influenced by the tyre pressures, the laden weight and the speed of the bike. The resistance reduces with increasing tyre pressure, hence the use of high pressures for record breakers, but again we tend to be restricted by the more important aspect of roadholding and have to use pressures appropriate to specific tyres and suspension settings. The main questions to be answered here are how does the rolling resistance vary with speed and what magnitude of forces are we dealing with? Are they of any significance?

Experimental verification can be carried out in one of two ways. The first option is to tow the bike and rider along at speed behind some form of screen so that the aerodynamic load is eliminated and at the same time record the force required to perform the tow. This is only really practical if you use a load cell and electronic data logging to record the force. It is generally a rather dodgy process for the rider and assumes that the bike exists which is not the case initially. Test centres would not normally contemplate having a rider on board during such procedures and replace the bike/rider with a loaded wheel carrier for obvious reasons.

The second method of determining the tyre's contribution to rolling resistance is to set up an indoor test bed in which the tyre can be loaded onto a rotating drum. This method generally gives much more repeatable results since the 'road' surface is consistent and it is easier to instrument the set-up reliably. It only takes account of the tyre properties given specific speed and weight conditions but this covers the major factors.

One common way of expressing the tyre's rolling characteristics is to introduce a coefficient of rolling resistance. This coefficient is similar in concept to a normal friction coefficient and it is equal to the rolling drag divided by the vertical tyre load. To obtain the amount of drag force due to rolling the coefficient needs to be multiplied by the weight on the tyre as shown in Fig 4.5. On a motorcycle there are of course two tyres to consider and the value of μ_{roll} will be greater at the rear tyre because it is transmitting torque.

In general there is no point in trying to differentiate between the wheels unless you have specific manufacturer's data. An average value is normally used. The weight figure then becomes the whole laden weight of the bike, clearly indicating another advantage of having less weight. It is perhaps worth noting that tyres do some very peculiar things when transmitting a lot of power and the use of a simple rolling coefficient would not stand up very well scientifically in these circumstances. However, these are problems for the tyre company. You will not go any faster by worrying about them.

The value of μ_{roll} is frequently assumed to be constant or to increase in direct proportion to road speed. Both assumptions are untrue but the latter will produce an approximation to the truth that is often adequate unless you are testing tyres to

Fig 4.5 *The rolling resistance of tyres is usually based on a coefficient of rolling resistance. The coefficient is not constant with speed.*

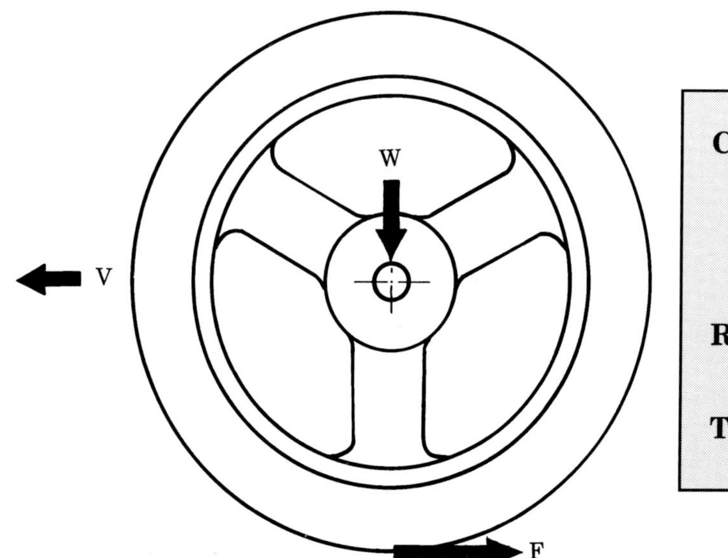

Coeff. of rolling friction = μ_{roll}

$$\mu_{roll} = \frac{F}{W}$$

Rolling drag force F = $W\mu_{roll}$

The value of μ_{roll} is speed related

their limit. If you do study the subject more closely then a number of things will be observed. Firstly, the rolling coefficient shows some dependence on higher powers of speed and a relationship to $(\text{speed})^2$ is probably more realistic. Although this sounds dramatic the figures are such that the graphs will show little variation from a straight line as far as practical results are concerned.

The really big changes occur when the tyre begins to approach its speed limit. At some speed a continuous deformation in the tyre casing is observed. This is called a standing wave. I do not know specific speeds for racing tyres but if you are using moped tyres on your superbike you may find out for yourself. Tyre speed ratings are important. Once this point is reached, the rolling resistance rises dramatically and terms as high as $(\text{speed})^{4.4}$ have been reported in various research papers (ref 1). Rolling resistance can thus rise rapidly but you should never encounter this.

For normal road speeds, the motor industry generally accepts a variation in rolling resistance that takes the form,

$$\text{Rolling resistance} = (a + bV)W$$

where a and b are constants
V = speed
W = laden weight

In this case the value of μ_{roll} is seen to be made up of two terms, one which is independent of speed (a) and one which is proportional to speed (bV). A somewhat better starting point was suggested by Hoerner in his masterpiece 'Fluid-dynamic drag'. It takes the general form,

$$\text{Rolling resistance} = \left(a + \frac{b}{p} + \frac{cV^2}{p}\right)W$$

where a, b and c are constants
p = tyre pressure
V = speed
W = weight

This shows a better fit to experimental data within the speed rating of the tyre. In his original work relating to car tyres, Hoerner proposed the following coefficients.

a = 0.005 b = 0.15 c = 0.000035

These are only valid if the weight is in lbf, the tyre pressures in lbf/in^2 and the speed in miles/hr. The resulting rolling resistance is also in lbf. Over the years several detailed studies have shown this representation to be very reasonable once the coefficients are modified to suit. Large tyres, eg lorry tyres, actually have relatively low rolling resistance, while motorcycles are somewhat worse.

This formula has been used by numerous people involved in record attempts. In the 1960's it was used to estimate rolling resistance for the Goldenrod land speed record car (684km/hr, 425miles/hr). For this application, the designers used the original values of constants a,b and c that Hoerner proposed, even though Hoerner's suggestions were for a normal road vehicle and Goldenrod was being used on salt flats with very different tyres. Note that if you read reference (4) listed, the value of 'c' is given as 0.0000162 but this assumes speed to be in ft/s.

Hoerner's expression, with the same constants, subsequently cropped up in several automotive applications and then, in the 1970's -1980's, it was employed by Kevin Cooper to estimate the rolling resistance of a Can-Am record-breaking motorcycle. Cooper's work initially related to conventional roadrace layouts and is therefore of much more interest to us. He also published many excellent papers on the subject of which reference (2) is one example.

In his work on behalf of Can-Am, Kevin Cooper accepted Hoerner's view, albeit with modification to suit 'modern' (1970's) motorcycle tyres and some concern at his lack of experimental data. Despite his reservations, the final comparisons of road tests and original theoretical estimates suggest that such relationships were indeed realistic.

For a 125cc roadracer, Cooper proposed the version of Hoerner's expression that is given overleaf in Fig 4.6. The bike concerned had a laden weight of 410lbf and tyre pressures up to 60lbf/in^2. At a speed of 140miles/hr the formula gives a force of 16.4lbf and this requires 6.1bhp at the wheel to overcome it, ie about 13% of that produced by a modern 125cc racer (metric equivalents: weight 1.824kN, tyre pressure 4.21kgf/cm^2, force 73N at 225km/hr). On this basis rolling resistance is not negligible but there is nothing you can do that will change the already small values sufficiently to reduce lap times. I have also given a direct metric equivalent of Cooper's expression in Fig 4.6 but please remember that there is nothing magic

For speeds below 150ft/s (102.3miles/hr)

$$\text{Rolling resistance (lbf)} = \left[0.0085 + \frac{0.255}{p} + \frac{2.771V^2}{10^5 p}\right]W$$

and for speeds above 150ft/s,

$$\text{Rolling resistance (lbf)} = \left[\frac{0.255}{p} + \frac{5.1V^2}{10^5 p}\right]W$$

where W = laden weight in lbf
V = speed in ft/s
p = tyre pressure in lbf/in^2

For speeds below 165km/hr

$$\text{Rolling resistance (N)} = \left[0.0833 + \frac{0.176}{p} + \frac{1.58V^2}{10^5 p}\right]W$$

and for speeds above 165km/hr,

$$\text{Rolling resistance (N)} = \left[\frac{0.176}{p} + \frac{2.91V^2}{10^5 p}\right]W$$

where W = laden weight in kgf
V = speed in km/hr
p = tyre pressure in kgf/cm^2

Fig 4.6 Top *Kevin Cooper's published expressions for rolling resistance as applied to a 125cc Can-Am record breaker of conventional roadrace layout.*

Bottom *Author's metric version of Cooper's formula effectively uses the same coefficients.*

about the constants in either of these expressions. Both reflect Cooper's specific appraisal for his chosen tyres running on salt flats. The figures were arrived at by working back from the difference between accurately known aerodynamic data and experimental road tests. I only quote them because you are unlikely to have anything better. The required values are totally dependent on the tyre/road surface combination.

In my own past experience, Cooper's assessment has proved to be a reasonable starting point for the maximum rolling resistance but you will have to adapt the basics to your own needs. Note that in my derivation I have used kgf for weight and kgf/cm^2 for pressure. Although neither are preferred units they reflect practical reality.

Conclusion

The general conclusion of this discussion is that rolling resistance is somewhat difficult to pin down and there is not much we can do to reduce it apart from minimising weight. Tyre aspects are generally in the hands of manufacturers and are determined by more important factors such as grip. Obviously bearing friction and the like should be minimal but this is simply good practice.

If you accept the Hoerner/Cooper assessment then certain things are considerably simplified. The formulae have a constant term that is not speed related, eg the term 0.0085W + 0.255W/P in Cooper's low speed adaptation, and you can check this out by pulling existing bikes along at a steady walking pace in still air using a spring balance. For example, if the bike weighs 500lbf laden with an average tyre pressure of $30lbf/in^2$ then the formula predicts a force that is not speed related of (0.0085x500 + 0.255x500/3) = 8.5lbf (38N). This is a very small force but it can be interesting to experiment with, especially at lower pressures. Pulling along a bike with a flat tyre will increase your awareness! In reality this exercise is actually not as easy as it sounds and it takes some practice to get a steady situation where the bike is rolling at a constant speed rather than accelerating or slowing down. Given the general order of forces involved you might as well forget it.

The speed-related part of the formula is larger at very high speeds and has been assumed to be dependent on $(speed)^2$. This is extremely convenient. Aerodynamic drag is proportional to the square of speed and there are practical methods of finding the total force related to $(speed)^2$ on the assumption that the rolling resistance is constant. This means that provided you are happy to accept that the total drag data obtained at the test strip will include a rolling resistance component, and that this aspect is largely beyond your control apart from reducing weight, then you may never need to worry about this topic ever again!

Rolling power

If you have gone to the trouble of estimating the force required to overcome rolling resistance at various speeds, then it is useful to know the power involved. This will allow better estimates of the aerodynamic drag to be made from road tests. The formulae you require are given below. Again I would stress the need to use appropriate tyre data when finding the forces initially.

$$\text{Rolling power (kW)} = \frac{FV}{3600}$$

where F = resisting force in N
V = speed in km/hr

or

$$\text{Rolling power (bhp)} = \frac{FV}{375}$$

where F = resisting force in lbf
V = speed in miles/hr

Example. Use Kevin Cooper's expression to estimate the rolling resistance of a bike weighing 463lbf (laden) at 125miles/hr if the mean tyre pressure is 28lbf/in^2. How much power is required to overcome this?

125miles/hr = 183.4ft/s (Table 4.1)

Since the speed is above 150ft/s,

$$\text{Force (lbf)} = \left[\frac{0.255}{28} + \frac{5.1\text{x}183.4^2}{28\text{x}10^5}\right]463$$

$$= 32.6\text{lbf}$$

$$\text{Power} = \frac{32.6 \text{ x } 125}{375}$$

$$= 10.86\text{bhp}$$

Example. Use the metric version of Kevin Cooper's expression to estimate the rolling resistance of a bike weighing 200kgf (laden) at 270km/hr if the mean tyre pressure is 2.25kgf/cm^2. How much power is required to overcome this?

Since the speed is above 165km/hr,

$$\text{Force (N)} = \left[\frac{0.176}{2.25} + \frac{2.91\text{x}270^2}{2.25\text{x}10^5}\right]200$$

$$= 204\text{N (46lbf)}$$

$$\text{Power} = \frac{204 \text{ x } 270}{3600}$$

$$= 15.3\text{kW (20.5bhp)}$$

Finally, to save you too much working out of these values, Fig 4.7 provides some graphical examples of the forces involved at different speeds and weights when the mean tyre pressure is 2kgf/cm^2 (28.4lbf/in^2). These graphs probably represent the maximum rolling resistance at the weight concerned. You can see how the lower tyre pressure raises the figures compared to those running at high pressure but you are probably powerless to change this. Fig 4.7 includes the total resistance graphs for road bikes so that you can see the contribution made by the rolling component.

Note that the lower graphs (Imperial) are not a direct equivalent of the metric ones (see note in lower graph).

Useful references

(1) 'Tyre rolling resistance'. Seki, Sasaki, Tsunoda. Automobile Engineer, March 1969, p88-91.

(2) 'A wind tunnel investigation of the steady aerodynamic forces and moments on a partially streamlined motorcycle'. Kevin Cooper. Canadian National Aeronautical Establishment internal report LTR-LA-144, June 1973.

(3) 'Tyre rolling resistance'. Anon. Automotive Design Engineering, January 1967, p 44-49.

(4) 'The Aerodynamic Design of the Goldenrod to increase stability, traction and speed'. Walter Korff, The Korff Company, Burbank, California, U.S.A.

To convert	To	Multiply by
kgf	lbf	2.205
lbf	kgf	0.4536
N	lbf	0.2248
lbf	N	4.448
kgf/cm^2	lbf/in^2	14.22
miles/hr	ft/s	1.467
km/hr	ft/s	0.9113
Note. The kgf/cm^2 is not a preferred unit of pressure but it is the unit you will find on many gauges, hence its use in the example given.		

Above. Table 4.1 *Unit conversions for those who wish to experiment with the formulae given.*

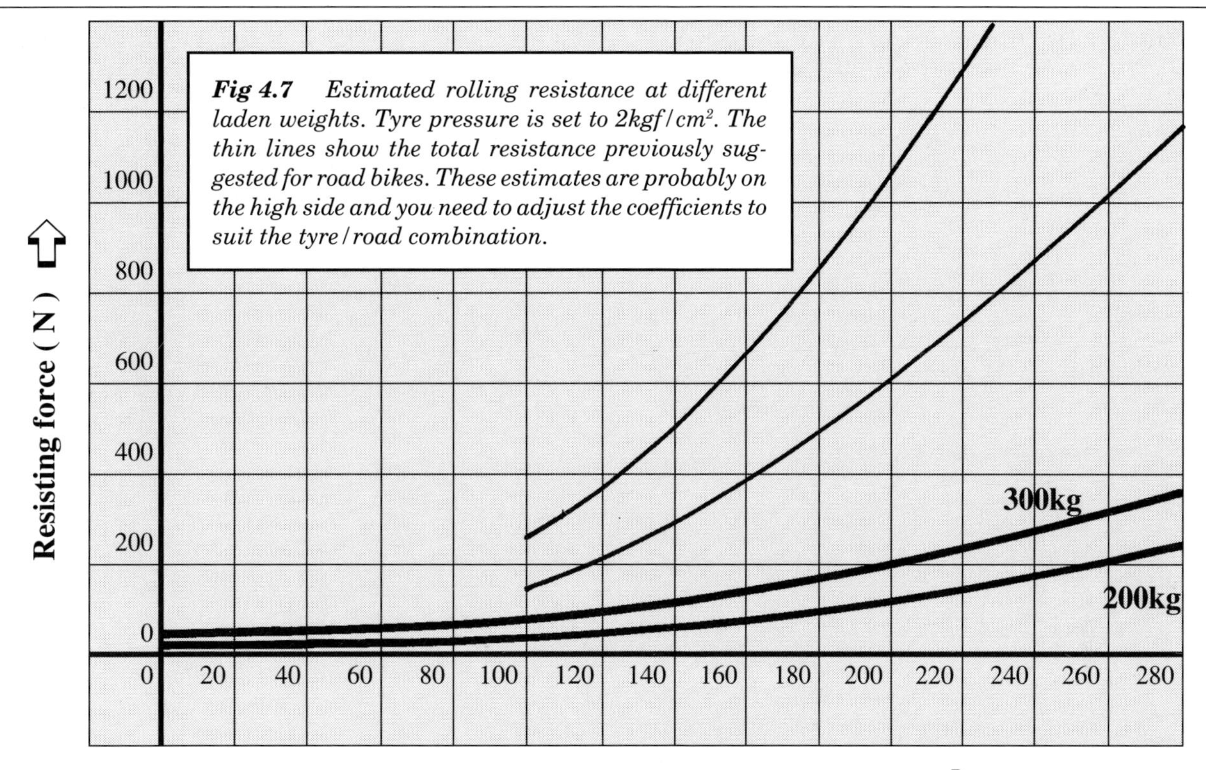

Fig 4.7 *Estimated rolling resistance at different laden weights. Tyre pressure is set to 2kgf/cm². The thin lines show the total resistance previously suggested for road bikes. These estimates are probably on the high side and you need to adjust the coefficients to suit the tyre/road combination.*

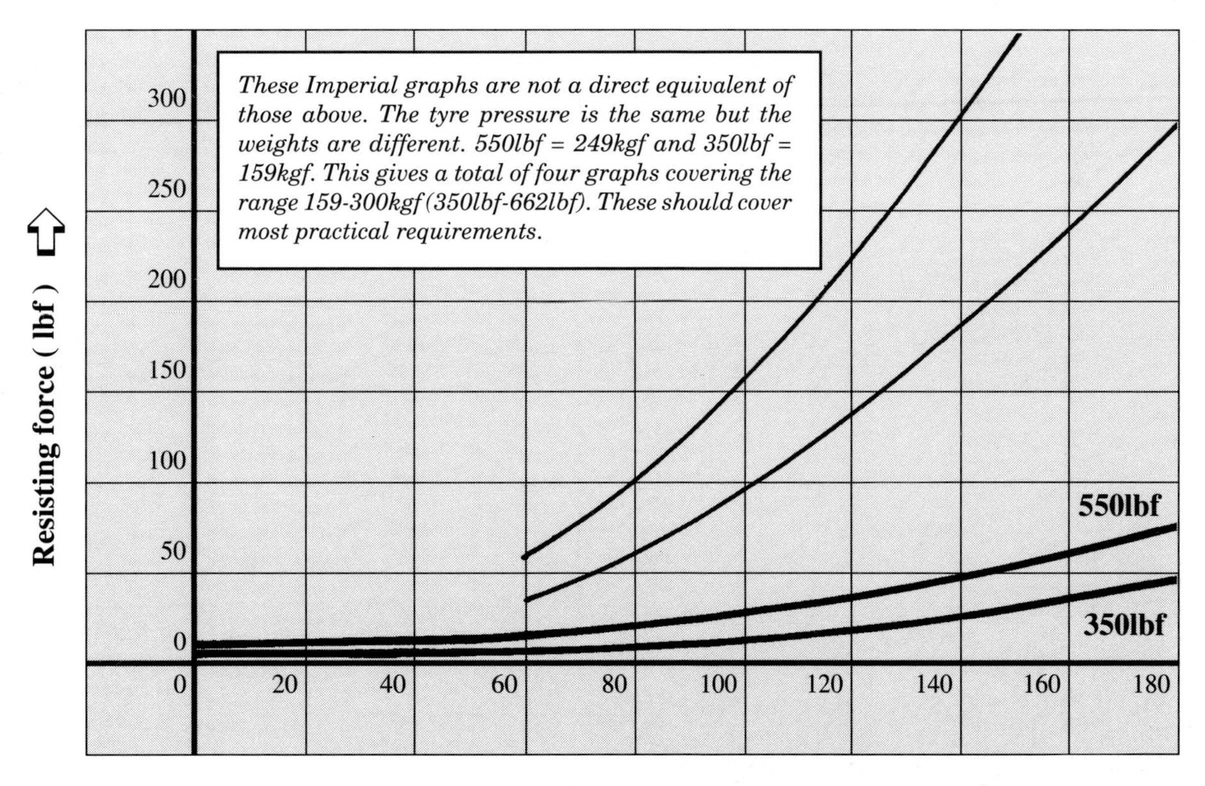

These Imperial graphs are not a direct equivalent of those above. The tyre pressure is the same but the weights are different. 550lbf = 249kgf and 350lbf = 159kgf. This gives a total of four graphs covering the range 159-300kgf (350lbf-662lbf). These should cover most practical requirements.

4.3 Origins of drag

Introduction

The resistance to motion experienced by a racing motorcycle is dominated by aerodynamic drag. Drag and weight are the major factors limiting performance and reducing either of them can bring significant improvements.

Weight is, in principle, easy to deal with, though in practice the reductions possible are limited by cost, strength and regulations. Pruning the last few grams off a motorcycle can be a very expensive process but this avenue must be pursued relentlessly. Reduced weight improves the acceleration of the bike from any road speed (see Section 6) though it only has a very minute effect on top speed which comes via reduced rolling resistance. Although no change in top speed is likely to be observed, you will get there in a shorter time.

Aerodynamic drag is a more complicated issue to deal with but the results of reducing it can be spectacular because it affects both acceleration and top speed. Reducing drag is not a substitute for reducing weight and reducing weight is not a substitute for reducing drag. You need to do both.

Aerodynamic drag is often said to affect only top speed. This is completely untrue and the influence on the acceleration of a racing motorcycle is particularly important because most of the acceleration takes place from high road speeds.

To illustrate this point I have included Tables 4.2 and 4.3. These results, together with many others in this section, have been provided by Kevin Cooper who is an aerodynamicist at the National Research Council in Ottawa, Canada. I am deeply indebted to Kevin for allowing me to reproduce these and other figures, all of which are the culmination of very expensive factory research programmes.

Some of the figures have been measured at the track, others are the result of extensive computer simulations that have been validated against numerous track tests. In each case only the aerodynamic design of the bike has been changed and all three configurations comply with the partially streamlined regulations, well almost!

The first set of examples in Table 4.2 gives acceleration times between certain speeds, together with figures for the maximum speed attained at Bonneville Salt Flats. In particular, note the times taken to accelerate from 113-145km/hr (70-90miles/hr) and 145-169km/hr (90-105miles/hr). Taking both ranges together, there is a saving of more than six seconds between the first and last configurations.

These figures are for a 125cc machine running in the last 50-70% of its speed range (see top speed figures). At similar speeds, more powerful machines would not show such a difference but once you get into the last 50-70% of their speed capability, the same sort of improvements appear and, the faster you go, the worse the drag problem will become.

Table 4.2 *Acceleration and top speed data obtained for three configurations of the same partially streamlined bike (source: K. R.Cooper, National Aeronautical Establishment, National Research Council of Canada).*

Configuration	Time(s) for stated speed interval						Top Speed	
	0 - 48	48 - 80	80 - 113	113 - 145	145 - 169	km/hr	km/hr	miles/hr
	0 - 30	30 - 50	50 - 70	70 - 90	90 - 105	miles/hr		
1	3.6	1.8	2.2	4.0	8.7	s	179.6	111.6
2	3.6	1.7	2.1	3.6	4.3	s	n/a	n/a
3	3.7	1.8	2.1	3.2	3.1	s	219.6	136.5

The second example, in Table 4.3, shows lap times at the Mosport road race circuit for the three configurations. Overall there is a one and a half second saving on each lap.

As a final indicator of the aerodynamic influence, you might consider the fact that for the first configuration in the tables to have achieved the speed of the last one using the original streamlining, its power output would have to be raised by 82%! This clearly represents an impossible achievement and shows how you should balance your time and effort between different areas. Aerodynamic drag is important and if these figures do not convince you then nothing will.

You might argue that this is all very well for aerodynamicists with factory bikes, budgets and wind tunnels, but not for you. True, there are many difficulties, but aerodynamics is a science and anyone can learn the basic principles. These can be applied and, even without a wind tunnel, improvements can usually be made, often quite dramatic ones. It all depends how bad the initial configuration is and, in aerodynamic terms, many motorcycles are pretty awful!

You can go a long way towards improving the aerodynamics without expensive test facilities. The main ingredients are time, enthusiasm and an appreciation of how the air behaves. For this reason, the chapter you are now reading is almost entirely theoretical. It only covers the most basic ideas but that is sufficient to make some practical progress in the next chapter.

Configuration	Lap Time (s)
1	80.3
2	79.5
3	78.8

Table 4.3 *Lap times at the Mosport circuit in Canada for the three different streamlining configurations. At the risk of stating the obvious, a saving of 1.5s per lap multiplied by ten laps is a very big saving considering it involves no extra power or riding ability!*

The air

Aerodynamics is concerned with the study of air and the way it interacts with other things, particularly moving objects such as motorcycles, cars and aeroplanes. Air itself is a mixture of gases, the main constituents being oxygen and nitrogen. Under normal circumstances the air is invisible and this makes it very difficult to appreciate what is happening when the air is disturbed by moving objects.

Because the air is invisible most people seem to adopt an unreasoned attitude to the way it behaves. We are very aware that pedalling a bike into a 30km/hr headwind is extremely hard work and yet when it comes to motorcycles the work involved, which is much greater, is somehow ignored because the engine does it! If you have this approach, it is essential that your 'out of sight out of mind' attitude is altered because the air is a most formidable adversary to performance even if you cannot see it.

Air is deceptive. It is much heavier than many people think. To estimate the weight of air we need to know its density (mass per unit volume) and, although this varies, a typical figure at sea level is 1.225kg/m^3(0.0766lb/ft^3). Using this figure, the air in a large workshop, say 5m x 4m x 3m, would weigh about 74kgf(162lbf) which is about the same weight as a light 125cc racer! The air in an average home probably weighs more than your road bike. It may be trivial, but it does help to make the point that air is certainly not weightless.

Anything with mass has inertia. To push it out of the way we have to accelerate it and that requires power, power which your engine must provide before it can even begin to accelerate you and the bike along the track.

Air also has a form of internal friction called viscosity. Most readers will be familiar with the general idea of viscosity, particularly in relation to oils, the more viscous ones being thicker and more resistant to flowing. The viscosity of air is much lower than that of oils and it also responds differently to temperature changes, cold air becoming less viscous. Since we cannot actually see it or feel it the viscosity of air also seems insignificant. Again this is incorrect.

Although the viscosity of air is indeed very small compared to that of liquids, it has a crucial effect on what happens to air that is close to the surface of the moving motorcycle and rider. This region is termed the boundary layer and its behaviour is controlled by the fact that the air is viscous. This in turn affects the pressure distribution around the bike, particularly to the rear of it, and it is the pressure distribution that is largely responsible for the forces that are generated. These are facts of life. We cannot render the air weightless or inviscid (no viscosity) so we have to understand the problems these properties create and seek to minimise them.

Aerodynamic forces

Once the motorcycle, or any other object, moves through the air, a force is created by the interaction of the two. The precise nature of the force depends on many things including the shape, size and orientation of the object as well as how fast it is moving. In some cases, moving objects can be shaped so that some part of the force generated can be used to our advantage. The obvious examples are aircraft wings which are designed to produce an element of lift and Formula 1 cars which are designed to produce an element of downforce as shown in Fig 4.8. Partially streamlined motorcycles are normally relatively neutral in terms of these vertical forces though some element of lift or downforce will generally exist.

Whatever the case, it is not possible to get something for nothing and a large proportion of the total force involved will always act in direct opposition to the direction of motion. This is what we call aerodynamic drag. For the wing, the total aerodynamic force generated is upwards and backwards while that on the F1 car is downwards and backwards.

Fig 4.8 *Vertical and horizontal components of aerodynamic force. The wing is deliberately shaped to create lift but the price is additional drag. The F1 car creates downforce (negative lift) but again extra drag is created. Even with no lift or downforce you still have drag!*

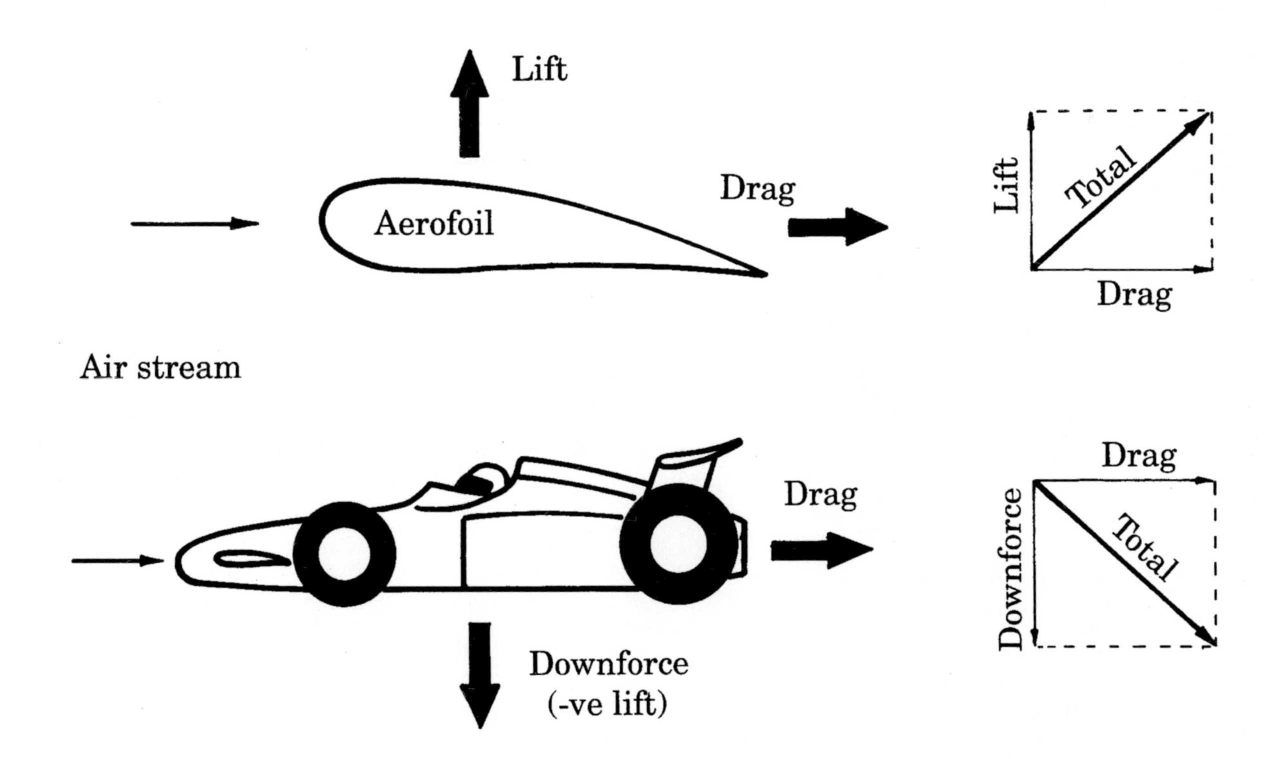

If the resultant of lift (positive or negative) and drag acts through the combined centre of gravity of the machine, then the force simply tries to push it in the appropriate direction. This is rarely the case. The point at which the total aerodynamic force can be considered to act is called the centre of pressure and it is most unlikely to coincide exactly with the centre of gravity. In this situation, the combination of lift and drag can also induce a pitching moment, ie when viewed from the side, the bike tries to rotate as well.

Next, we have to recognise that there are many conditions which will add an element of side force to what we already have. If the motorcycle is travelling in a straight line in still air, then the airflow is symetrical on either side of it and there is no sideforce but again this is rarely the case.

The most obvious cause of a side force is some element of side wind but when cornering the motorcycle can also present some side area to the direction of motion. Once a side force component exists it can combine with lift and drag to make things even worse. The bike can now roll or yaw as shown in Fig 4.9 if the centre of pressure does not coincide with the centre of gravity.

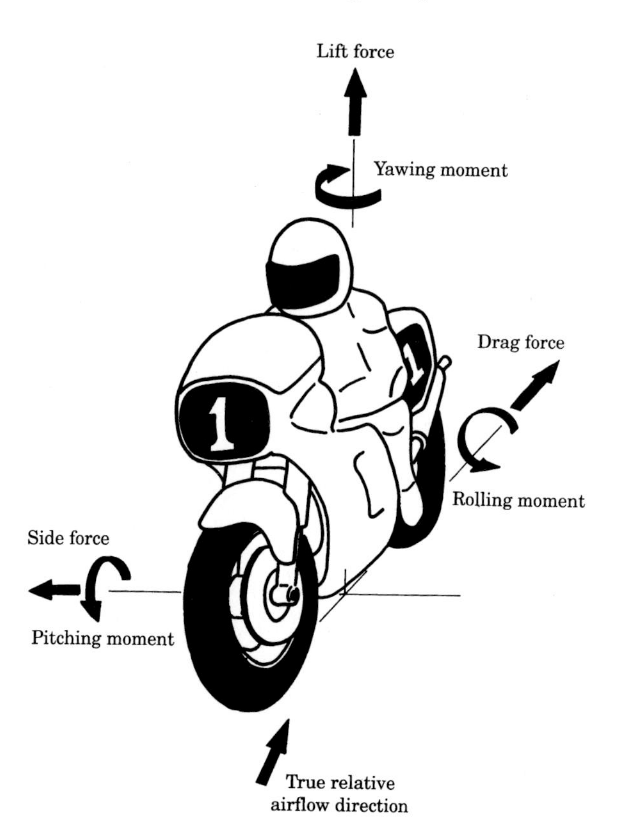

Dustbin fairings offered relatively low drag but they invited side forces like bees to honey. Because the fairings presented a large side area at the front of the bike the centre of pressure was invariably in front of the centre of gravity. This has a lot in common with negative trail on the steering, ie any problems tend to get worse. If the centre of pressure is behind the centre of gravity, then there is more straight line stability, though, as with trail, too much can be as bad as too little.

In general, full streamlining requires very careful design and is not suited to the gusting winds often encountered. It was banned in1957 after many riders had experienced severe high-speed handling problems though I don't think anyone actually died as a direct result. Despite these problems, the relatively low drag produced by the designs of this period is very evident.

- 1953 - NSU achieved 195km/hr (121miles/hr) from a fully streamlined 50cc bike producing only 9.7kW(13bhp).

- 1956 - The Moto Guzzi 250cc four stroke GP bike reached 227km/hr (140miles/hr) using just 30kW(40bhp). The V8 is reported to have reached 267km/hr (165miles/hr) on 60kW(80bhp).

These figures are a lot better than your latest superbike, a fact which is easily overlooked due to the manufacturers' recent obsession with power. Full streamlining is now restricted to outright record attempts.

All three components of the total aerodynamic force can be measured in a wind tunnel which of course you don't happen to have at the bottom of the garden - Fig 4.10. Fortunately, a lot of wind

Left. Fig 4.9 *Forces and turning effects that can occur due to aerodynamic loading. Drag is always present but everything else depends on shape and the direction of the airflow. The turning effects occur when the centre of pressure does not coincide with the centre of gravity.*

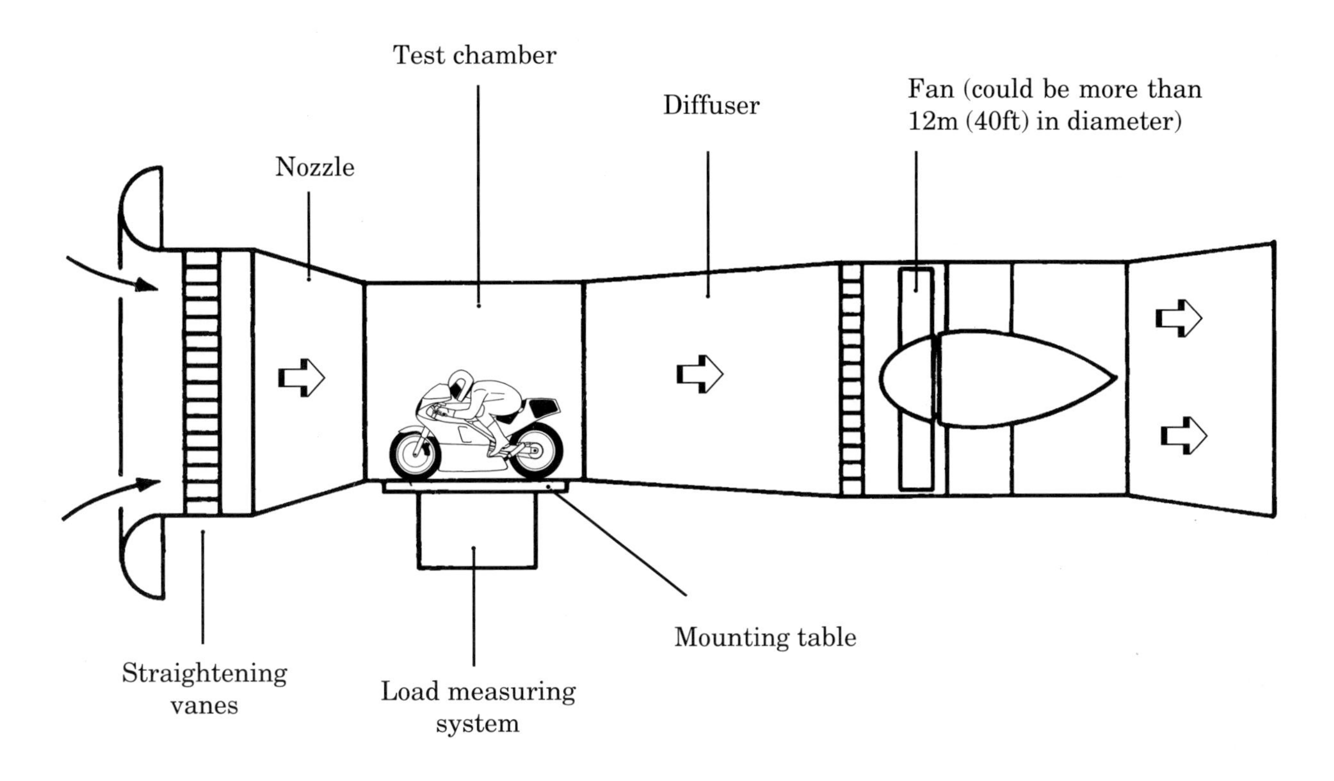

Fig 4.10 *The wind tunnel.*

Above. General layout. There are several variations on this theme, some of which have an 'open' test section to reduce the effect of the tunnel wall.

Right. Looking down the tunnel in the direction of airflow. The bike is on the load measuring platform, mounted on a turntable so that it can be set at an angle to the airflow to investigate the effect of side forces (photo K. R. Cooper, National Research Council of Canada).

tunnel data has been published and the force component most amenable to estimation, either theoretically or in track tests, is the drag. This is very convenient because from our point of view drag is the most important component since it directly opposes the motion of the bike.

This does not make other aerodynamic effects less important but the reasons are different. Firstly, everyone has a drag problem and always will have. You might, at some point, have a lift problem or a yaw problem etc but these are unfortunate instances rather than a guaranteed disaster. Problems like this can be very dangerous, possibly lethal, but the only way to sort them out is by experiment. If the finished bike shows any high-speed instability then it is always worth testing with no fairing and a simple flat plate seat. If the problem goes away then it is almost certainly aerodynamically induced and you will have to make changes. A useful test for lift is to fit a normal control cable to the moving fork leg so that the free end can be viewed when on the bike as shown in Fig 4.11. As you go faster, the acceleration reduces and the load on the front wheel should tend towards the static value as far as weight is concerned. If you find the forks continually extending at higher and higher speeds then you have a lift problem. In recent years some of the seats designed to give an element of downforce at the rear have only succeeded in providing lift at the front so you should investigate this as well as the fairing. Even small things like a road bike top box or handlebar fairing can produce quite dramatic problems that you have to sort out as best you can.

Fig 4.11 *A rod or control cable can be used to indicate the presence of lift at any speed provided the acceleration of the bike is negligible.*

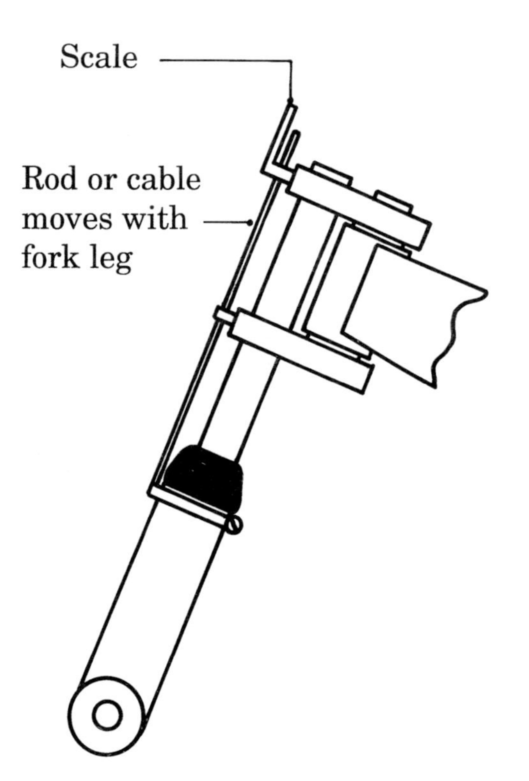

Pressure and force

Drag itself is a bit more approachable. The amount of experimental and theoretical data available in a readable form is vast. Even if a lot of it is mathematical you can usually get an idea of the important bits. Most of the data relates to aviation matters but the amount relating to vehicles in general is considerable.

The drag acting on a motorcycle and rider is produced by two different mechanisms, pressure changes and skin friction. Skin friction is a form of drag that is caused by the layer of air very close to the moving surfaces, ie the boundary layer. I will discuss it again later on but at this stage it is reasonable to say that skin friction represents a very small part of the total drag on a normal racing motorcycle. Fully streamlined bikes are different but for the standard partially streamlined case, most of the drag is due to pressure changes.

Pressure is defined as force per unit area. We live in a world that is at the bottom of a 'sea of air' and are thus exposed to the pressure generated by the weight of air above us. As you go higher there is less air above you and therefore the pressure is reduced. Because we have evolved in this environment, we only tend to notice changes in pressure and are unaware of its presence most of the time.

Pressure is not constant but we have to start somewhere and it is usual to assume that atmospheric pressure is close to 1.01bar (0.101N/mm^2, 14.7lbf/in^2) at sea level. Anything immersed in a fluid, as we are in air, experiences a force due to the pressure over its entire surface area. This force always acts normal to the surface but, since it is equal at both ends of the object, the net force trying to move the object along is zero as suggested in Fig 4.12.

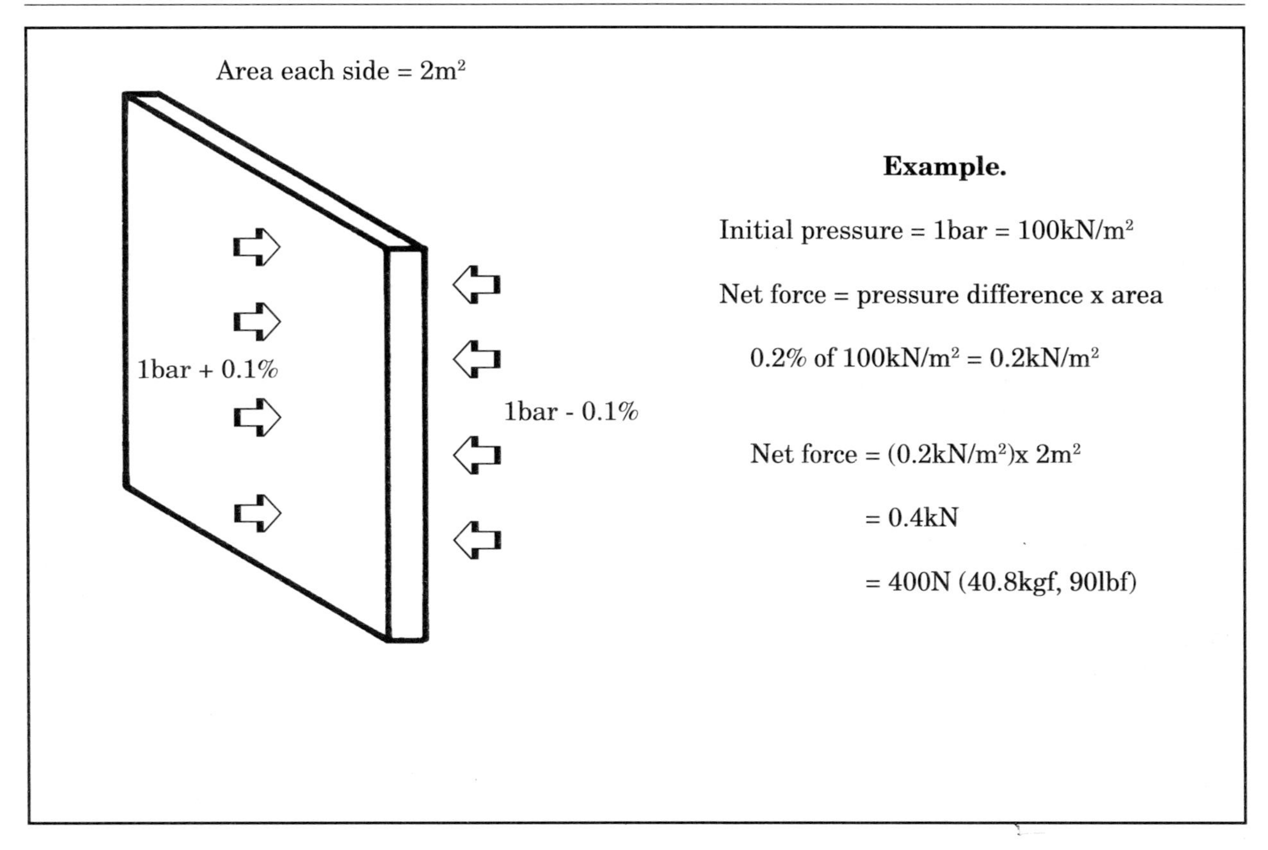

Below. Fig 4.12 *Air pressure produces a substantial force on large areas but if the pressure is equal at both ends of the object then the net thrust on the object will be zero. Any pressure difference will change this.*

Above. Fig 4.13 *Even small pressure differences can create large forces when they act over large areas. Most of the drag experienced by a motorcycle is caused by pressure rises at the front and, more importantly, pressure reductions at the rear.*

Air pressure acts on every surface

Net force zero

However, very small changes in pressure which act on only part of the surface area can generate suprisingly high forces that try to either accelerate or retard the object.

Fig 4.13 gives an example. The flat surface has an area of $2m^2$ on each side which is about that of a household door. The air pressure is initially 1bar all round. If it is somehow increased by 0.1% on one side and reduced by 0.1% on the other, then the force generated is 400N(40.8kgf, 90lbf) so you can see how important very small changes in pressure can be.

Also note that the force can be produced by a pressure rise on one side, a pressure drop on the other side, or a combination of the two. In the case of a moving motorcycle, more drag is created by reduced pressure behind it than by increased pressure in front of it. This is particularly important and goes against the common view that it is the front of objects that really matters.

Pressure changes

The drag force we are concerned with, and the pressure changes that produce it, are related to the relative speed of the air and object. This means that the problem can be studied either by moving the object through the air or by fixing the object and moving air past it. The latter method is much more convenient because objects can be mounted on load measuring fixtures and various tracers such as smoke can be studied as they move past the object. This is the general principle of the wind tunnel and because most of the results that follow come from wind tunnels, I will generally refer to moving air from now on. This is merely convenient and it simplifies certain things. In reality, it is of course the bike that will move.

The underlying principle behind the pressure changes is conservation of energy. A moving air particle has energy due to its velocity (termed kinetic energy), its pressure and the position it occupies. Changes in position produce a change in potential energy but, in the case of air, the changes in potential energy that would be experienced as the air negotiates any normal object are negligible. Thus as a first approximation,

Total energy	=	pressure energy	+ kinetic energy

Leaving the formal analysis aside (it can be found in any standard fluids textbook) we can obtain the following for a unit volume of air,

$$\text{Total energy} = p + 0.5\rho v^2$$

where p = pressure
ρ = air density
v = air velocity

This expression is one form of a common relationship known as Bernoulli's Theorem and the term $0.5\rho v^2$, which represents the kinetic energy, is often referred to as dynamic pressure (q).

The total energy is constant and therefore the pressure and velocity are linked. If the velocity rises then the kinetic energy increases and the pressure must fall. When the velocity reduces, so too does the kinetic energy and the pressure will therefore rise. To find out the 'normal' conditions we would have to consider the moving air stream when there is no object to negotiate. If the speed of the air stream is known then the kinetic energy , or 'dynamic pressure' term can be calculated. The normal or 'static' air pressure can be measured with a suitable barometer and the sum of the two figures gives the total energy per unit volume of air in the form of a 'total pressure'.

When an object is placed in the air stream the velocity of air particles in the vicinity of it will change. At some points the air is slowed down, indeed some of it is actually brought to rest. In this case the pressure at these points is above the static value. Other air particles will have to accelerate in order to pass around the object and, since their velocity is increased, the pressure in these areas will fall below the normal static value.

This is the fundamental mechanism by which the pressure changes occur, however the theory neglects the fact that the air has viscosity. Although the viscosity is small, it will have a crucial effect on air that is very close to the surface of the object and this will further modify the pressure distribution. Without viscosity, a shape such as a cylinder would show a symmetrical pressure variation that does not cause any drag. Viscosity ensures that all shapes produce drag!

Although I have discussed what happens in relation to a fixed object and moving air stream, the same result is achieved by an object moving in still air. The total energy can be determined from the atmospheric pressure at a point remote from the object and the velocity of the moving object. Where the air and object interact, the relative velocity of the two is modified and the aforementioned pressure changes appear.

Pressure differences produce forces and the simplest place to start investigating this is a point where the air is brought to rest. This is called a stagnation point and we can create one just to see what happens.

Fig 4.14 shows a device called a pitot-static tube placed in what is initially still air. The pressure on both sides of the pressure transducer is atmospheric and so no pressure difference is recorded when the air is still.

Once the air is moving, as in a wind tunnel, the pitot (pressure side) tube facing the air stream effectively 'captures' the air that enters it and brings it to rest. All of the kinetic energy is therefore converted into a pressure rise, hence the use of the term 'dynamic pressure'.

$$\text{dynamic pressure (q)} = 0.5\rho v^2$$

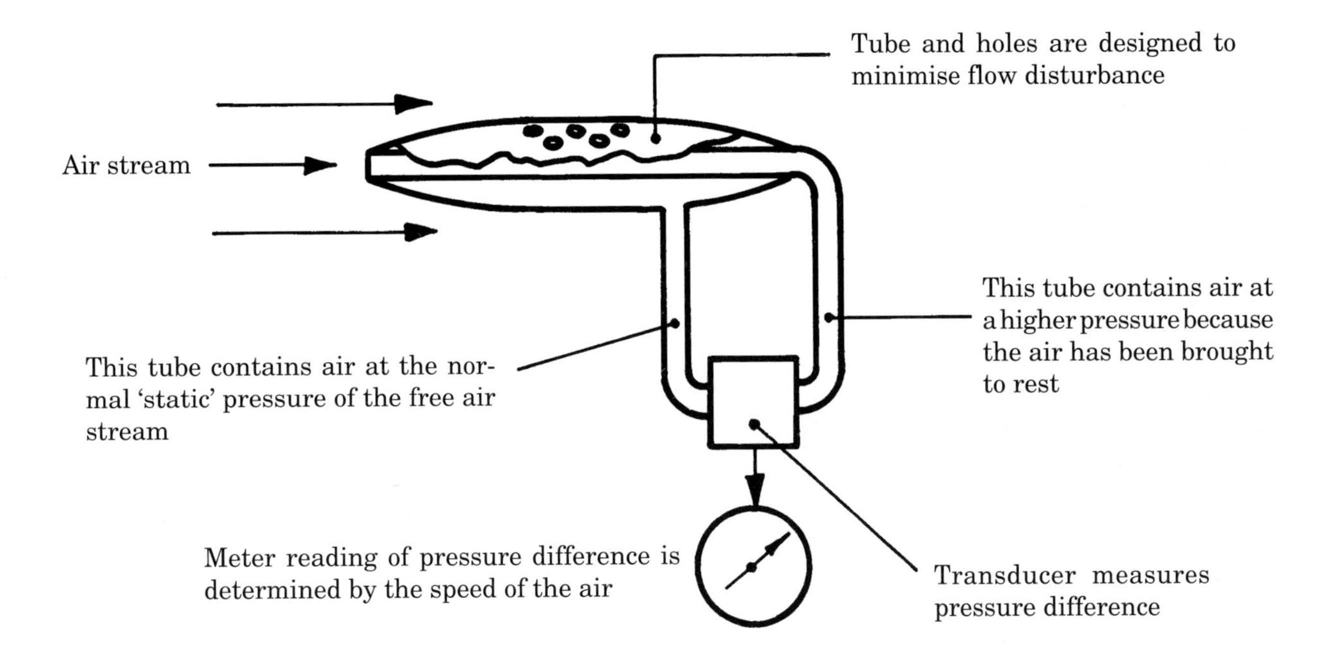

Fig 4.14 *The change in pressure caused by bringing air to rest can be measured using a pitot-static tube. When the air is still the meter reads zero but when the air is moving, the air brought to rest inside the tube creates a pressure that is higher than that in the free stream.*

As a result, the pressure in this tube is atmospheric pressure + dynamic pressure while that in the static tube is still just atmospheric. The difference recorded by this instrument is thus the dynamic pressure value and it can be used to indicate airspeed. Motorcycles do not normally have pitot tubes but the result is important because it allows us to measure the pressure rise that occurs when the air is brought to rest.

If the cross-sectional area of the pitot tube is A then the force acting on it, a drag force, is equal to pressure x area, ie $0.5\rho Av^2$. Density varies but to assist in comparing results it is usual to employ a density figure based on the International Standard Atmosphere. This standard gives a figure of $1.225 kg/m^3$ ($0.0765 lb/ft^3$) at sea level and we then obtain,

Force (N) = $0.0473Av^2$

where

A = projected area (m^2)
v = relative air velocity (km/hr)

or,

Force (lbf) = $0.0026Av^2$

where

A = projected area (ft^2)
v = relative air velocity (miles/hr)

These are the forces that would be produced if air was brought to rest over a flat area A. The formulae are of little use to you as they stand (hence they are not presented in the usual bold format), but later on you will see that the formulae used to predict the actual drag of the motorcycle and rider are almost the same. Unless it is specially contrived, as in the pitot tube, it is very difficult to bring air to rest over a flat area. If you simply placed a flat plate across the air stream then very little of the air will actually stop moving - Fig 4.15. Instead, most of the air is deflected and passes around the sides of the plate, assisted by the increased pressure where some of the air has been brought to rest. The path taken by individual air particles can be observed by using suitable tracers and streamlines can be drawn to indicate what the air is doing.

At this stage one might assume that the force produced by a flat plate is going to be less than when all the air is 'captured' but in fact it is about 20% greater. The problem does not lie at the front of the plate but at the back where the nice uniform flow suddenly breaks up into a chaotic motion characterised by swirling air movements known as vortices. In this region, called the wake, the pressure is below the normal atmospheric value associated with the free air stream and so the drag on the plate comes from both the pressure rise at the front and a pressure drop at the rear.

The wake is the region of air that 'buffets you' when a truck passes close by and it is clearly visible in the water behind a moving boat. More importantly, the wake is the so-called 'bubble of air' behind the bike in front that you have to enter in order to slipstream. The wake is a good indicator of drag. The smaller it is the lower the drag is likely to be and the more difficult it will be to ride in the slipstream of that motorcycle.

The flat plate is one extreme case but it can get worse as well as better. Fig 4.16 shows three examples. The cube at the top is actually worse than the flat plate, as is the cylinder below it. The large wakes are clearly visible in these flow visualisation shots. In the final example the wake is substantially less because this is a streamlined shape, ie one designed to produce low drag.

Although the maximum thickness of each section is the same, the drag force on the cube is more than sixty times that on the streamlined section! Think carefully about this. Although it is the same

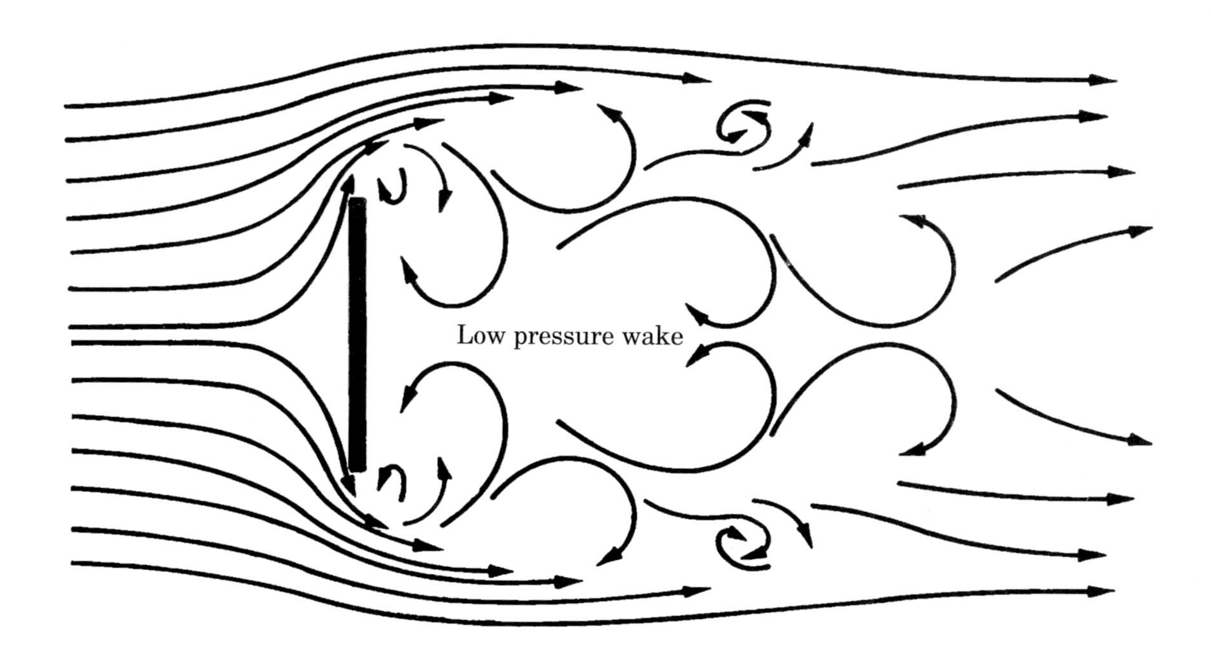

Fig 4.15 *When a flat plate is placed across the air stream, most of the air makes a good job of getting round it and does not come to rest. However once past the plate there is a void where the air flow is chaotic and the pressure is low. This low pressure acting on the area behind the plate, makes the drag higher than when all the air is brought to rest.*

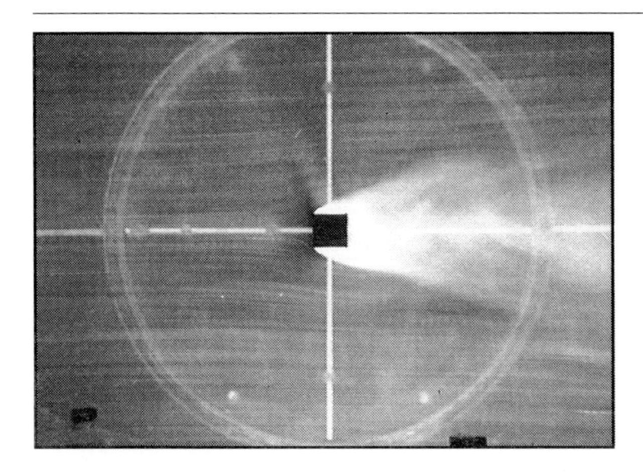

a) Flow past a cube.

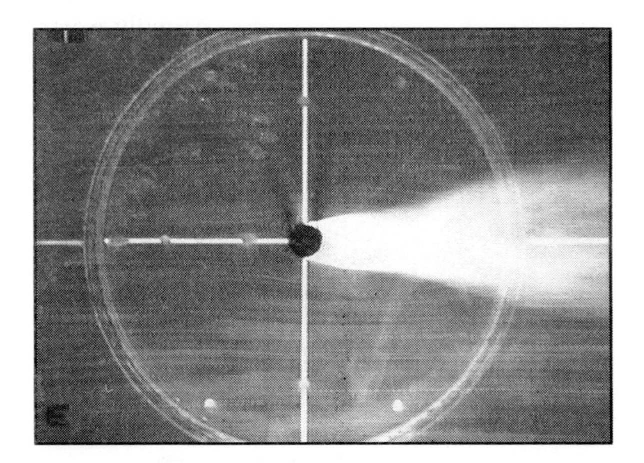

b) Flow past a cylinder.

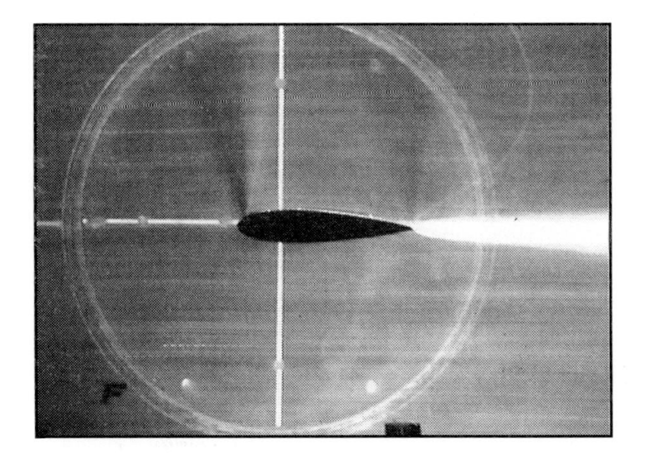

c) Flow past a streamlined section.

width, the streamlined section is clearly a larger object overall and yet the force required to move it through the air is minuscule compared to the other two shapes indicated. In this context, overall size is not the only factor.

It should be noted that even though one might produce a low drag shape, it will only generate low drag when the air meets it as intended. If the object meets the airflow at an angle (yaw or pitch) then the drag can rise dramatically. Fig 4.17 shows what happens when the streamlined shape from the last figure is presented at an angle to the airflow. The size of the wake clearly shows that this is no longer acting as a low drag shape.

There are two things we need to consider in relation to this. Firstly, why does this happen and what constitutes a low drag shape? Secondly, how can we estimate the drag that will occur for the shape we choose?

Left. Fig 4.16 *Flow visualisations showing the wake produced by three objects a) A cube, b) A cylinder and c) A streamlined section. Wake size is generally indicative of drag and the drag force acting on the cube is some sixty times that of the streamlined section when the widths are equal. Both size and shape are important (photographs by K.R.Cooper, National Research Council, Canada).*

Below. Fig 4.17 *Even a streamlined shape can produce a lot of drag if the air does not meet it at the intended angle. This example is a stalled aircraft wing. (K.R.Cooper, National Research Council, Canada).*

Boundary layer and pressure gradient

When the air and object meet at speed, the air tries to get out of the way. It actually receives a sort of warning that the object is approaching via pressure changes that radiate a long way in front of the object. Without this, the problems would be much greater. When objects move at the speed of sound, they are travelling as fast as the pressure waves can move out and so the warning is removed. Many nasty things occur, including a lot more drag! Fortunately, we are spared such problems and the flow past a rounded nose shape is generally like that shown in Fig 4.18.

In this diagram the lines with arrows on are called streamlines and they indicate the path taken by particles of air. Very little air actually comes to rest but any point where this happens is a stagnation point.

If these are true streamlines, as opposed to the pretty pictures often shown in the press, then they provide detailed information. Away from the object the streamlines are at a constant spacing. This tells us that the flow velocity is constant as is the pressure. When the gap between the streamlines alters we can deduce the following.

Diverging streamlines indicate falling air speed and rising static pressure.

Converging streamlines indicate rising airspeed and falling static pressure.

From this it is clear that the pressure is high in front of the object (as expected), but falls below the static value almost immediately the flow gets past the very front. This pressure drop can be very rapid and it has important implications as far as shape is concerned. At first it appears to be a good thing, since any reduced pressure at the front of an object should generate a force that acts in the direction of motion. Unfortunately, this assumes that the pressure behind the object remains unchanged and this is not the case.

As soon as the air has made contact with the object, some of it will attach itself to the surface and, by virtue of the friction present, will move along with the object. As such, the velocity of this air, relative to the object, is zero, while that only a few millimetres away may be very high. This creates a thin layer of air that does many peculiar things. It is called the boundary layer.

Fig 4.19 indicates some of the things that happen to the boundary layer and also the general form of pressure variation around the object shown. Note that the boundary layer has been enlarged for clarity and the pressure distribution is only for illustration. Minute changes in shape will yield very different pressure distributions but mine will suffice to convey the basic idea.

In front of the object the pressure is high but, as shown earlier, it falls rapidly as soon as the air begins to move past and a low pressure region is generated as the air negotiates the increasing cross-section. This is known as a 'favourable pressure gradient' because the air is moving against a reducing pressure.

The boundary layer has formed on the surface of the object and exhibits a quite orderly behaviour in which the air velocity varies from zero to the local 'free' value across the width of the bound-

Fig 4.18 *Streamlines showing the airflow at the front of a rounded object. True streamlines convey information about pressure and velocity changes, as discussed in the text.*

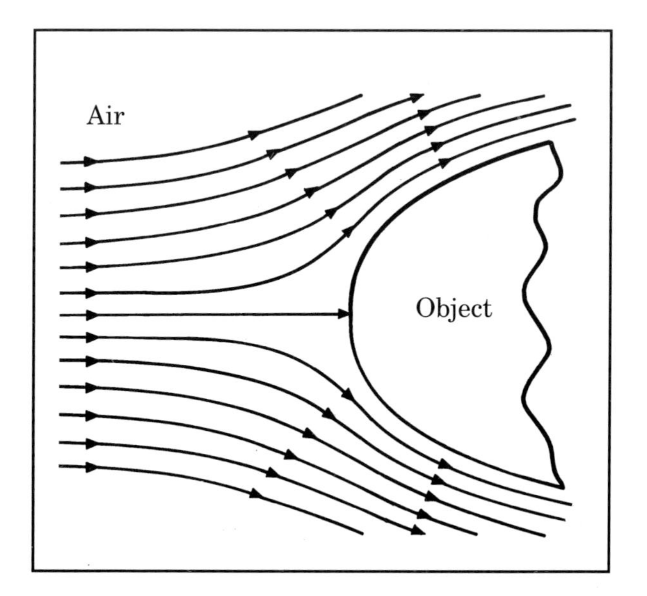

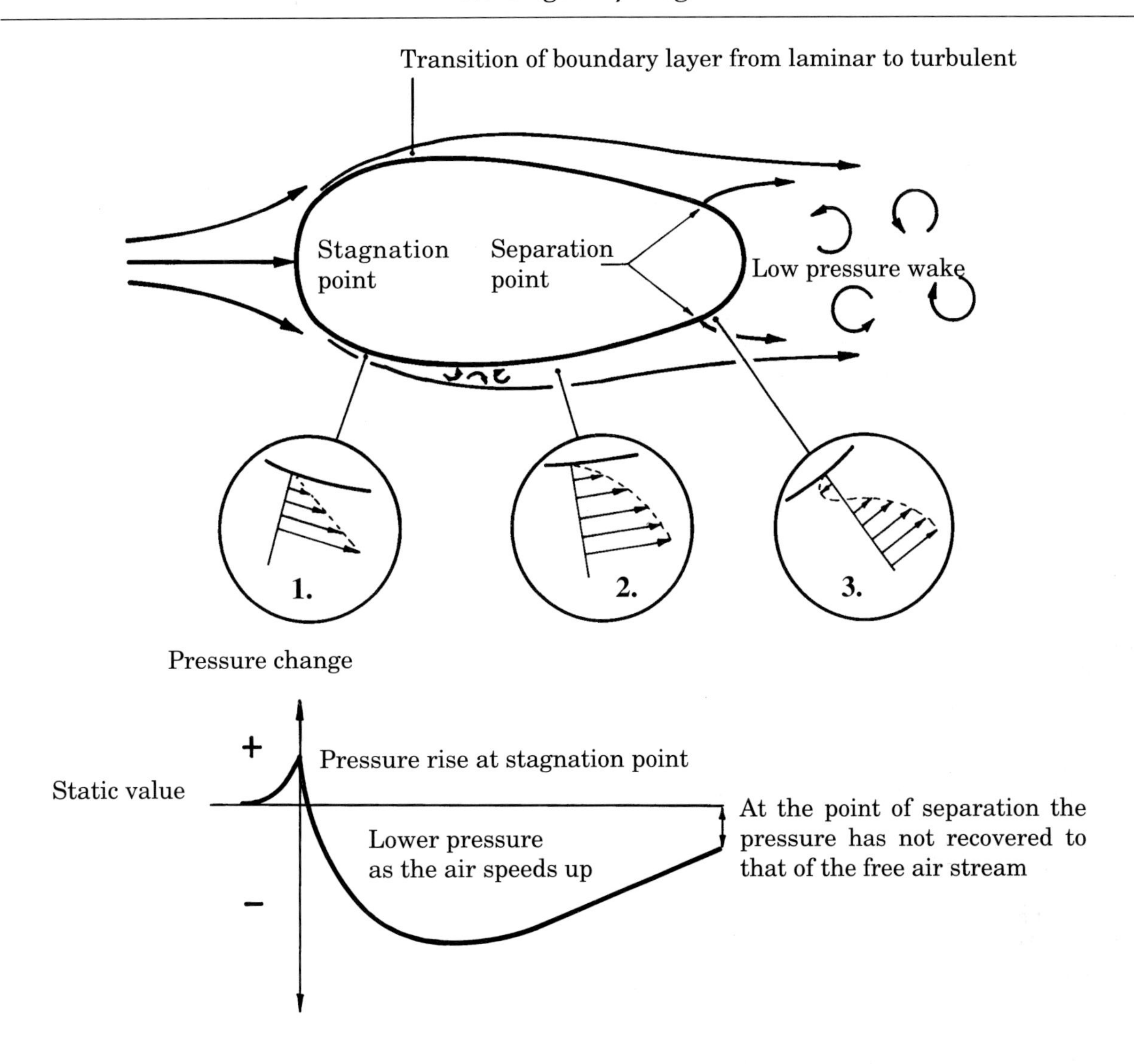

Fig 4.19 Development and final break up of the boundary layer, together with the general form of pressure variation. The drag is heavily influenced by the point of separation and the pressure that exists at this point. Base drag = base area x pressure at base and, for the sort of shapes we deal with, base drag is going to be the major element of total drag. Because of this, the trailing (rear) surfaces of components will be more important than the leading (front) surfaces.

ary layer - see enlargement 1 in Fig 4.19. The air shears like a pack of cards in order to accommodate this and the flow is said to be laminar.

However, the air is viscous, and that within the boundary layer tends to 'tire' as it shears. This soon produces a sort of wave motion within the boundary layer and it begins to get thicker. The flow within the boundary layer then becomes unstable, breaking up into a series of turbulent oscillations. Accordingly, the boundary layer is said to have passed through a transition point and the flow within it is now turbulent rather than laminar. The point where this occurs is determined by many things but the longer the layer has been in existence, the more likely it is to happen. Seemingly innocent things like flies, rivets, screw heads and panel joints can do the job once the layer is tired. Having a turbulent boundary layer is not entirely bad. It produces more skin friction than laminar flow but for our purposes this is not really a problem. The drag from skin friction is very small for a conventional motorcycle, relative to the drag produced by the pressure changes about to be discussed. Of course, if you start off with shapes that have low pressure drag, then the skin friction becomes very serious. It may constitute the bulk of the drag. Fully streamlined record breakers have this problem but we do not.

The good thing about the turbulent boundary layer is that it draws energy from the surrounding air and is much more active. This allows it to continue to form much further along the object and retaining this is our biggest problem. Also note that the variation in average flow velocity is no longer uniform - enlargement 2.

We must do everything to keep the boundary layer intact and prevent a complete breakaway of the air involved. Once this happens a wake has been created. The flow is very complicated in this region and within the boundary layer, flow reversal takes place - enlargement 3. The longer we can delay this, on an object of decreasing section, the smaller the wake will be.

The wake is characterised by a region of low pressure. You can see this from the pressure variation indicated in Fig 4.19. The pressure was recovering towards that of the undisturbed air stream but it is 'trapped' at a lower value by the separation. This lower pressure acts over the whole 'base area', ie the area of the object at the point of separation. The drag force due to this is (base pressure x base area) and this force 'sucks' the object back just as the increased pressure at the front 'pushes' the object back. Combined together, they produce virtually all the drag in our kind of applications.

Now that the basic idea has been covered, it is easy to explain why objects with pointed noses will produce reasonably high drag rather than low drag. Fig 4.20 shows a 'bullet like' shape and, because the area is continuously increasing, the air accelerates round it causing the pressure to fall well below the normal atmospheric value. This low pressure is present when the object suddenly ends so the large base area combines with a very low pressure to create a large amount of base drag. Shapes like this have no place on a motorcycle.

In order to minimise the drag we need to delay separation until the base area is very small. Once the point of maximum cross section has been reached, the air is starting to move against an adverse pressure gradient, ie as the cross-section reduces, the air slows down and the pressure is rising back towards the static value at a remote location. In this condition the boundary layer is extremely sensitive and is easily triggered into total separation. The area needs to contract very slowly to avoid this so, by implication, the object is going to be relatively long. Any attempt to ignore this and contract the area more rapidly will produce early separation, as will minor surface defects. If this happens, the pressure is still low, the base area is large and the drag is increased. We thus arrive at the basic form of streamlined shape shown in Fig 4.21. The general objective is to try and delay the separation as long as possible. To do this, the sides of such a section should not have an included angle of more than about 10 degrees at any point to the rear of maximum cross-section and the surface has to be free from defects.

The explanations I have given should be adequate to convey the general idea. It is tempting to adopt a more 'in depth' approach but this can be found in any formal aerodynamics text book along with the reasonable amount of mathematics that is necessary to convey the concepts more accurately. For the majority, the following summary will be adequate.

- Drag occurs due to pressure changes and skin friction. Pressure drag is the dominant part for a partially streamlined bike.

- The pressure changes because the air velocity changes. When the air accelerates around an object the local pressure will reduce. If the air slows down the pressure will increase.

- All changes are relative to the conditions in undisturbed air. If the air (or the motorcycle) is moving at 100km/hr and the atmospheric pressure is 1bar, then anything that forces the air to speed up will cause the pressure at that point to drop below 1bar. As the air slows down again towards 100km/hr, the pressure will rise back towards 1bar. If the air is slowed below 100km/hr, the pressure will rise above 1bar. The sum of the air pressure and the so called dynamic pressure ($q = 0.5\rho v^2$) remains constant.

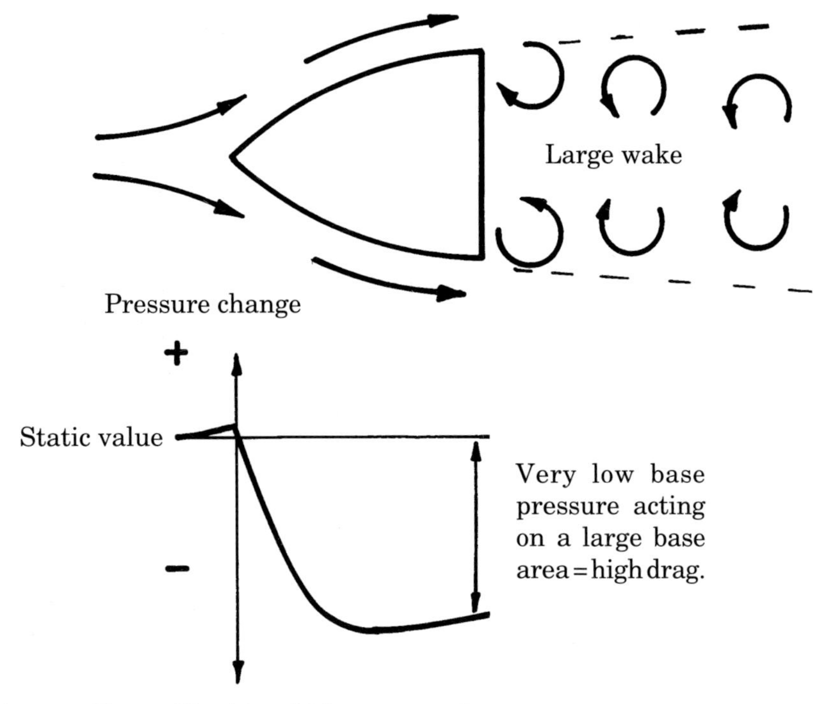

Above. Fig 4.20 *Shapes like this, which many people think of as having very low drag, do not. They suffer from high base drag because the pressure is still very low when the flow separates at the large base area.*

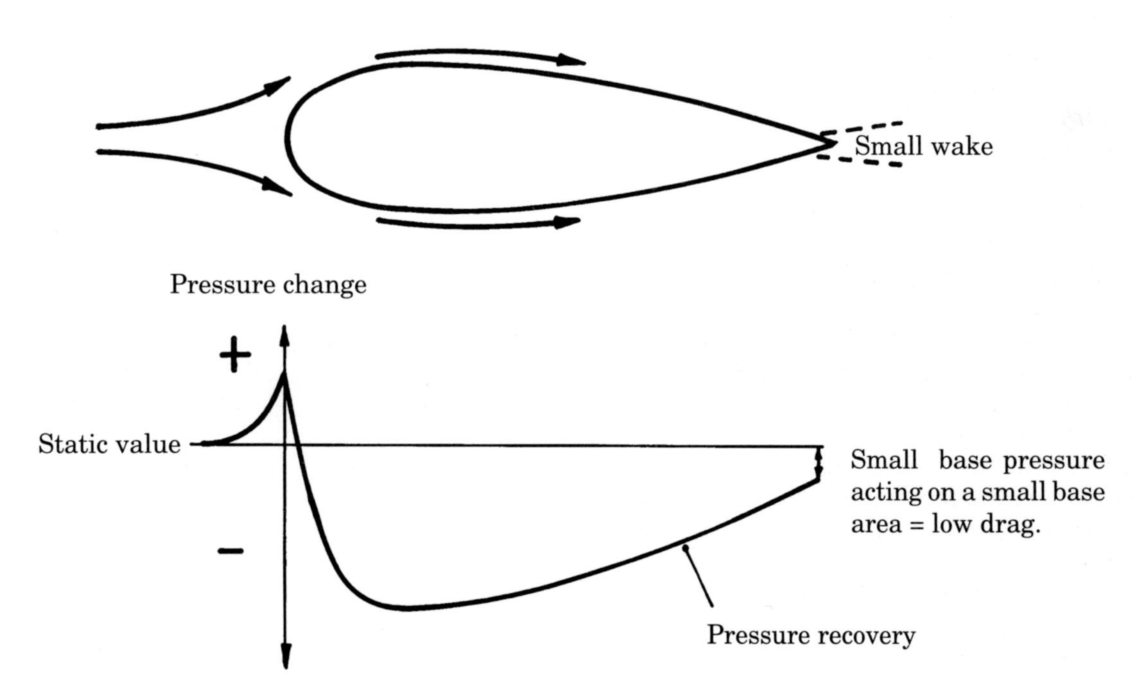

Fig 4.21 *A basic streamlined shape for low speed applications. The widest point is at about 25% of the length and the area reduces very slowly. Separation is delayed until the pressure has recovered to a higher value.*

- Some of the drag is generated by the increased pressure in front of the object but the greatest problem for a motorcycle is drag generated by low pressures at the rear. This is called base drag.

- To minimise base drag the flow must remain attached. It will only do this if the area reduction is very gradual and even then it needs a lot of encouragement to do so.

- Pointed shapes with large base areas generate much more drag than objects having moderately rounded fronts followed by slowly contracting sections.

- It is the the part of the motorcycle behind the fairing nose that is the major source of drag. Even if the whole motorcycle was a smooth surface this would still be a problem because there is insuffcient length available (on a normal roadracing machine) to contract the area gradually enough.

- In general, wake size is indicative of drag. A large wake implies high drag and vice versa. The wake produced by a motorcycle can be very large as you will see in the next chapter!

Nose shapes

As far as drag is concerned, the leading edge shape is not at all critical provided it is moderately rounded. This is fortunate because number plates are supposed to be virtually flat according to the regulations.

Fig 4.22 shows the effect of adding an increasingly large radius to a simple rectangular block. If we take the drag as 100% when there is no radius, then introducing the radius gives a dramatic change initially but this fails to continue. Once the radius has reached about 25% of the width, further increases give little gain. This shows up if we start with a well streamlined shape and square off the leading edge in a manner similar to the front of a fairing. For the specific section in Fig 4.23, the drag increased by 7%. It is not insignificant but we have much greater problems to face.

On a motorcycle, and most other vehicles, there is insufficient length to allow the desired shape to be achieved. It is tempting to contract the rear end more rapidly to suit the length but this is a disaster for the reasons already explained. Instead, we are faced with trying to delay separation by using a gradual reduction, but accepting the extra base area the short length will imply.

The consequences of this are also shown in Fig 4.23. Removing 14% of the length from the rear increases the drag by 47%! Removing 28% from the rear increases the original drag by 80%! If you still think that the front end is the most important, this should help to change your opinion of these matters.

As far as the motorcycle is concerned, it is not possible to create an ideal overall shape and we can only do our best with what we have. Other aspects of shape will be discussed in the next chapter but I think I have done enough to convey the general problem.

Top right. Fig 4.22 *Adding an increasingly large radius to a simple block gives a large reduction in drag initially but the reduction virtually ceases once the radius is about 25% of the block width.*

Bottom right. Fig 4.23 *The effect of departures from a well streamlined shape. a) Original shape, drag taken as 100%. b) Blunting the nose with moderate edge radii increases drag by 7%. b) Removing 14% of the length at the rear increases drag by 47%. c) Removing 28% of the length from the rear increases drag by 80%.*

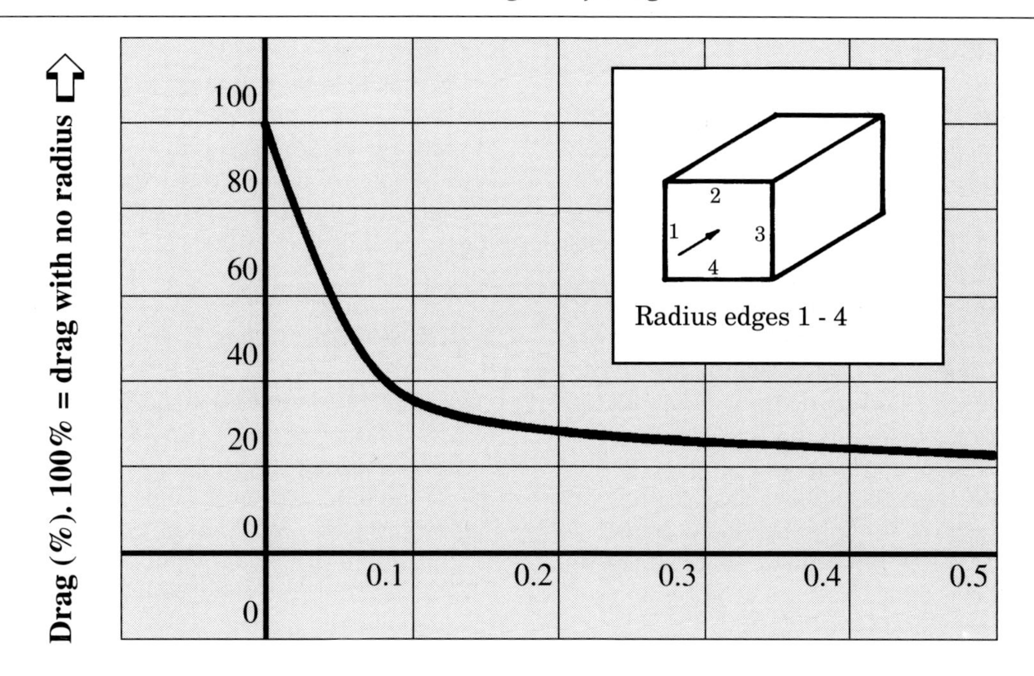
Drag (%). 100% = drag with no radius
100
80
60
40
20
0
0
0.1
0.2
0.3
0.4
0.5
Edge radius/block width
1
2
3
4
Radius edges 1 - 4

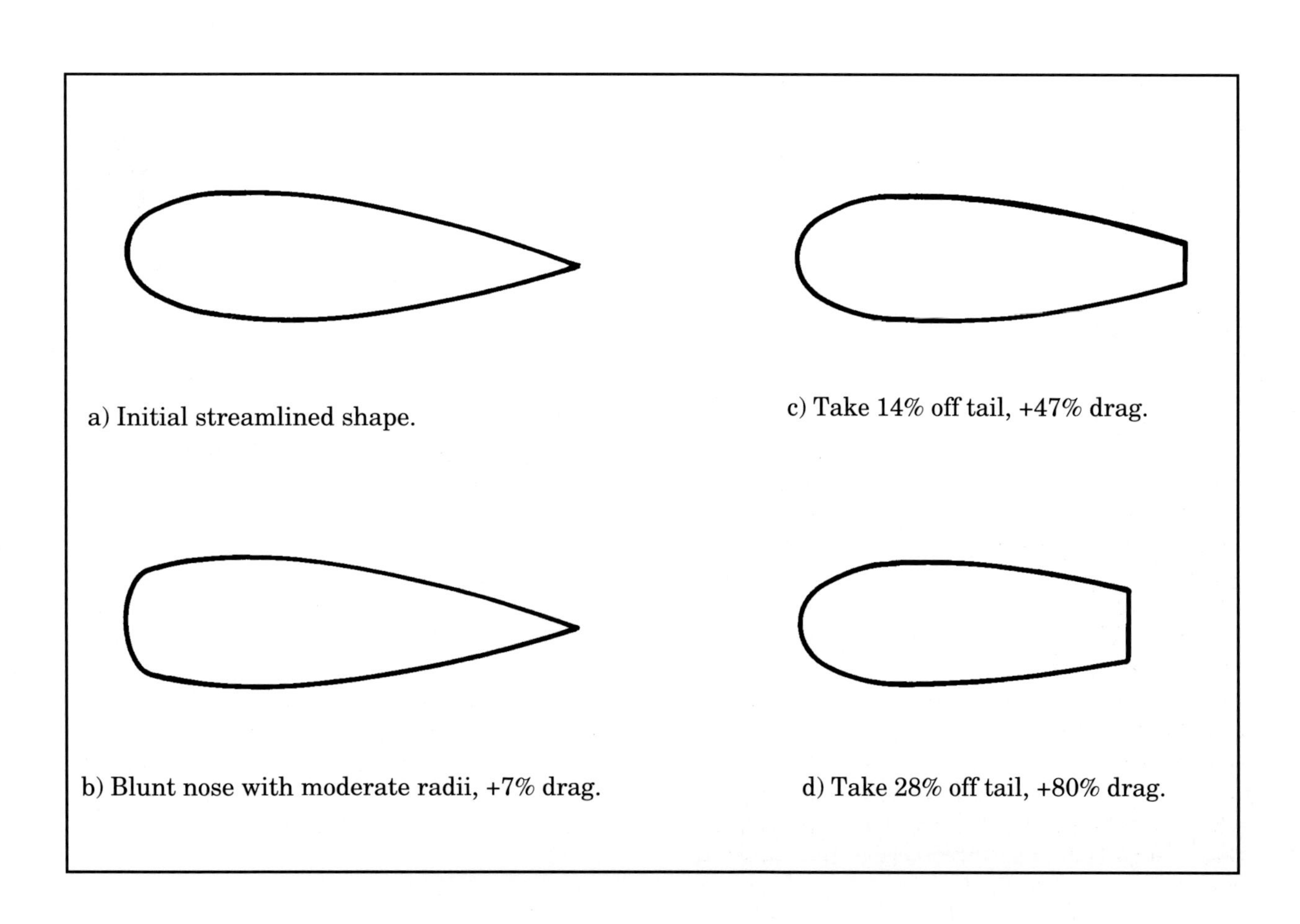
a) Initial streamlined shape.
c) Take 14% off tail, +47% drag.
b) Blunt nose with moderate radii, +7% drag.
d) Take 28% off tail, +80% drag.

Drag coefficient(C_d)

Earlier on I gave the formulae necessary to calculate drag force when the air was brought to rest. We have seen that this is not generally the case and have to contend with the effects of different shapes. This is done by introducing a figure called the drag coefficient into the formulae.

A drag coefficient gives the ratio of the drag force on the object to that which would be produced if the same airflow could be brought to rest on a flat plate of equal area. As such it allows objects of different shape and size, moving at different speeds, to be compared.

For example, if an object has a drag coefficient of 1.0 then whatever it might look like it behaves like a 'theoretical' flat plate and would produce the same drag force under the same conditions (projected area, speed and type of fluid).

The 'real' flat plate, where air flows around the edges and a wake is produced at the rear, has $C_d = 1.2$ while for the cube $C_d = 1.5$. For an unfaired motorcycle with the rider sitting normally a figure of $C_d = 0.7 - 0.75$ is reasonable. If the rider adopts a prone position this might fall to $C_d = 0.6$. This sounds quite reasonable until one realises that a housebrick with moderately rounded edges will probably do as well!

Suitably streamlined, the range of possibilities is very wide. At one extreme, a fully streamlined world record breaker might achieve $C_d = 0.07 - 0.1$ while a poorly streamlined roadracer could have as much drag as the unfaired motorcycle. Indeed it is quite possible that the drag coefficient with the so called streamling is higher than without! This is certainly true of many road fairings that are primarily designed to provide protection from the elements.

Unless considerable aerodynamic work has been done, the majority of roadracers probably occupy the range $C_d = 0.45 - 0.6$. Figures below 0.3 can be achieved within the roadrace regulations and if you started at 0.6 this represents a 100% improvement. Table 4.4 gives some general examples. Incorporating the drag coefficient into the previous formulae we obtain the expressions on the right. You can use these formulae to estimate the drag force on the motorcycle and rider, assuming that you know the required values.

I have already outlined some of the factors which will determine the drag coefficient though the term had not been introduced at that stage. It is useful to look at the other terms in the formulae as well because they are easier to deal with. It is also necessary to consider the power involved in overcoming these forces since this is always a shock if you are not already aware of it.

There are two other variables involved, relative velocity and projected area.

Relative velocity(v)

If the bike travels in a straight line in still air the relative velocity of the air and motorcycle is simply the road speed of the bike. Any wind will alter this. If the bike travels at 200km/hr directly into a 20km/hr headwind then the relative velocity is 220km/hr. The drag force would be that calculated using 220km/hr even though the bike is not going this fast. For the purpose of making comparisons it is usual to ignore this. When the wind does blow then everyone will experience more drag but the bike with the lowest drag coefficient will suffer the least. The most depressing aspect is the dependence on v^2. This is what causes the drag to rise increasingly rapidly with speed but it is a fact of life that cannot be altered. Attention has to be focussed on the projected area and drag coefficient.

Projected area(A)

Normal drag estimates are based on projected area, ie the cross-sectional area you would see in a head-on view - Fig 4.24. The drag force is directly proportional to this area so its reduction is a top priority. If you halve this area then you will halve the drag force at all road speeds provided your area reduction has not caused the drag coefficient to increase.

In some instances, attempts to reduce the area will raise the drag coefficient. Equally, it may be valid to increase the area with a view to reducing the drag coefficient by a proportionally greater amount. This will happen if the new shape is considerably better and many designs can benefit from this approach.

What really matters is the product of drag coefficient and projected area, ie C_dA. This is called the drag area. Lower the drag area and the drag force will drop. Increase it and the drag force will rise.

Drag force (N) = $0.0473C_dAV^2$

where

C_d = drag coefficient
A = projected area(m^2)
V = relative velocity(km/hr)

or

Drag force (lbf) = $0.0026C_dAV^2$

where

C_d = drag coefficient
A = projected area(ft^2)
V = relative velocity(miles/hr)

Vehicle	Drag coefficient	
	High	Low
Lorry	1.0	0.7
Bus	0.85	0.35
Unfaired motorcycle	0.9	0.65
Racing motorcycle	0.7	0.28
Delivery van	0.6	0.4
Modern car	0.5	0.28
Passenger train	0.4	0.3
Optimal 'clean' car	0.2	0.16
Goldenrod record car	0.1165	
Low drag wing section	0.06	0.03

Top right. Table 4.4 *Examples of vehicle drag coefficients. Compared to most other vehicles, the drag coefficient of a motorcycle is relatively high and performance owes a great deal to the substantial power to weight ratios that are obtainable. Nevertheless, the difference between motorcycles with good and bad aerodynamics is vast, especially at high speeds. Note that the low drag wing section is set for minimal drag, ie at zero angle of attack.*

Bottom right. Fig 4.24 *To determine the projected area, photograph the bike head on as shown and then follow the example given overleaf. The rider should be in a normal prone position and wearing normal riding gear.*

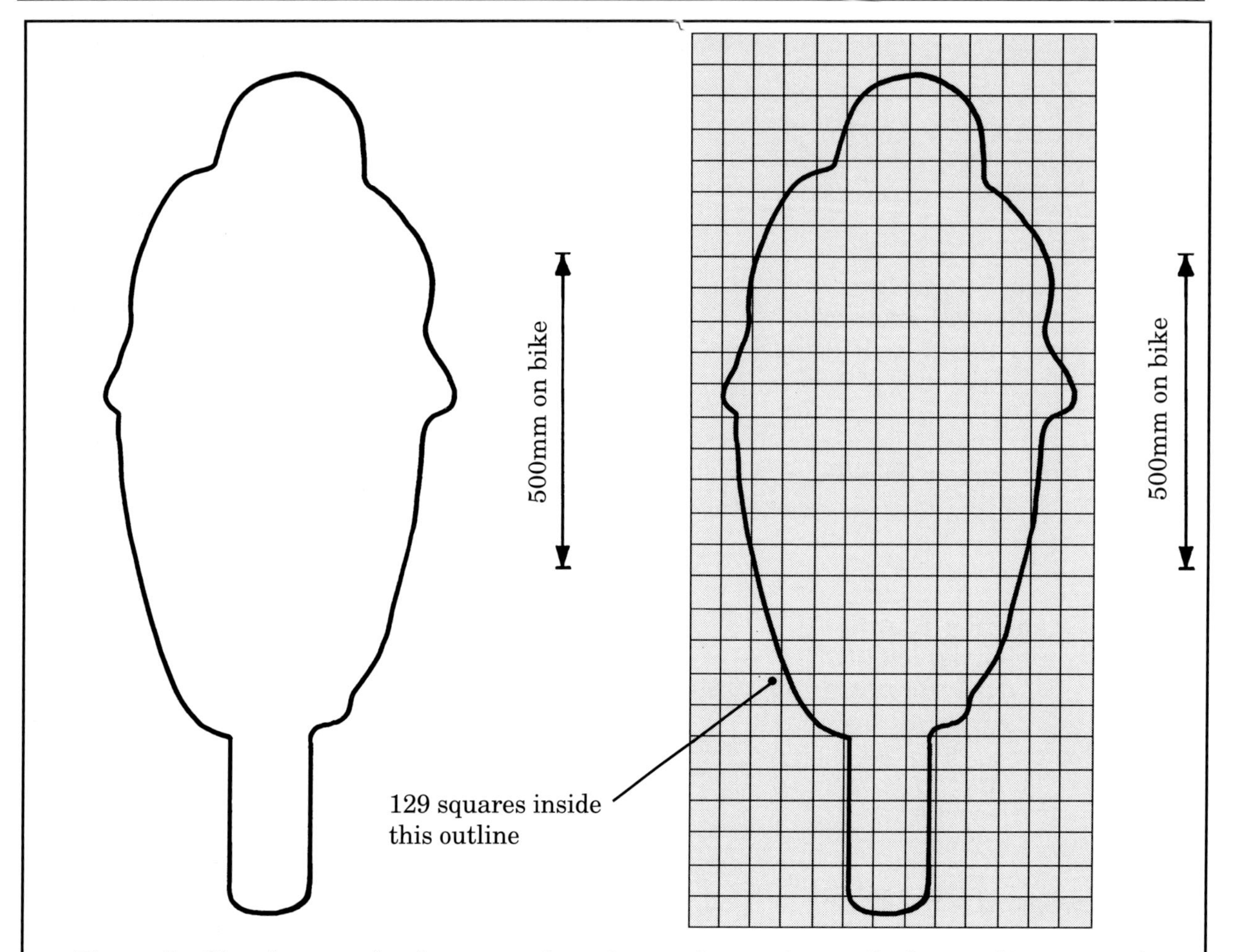

Example. The photograph taken was enlarged on a photocopier until a known dimension of 500mm on the bike became 100mm on the paper. The outline was then drawn in as shown above (left). The outline was placed on a grid of squares, each square being 10mm high and 10mm wide (above right). The number of squares was counted and found to be 129. Use common sense for incomplete squares, adding bits from different edges of the outline.

Each paper square has an area of 10mm x 10mm = 100mm^2.

There are 129 squares so the area of paper within the outline is 129 x 100 = 12900mm^2.

Every 100mm of paper is 500mm of bike, ie 1mm of paper corresponds to 5mm of bike. An area of 1mm^2 on paper is therefore an area of 5mm x 5mm = 25mm^2 on the bike.

The actual bike area is thus 12900 x 25 = 322500mm^2.

There are 1 000 000mm^2 in 1m^2 so the bike area is 322500/1 000 000 = 0.325m^2 (3.47ft^2).

The method is the same in Imperial units. eg, you might make 20in of bike equal to 4in of paper and use a 0.5in grid. The area scale is therefore 1in^2 paper = 25in^2 of bike. In this case, an area of say 80 squares would be 80 x 0.5 x 0.5 = 20in^2 of paper and that is equivalent to 20 x 25 = 500in^2 of bike, which is 500/144 = 3.47ft^2.

When a bike is being designed the projected area can be estimated, but as soon as it exists, even partially, the best method of obtaining the area is to photograph the bike and rider as shown previously in Fig 4.24 and use the method illustrated in Fig 4.25. The method is as follows.

- Take a suitable photograph. Ideally, the bike should sit in its normal laden position so a special stand may be needed to support it in this way. Adopt a normal crouched riding position. You must either include a suitable size reference in the photograph or measure some key dimension that can be seen in the photograph, eg from the ground to the tip of the handlebar.

- Enlarge the print on a photocopier until the size reference becomes a convenient value on the print. For example, if you know that the distance from the front wheel spindle to the ground is 300mm then enlarge the print until this becomes a round figure like 50mm on the copy. The scale of the copy is then 6mm of bike per mm of copy.

- Draw round the projected area.

- Draw a suitable grid over the copy or use a standard transparent grid from art shops.

- Count the total number of squares covering the area.

- Convert the count to area as shown in the example.

Left. Fig 4.25 *Estimating the projected area from a suitable photograph.*

Because it is often difficult or inconvenient to measure the projected area of something like a motorcycle, it is common practice in wind tunnel tests not to attempt to separate out the influence of drag coefficient and projected area but to keep them together in the form of 'drag area'.

Drag area (C_dA)

Drag area is the projected area multiplied by the drag coefficient, ie C_dA. Because the drag coefficient has no units, drag area has the same units as the projected area and it is easy to confuse the two. Drag area is easily determined from measurements of drag force and air speed so results are often published in this form.

For example, the drag area of an older Suzuki GSX-R750 road bike was published as 0.410m^2 (4.4ft^2) with the rider prone while that of a 1984 Honda RS500 racer was quoted as 0.243m^2(2.62ft^2). It is clear that the road bike has almost 70% more drag at a given speed than the racer but there is no indication as to whether this is due to a small projected area or a low drag coefficient. Common sense says it is a combination of both. I will discuss typical drag areas in the next chapter but the current (1995) style of superbike has a typical drag area of around 0.325m^2 (3.5ft^2).

Drag power

In addition to estimating drag force we can also estimate the net power required to overcome it and the figures may help to focus the mind on how dramatic the effects of drag are. They will also allow some drag estimates to be made using existing bikes. The formulae given on the right are only true in still air. If you wish to account for wind then any wind velocity (V_w) will only affect the original V^2 term giving,

$$\text{Drag power} = \text{constant} \times C_d A(V + V_w)^2 V.$$

The formulae now have a V^3 term. This means that if you double the road speed the power required to overcome drag will increase eightfold! This is why massive increases in power do not equate to large increases in top speed. Unless you can lower the drag coefficient as well, the extra driving force is simply swamped by the ever increasing drag force at higher speeds. You only have to look at the top speed of bikes and the power they produce to see what is happening. The following examples should reinforce this.

$$\textbf{Drag power (kW)} = \frac{C_d A V^3}{76173}$$

where C_d **= drag coefficient**
A **= projected area in m²**
V **= roadspeed in km/hr**

or

$$\textbf{Drag power (bhp)} = \frac{C_d A V^3}{146806}$$

where C_d **= drag coefficient**
A **= projected area in ft²**
V **= roadspeed in miles/hr**

Example. A bike has a projected area of 0.5m^2 and an estimated drag coefficient of 0.4 with the rider prone. What is the drag force at 150km/hr and how much power is required to overcome this?

Using,

$$\text{Drag force (N)} = 0.0473 C_d A V^2$$

$$\text{Drag force (N)} = 0.0473 \times 0.4 \times 0.5 \times 150^2$$

$$= 212.9\text{N}$$

Using,

$$\text{Drag power (kW)} = \frac{C_d A V^3}{76173}$$

$$\text{Drag power (kW)} = \frac{0.4 \times 0.5 \times 150^3}{76173}$$

$$= 8.86\text{kW}$$

Example. A bike has a projected area of 4.5ft^2 and an estimated drag coefficient of 0.6 with the rider prone. What is the drag force at 130miles/hr and how much power is required to overcome this?

Using,

$$\text{Drag force (lbf)} = 0.0026 C_d A V^2$$

$$\text{Drag force (lbf)} = 0.0026 \times 0.6 \times 4.5 \times 130^2$$

$$= 118.6\text{lbf}$$

Using,

$$\text{Drag power (bhp)} = \frac{C_d A V^3}{146806}$$

$$\text{Drag power (bhp)} = \frac{0.6 \times 4.5 \times 130^3}{146806}$$

$$= 40.4\text{bhp}$$

Example. A bike and rider has a projected area of $0.7m^2$ and $C_d = 0.6$. Development reduces the area to $0.6m^2$ and C_d to 0.4. How much is the power required to achieve 160km/hr reduced by?

Using,

$$\text{Drag power (kW)} = \frac{C_d A V^3}{76173}$$

For the first case,

$$\text{Drag power (kW)} = \frac{0.6 \text{x} 0.7 \text{x} 160^3}{76173}$$

$$= 22.58\text{kW}$$

In the second case,

$$\text{Drag power (kW)} = \frac{0.4 \text{x} 0.6 \text{x} 160^3}{76173}$$

$$= 12.9\text{kW}$$

Thus the saving is 22.58kW - 12.9kW

$$= 9.68\text{kW}$$

Example. If a bike has a drag area of $3ft^2$ how much power is required to overcome drag at a) 100miles/hr, b) 160miles/hr?

The drag area is $C_d A$ so for a),

$$\text{Drag power (bhp)} = \frac{3 \text{x} 100^3}{146806}$$

$$= 20.44\text{bhp}$$

For case b)

$$\text{Drag power (bhp)} = \frac{3 \text{x} 160^3}{146806}$$

$$= 83.7\text{bhp}$$

It is frequently useful to plot the drag force as a graph against road speed and this becomes rather tedious if you do not have a programmable calculator or a computer. To assist you I have compiled Figs 4.26 and 4.27 overleaf. These graphs, one in metric units and the other in imperial, give drag force vs road speed for a whole range of drag areas. You can read values directly from these graphs to suit virtually all applications and the captions give examples. Other useful data relating power and performance is given in the next chapter.

Reynold's Number (R_e)

Finally, a very brief discussion of a value called Reynold's Number may be useful. This term crops up in virtually every aerodynamics text and, although it is unlikely to influence what you do, some understanding can make things clearer.

Fluid flow is very complex. It is influenced by many different factors and situations which might at first seem similar may not be. To help categorise the type of flow involved, engineers have devised a number of different ratios that are extremely significant in the sense that they allow you to categorise the situation.

Reynold's number is one such ratio. The value effectively indicates the ratio of inertia forces to viscous forces and it is calculated from,

$$\text{Re} = \frac{\text{relative velocity x characteristic length}}{\text{kinematic viscosity}}$$

For air, and a relative velocity equal to road speed we obtain,

Re = 19026LV

where L = characteristic length (m)
V = road speed (km/hr)

or

Re = 9342LV

where L = characteristic length (ft)
V = road speed (miles/hr)

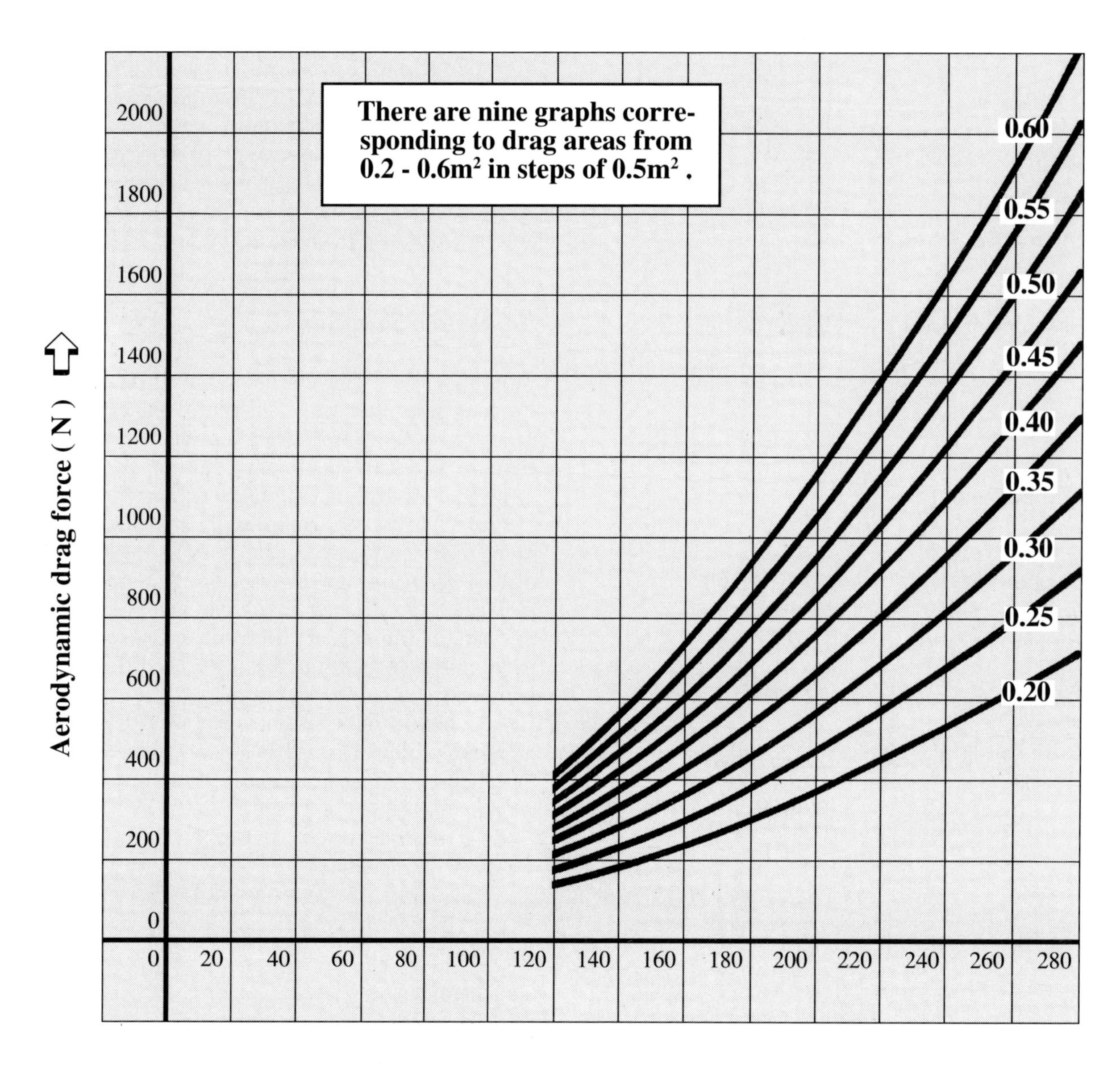

Fig 4.26 *Drag force vs road speed for a range of drag areas (m^2). Example: If the drag area is $0.4m^2$ then at 180km/hr the drag force is approximately 600N.*

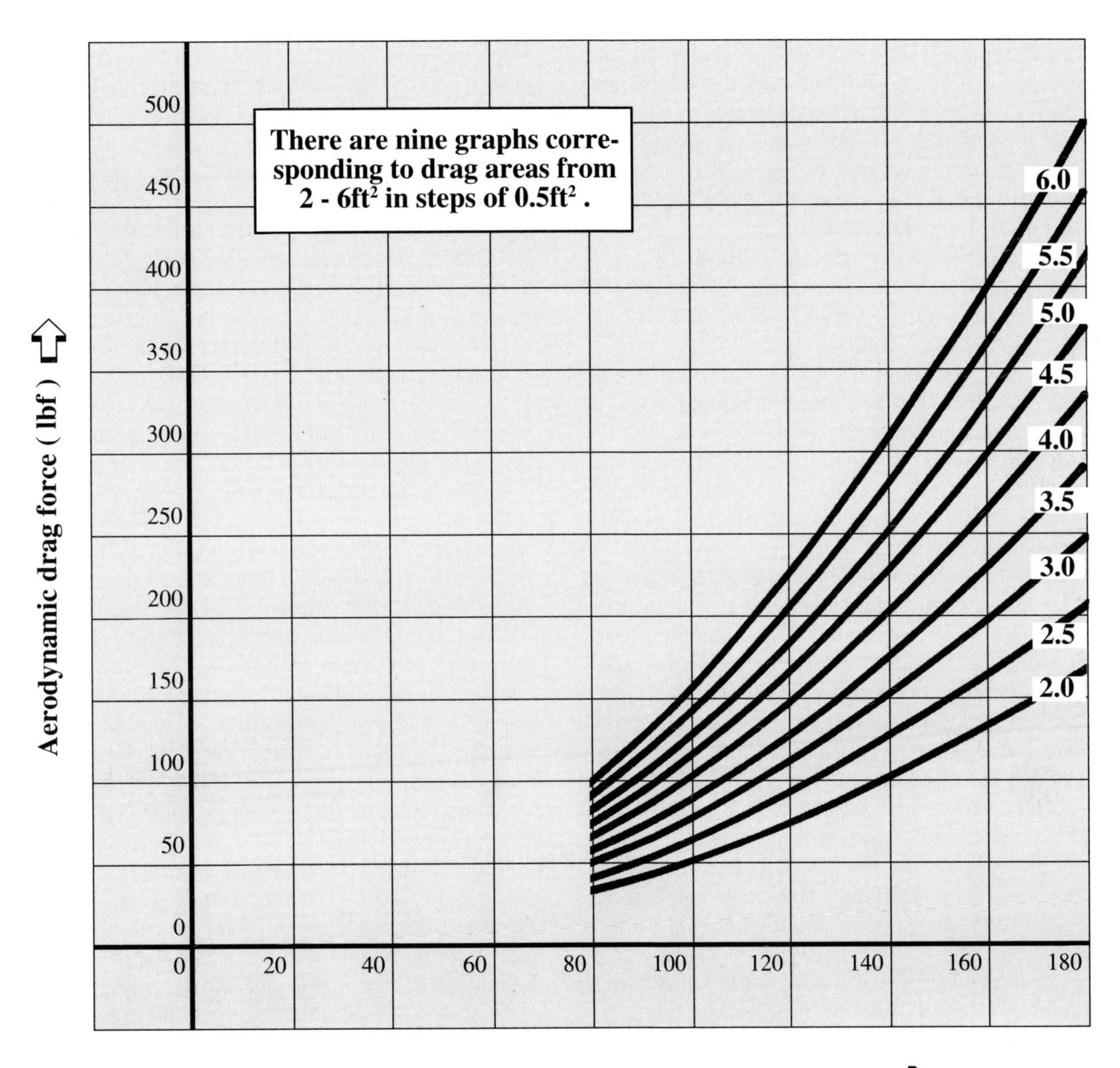

Fig 4.27 *Drag force vs road speed for a range of drag areas (ft²). Example: If the drag area is 4.0ft² then at 140miles / hr the drag force is just over 200lbf.*

Reynold's number has no units since it is effectively the ratio of two forces. This means that any quoted figure can be used without concern for the units involved.

The characteristic length used depends on the object. Aircraft wings use the chord (distance from front to rear) and for cylinders, spheres etc the diameter is employed. In the case of a complete partially-streamlined motorcycle the decision is not simple but it is usual to take the length as being equal to the wheelbase.

Given a typical wheelbase of 1370mm (53.9in), a road speed that varies from 100 - 300km/hr (62 - 187miles/hr) yields Reynold's Numbers in the range, 2.6×10^6 to 7.8×10^6.

This may seem meaningless but it tells an aerodynamicist what to expect. It categorises the flow situation around the motorcycle as being similar to that experienced by airships and old aircraft rather than fast jets! This is why many of the shapes with low drag lack the rakish lines the stylists much prefer.

Another useful feature of Reynold's Number is that is allows the drag coefficients of various components to be estimated from standard test data. Contrary to what I may have implied so far, drag coefficients are rarely constant, they vary with the speed of the object, its size and the type of fluid the object is moving through.

The drag coefficient of a cylinder can vary from about 0.3 up to several hundred (in thick oil) and in previous notes I have only quoted the value most applicable to small parts (1.2). Furthermore, in the case of a cylinder, the drag coefficient changes relatively suddenly at a Reynold's Number of about 3.5×10^5.

Situations like this are said to have a critical Reynold's Number and the flow can be either subcritical or supercritical. As far as a complete motorcycle is concerned, I have never seen any figures which suggest that a critical Reynold's Number will exist within the normal working range. Drag coefficients do certainly vary. Some test figures I have show a 20% rise in drag coefficient as R_e changes from 3×10^6 to 6×10^6 while others show a 10% fall over the same range. There are no simple rules for the complete package and in the absence of serious testing you have no choice but to assume that the drag coefficient is constant. For individual shapes, make sure you know the Reynold's Number at which the drag coefficient is quoted before taking it at face value.

Conclusion

In this chapter I have tried to outline what aerodynamic drag is and the features that increase or reduce it. The formulae given allow the drag force acting on any object moving in air to be calculated, together with the power required to overcome it. The drag is determined by the composite figure, drag area, and this gives us two major avenues to explore on the bike.

Minimising projected area is a relatively straightforward task provided it was considered during the initial design. Reducing the drag coefficient is much more complicated. A motorcycle is not a simple streamlined shape. Air passes around it, through it and into it, all of which influence the drag. Nevertheless, improvements are usually possible if you are prepared to work at it and apply the principles discussed to the best of your ability.

One problem that you will certainly encounter is the difference between what seems to be correct aerodynamically and current styling. This can be very confusing because the rakish lines of many bikes suggest that this is the way things should be.

You should not underestimate the role of the stylists and market forces. As one senior aerodynamicist told me, 'You think that they (the factories) know something that we don't but when you put the bikes in the tunnel it is obvious that many are very poor aerodynamically. There is no question of the factories using something which is efficient but lacks style'.

This situation is slowly changing, mainly because companies like Derbi and, more recently, Aprilia, take aerodynamics very seriously indeed and have demonstrated what can be done. If you look at the 125cc and 250cc Aprilia bikes you will see relatively bulbous, rounded fairings that do shield the rider properly and still look the business. Conversely, the current Japanese 125cc over-the-counter racers come with fairings that offer virtually no streamlining to anyone larger than a 10 year old child but the styling is very smart! The fact that Honda's new Blackbird is rumoured to have better aerodynamics than the NSR250 does make you wonder, though the length of the Blackbird plays a significant role.

If you have wind tunnels at your disposal then you can of course work at things until some compromise of style and function is achieved but if you are restricted to 'suck it and see' methods it is better to stick to the basic principles.

4.4 Minimising motorcycle drag

Introduction

Chapter 4.3 indicated that any reductions in drag force must come from a reduction in drag area, ie the product of projected area (A) and drag coefficient (C_d). Reductions can be achieved by reducing either of these quantities but do remember that inappropriate reductions in area can easily raise the drag coefficient and therefore cancel out any gain you perceive.

The drag coefficient of the bike and rider will only reduce if the 'shape' of them is improved from an aerodynamic viewpoint. In this context 'shape' is an all-enveloping term that includes the way we deal with internal airflow, surface details and even the rider's clothing. You may laugh, but wind tunnel tests have shown a 15% reduction in drag achieved through changes in rider clothing alone. Unfortunately, you will not see any such improvements since tight fitting leathers already represent the best clothing that meets the safety regulations. If, on the other hand, your leathers are several sizes too large, then you should address this problem as soon as possible!

Motorcycles present serious problems as far as drag is concerned. They are not a smooth continuous shape and most of the bits that do meet the air have very high drag coefficients, typically 1.2. On this basis, a small area generates a lot of drag and it is incredible how all the seemingly innocent bits add up.

Projected area

Minimising projected area has to be the top priority because it is relatively straightforward to do, provided you think about it before the bike is built. Making changes to an existing layout is much more difficult. Again, I would remind you about the dangers of trying to reduce the projected area without bearing in mind the need for a suitable shape. Although I am now going to discuss minimising the area, you should not be afraid of area and many bikes suffer from high drag coefficients that result from things like narrow fairings. The overall result may be little better than an unfaired bike with the rider prone.

One of the main requirements for success is to minimise the projected area of the unfaired bike and rider. You then attempt to wrap a reasonable shape around this, accepting any small increases in area that this implies.

If you look at the projected area of motorcycles in photographs then it is clear that the area presented by the rider is the dominant factor. This is confirmed by experimental data.

Standard aviation design data tells us that 'average man' has the following drag areas when placed in a wind tunnel. Note that these figures are C_dA not A, I do not have the breakdown of area and drag coefficient.

- Standing: $0.83m^2$ ($9ft^2$).
- Sitting: $0.56m^2$ ($6.0ft^2$).
- Crouching: $0.28m^2$ ($3ft^2$).

The drag area of a medium sized classic bike with no form of streamlining is about $0.35m^2$ with the rider prone and about $0.55m^2$ - $0.6m^2$ with the rider sitting upright. As you can see, these figures are a reasonable reflection of the drag area presented by 'average man' alone.

Compared with the unstreamlined classic bike, modern sports/road bikes are likely to have higher figures when the rider is prone and lower ones when the rider is upright. Typical values would be $0.4m^2$ with the rider prone and $0.45m^2$ with the rider upright. The higher figure with the rider prone reflects the bulk of the bike, ie an increase in projected area, while the reduction with the rider upright reflects the improved integration of rider and streamlining, together with a more favourable riding position, even when sitting up. Wind tunnel tests on current stock superbikes give figures around $0.32m^2$ ($3.5ft^2$). Whatever the case, the cross-section is dominated by the rider. Conversions for projected areas and/or drag areas are given in Table 4.5 overleaf.

These figures tell us two things. Firstly, the size of rider is extremely important, with the proviso that the bike is designed to capitalise on this fact. Secondly, a lot of so-called streamlining does not offer much improvement over a naked bike and

To convert	To	Multiply by
m^2	ft^2	10.764
ft^2	m^2	0.0929
in^2	ft^2	0.0069
ft^2	in^2	144
cm^2	in^2	0.155
in^2	cm^2	6.45
cm^2	m^2	0.0001
m^2	cm^2	10000

Table 4.5 *Useful conversion factors for projected area or drag area.*

the weight of the streamlining may be detrimental to acceleration and hence lap times. It is always essential to bear in mind the weight of any proposed streamlining because unless the streamlining works more effectively, you are going downhill all the time.

The first practical step you can take to minimise drag is therefore to start with a small, thin rider and design the bike around them. The advantages of a small, light rider are so great that they cannot be ignored, particularly on small bikes.

If, like me, you are tall, reasonably built and cannot survive on a bowl of rice a day, then do not get too depressed because with a bit of thought and effort you can reduce the problems you create. This will allow you to compete with similar riders, though the small rider will always have an acceleration advantage when on equal equipment.

Riding position is extremely important. A good position provides two key requirements in one go. Firstly, the rider's back is relatively flat and this can lower the drag coefficient significantly. Secondly, the projected area is reduced by virtue of the reduction in overall height - Fig 4.28.

At the moment we are primarily concerned with projected area and to achieve a well compacted position like that shown in Fig 4.28 the bike has to be designed to suit. The tank top must be low enough to allow the position to be achieved but it should not be any lower. One of the key requirements in what follows later on is obtaining a riding position that is repeatable. The rider will only be able to do this if they can 'lie' on a solid surface when in the prone position.

Most riders of normal build will struggle to combine a flat back with an acceptable footrest height if the seat base is horizontal. Regulations prohibit the seat base being inclined at more than a few degrees though many bikes break this rule. The regulations do not actually state an angle, but they do state that the height from the lowest part of the seat base to the top of the rear seat 'fairing' must not exceed 150mm as shown in Fig 4.29. You will be hard pressed to find a bike that complies with this!

Similarly, the rider shown in Fig 4.28 is breaking the screen to helmet clearance regulations which specify a minimum of 100mm. This rule is also frequently flouted, even (especially?) at GP level but you may have to do battle with an enthusiastic scrutineer.

The other aspect of rider size is width and if you are of normal build your shoulders are the widest part. This is a blessing because the shoulders will be well forward where the widest part of the bike needs to be. However, if your backside is just as wide then this presents a problem.

Fig 4.28 *The rider testing this bike in the wind tunnel has a good, though possibly uncomfortable, riding position. His back is flat and he is well tucked in. Note the wool tufts used to check airflow (photo K.R.Cooper, National Research Council, Ottawa, Canada).*

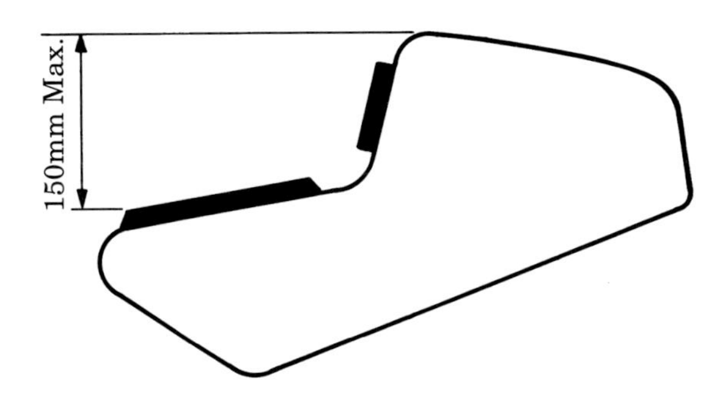

Above. Fig 4.29 *Seat inclination and the height of the rear fairing are both restricted by this regulation. The regulations do not state a specific maximum inclination for the base but, the more inclined you make it, the lower the rear fairing has to be. Many bikes break this regulation. The 150mm is measured from the lowest point on the base.*

At this stage, we might assume that the bulk of the bike can be accommodated within the rider's cross-section and the shoulders fit into this maximum area. If your backside and hips are wider then you will not be able to achieve the most advantageous shape without widening the front end even more, thereby increasing projected area - Fig 4.30. The trade-off between more area and a lower drag coefficient can only be found by experiment so, if you are built in the manner described, you have a lot of testing to do!

Below. Fig 4.30 *The widest cross-section needs to be near the front of the bike. This suits a rider with narrow hips. If the hips are wide, it is necessary to increase the frontal area in order to maintain a closing section. However, if the design is poor, and the flow separates very early on, a better result might be achieved with a fairing to match the original rider area. This is always a dilemma and the best solution can only be decided by testing.*

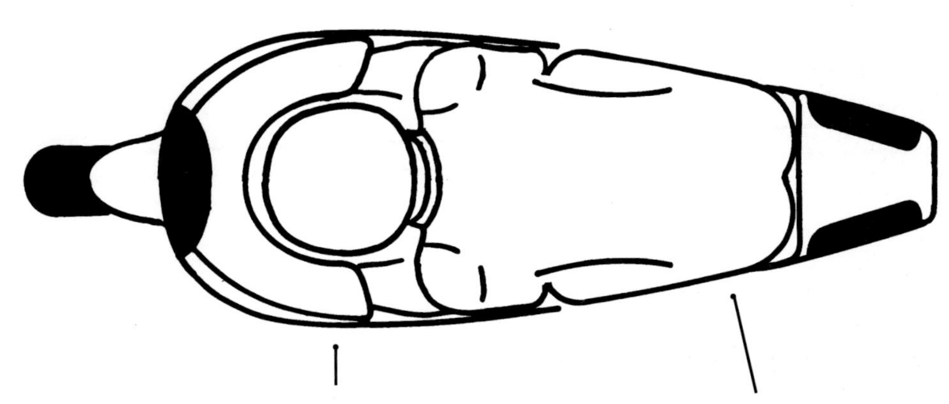

The widest sections should be near the front of the bike. It may be necessary to add area to achieve this. Results then depend on the relative increase in area and reduction in drag coefficient.

This region should be tapering inwards. If the hips are wide, the front of the bike needs to be wider as well in order to maintain shape.

Because the rider forms such a large part of the overall shape, the rider's legs should taper rearwards when viewed from above, though not by very much. This is largely determined by the design of the seat, tank and frame.

Many bikes have wide top frame tubes and tanks that splay out the rider's legs quite sharply. This is virtually guaranteed to increase the drag coefficient if it was low to start with. If it was poor initially it will stay that way. A solution is to scallop the tank and reduce the frame width until you achieve what you want. Fig 4.31 is an extreme example from one of my own bikes a few years ago. It is like this because I have a large, injured thigh that would otherwise stick out considerably. This tank does pose certain risks in the event of a crash!

Fig 4.31 *Scalloping the tank allows the rider's legs to adopt and hold a good position. This example, from one of the author's bikes is rather extreme, but was necessary because of a large, permanently damaged thigh.*

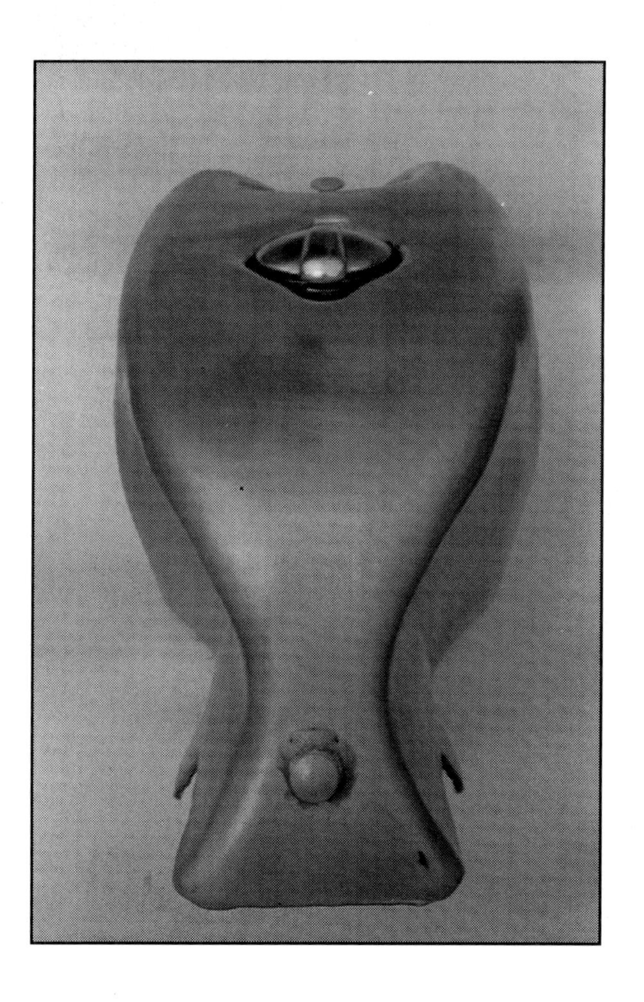

The influence of the seat base and frame is determined by the riding position and other requirements. On small bikes, ie 80cc, 125cc and some 250cc, the rider's thighs point significantly downwards, a consequence of obtaining a flat back. In this case the legs will splay out when viewed from the front unless the seat base and frame are very narrow. Most small bikes are like this and the factory Derbi from a few years ago is a particularly nice example - Fig 4.32.

On larger bikes the situation is different. The space beneath the seat is often required for exhausts and the rider also has to be able to adopt a position in which he or she can physically 'wrestle' the bike about. The upper thighs tend to be more horizontal. In this case the solution is to widen the seat base and form a sort of platform that the air can adhere to if conditions are right - Fig 4.33.

Whatever the case, the rider and riding position are the first things to consider and every attempt should be made to reduce the projected area they occupy. Do remember that the chosen position may have to be maintained for long periods of time. This will test your thigh and neck muscles at the very least.

Finally, if you can get a good position in terms of the features described, then you need to do so with the rider as far forward as possible. This will usually fit in with the centre of gravity requirements and may allow you some freedom in respect of things like radiator location (discussed later). Screen clearance and handlebar position are the limiting factors but if you look at any winning GP bike you will see that maximum width is pushed as far forward as possible. This will allow maximum streamlined length and that is extremely important.

Top right. Fig 4.32 *On small bikes, the seat base and top frame tubes are made very narrow to combine low projected area with a very flat riding position. This is the factory Derbi that won the 125cc World Campionship a few years ago. Derbi spent many days in the wind tunnel with this bike and the design reflects this effort (photograph WP Suspension).*

Bottom right. Fig 4.33 *On larger bikes the space under the seat base is needed and the riding position cannot be so extreme. In this case the base is wide and comes out under the rider to pick up the airflow. The rider's thighs are more horizontal. See also Fig 4.36 (photograph WP Suspension).*

3
DUCADOS
CEPSA
DERBI
DUCADOS
CEPSA
DERBI
CLIMAX
RENAULT
BOSCH

8
DE VRIES
YAMAHA

Once the riding position has been finalised, the objective is to build everything else into the projected area it represents. This is unlikely to be possible but it is still a goal to aim for. The first increase in area is likely to come from the crankcases due to the conflicting requirements of cg location and footrest height. The crankcases are almost certainly below your feet and there is not much you can do about it. Exhausts may further aggravate the problem and the projected area will start to creep up. Since most of these things are decided by engine configuration, this is another thing to think about before spending money. The Britten and the Ducati are more than just powerful motorcycles.

Fig 4.34 *Two laboratory photographs of a model motorcycle in a water tunnel (water tunnel testing is less expensive than full size wind tunnel testing). Note the substantial wake, with or without the fairing. The photographs are not good enough to show detail but you can just detect the early separation on the rider's arms and legs when no streamlining is used (photo K.R.Cooper, National Research Council, Ottawa, Canada).*

Shape

Once the projected area has been minimised, the next task is to achieve a low drag shape around it. This is not easy and the wake produced by a moving motorcycle is something to behold as shown in Fig 4.34. I apologise for the poor quality of the photographs but they were taken as a record of events, not as a picture for use in my book. As with several other examples in this section, I thought that the information they convey was too important to leave out.

The most fundamental problem is lack of streamlined length. We cannot obtain a particularly good shape no matter what we do so we have to look at how relatively poor shapes behave in the wind tunnel. A partially streamlined motorcycle is not dissimilar from a block with a rounded front and corners. You may not like this idea, but the humble block will do better than most bikes if it is the right length. The key to this is demonstrated in Fig 4.35. This shows the drag of a smooth block that has an elliptical front and moderately rounded edges. The graph indicates the drag coefficient achieved as the slenderness ratio (length/width) is varied by increasing the length.

When the block is very short the drag is high as you would expect for a cube with rounded edges. As the length increases the drag falls quite dramatically because the length at constant cross-section allows a partial pressure recovery, thereby reducing base drag. However, a point is reached where the drag begins to rise again. This is caused by a build up of skin friction and a very tired boundary layer. Minimum drag occurs when the slenderness ratio has a value of seven. This graph is surprisingly close to reality as far as motorcycles are concerned so length is the first problem. In this context length means the streamlined length over which the air remains attached.

Width and depth will vary. Width is less than depth on a motorcycle so using width indicates the best case. If the widest point is 0.5m (1.64ft) then this very narrow machine needs a streamlined length of 3.5m (11.5ft) for minimum drag. You will not achieve this and you will not get the drag

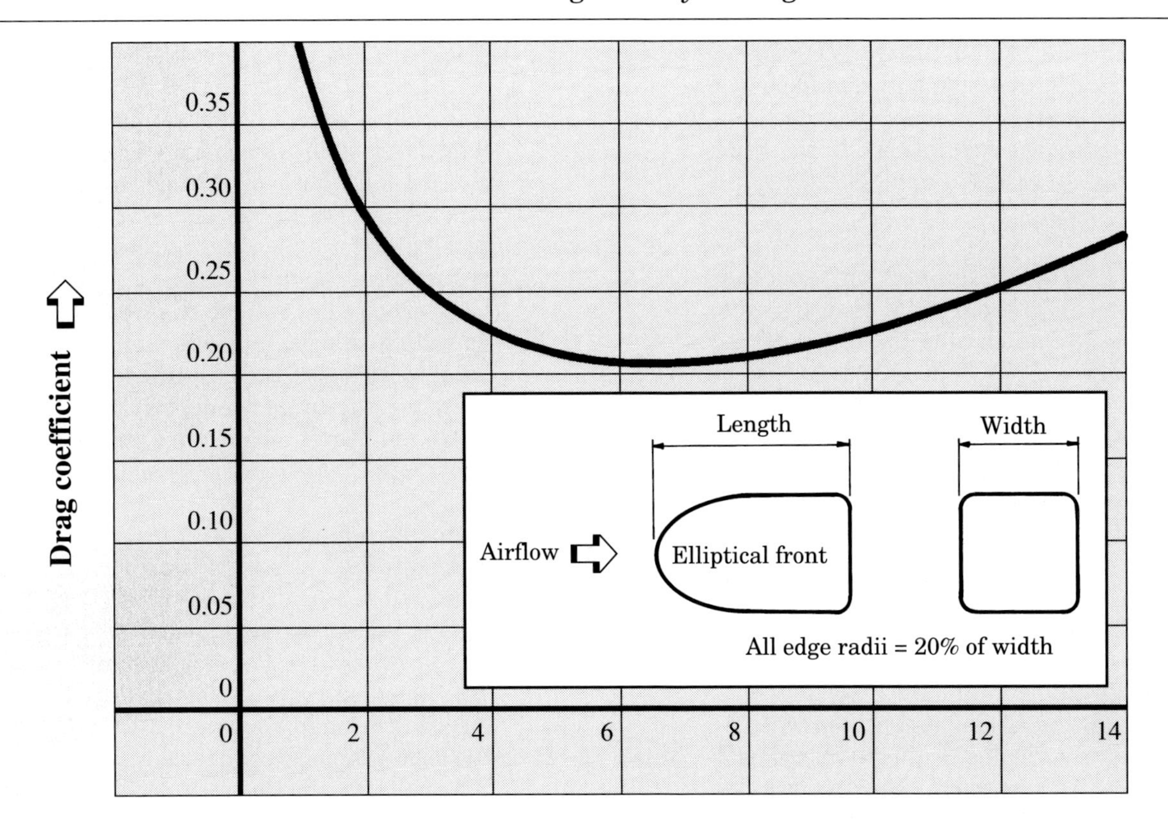

coefficient anywhere near the 0.21 this implies. Wheelbase is unlikely to exceed 1.5m (4ft 11in) on any bike and you cannot streamline this full length because of the regulations. If you combine this with realistic width and depth measurements you can see that you are working on the portion of the curve where the drag coefficient is about 0.25 - 0.4. These figures are for a smooth shape but a simple one. You will not be able to do better than this at Cd = 0.25 but you could do a lot worse, 0.4 - 0.6 being common. To approach the values on this graph the bike must be narrow, shallow and long. I have already dealt with area.

The restrictions on length are many, the first one being wheelbase as just mentioned. The second restriction comes from the regulations. The streamlining must not start more than 50mm in front of the front wheel spindle, another rule that is often broken, and the seat must end at the back of the rear tyre. Everything in-between forms an approximate streamlined shape and the object is to keep the air attached to the bike and rider for as long as possible. On many bikes, separation occurs very early, often around the rider's shoulders at the top and where the fairing sides end at the bottom. Given this situation your efforts will have little effect on drag because the difference between various front ends is not great in terms of drag. To make progress, the main requirements are as follows.

Fig 4.35 *This graph is particularly important. It shows the drag coefficient of a smooth rectangular block which has an elliptical nose shape and rounded edges. If the length of the block is increased while maintaining the cross-section constant, the drag falls substantially in the early stages but then rises again for reasons given in the text. Partially streamlined motorcycles behave in a very similar way and therefore one aim is to achieve a slenderness ratio around seven. We cannot do this but it shows why the bike needs to be long and thin.*

- The fairing must start as far forward as possible and should shroud the wheel as much as possible within the regulations. Look at the Honda NSR500 and NSR250 in Fig 4.36.

- The front mudguard, while not legal streamlining, should be designed to deflect air around the sides of the bike.

- Airflow into the bike will increase drag but you must have air for cooling and induction in surprisingly large quantities. Making the best of this is discussed later.

- The widest part of any cross-section needs to be near the front of it, say 25% along its length. This means that the fairing and screen will have a closing profile in any view - Fig 4.37 overleaf. Many bikes have an opening profile and that is very bad for drag.

- The fairing must be wide enough to prevent the air stream hitting the rider, especially on the shoulders. If this happens, the airflow will certainly separate early. Many fairings are much too narrow in this respect and the rider should not be able to feel wind force when prone. I do not have a photograph available, but look at the 1996 250 Aprilia which is extremely fast and compare the width with many club bikes.

- The most important thing is the blending of rider and fairing/screen as if the two were one. The rider should represent a continuation of the desired shape and a large void is almost as bad as the rider sticking out everywhere.

- The seat must try to pick up the air as it leaves the rider so that full wake development is delayed as long as possible. To do this it has to be extremely large on any size of bike. This looks rather silly if it is a small bike for a big rider but drag reductions of 8 - 10% are possible. Use carbon fibre to keep the weight down. Notable examples include the John Mocket designed Yamaha seats together with the factory Derbi and Garelli from a few years ago.

- Do not be tempted to pull the seat section in too sharply. If the air has managed to stay attached this far then it will surely separate at a steep contraction. The seat should only approach a point if the rider's backside is small enough to allow the seat section to reduce slowly in the available length.

- The area behind the rider's legs should be filled out but this is limited by access and regulations.

- Surfaces should be free from defects and fasteners whenever possible. This is discussed next.

These are the most basic ideas and they are summarised in Fig 4.38 overleaf. If you apply them rigorously you can improve most bikes to the point where it shows up in lap times.

Fig 4.36 *Two examples of current thinking. At the top is Mike Doohan's 1995 NSR500. Note how far forward the fairing is and the way the width varies. The widest point is well forward. The belly extends right to the wheel and the seat is massive. It still has a significant inclination when normally laden (photo R.Shuker). The second example is Nobuatsu Aoki's Team Rheos Molenaar Racing NSR250. In this excellent shot you can see the same features. The shape of the seat and belly pan are particularly clear. Note the 'clean' lines (photograph supplied by WP Suspension, Netherlands). In both cases the mudguard does more than keep the engine clean! Hot air from the radiators is delivered to the low pressure region at the sides of the fairing.*

HONDA
HRC
SHOWA
REPSOL
MICHELIN
NGK
RK
BENETTON
SPORTSYSTEM

MICHELIN
HRC
Boldor
MOTUL
HONDA

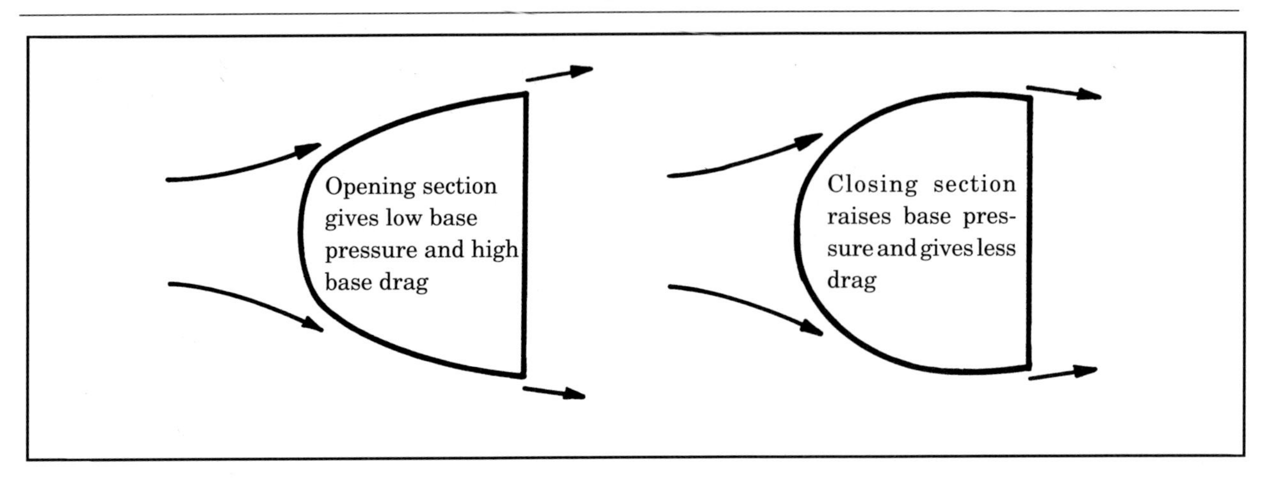
Opening section gives low base pressure and high base drag
Closing section raises base pressure and gives less drag

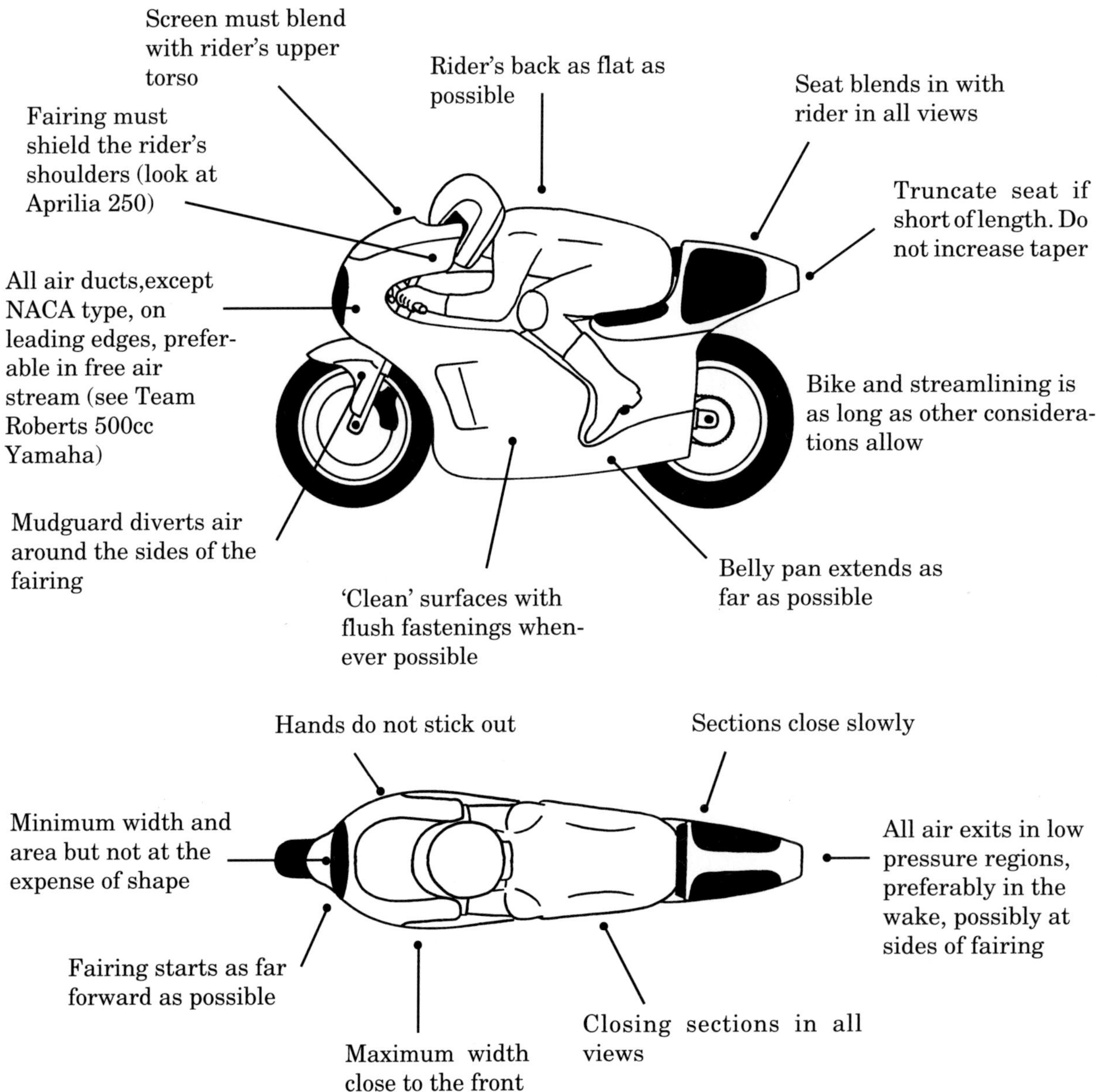
Screen must blend with rider's upper torso
Rider's back as flat as possible
Seat blends in with rider in all views
Fairing must shield the rider's shoulders (look at Aprilia 250)
Truncate seat if short of length. Do not increase taper
All air ducts,except NACA type, on leading edges, preferable in free air stream (see Team Roberts 500cc Yamaha)
Bike and streamlining is as long as other considerations allow
Mudguard diverts air around the sides of the fairing
Belly pan extends as far as possible
'Clean' surfaces with flush fastenings whenever possible
Hands do not stick out
Sections close slowly
Minimum width and area but not at the expense of shape
All air exits in low pressure regions, preferably in the wake, possibly at sides of fairing
Fairing starts as far forward as possible
Closing sections in all views
Maximum width close to the front

Surface details

One of the most important aspects of aerodynamics is attention to detail. Small features can produce drag that is far greater than their size suggests and there are two main reasons for this.

Firstly, the exposed parts of motorcycles are usually round tubes, fasteners, flat surfaces and so on. The drag coefficients of little bits like this will range from perhaps 1.0 to 1.5. If you expose such parts to the air stream then, compared to something with a drag coefficient of 0.3, they behave as if they have 3 - 5 times the area they actually do have. On this basis, something like a fully exposed handlebar generates as much drag as a very large piece of fairing, even though it looks insignificant.

Things can get worse. The second problem is interference and cars provide a good example. Back in 1978 Pininfarina produced a superbly styled car that was a reasonably normal saloon shape (rather like a Ford Granada). It had a drag coefficient of only 0.17. However, adding a pair of windscreen wipers, two mirrors and a hole for cooling air increased the drag coefficient to 0.23, ie a rise of 35%.

The motor industry is littered with such cases and they illustrate the problem of interference. Innocent little things like bolts and fasteners not only add their own drag element. They can also mess up what was originally a nice low drag surface. For, example, the wake generated by a row of small fasteners can destroy the airflow over a previously good surface. As a result you get the drag increase from two sources, the fasteners themselves and the interference.

Top left. Fig 4.37 *Any cross-section must be a closing section. Many bikes have fairings and screens that fail to do this when viewed from above.*

Bottom left. Fig 4.38 *Summary of the most basic features required to reduce drag. Once this is achieved, pay particular attention to small details. These are like the weight of small parts - you only notice the effect when you put them all together.*

Right. Table 4.6 *Examples of the drag changes associated with a variety of fastenings located in a boundary layer. Adapted from Fluid Dynamic Drag by Hoerner.*

The message is very simple. Clean up every surface wherever possible and use flush fastening if you can. The drag penalty associated with some of the changes from flush fastening are given in Table 4.6. As you can see, it is easy to increase drag from an accumulation of minor details.

Fastening type (airflow left to right)	Drag relative to datum type
	Datum
	x20
	x160
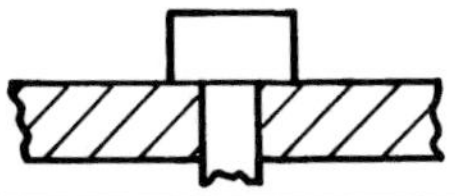	x210
	x400
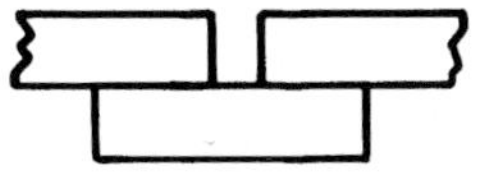	Datum
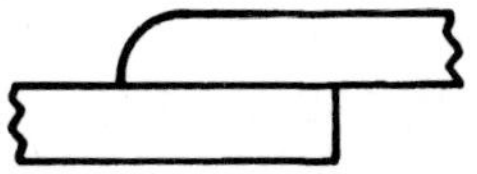	x4
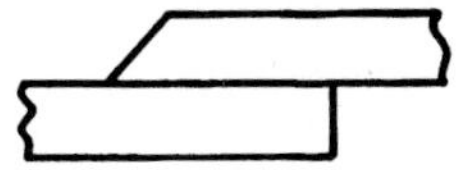	x11
	x13
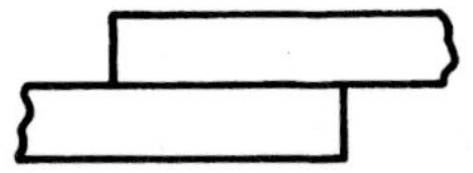	x40
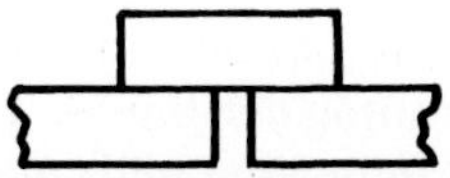	x70

An example

Before I go on to discuss the provision of air for induction and cooling, it will be useful to consider some real data that shows what can be achieved in practice. Again, I am indebted to Kevin Cooper and the National Research Council in Canada for allowing me to reproduce all their figures which relate to development of a factory 125cc bike a few years ago. The bike achieved world records at Bonneville Salt flats in both the partial and fully streamlined categories, indeed I think one record still stands. I will only discuss the partially streamlined case here. Although the figures are somewhat dated, none of the principles has changed.

The original bike was a standard short circuit racer. Unfortunately, the photographs no longer exist but Fig 4.39 was taken from various photocopies. It is a typical club racer of the time and not that different from many club specials even now.

In this form the drag coefficient was measured at 0.608 with the rider prone. The projected area was $0.414m^2$ ($4.5ft^2$) giving a drag area of $0.252m^2$ ($2.7ft^2$). A major defect was confirmed when the bike was tested without the rider. The drag coefficient dropped to 0.45 indicating that the rider made everything much worse and so the streamlining was not actually effective.

In common with many others, the fairing was too small and the rider's back was much too curved. This can be verified if the leathers are slack, since the low pressure air negotiating the curve will suck them upwards. The first step was therefore to alter the riding position and design a new fairing which is also shown in Fig 4.39. These changes reduced the drag coefficient to 0.374 with the original projected area. This represents a 39% reduction in drag! With this new fairing, adding the rider no longer increased the drag.

This major change was followed by a series of smaller but very vital changes together with a general 'clean up' campaign. The major changes are listed in Table 4.7 overleaf. Note the change produced by the seat. There is even a 2.8% reduction due to putting small fairings on the back of 229mm of fork slider! Each change is fairly small but the overall drag was reduced by 55%.

The effect of these changes on the power required to overcome the drag is shown in Fig 4.40 overleaf and this leads to the performance improvement given at the beginning of Chapter 4.3, ie 40km/hr on top speed (25miles/hr) and, more importantly, 6.4 seconds of the time to accelerate between 113 and 169km/hr (70 - 105miles/hr). You cannot fail to be impressed.

I am not going to pretend this is straightforward, even with a wind tunnel and the necessary expertise, but it does show what can be achieved if the initial configuration is not particularly good. If you managed half this with suck it and see methods the result would show up in lap times.

For readers with a particular interest in this area, Table 4.8 details all the wind tunnel runs. One very interesting result is the negligable effect of having the front wheel running at road speed. With the wheel fixed (run number 18), the drag coefficient is 0.356 at 123miles/hr. When the wheel is running at full road speed (run number 20), the drag coefficient is 0.355 at 125miles/hr. This suggests that although the rotating wheel adds a vortex into the airstream by virtue of its rotation, the practical implications for this bike are negligable. Note however that fairing the wheels with discs does give a drag reduction.

A lot of the work done in thes tests relates to side force and lift but further discussion is beyond the scope of this text. The idea is simply to show you that results can be achieved if you are prepared to work at it.

Fig 4.39 *These pictures are taken from photocopies but they still convey useful information. The pictures at the top show the original bike. Note the relatively upright riding position, the short streamlining, ineffective seat and inadequate width of fairing. The pictures at the bottom are of the new configuration during wind tunnel tests. The fairing width now prevents air hitting the rider's shoulders but the projected area remains the same. Width was taken from where it was not required and moved to places where it was essential. The new fairing is considerably longer and in this shot experiments are being carried out using taped on panels in front of the new seat, over the forearms and around the rider's legs. Note how much flatter the rider's back is. Apart from the wheel discs and dubious screen / helmet clearance, this bike meets the current partially-streamlined regulations (from material supplied by K.R.Cooper, National Research Council, Ottawa, Canada).*

104B

BELL

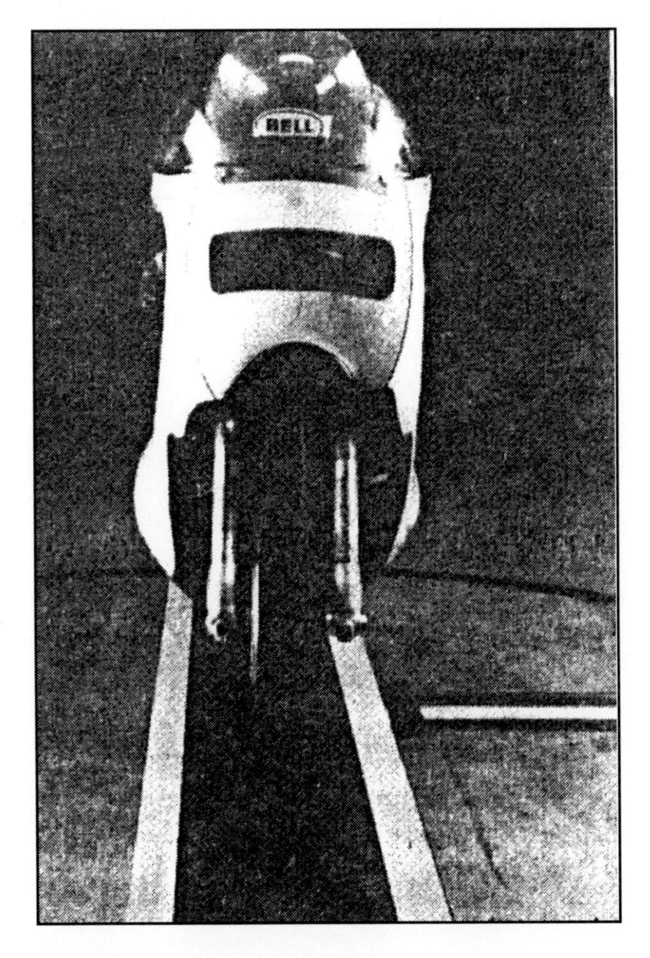
BELL

61

Configuration	Drag coefficient Cd	Drag as % of original
Original	0.608	100
New fairing, otherwise bare	0.374	61.5
As above + wheel covers	0.343	56.4
As above + fair lower fork legs	0.326	53.6
As above + small hand fairings	0.319	52.5
As above + fair in front forearms	0.312	51.3
As above + larger seat	0.281	46.2
As above + improved belly pan	0.274	45.0

Above. Table 4.7 *Major steps in drag reduction for the bike concerned (data K.R.Cooper).*

Below. Fig 4.40 *Calculated power requirements at the back wheel for both configurations.*

Right. Table 4.8 *Full details of the wind tunnel tests discussed in the text (data K.R.Cooper).*

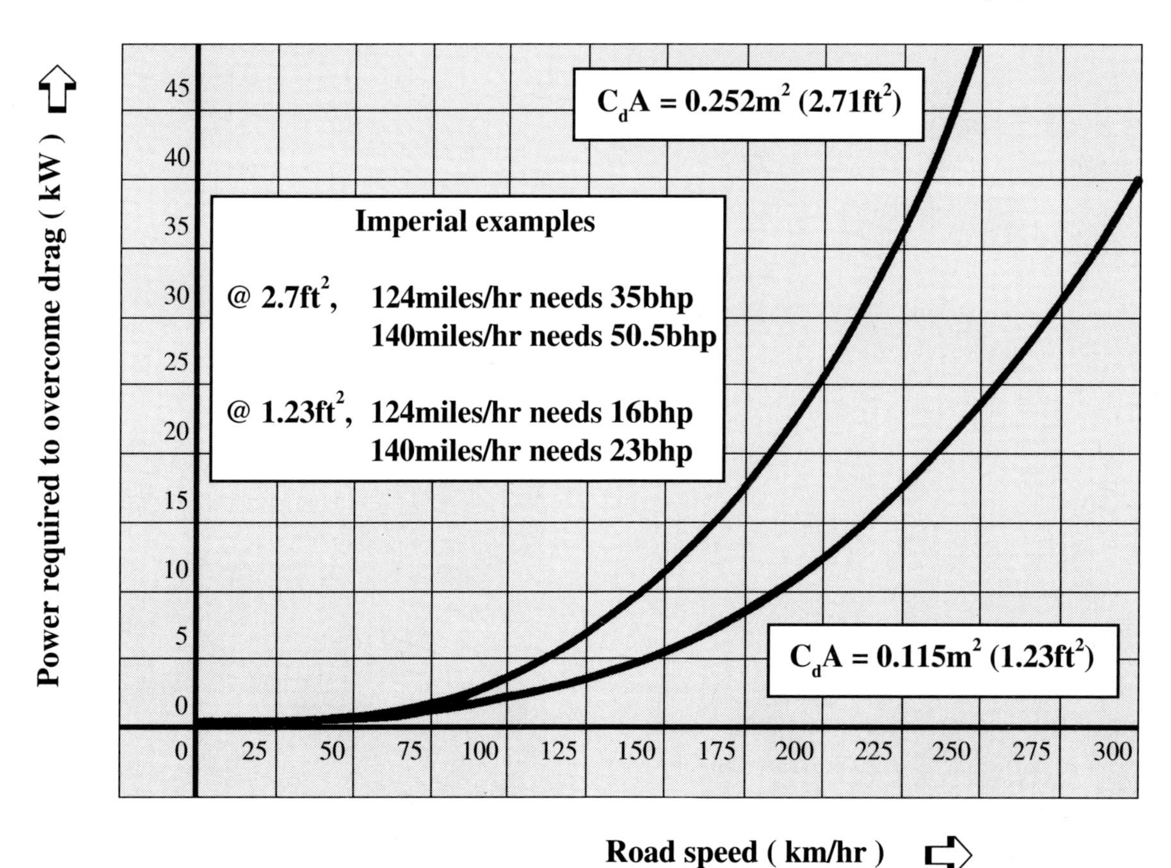

Run No	Yaw angle (deg)	Speed (mph)	Configuration	Drag coeff at zero yaw
1	0 to 12	66	Original machine, no modifications	0.518
2	0 to 12	86	Original machine, no modifications	0.560
3	0 to 12	102	Original machine, no modifications	0.566
4	0 to 12	129	Original machine, no modifications	0.583
5	0	133	Original machine, no modifications	0.598
6	0 to 5	143	Original machine, no modifications	0.608
7	0	150	Original machine, no modifications	0.621
8	0 to 5	125	Original machine, front wheel running	0.574
9	0 to 5	102	Original machine, rider off	0.451
10	0 to 5	82	Original machine, pitched down 1.5deg	0.574
11	0 to 5	102	Original machine, pitched down 1.5deg	0.583
12	0 to 5	123	Original machine, pitched down 1.5deg	0.560
13	0 to 5	82	Original machine, pitched up 2.2deg	0.606
14	0 to 5	102	Original machine, pitched up 2.2deg	0.604
15	0 to 5	123	Original machine, pitched up 2.2deg	0.581
16	-1 to 3	82	Machine with new fairing and riding position	0.361
17	-1 to 3	102	Machine with new fairing and riding position	0.354
18	-1 to 3	123	Machine with new fairing and riding position	0.356
19	-1 to 3	143	Machine with new fairing and riding position	0.372
20	-1 to 3	125	With front wheel running	0.355
21	-1 to 3	123	With rider off	0.357
22	-1 to 3	82	With disc fairings on wheels	0.337
23	-1 to 3	102	With disc fairings on wheels	0.335
24	-1 to 3	123	With disc fairings on wheels	0.334
25	-1 to 3	143	With disc fairings on wheels	0.343
26	-1 to 3	125	As above with wheel running	0.324
27	-1 to 3	123	With discs and fork fairings	0.329
28	-1 to 3	143	With discs and fork fairings	0.326
29	0	143	As above with wheel running	0.320
30	-1 to 4	144	With disc, fork and hand fairings	0.319
31	-1 to 3	144	As above plus arm fairing	0.312
32	-1 to 3	144	As above plus large seat	0.281
33	-1 to 3	144	Arm fairing off, small seat mod	0.284
34	-1 to 3	123	As above plus belly pan	0.311
35	-1 to 3	143	As above plus belly pan	0.296
36	-1 to 3	164	As above plus belly pan	0.295
37	-1 to 3	143	As above plus feet gaps closed	0.298
38	-1 to 3	143	As run No 33 with modified belly pan	0.274
39	0	143	As above with helmet fairing	0.276

Air for induction

The provision of air for induction and cooling is vital but it increases drag. All you can hope to do is to minimise the damage and gain other benefits in return. Most engines receive a very inadequate supply of air that is in poor condition. As such they are unlikely to develop the same power on the track as they do on the dynamometer.

With no serious intervention, the engine receives hot air from the rear of the cylinders and invariably not enough of it. Some motors are positively gasping for air when the bike is travelling at high speeds. Two-stroke cylinders need their own capacity of air every revolution of the crank and four-strokes need it every two revolutions. Don't even bother about volumetric efficiency, the situation is so bad that you probably need two and a half times as much air coming into the bike as the calculation suggests because in most cases the supply is severely degraded before it even reaches the carburettors.

The only way to keep the air cool (hence increasing charge density and power) and ensure that it gets to the right place is to duct it. Anything else is a gamble. This leads us into several areas, ie ducts, airboxes and ram-air technology.

Ducting

The basic requirements are as follows.

- Ideally, the air inlet needs to be in a high pressure region at the front of the fairing.
- The ducting needs to be as straight as possible.
- The duct should gradually increase in size as it nears the airbox. The object is to decelerate the air and thereby raise its pressure. The more you can raise the pressure the more power you can obtain, provided you can sort out the carburation.
- The air inlet should have a rounded entry and must be relatively large. If it is too small, the motor will be starved of air when trying to deliver high power at low road speeds.
- The airbox should be at least as large as the capacity of the cylinder(s) it is feeding. Most are a lot larger because of the rate at which the engine empties the box!

Fig 4.41 *General layout of air duct for induction. The best examples I have seen are on the Aprilia 125cc and 250cc GP bikes.*

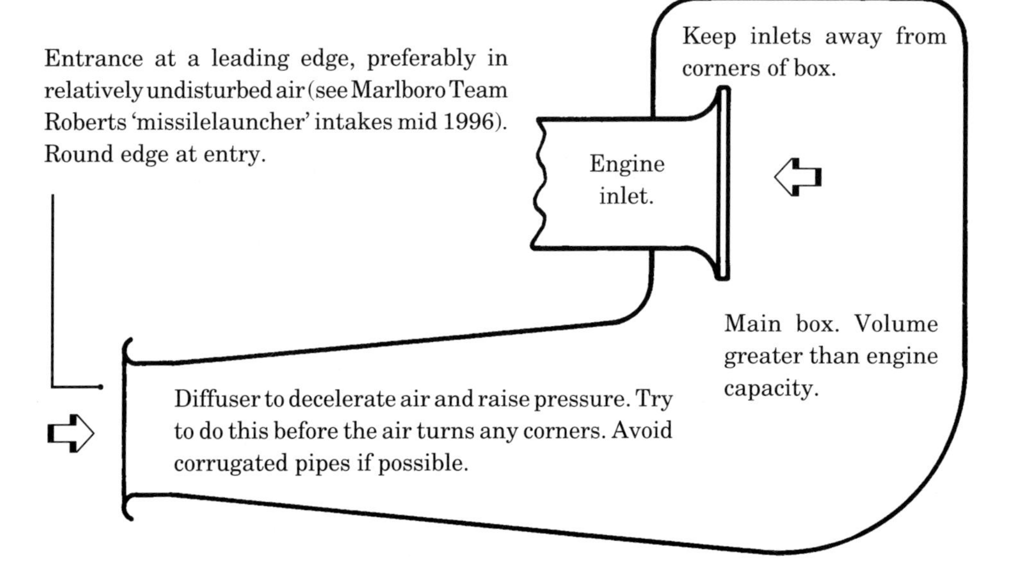

The airbox should be sealed if you are intending to capitalise on ram-air effects but for most people the main advantage lies in the availability of a cool air supply in adequate quantities. Fig 4.41 outlines these ideas.

How big should the inlet be? This is a good question and, although sums will get you started some experiment is essential. The engine requires an air flow rate which is proportional to its crankshaft speed. The duct delivers an air flow rate that is proportional to how fast the bike is going. You can calculate the air the engine needs at full power. Ignore the volumetric efficiency. You can then calculate the size of duct required to give this at top speed.

Simple; but what happens when the engine is making full power at much lower road speeds? The answer is equally simple, it starves of air. A reasonable compromise seems to be as follows.

- Calculate what the engine needs at full power.
- Multiply it by 2.5 to allow for all the various losses. This is not a joke. If you are getting in 40% of the free air stream theoretically available you have made a good start. With a very well located air inlet (eg the Marlboro Team Roberts 'missile launcher' intakes, mid 1996), you can reduce this considerably but don't start out with undersized inlets.
- Calculate a duct inlet area based on half your maximum speed attainable or the average lap speed. Use the lowest figure.
- Try it. You can always make it smaller but increasing the size usually means starting again.

All the necessary formulae are given on the right. Volumetric efficiency is taken to be 100% for working out a nominal value. Two examples are given overleaf.

Nominal intake air requirements

4 Strokes

$$\text{Flow rate (litres/min)} = \frac{CN}{2000}$$

or

$$\text{Flow rate (ft}^3\text{/min)} = \frac{CN}{56634}$$

2 Strokes

$$\text{Flow rate (litres/min)} = \frac{CN}{1000}$$

or

$$\text{Flow rate (ft}^3\text{/min)} = \frac{CN}{28317}$$

where

C = Cubic capacity in cm^3
N = Engine speed in revs/min

Required area (no losses)

$$\text{Area (cm}^2\text{)} = \frac{\text{Flow rate (litres/min)}}{1.67 \times \text{Air speed (km/hr)}}$$

or

$$\text{Area (in}^2\text{)} = \frac{1.6 \times \text{Flow rate (ft}^3\text{/min)}}{\text{Air speed (miles/hr)}}$$

For a circular entry

$$\text{Diameter} = 1.128\sqrt{\text{Area}}$$

Example. Estimate an air inlet size to suit a 125cc two-stroke engine peaking at 12000revs/min. Top speed is 209km/hr and an average lap at the slowest circuit is 116km/hr.

Using Flow rate (Q) $= \frac{CN}{1000}$

$Q = \frac{125 \times 12000}{1000} = 1500$litre/min

Allowing for ducting and entry losses,

Required flow rate $= 2.5 \times 1500$litres/min

$= 3750$litres/min

Half top speed is 103km/hr which is less than the lap average,

Using Area $= \frac{\text{Flow rate}}{1.67\text{xAir speed}}$

Area $= \frac{3750}{1.67 \times 103}$

$= 21.8\text{cm}^2$

Diameter of entry $= 1.128\sqrt{21.8} = 5.26$cm

Example. Estimate an air inlet size to suit a 1000cc four-stroke engine peaking at 13000revs/min. Top speed is 170miles/hr and an average lap at the slowest circuit is 86miles/hr.

Using Fow rate (Q) $= \frac{CN}{56634}$

$Q = \frac{1000 \times 13000}{56634} = 230\text{ft}^3/\text{min}$

Allowing for ducting and entry losses,

Required flow rate $= 2.5 \times 230 = 574\text{ft}^3/\text{min}$

Half top speed is 85miles/hr which is less than the lap average,

Using,

Area $= \frac{1.6 \times \text{flow rate}}{\text{Air speed}}$

Area $= \frac{1.6 \times 574}{85} = 10.8\text{in}^2$

Diameter of entry $= 1.128\sqrt{10.8} = 3.7$in

These calculations are the best I can offer based on my limited experience. I suggest you try them out and adjust the 2.5 multiplying factor accordingly. However, you will be surprised at just how inefficient entry ducts can be. I have assumed a 40% efficiency. You are unlikely to exceed 50% but could go down to 25% or less if the entry is not well located.

Ram-air induction

This is something that people get very excited about, especially if they only use the bike to go to the shops. In reality ram-air concepts are of no use under these conditions, they are of little use on short circuits, and only provide real benefit on ultra-fast circuits. They also cause a lot of problems.

The idea is very simple. As you go faster more air comes in. The duct decelerates the air and raises its pressure. The airbox holds air at higher pressures and this ‘rams in’ the mixture.

There are two problems. The first one concerns the pressure rise you can achieve. Your ducting will not be 100% efficient. The boundary layer causes all sorts of problems, there are momentum losses and some ducts choke up completely. However, let us ignore this for now. If you manage to bring the air to rest and achieve a fully ‘charged’ airbox at the right time then the maximum pressure rise obtainable is that of the dynamic pressure, ie $0.5\rho v^2$. Fig 4.42 shows what this amounts to at different speeds. The faster you go, the greater the pressure you can generate.

The result is not really significant until you are going at speeds above say 260km/hr (161miles/hr). Even then it is marginal. At 280km/hr (174miles/hr) you could get a 4% power gain but 2% is more likely given the problems of duct

Right. Fig 4.42 *Maximum pressures that can be generated by bringing air to rest from different speeds. The graph at the top is in metric units, the bottom one is in imperial units.*

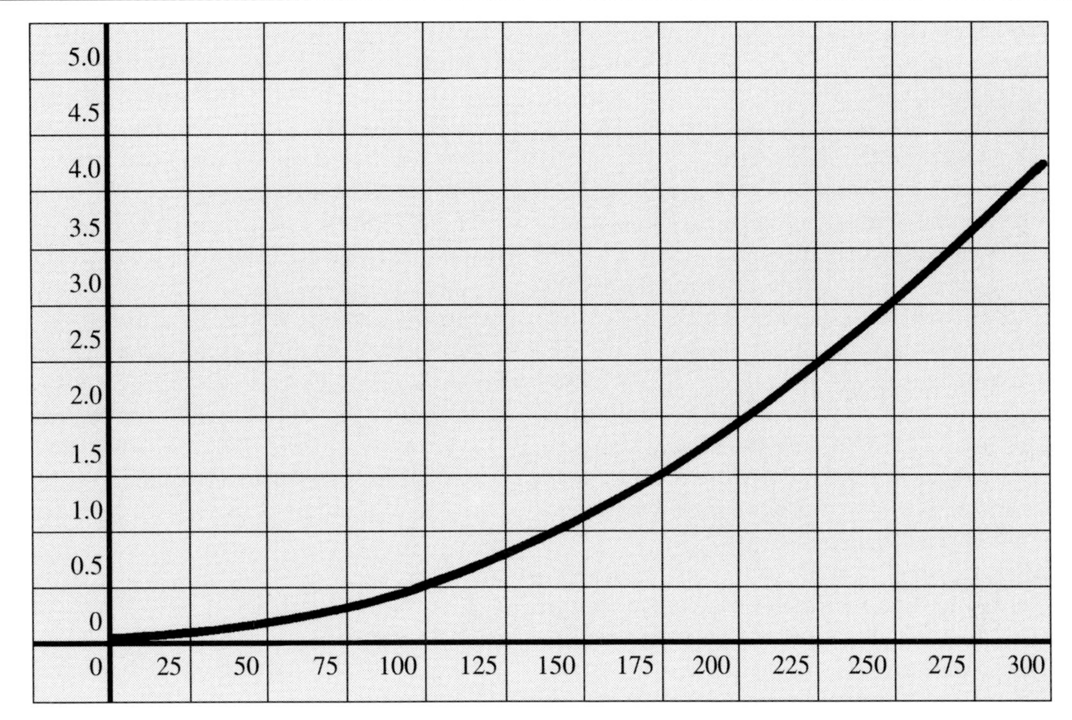

Road speed (km/hr)

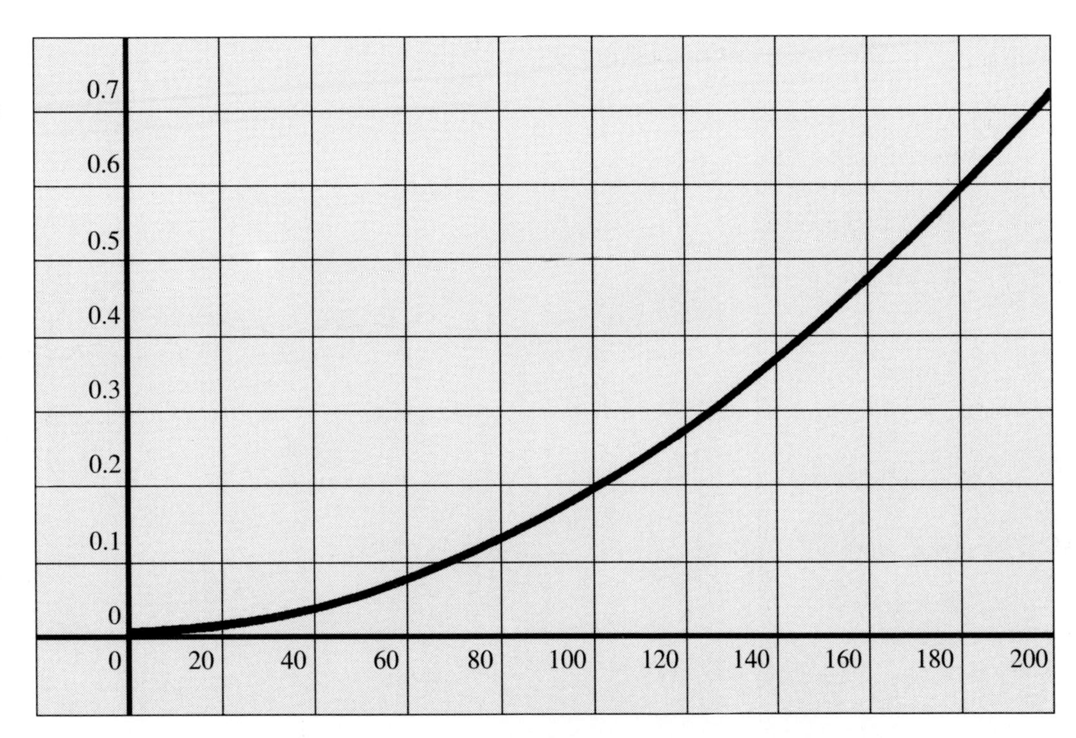

Road speed (miles/hr)

efficiency. This will only translate into a minuscule speed advantage (power required is proportional to speed[3]) but for GP front runners at Hockenheim this means everything. At Darley Moor it will not change the world!

There is also a price to pay. Unless you have fuel injection capable of dealing with it, the air:fuel ratio will be modified according to road speed. The engine will get more air without getting more fuel in the right proportions. This will either lean out the mixture at high speeds or enrich it at low speeds according to how you set up the carburation. Accurate compensation is only possible with the interjection of electronics and that is the way things are going - Fig 4.43. For the average racer it is all a mixed blessing and the main objective is to obtain a decent supply of cool air.

Another aspect of ram-air induction is the possibility of using the airbox as a resonance chamber. In this case the objective is to get the pressure in the box to vary in sympathy with the induction requirements, ie a high pressure occurs when the inlet starts to open. I have no experience of this but can comment as follows. The idea is not new but it is difficult to sort out unless you have the appropriate instrumentation to investigate it properly. For a single-cylinder two-stroke a mathematical solution seems reasonable since it is fundamentally the same as the calculations required to achieve crankcase/transfer/exhaust resonance. Many people have now got this sorted out because we have been doing it for many years.

With multi-cylinder engines a whole new set of problems emerge because you are trying to synchronise the airbox frequency with each cylinder. Nevertheless, this is where the real gains can be made and a well designed airbox can go a long way towards removing mid-range troughs from the torque curve, thereby smoothing out the power delivery. You can experiment with airbox volume, the entry duct and the inlet tracts, particularly their lengths, but your chances of success without a lot of dyno time and good instrumentation are very slim. I must have a dabble at this sometime but at the moment my useful knowledge is nil!

The NACA duct

While on the subject of induction air, a brief discussion of the so called NACA duct is probably called for. These ducts are very common on racing

Below. Fig 4.43 *The airbox on a factory 125cc Honda. The tank is also at airbox pressure and when the throttle is closed the tank vents to the atmosphere. This is initiated by an electronic sensor on the throttle.*

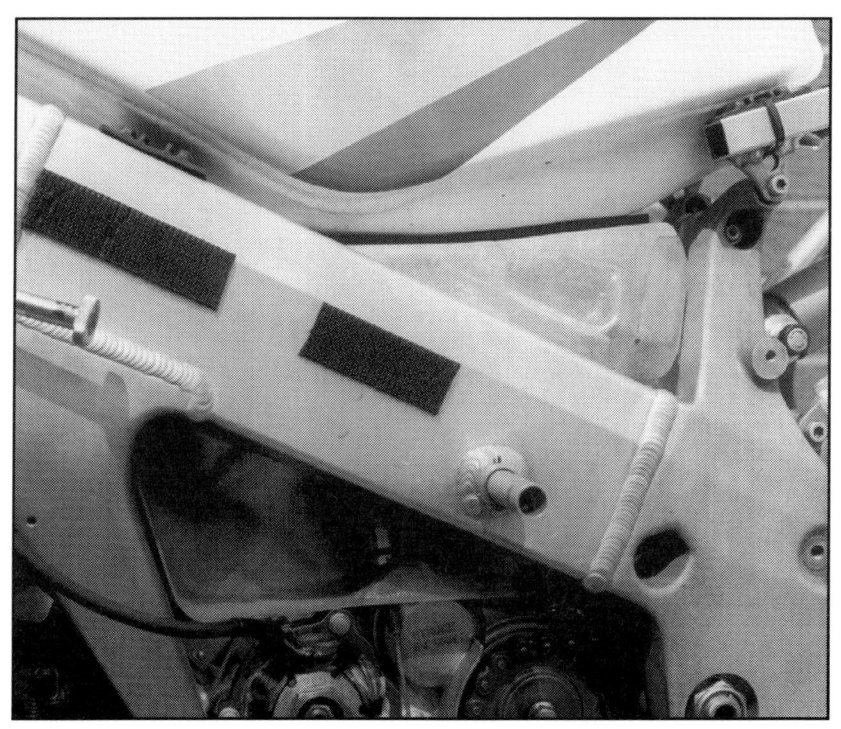

cars, reasonably common on sidecars and sometimes seen on solos. An example is shown in Fig 4.44. Some of the ducts you see will not work in the way the duct is intended to because they are not the right shape or in the correct location. They may well take in air but do so with a significant drag penalty. If the NACA duct is correctly designed and located then the increase in drag coefficient of the bike due to the duct can be less than 1% of its original value.

The NACA duct was developed by the aerospace industry as a means of providing maximum air flow rate with minimum drag. Any form of inlet that sticks out in the air stream will generate drag of its own and interfere with the normal flow as described earlier. The NACA duct is flush with the surface and is a very subtle device.

First a word of warning. The NACA duct fails to perform when it is yawed to the air stream. It is easily shrouded or placed in a wake and only works at its best when it is located in a relatively flat smooth panel where the relative air speed is high, hence the use on cars and sidecars. Short fairings with a lot of curvature are not ideal.

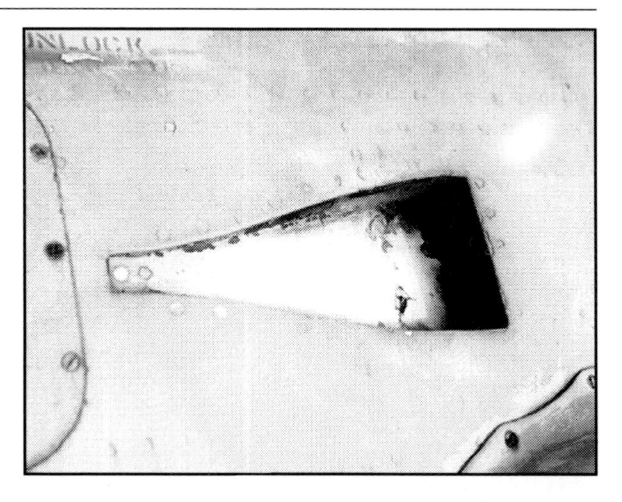

Above. Fig 4.44 *A 'real' NACA duct. This one is on a Hawker Hunter jet aircraft. Most aircraft have them.*

Below. Fig 4.45 *The key to the operation of the duct is the S shape and the sharp corners at all side edges. The rear outer lip should, theoretically, be quite thick but tests show that it will still work using just the fairing skin.*

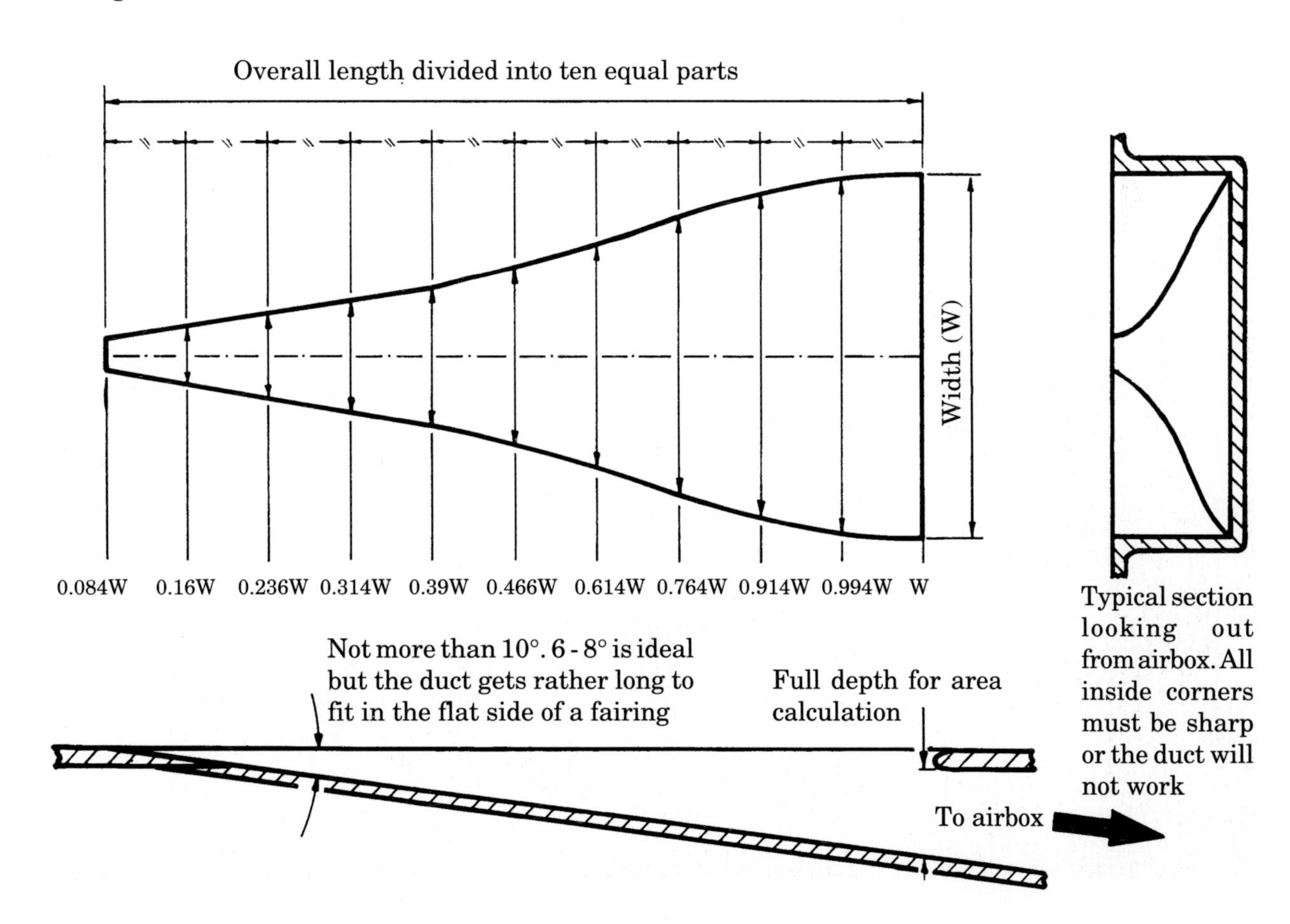

Given the right conditions and design this duct is one of the most efficient but it must be made to the correct dimensions and, even more important, the edges must have sharp corners - Fig 4.45. This is because of the way the duct works.

When the air passes the sharp edges at high speed a vortex is set up, ie a rotating air flow. The effect of this is to scavenge the floor of the duct and thin out the boundary layer that would otherwise build up and block the duct. Provided this happens, the air is persuaded to jump into the hole it would otherwise ignore. The key is the sharp edges and the S type shape.

Theoretically, the trailing edge of the duct should have a relatively thick streamlined section of specific proportions but NACA ducts using just the thickness of the fairing skin have been shown to work perfectly well in wind tunnel tests. They are not quite as good, but much easier to construct.

To estimate the duct size, use the method given previously to calculate the required entry area. This will then be equal to maximum width multiplied by the depth at that point. Make the width at least three times the full depth and preferably more, up to five times if you have the space to do so. Keep the floor angle to less than ten degrees, preferably six, and use this to calculate the length. Make a card template first. Once you have decided on the width and length, divide the length up into ten equal strips and mark off the widths according to Fig 4.45. Do it as accurately as you can and then create the full duct in the fairing. Don't forget the sharp corners.

Example. Design a NACA duct to provide an area of 30cm^2.

Use a width that is four times the depth (3 to 5 acceptable). Calculate the depth using,

$$\text{Depth} = \sqrt{\text{Area}/(\text{Width : depth ratio})}$$

$$= \sqrt{30\text{cm}^2/4} = 2.74\text{cm}$$

Thus, width = 4 x 2.74 = 11cm approx

For a six degree floor,

Length = Depth/Tan(6°) = 2.74/0.105 = 26cm

Fig 4.46 *Duct shape developed in the example.*

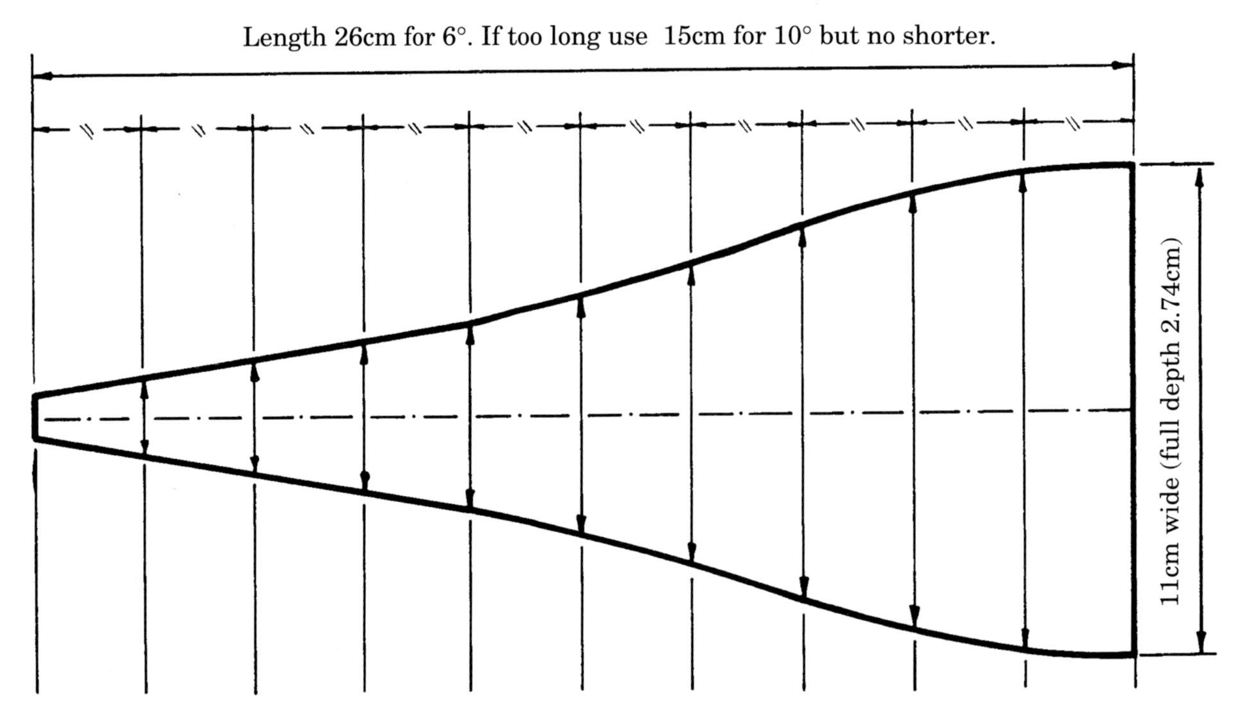

Values are listed as calculated. Just make the shape as accurate as you can. Widths given every 26mm.

If this is too long to accommodate, ten degrees gives 15cm but do not go any steeper. Using 26cm, divide a pattern into ten strips each 2.6cm long and obtain the widths at each stage using the data given previously in Fig 4.45. Fig 4.46 shows the final design.

Cooling

Cooling is one area where there will be a lot of changes in the future, simply because at the moment we make a poor job of it. This is an undisputable fact, but as you might imagine there are reasons. Design is a compromise in which some things have to take priority over others and on most bikes the bit that loses out is cooling.

It does not lose out in the sense that the cooling is totally inadequate. When the cooling is inadequate the problems are very obvious. Water boils, pistons melt, power dwindles and so on. No, the real problem is the price we pay in drag for obtaining sufficient cooling.

The goal is very simple. The less air you allow to pass through the bike, as opposed to around it, the lower the overall drag will be. Set against this is the need to provide sufficient cooling and there is a great deal that can be done before you even consider the air.

It is essential to make the heat transfer as effective as possible at cylinder level, irrespective of whether you have water cooling or air cooling. The thermal conductivity of most aluminium alloys is about sixty times greater than that of carbon so carbon is a severe barrier to heat transfer. Similarly, the most minute amounts of metal oxides inside the water jacket (the creamy brown bits) also have a dramatic effect and it has been estimated that an even coating 0.5mm thick would reduce the overall conductivity by some 50%.

If your heads and cylinders are a carbon/aluminium/oxide sandwich then, assuming there are no overheating problems, the engine is overcooled. Keep it free from carbon, clean out all deposits and use a decent corrosion inhibitor. You can then get away with less air.

There are many other checks to make but I do not want to digress too far from the main topic. Most tuning books give some coverage to this even if it only amounts to the advice that black surfaces are best. Note that a thin high quality black coating might gain you 10% in heat dissipation. A thick one may make things worse.

Once the heat energy is transferred through the cylinder/head walls you then have the choice of air cooling or water cooling. Again, the pros and cons can be found in tuning books. Water cooling is the norm, but the advantages are often overstated. Water does provide more thermal stability, it does allow more power to be produced from two-stroke cylinders and it is virtually essential for two-strokes with cylinders that are close to each other. Despite this, it is generally heavier, there is much more to go wrong and it makes engine work more time consuming. It also lacks the air cooled engine's ability to increase its heat transfer by radiation when the bike is still.

Everything depends on what you are doing. If your racing consists of four laps at an airfield then you are not operating under GP conditions. At the risk of offending those who assume that only water cooling is acceptable, I would suggest that some people do not need it and can benefit from the simpler air cooling, provided the air does actually get to do the job required of it. This is particularly true of four-stroke single-cylinder engines.

If you are using water cooling, you have many other areas worthy of great experiment, ie the radiator, the volume of water, the block pressurisation and the water flow rates to name just a few. Radiators vary incredibly. There are tube and flat fin types, corrugated fin types, cellular cores and so on. If you broaden your horizons and look at heat exchangers in general the range of possible constructions is vast. Some are much more efficient than others, ie they need less area to do the same job and those are the ones you need to sort out. Unfortunately there are no simple rules and it is a case of experimenting. One useful observation is that increasing the thickness of the core does not produce a proportional increase in heat dissipation. Indeed, the gains can be very small for quite large increases in thickness. Do not even consider doing any sums on the size of radiator you need, they are too complex. Just look around at what is being used elsewhere remembering that most bikes have much bigger radiators than they need because the air is so badly managed.

Managing the air

Irrespective of whether you have air cooling or water cooling you are relying on air to do the final job. On a large number of bikes this stage is appallingly inefficient. It does not have to be like this and you need only look at the Britten V-Twins to see one well thought out solution. They have made a serious attempt to obtain an efficient, low drag cooling system. The result is an air intake that blends in as if it's not there, a radiator that is smaller than that fitted to some 125cc bikes and a clear exit of hot air that goes straight into the wake. The radiator is under the seat and, while I do not have any power figures, this bike was speed trapped at 304km/hr (189miles/hr). You can draw your own conclusions.

Compare this with the majority of installations. The radiator represents a big flat plate stuck right behind the front wheel. You may be surprised know that although the radiator presents a formidable element of drag area, it does not actually take in anything like the air it should and the air it does take in is far from ideal for cooling.

Once heated, the air is left to battle its way past every obstruction known to man and is particularly keen to linger around carburettor inlets and electronic components, both of which spend their days dreaming about cool air.

Many air-cooled bikes do little better with a massive hole in the fairing that allows most of the air to bypass the engine altogether. By the time it has bounced around every bit of metal the drag penalty is substantial.

Of course not all bikes are like this and a significant improvement came about when radiators split to the two sides of the fairing and the hot air went out through the sides of the fairing. Nevertheless, this only happened when it had to and even so many such configurations increased the projected area quite dramatically.

Viewed from the front, some big bikes are all radiator. Even some factory bikes were like this and I remember being surprised at the front view of the YZR500 before Team Lucky Strike got hold of it and sorted it out.

Cooling will become the 'in thing' very soon. For years the only thing of interest to the Japanese was power. When that got out of hand they became interested in handling. Now they are developing an interest in real aerodynamics as opposed to styling. They need to, because companies like Aprilia and Britten have shown what can be achieved in this area on relatively small budgets.

However, I am running ahead of myself here. Why are bikes like they are? Does it matter anyway and what can you do to improve them.

There are two totally different situations facing you. The first is designing a new bike from the ground up. The second is improving what you already have. To obtain vast improvements, the only way is to design a new bike around the aerodynamic requirements including cooling. This will inevitably lead to composite frames with everything moulded in as per F1 car technology. It is not good news for the average racer trying to pay the mortgage.

If you have an air-cooled bike there are no excuses. The air needs to be ducted so that what you do get actually passes over the fins. I remember being staggered by the difference this made many years ago. Like everyone else I had a massive hole in the fairing but, following a seizure, I was worried about the cooling so I made up a simple duct to ensure that the air reached the fins - Fig 4.47. As a result, the bike would barely run because it would not stay hot enough. A hundred metres was enough to cool it right down. I therefore made the hole smaller and by the time it worked well the hole was tiny compared to the initial set-up.

Designers of water-cooled bikes, especially modern ones, have a few more excuses. Where can you put the radiator? Because most bikes are the

Fig 4.47 *Even an elementary duct will deliver air to the fins more efficiently and dramatically improve the cooling achieved.*

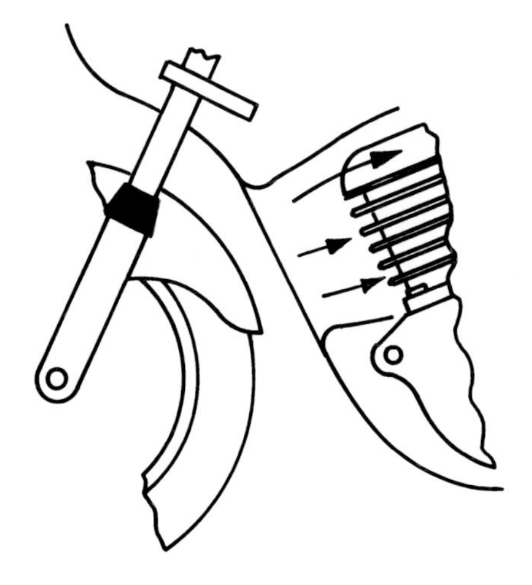

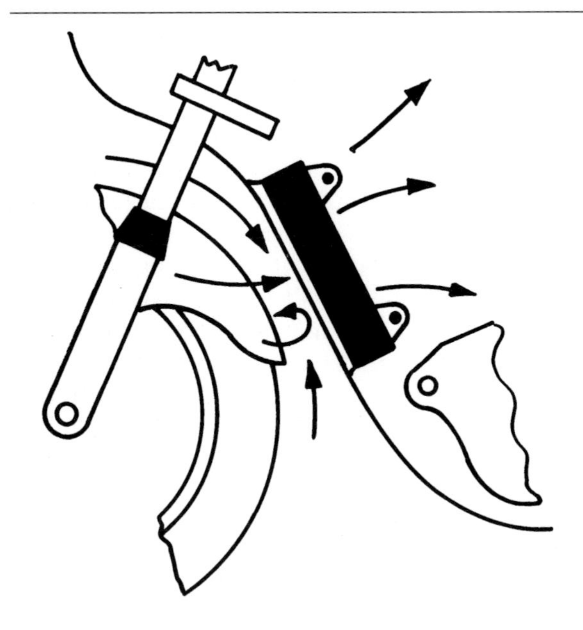

Above. Fig 4.48 *Most radiators are wedged in the available space between the engine and front wheel. They receive much less air than they could from a better position and tests show that they would actually receive more air if tilted backwards. Space generally precludes this.*

Below. Fig 4.49 *The ideal layout of radiator duct is rarely achieved but it is worth trying.*

development of what went before, the change-over from air-cooled to water-cooled meant that the radiator went where there was space and the air could meet it, ie in front of the engine.

Given the fact that the engine is invariably sitting right behind the tyre to produce the desired cg location, most radiators tend to be squashed into the available gap at an angle - Fig 4.48.

In fact, wind tunnel tests show that these radiators do not get anything like the air you would think. Air in the region behind the wheel and forks is much more sluggish than it might appear and much of the airflow that does exist passes parallel to the face of the radiator and does nothing.

I am assured by Kevin Cooper, that his wind tunnel tests on current Superbikes show that the radiator would receive a lot more air if it were tilted in precisely the opposite direction, ie leaning backwards and that this far outweighs the natural convection possible with the existing layout. The main problem is, you cannot physically do it because the engine is in the way. The basic conclusion is that radiators behind the wheel are in the wrong place and the radiator on the Britten is in a better place.

Whatever the case, the ideal situation is shown in Fig 4.49 The air needs to be carried to the radiator via a sealed duct. The entry to the duct should be well rounded and a starting point for the

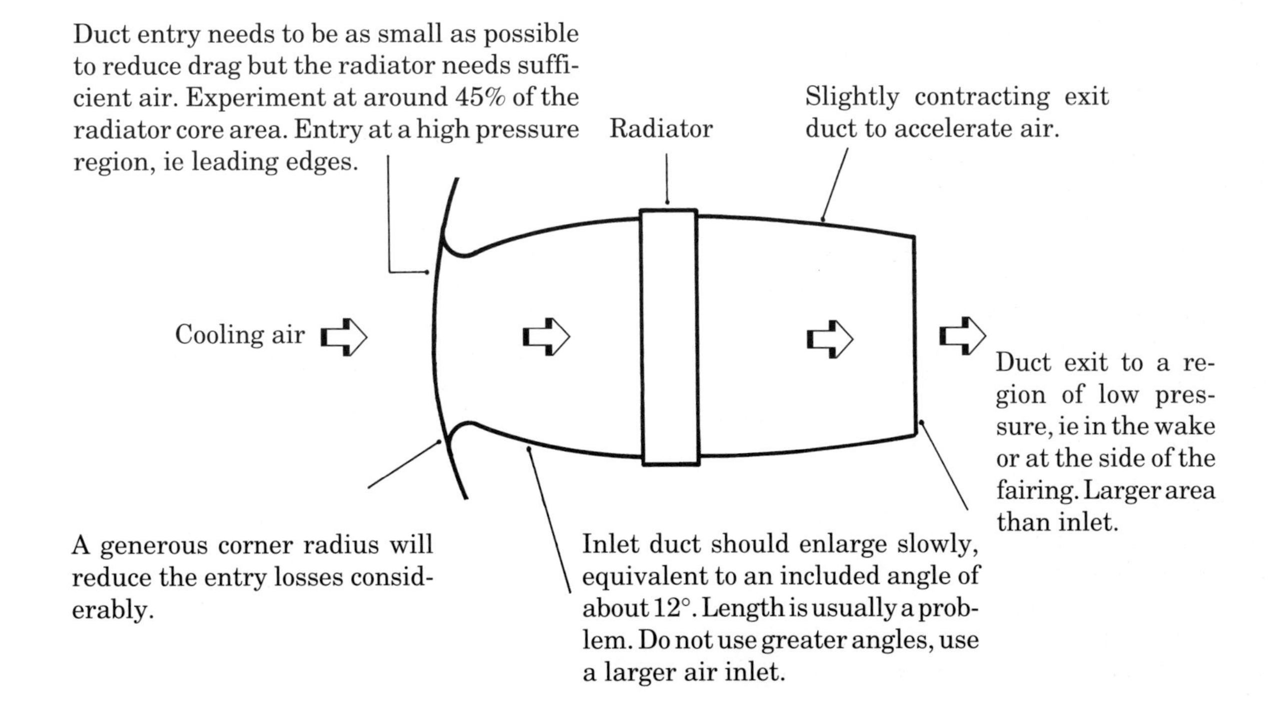

area is 45% of the radiator core area. If the duct has to be very short, the entry area will have to be greater than this because the duct needs to expand slowly. This allows the air pressure to rise as it approaches the core. Slowing the air down also allows it to spend more time acquiring heat energy and there is an optimum air speed that can be found by experiment. Lack of duct length is one of the main problems with the normal installation. In terms of aerodynamic efficiency, ie heat dissipated/drag force produced, the radiator is more efficient at lower air speeds. An element of turbulence is also essential to transfer the heat from one air molecule to the next.

Overall, this is not an efficient process due to boundary layer problems but it is much better than the usual solution. If you really want to get serious you can use boundary layer scrapers/ diverters as per Formula 1.

Once it has passed through the core, the hot air should again be ducted or at least diverted away from anything to do with carburation. To get the air through the radiator efficiently the final destination needs to be a low pressure region, ie in the wake at the rear or at the sides of the fairing. Duct the air whenever possible. The duct should converge slightly to help accelerate the air towards free stream conditions but make sure that the final outlet is larger than the inlet because the air is now hot.

Is it worth the trouble? Unfortunately I do not have any solid wind tunnel figures for bikes but on a typical saloon car the cooling can account for 12 - 15% of the total drag. Re-design can reduce this to 5%. The conventional centrally mounted radiator on a bike is probably even worse. Not only that, but the arrangement encourages air to spill out and mess up the flow around the fairing thereby raising the basic drag. Overall, this has to be one of the areas with the greatest potential for improvement.

Testing

If you do not have a wind tunnel then there is a lot of airfield/track testing to be done. There are several methods available to you.

- Coast down tests.
- Top speed tests.
- High speed acceleration tests.
- Tuft testing.

Testing, and the instrumentation involved, is a very specialised area. I can comment with reasonable authority because most of my industrial work concerns various forms of instrumentation and data gathering.

It is usually fairly easy to come up with some numbers but it is normally rather difficult to be sure the numbers are correct! There are many sources of errors. Calculated values may change by a large amount for a small change in the input data and so on.

Because of this it is essential to focus on what you are really trying to do. For most people, the object of aerodynamic testing is not to find the drag coefficient or the drag area but to see if the performance has been improved. The more direct the chosen measure of performance, the more chance you have of getting repeatable results, without which the tests are a waste of time and money. Adopting this view leads to the following conclusions for the average constructor.

Coast down tests are one standard automotive means of finding a drag coefficient. The vehicle is allowed to freewheel from some speed and the deceleration is measured. Using this, the drag coefficient can be calculated. The problems are as follows.

- On a racing bike it is very difficult to select neutral (unless you are in a race!). Clutch/gearbox drag can be significant.
- Suitable accelerometers are rather expensive though you can build something for about £150 with a simple readout. Assuming you do not do this, you need to measure four road speeds and two time intervals. The errors can be large.
- Wind can have a big effect.
- If you actually want a drag coefficient value, you need to know the inertia of the rotating parts.

Overall, this method is very prone to error unless you have the right instrumentation. A top speed test possibly has more potential for most people but there are still problems.

- You need somewhere to run the bike at the maximum speed possible. This can be difficult or expensive. Best potential with relatively low-powered bikes.
- The gearing has to be optimised. This takes time, several runs, and engine performance can change as well as wind conditions.
- The result will include rolling resistance unless you allow for it. Any allowance is probably a big guess!
- You need to have dyno data showing the net power at the back wheel vs engine speed.
- The calculated value of drag coefficient is extremely sensitive to errors in speed measurement so the first requirement is to get your revcounter accurately calibrated. The appropriate formulae are given on the right and here are two examples.

Example. A bike reaches top speed at 11000revs/min in top gear. The road speed is calculated to be 240km/hr and the engine delivers 60kW at the back wheel at 11000revs/min. Neglect rolling resistance. What is the drag area ?

Using,

$$\text{Drag area (m}^2) = \frac{76173P}{v^3} = \frac{76173 \times 60}{240^3} = 0.33\text{m}^2$$

If the power to overcome rolling resistance can be estimated, this should be subtracted from the total power at the wheel first. This will give a lower, and more realistic drag area.

Example 40bhp net gives a measured top speed of 130miles/hr. Find the drag area. How much error is involved if the speed is really 135miles/hr?

Using,

$$\text{Drag area (ft}^2) = \frac{146806P}{v^3} = \frac{146806 \times 40}{130^3} = 2.67\text{ft}^2$$

Using 135miles/hr gives a drag area of 2.36ft^2 so a 3.7% error in the speed data gives an 11.86% error in the drag area. This aspect can cause large errors if you are not careful.

$$\textbf{Drag Area (m}^2) = \frac{76173P}{V^3}$$

where

P = net power available to overcome aerodynamic drag in kW

V = maximum speed in km/hr

or

$$\textbf{Drag area (ft}^2) = \frac{146806P}{V^3}$$

where

P = net power available to overcome aerodynamic drag in bhp

V = maximum speed in miles/hr

In my opinion, high speed acceleration tests are the most reliable means of checking any changes in performance. You cannot easily calculate the drag coefficient from the result but, as I said earlier, the real aim is to look for improvement.

Use any reasonably high gearing and run the bike up to speeds over 60% of its capability, the faster the better. What you need to record is the time taken to accelerate between any two speeds but you do not need to know the speeds, only the chosen reference points.

Do a test run and then make a decision. For example, you might record the time it takes to accelerate from 7000revs/min in top gear to 11000revs/min in top gear. A long interval that spans gearchanges makes improvements easier to see but introduces the time to change gear. Provided your gearchanges are sweet, this is not a problem because it should be very short compared to the time taken to accelerate through a couple of gears. Any worthwhile drag reductions do make a big difference to the test result. If you cannot detect changes using this method your lap times will certainly not improve.

For timing, it is usually adequate to use a large handlebar-mounted digital stop watch of the type available for push bikes. The rider can start and stop this with reasonable accuracy but if you can arrange an electronic triggering system via the revcounter so much the better. A good data logger is the obvious tool but only a minority can afford them.

In all cases, the first tests should be carried out with no streamlining whatsoever. Use a simple 'plank' seat. Get several sets of data for this configuration with the rider prone because it represents your base line. It might be the best result you get! Try to do all the testing at one session and keep an eye on the wind. Wait for a calm day unless you are desperate.

Finally, the use of tuft testing can provide a lot of information about what the air is doing. Previous photographs have shown typical tufts. Use ordinary wool and attach it with Sellotape. Superglue either fails to work or leaves a big mark when you pull the wool off.

Attach the tufts in rows at several points on the bike and rider as well as near to key points such as inlets. Now head off down the test track while friends drive alongside, one using a camcorder or cine camera and the other driving the car. Go as fast as possible and study the film.

When the airflow is steady, the tufts will lie flat and point in the direction of airflow. Where the airflow is changing, as with separated air, the tufts spin like sycamore seeds. From this you can, with some experience, build up a picture of what is happening and hence try to improve it.

The nice thing about all this is that it is mainly time and effort. The costs are not great if you do the work and, once you have reached a plateau with engine development, it represents the best way forward as far as straight-line performance is concerned. Table 4.7 gives you some idea of what to aim for.

Table 4.7 *Examples of motorcycle drag areas. The data is from several sources, but many were published in the March 1987 issue of Das Motorrad.*

Bike	Drag area (m^2)	Drag area (ft^2)
BMW K100RS, sitting	0.429	4.62
BMW K100RS, prone	0.402	4.33
Honda VF1000F, sitting	0.455	4.89
Honda VF1000F, prone	0.400	4.30
Kawasaki GPZ900R, sitting	0.433	4.66
Kawasaki GPZ900R, prone	0.361	3.88
Suzuki GSX1100EF, sitting	0.444	4.77
Suzuki GSX1100EF, prone	0.412	4.43
Yamaha FJ1100, sitting	0.483	5.20
Yamaha FJ1100, prone	0.433	4.66
Honda RS500 GP, prone	0.243	2.61
Chevallier 250 GP, prone	0.223	2.40
Typ. 1996 Superbike, prone	0.300	3.23
125cc club racer, prone	0.247	2.66
125cc GP racer, prone	0.120	1.30

5.1 Suspension overview

Introduction

Suspension has always been a major topic of discussion amongst motorcycle racers and this will no doubt continue. Apart from the engine, the suspension components are some of the most expensive individual items on the bike and yet they often receive the blame for most of the problems encountered on the track. It seems that everyone who fails to win a race, at any level, either has tyre problems or suspension problems!

I will avoid being too cynical about this and simply start by saying that the suspension is frequently not guilty of the problems it is credited with. Admittedly suspension has an impossible job. It is expected to cope with such a vast range of conditions that it cannot possibly be set up to offer ultimate performance under all these conditions, but even simple suspension systems can be set up to provide an acceptable level of performance under most conditions.

What suspension cannot do, no matter how much it costs, is to compensate for inadequacies in the design of the frame or poor engineering workmanship. The frame structure, particularly the swinging arm and its connection to the steering head, must be rigid enough to resist the loads it receives without deflecting significantly. The swinging arm pivot and any linkages involved must all be engineered to a high standard. Mountings for suspension units must not flex. Bolts and spindles must be of suitable sections so they do not bend. Bearings must be in top class condition, devoid of play and well lubricated, especially if complex linkages are to be employed. I could go on and on with this list but I'm sure the point is made.

Suspension has something in common with aerodynamics. Like aerodynamics it is based on a number of very well-established principles that frequently get ignored or forgotten. Even if you understand the concepts it can be extremely difficult to interpret what is happening on the track. With no understanding it is virtually impossible.

Most information on suspension concentrates on how the actual suspension units behave. Important as this may be, it is not what really matters. The thing that really matters is the way that the wheels behave. Any discussion on suspension should concentrate on what is required at the wheel and the individual can then decide on the best way to achieve such characteristics, selecting suspension units that are built to match their requirements. These requirements will be entirely dependent on the mechanism used and therefore the suspension units are not the place to start but the place to finish. Always start with what you want to achieve at the wheel.

Basic requirements

The purpose of suspension is threefold.

- To keep the tyres in contact with the ground so they can grip.
- To isolate the bulk of the motorcycle from vibration and impact loads, thereby lowering stress levels and reducing the risk of fatigue failure.
- To provide rider comfort.

On a roadrace machine, keeping the tyres in contact with the road is the main priority but in off-road applications the need to isolate the bulk of the bike from repeated impact has almost equal status. Modern motocross bikes would need to be a lot stronger than they currently are if existing courses were used without modern suspension systems. The concept of leaping off table-top jumps using a twin shock system with 100mm of wheel movement is painful even to think about!

Comfort is of course a secondary priority for all racing machines and riders of competition bikes generally accept a much harsher ride than they would wish to tolerate on a road bike. When comfort becomes a real problem, then it is necessary to utilise fully the suspension properties of the seat, otherwise the main suspension may need to be unacceptably compromised. Roadracers survive with a thin layer of foam on the seat but the seat design for motocross bikes is a more serious business altogether. The great variety of conditions which the suspension has to cope with come from four main sources.

- Variations in laden weight.

- Changes induced by motion of the bike and the transfer of power, ie weight transfer during acceleration and braking, pro-squat or anti-squat forces due to swinging arm layout, radial accelerations associated with cornering (discussed later) and various torque reactions.

- Variations in terrain. Bumps, hollows, ripples etc.

- Tyre characteristics.

Changes in laden weight are a very important feature of road bikes since they have to cope with passengers and luggage at regular intervals. For a competition bike these changes are restricted to the variation in the weight of individual riders which is, hopefully, substantially less. Even so, the influence of rider weight is very significant, especially on small, light bikes such as a 125. This means that to get the best suspension performance, rider weight must be accounted for.

Some of the biggest problems for a roadrace bike come from motion-induced forces. Acceleration, braking and cornering all set up relatively large forces and I have already discussed how weight transfer frequently places the full weight of the bike and rider at either end of the machine. Since this roughly doubles the load supported by the suspension at front or rear it is obvious that it will be difficult to get what we want under all conditions.

A complete contrast in requirements comes from the road surface. Although roadracers are not faced with the sort of terrain that motocross bikes have to cope with the track surfaces are far from smooth. Thanks to the invention of miniature cameras we are all more aware of this. TV coverage invariably includes several shots taken from the centre of the bike looking backwards and there for all to see we have a back wheel jumping up and down like something possessed despite the apparently smooth track.

Notice the difference between this and motion-induced changes. Acceleration, braking and cornering impose high loads that use up lots of suspension travel but they tend to be fairly gradual in nature. Surface irregularities are generally fairly small but they are encountered at a range of speeds and the suspension has great difficulty in getting the wheel to follow them. On many occasions the movement of the wheel you observe is substantially greater than the bumps that produced it. Conditions change very quickly.

There is really no simple way of dealing with these requirements and no doubt in a few years' time everyone will be using microprocessor controlled 'adaptive' suspension systems. Systems that adapt in real time are extremely demanding in terms of actuator response and signal processing speed but some 'compromise' systems using circuit 'maps' or rider adjustment have already been experimented with. Until this represents the norm you will have to accept the best compromise you can achieve at any given circuit.

Finally we have the response of the tyres. Tyres are a complete self-contained suspension system that have a considerable influence on their more obvious counterparts. Changing tyres will alter the behaviour of the complete system and so they too need to be considered.

From this very brief discussion it is obvious that the suspension system has to cope with a wide range of requirements and that some degree of adjustment is almost certainly necessary even if the system is put together well in the first place. Modern systems provide such adjustment but setting them up well requires both knowledge and experience.

History

Before looking at the principles of suspension it is useful to examine briefly some of the ideas that have surfaced over the years. Inevitably this mainly involves road bikes and seems out of place but it is only in recent years that bikes have diversified dramatically towards the various specialisms. For many years people rode to work on the bike they raced at weekends! One of the things that this reveals is that most of the 'modern ideas' have been around for a very long time in one form or another. Apart from one or two experimental systems, rear suspension was restricted to the tyres and saddle until about 1930. However, at the front of the motorcycle were a variety of 'girder forks' - Fig 5.1. The interesting thing about these is that they are a form of mechanical linkage system and employ a single 'suspension unit'.

Although the 'suspension unit' was simply a spring, the concept is similar to the latest linkage mechanisms that are now employed for the rear suspension of many motorcycles.

The period 1930 - 1940 saw major changes with the development of telescopic front forks and 'plunger' rear suspension. Crude though they may have been, the telescopic forks came in both 'upside down' and 'conventional' forms, though you might be forgiven for applying such titles to the examples of the time. It is well known that the telescopic fork suffers from a lack of stiffness and most standard forks, as opposed to purpose built race forks, can be visibly twisted out of line by placing the wheel between your legs and turning the handlebars. Nevertheless they have an enduring aesthetic appeal and still have some development life. Single-sided systems using machine tool type pre-loaded bearings have already been tested on modern roadracers by companies like WP Suspension. Apart from such developments the telescopic fork remains much as it always was except for a massive improvement in materials, detail design and quality of manufacture. These are important factors that I shall refer to again. For the average bike builder cost is the main restriction with some of the better front forks costing well over £1500.

Plunger rear suspension represented an improvement on rigid frames but suffered from many problems. Vertical wheel movement tightened the chain considerably when the wheel moved up or down so travel was generally limited. Bearings were simple bushes that required clearance and thus allowed the wheel to tilt out of line. It wasn't long before the swinging arm replaced it and that too has remained to the present day.

Fig 5.1 *The girder forks employed on vintage bikes are a form of linkage system with a single spring element. As such they are the forerunners of the linkage systems commonly employed at the rear of modern bikes.*

The use of a swinging arm paved the way for better control of the rear wheel via specially designed 'suspension units'. A key feature was the use of hydraulic damping. Damping is discussed in detail later on but a brief outline is as follows.

To provide suspension you have to include something that will allow the wheel to deflect independently of the motorcycle but which will also return the wheel to its original position soon afterwards. This requires something that will store up the work done in deflecting the wheel as energy and then use it to return the wheel. This is the characteristic of 'stiffness' and it is normally provided by a coil spring though other solutions such as rubber in shear, leaf springs or steel torsion springs have been used. The spring can isolate the bike from impact by absorbing the energy from sudden 'shocks' but it then takes a while to dissipate this energy. As it does so the bike bounces up and down on the springs in a most unsatisfactory manner. Other related aspects will be discussed later. To overcome such problems the excess energy stored in the spring(s) has to be used to do something that is not detrimental to the suspension behaviour before it can be transferred to the bulk of the bike. On girder forks the solution was to have a form of 'friction brake' that converted the energy to heat. The principle is fine but the nature of the friction is not at all suitable. A much better solution sees oil forced through small holes in chambers and this is the basis of modern hydraulic dampers. It is interesting to note that it is the spring element that is the 'shock absorber' and the role of the damper is to introduce an additional force which opposes the relative move-

Fig 5.2 *Velocette road bikes provided slots so that the angle of the rear suspension units could be altered. This changes the springing and damping characteristics seen by the wheel. It was used to account for load changes associated with carrying a passenger.*

Fig 5.3 Vincent bikes employed triangulated swinging arms in the 1950's. Twin inclined units were later replaced with a single 'monoshock' system. Similar systems appeared on some bikes even earlier but this was the one that caught riders' imagination.

ment of wheel and bike, thereby dissipating excess energy. The heat produced raises the oil temperature and, hopefully, this is transferred to the surrounding air. This is the basis of all modern suspension and identical observations apply to front forks. Several variations on this theme appeared. It was soon realised that although the characteristics of the suspension units were essentially 'fixed', the way the wheel responded to them could be altered by setting the units at an angle. If the angle was adjustable then changes could be made at will.

Velocette offered adjustment as standard using the system shown in - Fig 5.2. Vincent on the other hand realised that flexure of the swinging arm was excessive unless the arm was built rather substantially making it very heavy using the materials available at the time. They adopted a triangulated fork using smaller tubes and suspended with two almost horizontal units - Fig 5.3. These were later replaced by a single unit and the cantilever/monoshock system was born. In fact several similar systems had appeared much earlier but Vincent acquired a reputation for making it work fairly well. It was subsequently adopted by Yamaha around 1979 and became de rigeur for many years, irrespective of the bike's application.

Although production bikes of all types were now appearing with monoshock units and cantilever swinging arms there had, for several years, been experiments with linkage type systems for rear suspension. The first written confirmation I have of this is a thesis by S.H.Black at Cornell University which describes a linkage system fitted to a Kawasaki 250. This was in 1978. Several other variations on the theme appeared, notably the Villa 250 Adriatica in 1980 and within a few

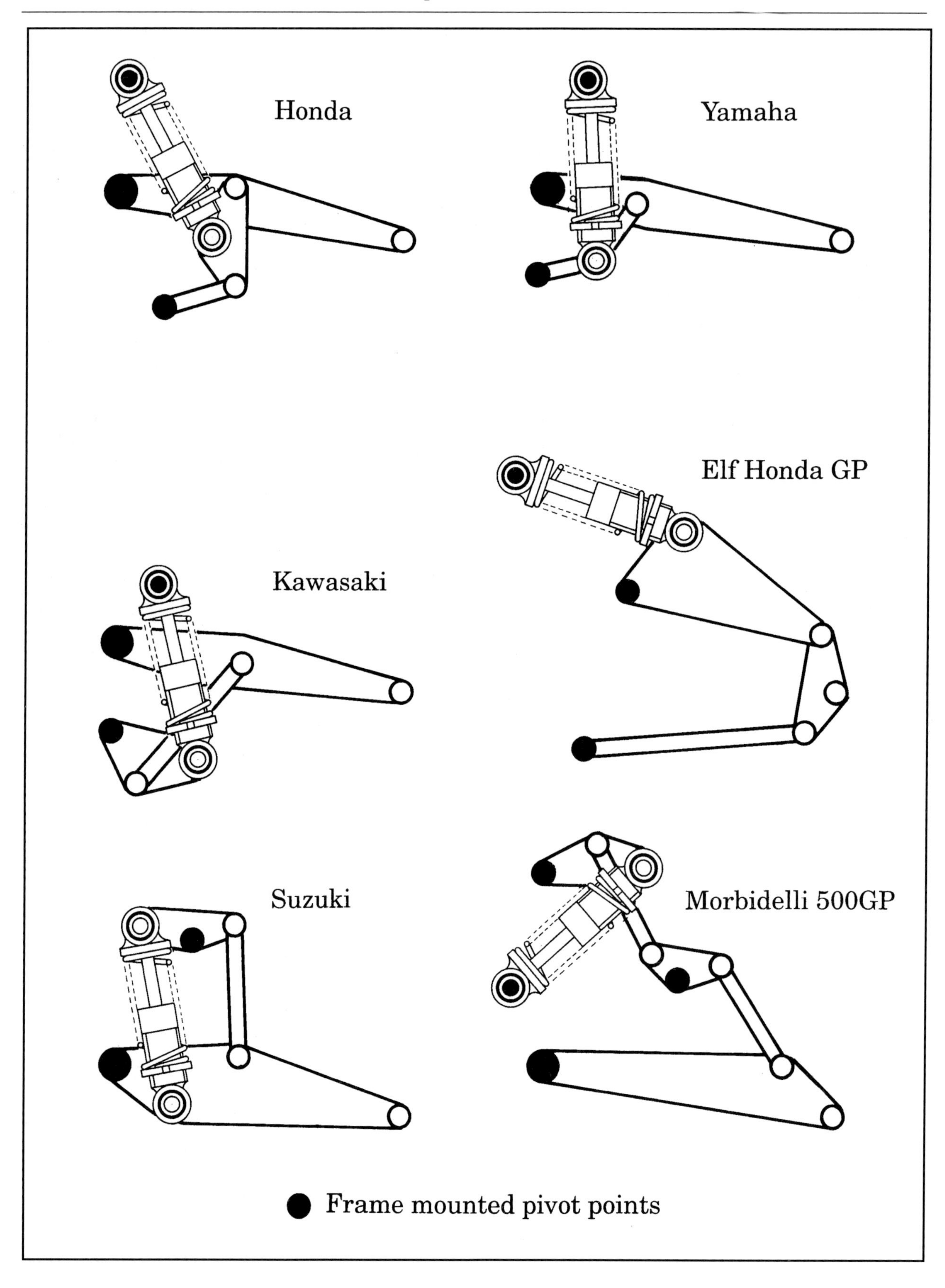
Honda
Yamaha
Elf Honda GP
Kawasaki
Suzuki
Morbidelli 500GP
Frame mounted pivot points

years all the major manufacturers had linkage type systems on at least some of their motorcycles. Various examples are shown in Fig 5.4 .

As with the earlier monoshock systems, the use of linkages then spread to include road, roadracing and trials machines. Clearly these systems are complicated. They are more difficult to construct and require much more maintenance so why use them? As far as motocross and trials were concerned there were two main problems to overcome. Firstly, the tracks were becoming ever more dramatic and more and more suspension travel was being sought. To achieve this, the rear units on existing twin shock bikes were being moved further and further along the swinging arm. If they are located at the mid-point then the wheel travel is approximately twice that required of the suspension unit itself. However, this approach introduces other problems. Along with the increase in travel comes an increase in the force applied to the middle of the arm. The arm is being bent and failure is more likely. Despite this, the system was very common in the early 1970's. Riders soon realised the potential problems and swinging arms suddenly became a lot stronger.

In one sense the monoshock layout overcomes this problem. Wheel travel can be much greater than that of the suspension unit itself and the triangulated arm is far better suited to the increased loads involved, taking most of the force as compression of the upper tubes rather than as bending of the arm itself. However, like the normal twin shock layout the geometry of the cantilever system means that the characteristics of the suspension actually seen at the wheel are not ideal for motocross use and it is not easy to overcome this with simple systems.

The problem lies in the relatively fixed characteristics of normal suspension units and the extremely variable requirements of the wheel. It is very difficult to produce a suspension unit which can offer good behaviour on minor ruts, ripples and bumps and still cope with the massive leaps encountered in motocross. If the behaviour is acceptable for the majority of conditions then the suspension is almost certain to bottom out with a bang on the larger jumps and bumps. By using linkages it is possible to alter considerably the springing and damping characteristics that the wheel experiences at different points in its travel. This can, to some extent, be achieved by using special springs and damping arrangements within the unit but linkages provide much more scope and a greater degree of alteration which can prevent bottoming out completely. By combining sophisticated suspension units and linkage systems an almost limitless range of possibilities presents itself. There is no doubt that these systems are beneficial for motocross. They provide substantial travel, soft suspension at small amounts of travel and much harder suspension as the travel increases. This is commonly called 'rising rate' and I will discuss it in detail shortly. The change in characteristics can be vast and the application clearly supports this.

The use of complex linkages, large amounts of travel and dramatically rising rates is of much more doubtful benefit on tarmac. Indeed, at the time of writing the latest factory KTM motocross bikes are experimenting with non-linkage systems so perhaps a new trend is about to start. Personally I think this is the most sensible approach, ie the flexibility should be built into advanced suspension units rather than being achieved by linkages. Linkages require a lot of maintenance, especially on off-road bikes. They are exposed, they attract dirt and they wear out. Friction soon becomes higher than one might like.

Despite these problems, market forces have ensured that linkage systems have appeared on just about every type of bike. The problem is, few constructors know what type of rising rate characteristic will suit them and many linkage systems on road and roadracing bikes do no more than could be achieved with either a twin shock or cantilever layout. Many road races have been won using bikes that do not have rising rate characteristics and some actually have falling rate characteristics. There are no clear cut rules here.

Even if you go along with the idea of having a rising rate and can specify its nature you then have to achieve it. Since translating any new characteristic into linkage geometry is a substantial challenge without sophisticated Computer Aided Design facilities, you really do need to believe in this in order to justify the work involved. Experiments can be very time consuming.

Left. Fig 5.4 *Some of the many linkage systems that have been employed for rear suspension by different manufacturers.*

This then is a rather brief history of motorcycle suspension. We note that although Grandad's bikes were crude in construction the designers were not short of ideas and virtually all the modern concepts have been around for years. However, today's materials and engineering precision allows these ideas to be used without the problems experienced in the past. The manufacturers now produce ever more exotic systems with beautifully sculptured 'gull' and 'single sided' swinging arms together with very sophisticated suspension. Just how much of this is driven by need and how much is market appeal is often difficult to judge but the majority of riders will never push bikes to the point where it really matters. As such, we are really dealing with aesthetic appeal and only the individual can accept or reject the cost involved.

For those who know they genuinely cannot outride moderately good suspension, the progress with materials and engineering precision has brought another bonus. Given the quality of components available it is by no means essential to use complex systems and a simple swinging arm with twin shocks or a cantilever monoshock has much to recommend it, especially if your precision engineering facilities are limited. Provided the structure is sound and the suspension units chosen are of high quality, the systems can be made to work extremely well, eg Brian Crighton's Nortons or Moriwaki's NSR250 Honda. Each system has its enthusiasts but a general summary is given on the next two pages. Readers will have to form their own opinion regarding the balance of needs and market forces.

Fig 5.5 *Is this the future? The single-sided fork was designed by WP Suspension several years ago and has been fully developed using a variety of bikes. The technology is there but the market is not yet ready.*

Twin shock suspension

- Simple to construct requiring much less precision engineering than linkage systems.
- The heat generated in each damper is less than when one single damper is used. This helps to keep temperatures down and reduces the possibility of fade.
- The location of the suspension units is much more favourable in terms of heat transfer. The units are close to the free air stream and are not trapped directly in hot air coming from the engine. Again, this reduces the possibility of fade.
- If the units are badly mismatched they tend to twist the swinging arm. Given modern materials and suspension unit design this should not be a problem.
- The travel of the suspension units themselves is greater than that found on 'short' monoshock types. It is possible that this gives the manufacturer more scope to control damping characteristics at their intended values, though very long units have space problems.
- Because 'fashion' dictates that these systems are obsolete it can be difficult to source high quality suspension units with the variety of adjustments that are available on monoshock type units.
- Minimal loads are transferred into the frame.
- The suspension loads are shared by two units which are generally less heavily loaded than a single unit.
- The swinging arm is more flexible in its untriangulated form. The solution is to brace it where there is found to be a problem.
- Wheel travel is limited. This is a major problem in off-road applications, less so on tarmac.
- The suspension units move at roughly the same speed as the wheel and are located near the wheel. As such they add significantly to the effective moving mass and make it more difficult to control. See 'sprung and unsprung mass'.
- The majority of swinging arm layouts give a roughly constant 'rate' characteristic. They can be set to rise by perhaps 70% or fall dramatically, neither of which is of much use to those seeking vast rises in rate. Any major alteration in suspension characteristics with wheel travel has to be built into the suspension units themselves.
- The layout is perceived as old fashioned which can affect resale value however well it may work.

Cantilever - monoshock suspension

- Relatively simple construction, again not requiring the precision of linkage systems.
- Long suspension units were used originally but few of this type are available now.
- Imposes higher frame loads than most twin shock systems.
- The unit makes less contribution to the unsprung mass.
- The location of short units immediately behind the engine is far from ideal thermally but it is, in a sense, convenient.
- The use of a single unit means there are no matching problems.
- Large range of sophisticated units available with springs and damping characteristics to suit virtually any desired application. Considerable adjustability on race units.
- The mechanism has very limited ability to impose desired changes in rate characteristics with wheel travel. As with twin shock, anything dramatic has to be built into the suspension unit.
- Allows greater wheel travel than twin shock systems in most cases.
- Stiff, light swinging arm layout.

Linkage suspension systems

- Ultimate flexibility in characteristics obtainable.
- Must be well engineered. High precision is required to avoid excess friction and this increases costs.
- Easy to experiment with by making different rocker arms, using adjustable links etc.
- The current 'fashion', hence marketable. Few people can tell what the system really does just by looking.
- High forces are generated at some points in the mechanism.
- Designing a completely new linkage system to produce a specific characteristic is extremely difficult.
- Most bike builders will need to copy existing systems and experiment from there.
- There does not appear to be any 'magic' characteristic that gives best results on tarmac.
- Linkage systems require careful design, especially near to full travel. Some have been known to 'wind up' in this region.
- Very small dimensional changes can sometimes yield very large changes in characteristics.
- Require a high standard of maintenance if they are to perform correctly. This should be routine on a racing motorcycle.

Sprung and unsprung mass

Whatever the type of suspension system chosen, some parts move with the wheels and others form the bulk of the bike. The bulk of the bike on which you sit is supported by the suspension system and it is therefore called the sprung mass (or sprung weight). Strictly speaking we are dealing with mass though in normal conversation most people would refer to weight. The distinction is probably only important when you start working things out and the reader is referred to Appendix 1 which discusses this topic in more detail.

The parts which move with the wheels when the suspension operates are collectively termed unsprung masses (or weights). At the front of the bike the unsprung masses are those contributed by the wheels, tyres, brakes and moving fork legs.

At the rear the situation is considerably more complicated but in essence we have the wheel, tyre, brakes, sprocket, chain, swinging arm and various suspension components. A substantial part of the suspension units moves up and down with the wheel and it is therefore classed as unsprung. The remainder is attached to the frame and is thus part of the sprung mass.

The term unsprung mass is actually an equivalent value rather than an actual value. When the wheel encounters a bump the force generated has to accelerate all the unsprung parts around the swinging arm pivot. These have a certain moment of inertia and this will determine how easy they are to accelerate. Analysis would show that while the wheel assembly can be handled directly some serious sums are required to sort out what percentage of the swinging arm, chain and suspension units is involved. The final result depends on individual masses and where they are concentrated. As an example, if most of the weight of the swinging arm was near to the pivot then it would be easier to accelerate it than a similar system with most of the arm weight at the wheel spindle. Similar observations apply to the suspension units and normal twin shocks generate the greatest inertia because of their location. Most of the suspension unit moves at relatively high speeds.

I will consider this again shortly but we do not need any sums to achieve a good practical result. If the entire assembly has a low moment of inertia then a relatively small torque is required to accelerate it around the swinging arm pivot. To achieve this we must,

- Reduce the total mass, hence weight, associated with any unsprung components, ie those that move with the suspension.

- Within the limits of required strength and other considerations, try to concentrate the weight at the smallest radius from the swinging arm pivot.

Although these principles are fundamental there are obviously limits to what you can achieve. The wheel, tyre, sprocket and brake components normally sit on the end of the swinging arm though some people, notably Harley Davidson, have experimented with rear brakes that run on the gearbox final drive shaft. This idea appeals in terms of reduced unsprung inertia but there are all sorts of other problems to be overcome.

Given this situation, once you have purchased the best components you can afford and have lightened everything to the limit then there is little else that can be done with a given layout. Even this takes a lot of work and I recently had the pleasure of picking up the wheels of a leading 500cc classic racer. They looked normal enough until you actually lifted them up, at which point I thought they were off a 125! Tales of re-machining the rim profiles and modifying every spoke nipple then followed, not to mention the specially made magnesium hubs. The amount of work involved was clearly astronomic but the results were very impressive. Given the fact that they have been in use for some time and have won many races it is clear that they are still strong enough. Most components are over-engineered but you have to think very seriously about the consequences of any lightening regieme.

As far as the suspension itself is concerned, the same observations apply. The less the moving parts weigh and the smaller their effective radius from the pivot the better. If the radius is not obvious then look for amount of movement, less movement giving a similar result.

Twin shock layouts are clearly the worst in this respect but I think the problem is often exaggerated. Taken as a percentage of the total inertia their contribution is not so great that it renders the suspension unworkable! Individuals should simply select the system that suits them and then try to implement it as efficiently as possible.

Influence of unsprung mass

Any vertical force that appears at the wheels is passed directly to the sprung mass by the springs in the suspension. The force involved will depend on the vertical acceleration imposed on the equivalent unsprung mass and the unsprung mass value m , ie force = mass x acceleration.

This force is now passed on to the sprung mass. If the force concerned is F and the sprung mass is M then the bulk of the bike and rider will be accelerated upwards such that,

$$a_s = \frac{F}{M}$$

thus

$$a_s = \frac{ma_{us}}{M}$$

where

a_s = vertical acceleration of sprung mass

a_{us} = vertical acceleration of unsprung mass

m = unsprung mass

M = sprung mass

F = force transmitted

This shows that the acceleration of the sprung mass upwards when the bike hits a bump depends on the value of (unsprung mass/sprung mass). To obtain the most comfortable ride and isolate the bulk of the bike from what the wheels are doing we need to minimise this value. Large road bikes are usually best in this respect. Although they are very heavy a high proportion of the mass is sprung mass. The value of (unsprung mass/sprung mass) is relatively small and as a result the ride is extremely smooth. Some large tourers glide along as if the roads were glass. Unfortunately, roadracers do not come out of this very well. Most builders will lighten the bike as much as they can within available budgets but there is a limit to how much you can remove from unsprung components. Nothing can be done about tyres and the lightest wheels are extremely expensive. By the time it reaches the track, the race bike will be much lighter than the road bike overall but the final m/M ratio is likely to be higher. The result is a harsher ride on a given surface, irrespective of how well the suspension is set up.

In addition to limiting comfort, the unsprung mass is very influential as far as roadholding is concerned. At any point where the wheel is losing contact with the ground its return is driven by the available spring force. If the unsprung mass is small, the resulting acceleration is increased and the wheel makes contact again fairly quickly. The greater the unsprung mass the more sluggish this process becomes. It is important to acknowledge these aspects and do everything you can to minimise the unsprung weight (hence mass), irrespective of the type of suspension you intend to use.

Finding unsprung mass

In practice I do not think it is worth doing reams of sums to find the exact equivalent unsprung mass. The reasons for this are quite simple. Firstly, you are always restricted by cost and strength. You will use the best components you can afford and lighten everything as much as you think is safe. Secondly, the majority of the moving parts involved are concentrated at the wheel spindle where their equivalent unsprung mass is no different (numerically) to the value you would obtain on a set of scales. Note that mass in kg is numerically equal to weight in kgf. The same applies to lb and lbf but not newtons (see Appendix1).

The swinging arm is usually fairly light in comparison and most of the material is concentrated near to the pivot. For these reasons I think it is more than adequate simply to weigh the final assembly as shown in Fig 5.6. The same technique can be used at the front of the bike.

- Support the bike under the frame or engine so that the wheels just touch the ground.

- Free off the springs to the extent that the swinging arm just 'hangs'.

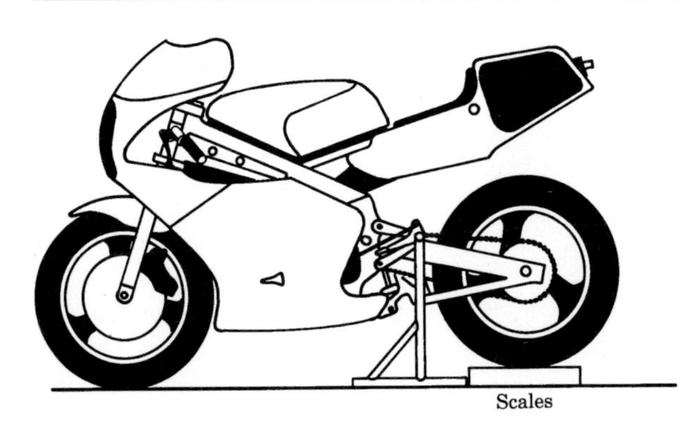

Fig 5.6 *Weighing everything that 'hangs' onto scales set as shown will give an unsprung weight that is more than adequate for most practical purposes. Make sure the swinging arm is completely free and the suspension is not fully extended. Springs must be uncompressed.*

- Place a set of scales beneath the wheel and take a reading. This figure will be an adequate unsprung weight for most purposes.

The value you will read at the rear is not the true unsprung weight but it is a reasonable approximation that can be used for comparison. If you reduce this then progress has been made.

Although a true calculation is generally out of the question, some discussion of the source of error in the above method may be of interest.

Fig 5.7 shows various examples. If we have a concentrated mass m at radius r then its moment of inertia about centre O is mr^2. If we attach this to the pivot using a weightless arm of length L (diagram b), then the moment of inertia is mL^2. Taking m to represent the complete wheel assembly, if we let it hang on a set of scales as described earlier then the scale reading does give a true equivalent unsprung mass and we could calculate the moment of inertia using this figure and the value of $(\text{length})^2$.

However the arm itself is not weightless, nor is the chain etc. Diagram c) is the simplest representation possible, an arm in which the weight is uniformally distributed throughout. This has a moment of inertia equal to $mL^2/3$ (derived by calculus). If we support this horizontally on the scales, the value we get will be half of the total weight, hence mass, ie m/2 as shown in diagram d). A mass m/2 at radius L has a moment of inertia $=mL^2/2$ so the scale reading gives us the wrong answer, it should be $mL^2/3$. In practice this is not really a problem. The heaviest element is the combination of wheel, tyre, brake, sprocket etc that is a concentrated mass at arm's length and the scale reading copes with that correctly. The scale reading does not give a true value of the mass required to calculate the inertia presented by the arm, chain etc but it does make some attempt. Since it will take you almost as long to do the sums accurately as it does to build the bike the method I have described should be acceptable for the majority. Boffins can read appropriate text books.

Fig 5.7 *Moment of Inertia for a number of simplified situations. The text uses these to show why weighing everything that 'hangs' on to the scale does not give a truly representative figure of unsprung weight. However it is more than adequate as a means of comparison.*

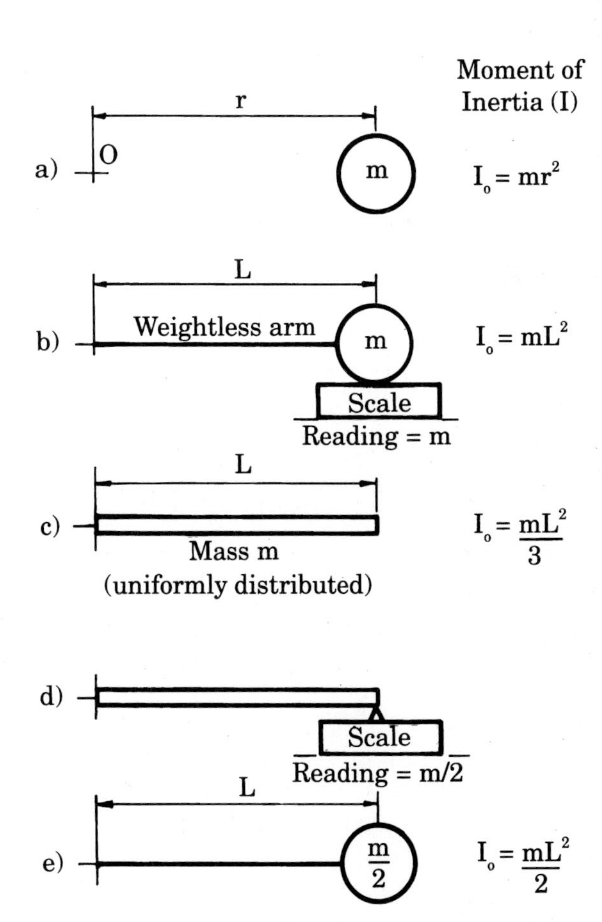

5.2 Stiffness requirements at the wheel

Introduction

Although the purpose of suspension is common to all systems the method used to achieve a final result is entirely at the discretion of the builder. In the previous chapter I have identified some of the more common systems and a search through the history books would reveal many other solutions. Every constructor has ideas they wish to experiment with.

I do not think it is possible to stand up and say that any one system is better than another. Riders differ considerably in their opinions and it is not possible to compare like with like. For example, you cannot ride a twin shock bike fitted with ex-WD dampers and then pronounce all such systems inferior. Most twin shock systems fitted with state-of-the-art dampers feel a lot better than linkage systems fitted with 'economy' units.

However, the purpose of all these systems is the same and in this book I am therefore going to concentrate on the overall requirements. You can then apply the ideas to whatever configuration appeals to you.

A detailed analysis of suspension is beyond the scope of this book and it does not really lead anywhere beyond what can be determined from a few basic ideas. Suspension requirements depend on a vast range of parameters including rider weight, machine weight, cg location, wheel travel, tyres, steering geometry, track surface, riding technique, braking capacity, power available etc. With all these things to consider the best way forward is to combine simple concepts with practical experience and the more data you can acquire relating to existing bikes the better. It is particularly important to study any set-up that does not suit you and try to find out why. Eventually a clear, or probably rather murky, picture of your requirements will emerge.

Because all suspension systems are different I want to begin by looking at the overall requirements, ie what happens at the wheel. Once you can establish what is required at the wheel you can then design any weird system you like and estimate the requirements of a suspension unit to suit. In some systems, small changes in geometry or rider preference require substantial changes in the suspension unit characteristics so without some attempt to estimate the requirements, experiments can get rather expensive.

As with most other areas, the sensible course of action is to discuss your requirements in detail with the manufacturers. They have more experience than you or I and they have much more data to fall back on. Obviously you have to sort out the people who know from the people who just want your money but this is not too difficult to do.

Stiffness

Stiffness is something that crops up in many different forms on a motorcycle. It expresses the relationship between the forces or torques applied to things and the deflections they produce.

$$\textbf{Stiffness} = \frac{\textbf{Change in load}}{\textbf{Change in deflection}}$$

Stiffness can be measured in any appropriate units, common ones being N/mm, N/cm, kgf/mm, kgf/cm and lbf/in for force and linear deflection. N-m/deg, N-m/rad, lbf-ft/deg etc apply to torque loads and the resulting twist. Stiffness is often constant for relatively small deflections, but rarely so over very large deflections. It is frequently presented in the form of a graph showing load vs deflection. Stiffness can be calculated from the slope of the graph at any point and changes in stiffness are very evident when the data is presented in this way.

Something with a high stiffness value shows little movement for a given load change and in the case of structures the deflections produced by normal working loads may not be visible. For example, if a load is applied to the end of a steel bar, 50mm diameter and 100mm long then it takes about 390kN (39tonf) to compress it by 0.1mm (about 4thou).

This is serious stiffness and the piece of metal is, for most practical purposes, rigid. Once we start building motorcycles however, the structures, stiff though they may appear, are very flexible in comparison. If you held the pivot of a typical swinging arm from a large bike perfectly still, then a force of perhaps 300N (67lbf) applied at the wheel spindle would deflect the wheel sideways by 1mm. A purpose built arm for a 750cc race bike might require twice this load but you can see that compared to the original example the swinging arm is like a rubber band!

As far as suspension is concerned the stiffness involved is much lower than my structural examples, as indeed it should be. There are in fact three stiffness values involved here. Firstly there is the stiffness of the tyres, secondly the stiffness offered by the suspension mechanism and finally the stiffness associated with the seat. For roadracing the seat can be ignored but riding a motocross bike with 10mm of foam to sit on would adequately demonstrate the suspension properties of a good seat. I will consider the main suspension stiffness first and look at the tyres later.

Wheel rate

Whatever the actual mechanism involved, the 'real' stiffness offered by the suspension presents itself as a value that can be determined by recording the wheel's vertical deflection when different vertical loads are applied. This particular stiffness is commonly called wheel rate (the term rate is often used for stiffness but unless it is further qualified confusion is likely). Thus,

$$\text{Wheel rate} = \frac{\text{change in wheel load}}{\text{change in wheel position}}$$

where both the load and deflection are measured vertically and the bike is assumed to be upright

As before, it is usual to present such data as a graph, particularly if the wheel rate is not constant. Fig 5.8 gives examples. When the wheel rate is high the suspension is stiff and vice versa.

Wheel rate is the fundamental outcome of your suspension system as far as 'springing' is concerned. Taking all motorcycle applications, the range of values is probably 7-23N/mm (0.7-2.3kgf/mm, 40-130lbf/in) but for a given type of bike, weight of rider and riding style this reduces to a much narrower range of values. The use of a swinging arm and different mechanisms will ensure that the stiffness associated with the actual spring(s) on the suspension unit(s) is not the same as the wheel rate. The basic objective is to determine a suitable wheel rate and then work from there to establish what actual springs are required to achieve it using your chosen mechanism.

You might consider the situation to be represented by Fig 5.9 in which each wheel is connected to a single, vertical suspension unit. The wheel can only move vertically and in this situation, with just one unit per wheel and no arms or linkages, the required spring stiffness (rate) would indeed equal the wheel rate. Although the system in Fig 5.9 is hypothetical in the sense that it is impractical, it is a very convenient representation of the system and I will use it again later on to develop various ideas.

As far as wheel rate is concerned there are three things to be decided. What should the rate be and should it remain constant? If it does not remain constant how should it change?

Top right. Fig 5.8 *Graphs showing the vertical force required to move the wheel vertically against the suspension stiffness. The wheel rate is equal to the slope of such a graph. Graph a) is a straight line so a given increase in force always gives a proportional increase in wheel movement. In graph b) the slope is increasing. It takes more force at the wheel to move it by a given amount later in the travel than it did at the start of the travel. This is called a rising rate. Both graphs show a 'step' at the beginning where a certain force is required before the wheel moves at all. This is due to preload which is discussed shortly.*

Bottom right. Fig 5.9 *A physical representation of wheel rate. The wheel is supported by a single vertical suspension unit and can only move vertically. This system is not a practical layout but a convenient representation for outlining the basic ideas.*

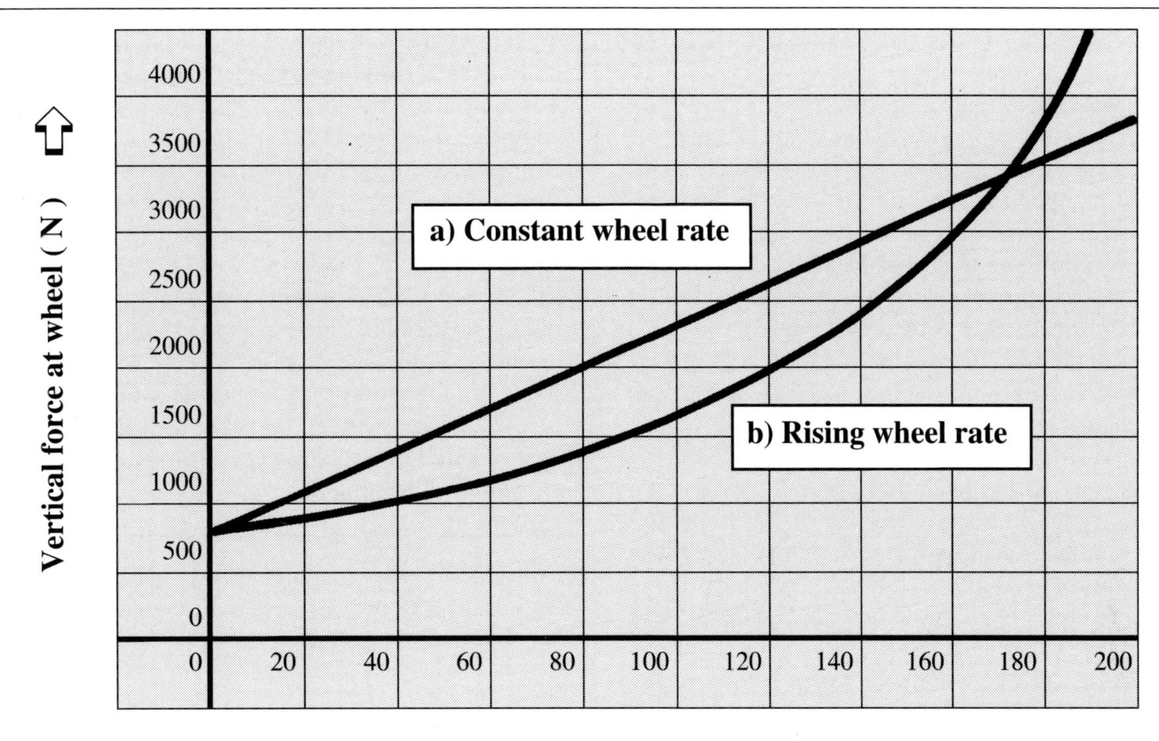

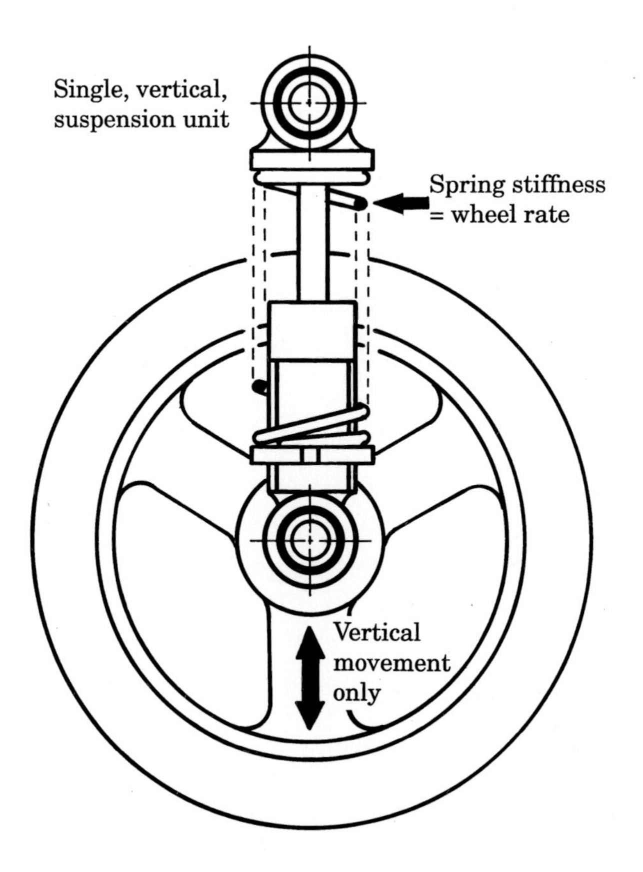

Wheel rate requirements

Wheel rate is best determined by a combination of simple analysis and practical experiment. If you have two broadly similar bikes with totally different suspension systems then it is suprising how similar the wheel rates will be when you find them both acceptable, even though the actual spring stiffness may be very different. What I am talking about here is the initial wheel rate over perhaps the first 50% of suspension travel. The situation at greater travel needs to be looked at separately.

One role of any suspension system is to isolate the sprung mass from the road, ie we want the bike to carry on undisturbed while the wheels bounce up and down. In moving along the road the bike experiences all sorts of bumps and troughs. It meets them at different road speeds and the bumps or hollows are at any random point on the road so they 'arrive' at all sorts of different rates.

When you have forces transmitted repetitively through suspension to a sprung mass then, with very little damping, some funny things happen. Two common examples will demonstrate this.

First, consider a car engine. When it ticks over the engine moves about, often quite violently, but as soon as you rev it up it remains virtually still. This system consists of a sprung mass (the engine), a suspension system with stiffness and some damping (the rubber mounts) and a force that varies with engine speed (out of balance engine forces). Similar behaviour is observed with rev counters which sit still under normal conditions but tend to flap about on the mounts at tick over.

The suspension we are dealing with is no different. Given little damping and a road that bumps away at the wheels ever more rapidly you would find a point where the sprung mass, which includes you, starts to move up and down very violently. The result can be so severe that components are easily broken, however if it was possible to increase the frequency of movements continuously then the effect would largely disappear, the sprung mass responding less and less to the moving wheel. Indeed, with very rapid wheel movements, the sprung mass will remain virtually still. This is shown graphically in Fig 5.10 and the system is said to have a resonant frequency at the point where the movement of the sprung mass is greatest. Real suspension does not exhibit such a smooth curve due to factors such as seal stick/slip characteristics but the general shape is similar. This resonant frequency is related to the wheel rate, the sprung mass and the amount of damping. It is influenced by the stiffness of the tyres. Typical values for reasonable suspension lie in the region of 1-2.5Hz (Hz: hertz or cycles per second, ie one or two peak movements every second). If there is a lot of damping the large movements are prevented and the frequencies lowered, possibly to zero, but we must start by assuming just a small amount of damping.

Fig 5.10 *Graph showing the way the sprung mass responds to repetitive movements at the wheel when it is lightly damped. At a certain point called the resonant frequency the sprung mass jumps up and down excessively but for much more rapid inputs it barely moves.*

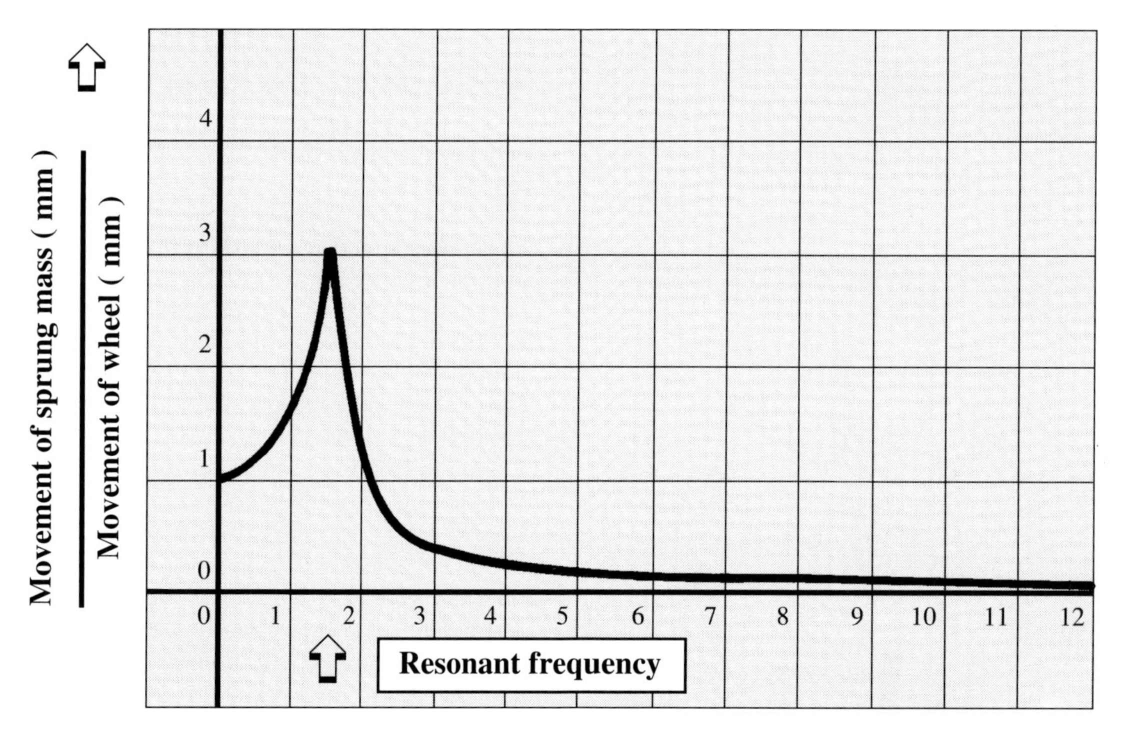

Now, suppose that this resonant frequency is very low. If it is, then the majority of wheel movements, which occur at higher frequencies, do not result in large movements of the sprung mass. If the resonant frequency is extremely low then the sprung mass will almost sit still when the wheels move up and down rapidly. This is what happens with the engine and the rev counter and it is also the main suspension requirement for a smooth ride, alongside the need for a low unsprung mass.

To achieve this situation, the value of wheel rate/sprung mass needs to be as low as possible. Thus the suspension needs to be as soft as possible, ie a low wheel rate, to minimise movements of the sprung mass in response to the majority of wheel movements. We could do some sums to demonstrate this but it is not really necessary.

Unfortunately this is only one of many requirements. If the wheel rate is low then the wheel travel in response to a given load is relatively long. Wheel forces are passed to the sprung mass via the suspension and they need to be high enough to lift the bike over normal obstacles before all the travel is used up and the suspension 'bottoms out'. Additionally, the system has to be able to cope with loads produced by acceleration, cornering and braking. Any of these situations, and especially combinations of them, will generate relatively large forces at the wheel. During braking and acceleration the full weight of bike and rider can be transferred to the front and rear wheels respectively. Typically, this represents a 100% increase in load compared to that associated with riding at a steady speed.

The next problem is cornering. Fig 5.11 overleaf represents a bike cornering and considerable increases in suspension load can take place. When the bike goes round the corner it is subjected to an acceleration that is directed towards the centre of curvature, ie radially inwards. This is called centripetal acceleration and without it the bike would simply carry on in a straight line. For the bike to follow a circular path of radius r, the tyres must provide a friction force that will generate the required centripetal acceleration. This acceleration is equal to v^2/r where v is the bike's road speed.

As you go faster for a given corner radius the centripetal force required to keep the bike on line gets larger. If you demand more than the tyres can provide then they let go, you fall off, and the bike goes off at the tangent it prefers! For the purpose of illustration Fig 5.11 is simplified to indicate the forces all at one tyre but they are of course shared between both tyres. The total (resultant) force acting at the contact patch is given by, $m\sqrt{g^2 + a_r^2}$. The notation is included in the diagram. How this is shared between front and rear depends on the weight distribution at the time. This total force will act roughly in line with the suspension, the precise situation is determined by how wide the tyres are and where the combined cg lies.

On the race track the value of centripetal acceleration a_r is typically 1g or slightly greater. Most good club racers reach these sort of values on low to medium speed corners, though only very good riders can go fast enough to do so on very high speed corners. To maintain 1g, the lean angle of a line drawn between the cg and the contact patch has to be 45°. The resultant force gives a 41% increase in the wheel load, most of which acts straight through the suspension. However, the real problems start when you are combining hard cornering with hard acceleration or braking. Fortunately, at this point the tyres impose strict limits on what you can achieve.

So, irrespective of how desirable it may be to have a low wheel rate, the combination of wheel rate and available travel must be such that the suspension can support these loads without bottoming out. Indeed, an optimum set-up frequently allows the system to just bottom out on rare occasions, say once a lap, so it is at the lower practical limit of wheel rate.

Finally, it is necessary to acknowledge one other possible problem associated with very low wheel rates. If the frame lacks stiffness then the bike will not take to low wheel rates very well. On fast corners it may tend to 'wallow' badly. This is one reason why suspension used to be somewhat stiffer than it is today. Only experiment will provide the final answers.

Wheel travel

Wheel rate and wheel travel are inextricably linked together because the lowest wheel rate you can use depends on the wheel travel available. The amount of travel used has increased steadily in all applications over the past 20 years or so. Some of this has been for good scientific reasons and some of it is pure fashion. The trend began with motocross where movements of perhaps 120-200mm (4.7-7.9ins) soon reached the current values of

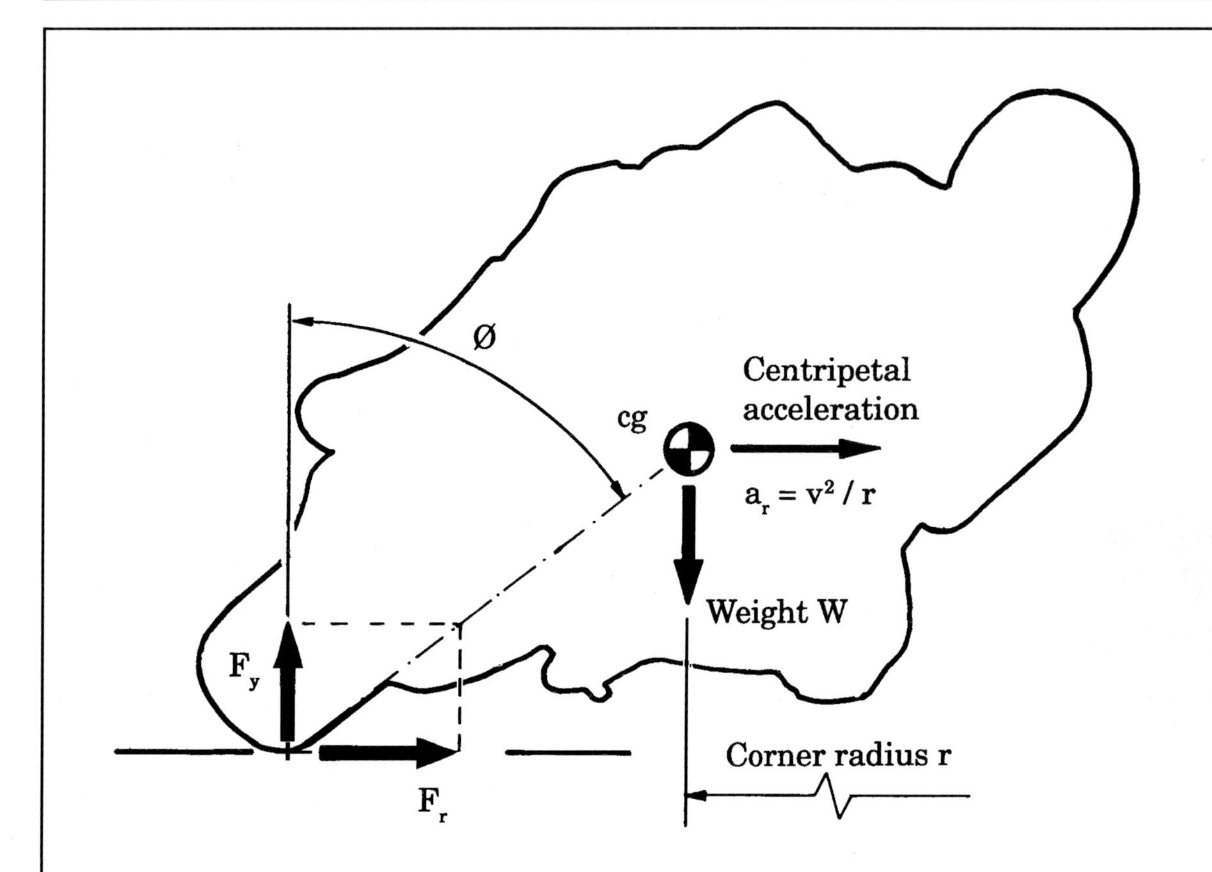

Notation

F_y = Vertical force acting on tyre.
F_r = Radial (friction) force on tyre.
Ø = Lean angle of cg from vertical.
r = Corner radius to cg.
v = Forward speed of bike.
a_r = Radial (centripetal) acceleration.

Forces

The bike has no vertical acceleration so the force F_y is equal to the weight, ie mass x g.

The radial acceleration is a_r so using force = mass x acceleration gives, $F_r = ma_r$.

The total resultant force at the tyre is therefore

$$\sqrt{F_y^2 + F_r^2} = \sqrt{(mg)^2 + (ma_r)^2} = m\sqrt{g^2 + a_r^2}$$

A typical centripetal acceleration value for quick cornering is 1g or slightly higher. This makes the total force 1.41mg, ie 1.41 x weight. Most of this goes through the suspension.

Lean angle

The required lean angle Ø is given by,

$$\text{Tan}Ø = a_r/g \text{ or } v^2/gr$$

Thus a centripetal acceleration of 1g gives a TanØ value of one and Ø = 45°. The actual lean of the bike will be slightly different to that given. It depends on the location of the contact patch and combined cg. Changes in cg height do influence the actual lean of the bike, as opposed to the cg position, when the tyres are wide.

Fig 5.11 *Cornering requires a radially inward acceleration. The tyre force that provides this increases suspension loads as described.*

Fig 5.12 *Modern motocross often involves high impact loads. This makes it difficult to achieve acceptable suspension without a rising rate characteristic.*

about 300mm(11.8ins) front and 320mm (12.6ins) rear. The idea transferred to roadracing where typical movements of 70-100mm (2.75-4ins) gradually increased to around 120-200mm (4.7-8ins) at the rear of the bike. The original principle of long travel is heavily based on energy storage. When they compress, springs store energy and the energy they can store increases with the square of travel, assuming a fixed wheel rate. A bit more travel gives a very worthwhile increase in energy storage, every bit of which is needed when you land at the bottom of a big jump on a motocross circuit - Fig 5.12. Conditions like this impose serious problems for suspension designers even now. It is all very well cushioning the bike and rider by storing large amounts of energy in springs but you then need outstanding dampers to dissipate it all before it is released into the sprung mass. Motocross 125's are particularly problematic because they have virtually the same wheels and swinging arms as large bikes giving a high unsprung mass alongside their very low sprung masses. Lightening the wheels etc makes for better suspension but then they break up!

Transferring the idea of very long travel to tarmac is rather different. There are no table top jumps, indeed anything above 40mm is hard to find so why use a lot of travel? The reason lies in our original analysis. If you increase the travel you can use a lower wheel rate to handle given loads. If the wheel rate is lower the resonant frequency is lower and the suspension quality is therefore better, though in my opinion many bikes go too far in this respect. Very low wheel rates allowed for by long travel lead to severe changes in the pitch orientation of the bike. Steering geometry, ground clearance and cg height can change fairly radically and this may lead to a variety of handling problems. If you adjust the values to cope in one position then the handling in other positions is compromised.

Whatever the theory, riders and special builders have formed their own opinions. In the early days there were a lot of riders who preferred less travel but this may have had as much to do with past experience as it did with rational assessment. Today's riders have grown up on long wheel travel and, given the level of engineering refinement that is currently available, most would find reductions in wheel travel a retrograde step. There are no rules only theories and preferences.

Tyre influence and stiffness

Until now I have only considered the isolation of the sprung mass from large wheel movements and the conclusion is that the wheel rate should be as low as possible. The more wheel travel you use the lower the wheel rate can be.

Now it is time to consider the influence of the tyres in all this and look at the problems associated with the unsprung mass moving up and down, rather than the isolation of the sprung mass. If you bounce the bike up and down it is clear that the wheel rate is considerably less than that offered by the tyres which only compress a relatively small amount. In fact, if you press on the seat with the tyres on the floor then strictly speaking you are not observing the wheel rate due to springing alone but a composite rate produced by both wheel rate and tyre stiffness. Fig 5.13 shows the radial stiffness of some Michelin race tyres as a graph of load against deflection. The stiffness is calculated by taking any convenient change in load and dividing it by the change in deflection. This gives values of 218.75N/mm (1249lbf/in) for

Fig 5.13 *Radial stiffness of some racing tyres. Rear tyres can be suprisingly stiff but this is a consequence of the high power they have to transmit.*
(Data courtesy of Michelin competition department).

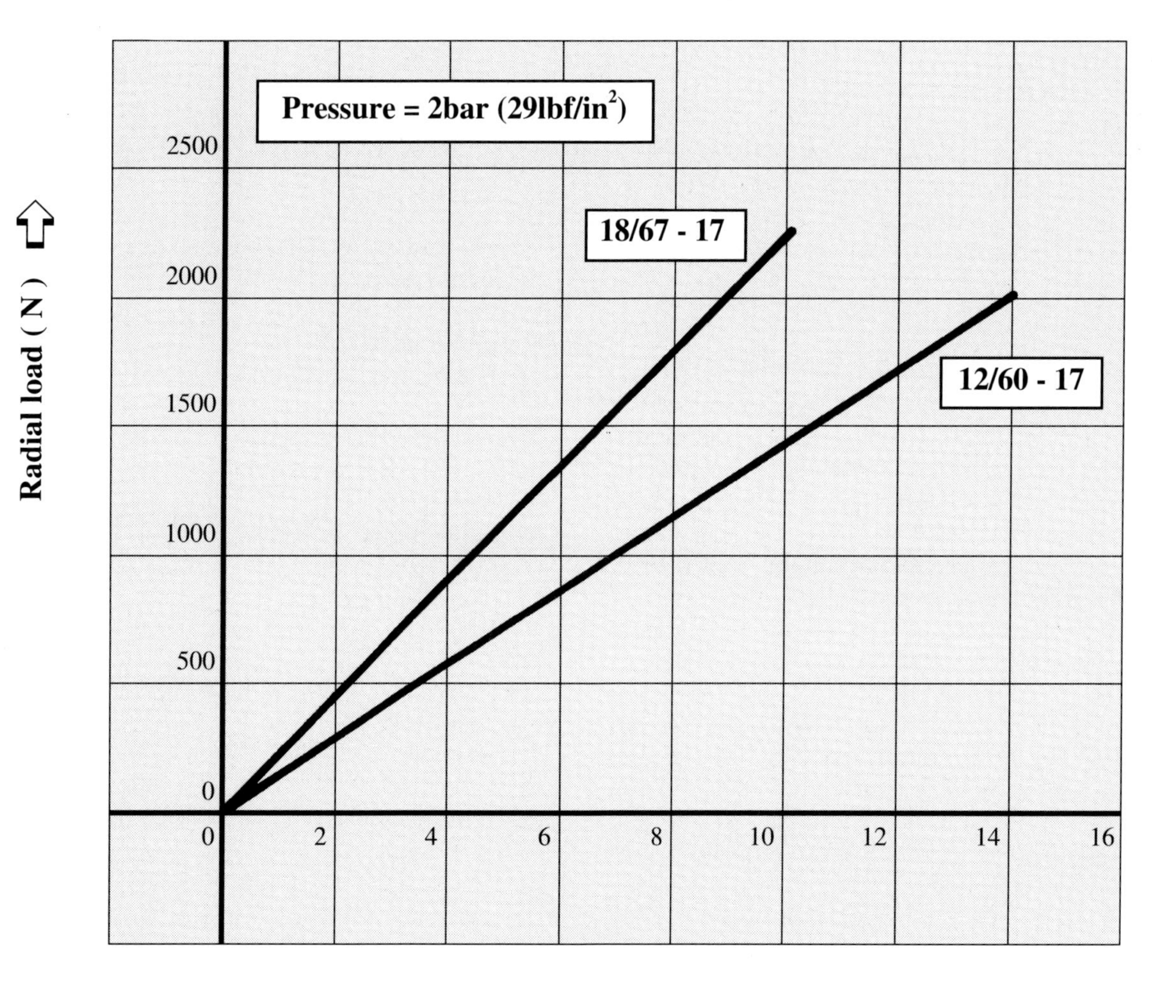

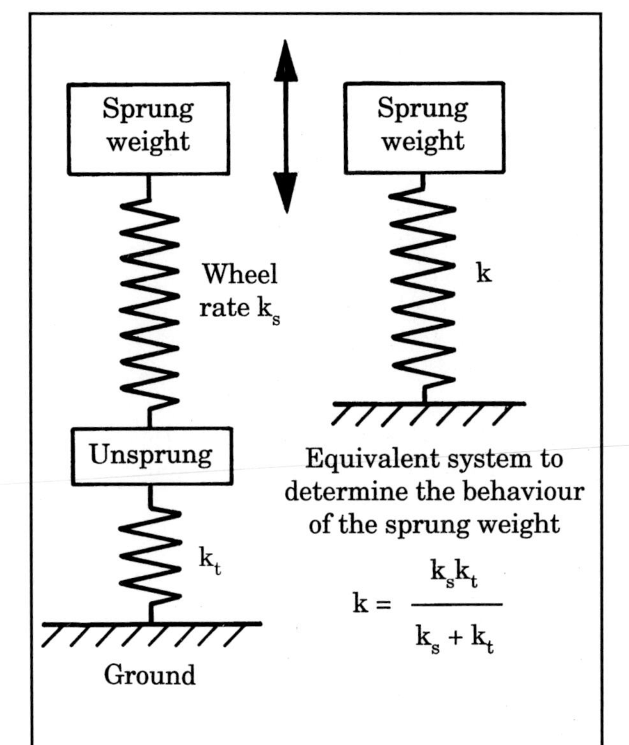

The approximate stiffness seen by the sprung weight is given by,

$$k = \frac{k_t . k_s}{k_t + k_s}$$

If $k_t = 10k_s$ then $k = 0.909k_s$

ie the tyres give roughly a 10% reduction in the wheel rate that would have been achieved by the suspension alone.

Above. Fig 5.14 *Tyre stiffness slightly reduces the wheel rate due to suspension alone.*

the 18/67-17 tyre and 142N/mm (810lbf/in) for the 12/60-17. As you can see, the stiffness of tyres is very variable and this is important. Some, like the 18/67 -17 example, have suprisingly high stiffness values. This is the rear tyre for a 750cc race bike and such tyres need to be of substantial construction in order to withstand the power delivery. In addition, the manufacturers offer GP riders several choices of tyre stiffness each with a variety of different compounds. The variation in tyre stiffness and compound is the main reason why changing tyres often demands changes to the suspension, particularly when 'soft' wet tyres are fitted. Note that the stiffness results from both the construction of the tyre and the pressure, so pressure variation is another important factor.

Broadly speaking, the stiffness of the tyres is going to be perhaps ten times that of the basic wheel rate. This relationship varies a lot because of the range of tyres produced and the range of possible wheel rates but it will do for now. The combination of tyre and suspension gives an 'effective wheel rate' that is slightly lower than that due to the suspension alone - Fig 5.14. The reduction is about 10% for the situation given rising to 12% when the tyres are only eight times as stiff as the wheel rate. In the case of wet tyres, quite large changes are possible but correction for this is as diverse as the manufacturers. Every tyre is different and the suspension changes to suit one make may be exactly the oposite of the corrections required to suit another. Experience is everything.

We also have to consider the condition in which the tyres flex on the road. This is crucial to roadholding because it can easily turn into pattering and the wheel starts to hop about the track, especially when it is lightly loaded, eg at the front when accelerating or at the rear when braking. In this case it is the unsprung mass that is making small movements, 'sandwiched' between the tyre stiffness and the wheel rate due to the springs. The sprung mass can be considered fixed for these small inputs and the effective stiffness acting on the unsprung mass is the sum of the basic wheel rate and tyre stiffness as shown in Fig 5.15 overleaf. As such, the resonant frequency of the unsprung mass is relatively high, compared to that of the sprung mass. It is dominated by the tyres, and slightly altered (10% again) by the wheel rate. The less the unsprung mass and the stiffer the tyres the higher the resonant frequency will be. If the tyres are particularly stiff and the wheel rate employed is much higher than it should be then the rear will tend to spin because the tyre cannot comply with road variations. A typical result is losing the back end when it is lightly loaded on corner entry. Similarly, wheel rates that are too high increase the likelihood of losing the front end when braking deep into corners. Many problems show up as strange wear patterns on the tyres and experienced tyre technicians are usually the best people to talk to about these matters.

For most riders and special builders little of this matters too much. Their choice of tyres is restricted to off the shelf varieties which the manufacturer has produced as the best compromise for 'average' conditions. If your wheel rates and unsprung masses are far from average then you will not get the best out of the tyres.

Modern race tyres have now developed to the point where virtually every tyre, whatever the compound, will go full race distance provided the working conditions imposed by track, temperature, tyre stiffness and wheel rate are correct.

Unfortunately, the only means of assessment, ie rider feedback and temperature checks, are usually based on final practice data and it is easy to get it wrong. Most tyres work best at around 90 -100°C rear, 65-70°C front and it does not require very big changes in track conditions and suspension settings to cause problems. If the rear tyre is worked too hard then by 120-130°C the rubber is too fluid and the tyre will not last. At 60-70°C it will not warm up to the point where it really sticks.

Given that 10°C changes in road and air temperature are common, the suspension needs to be finely tuned to the tyre chosen to get the best from it, or, put another way, the choice of tyre is critical in relation to the way the bike is set up. How well you actually set it up is rarely discovered until it is too late, ie at the end of the race.

Overall, the interaction of tyre stiffness and wheel rate is not dramatic if everything is up to date. Most Club and National racers rarely need to change the springing once it is sorted out. Classic racers set up for the tyres of 25 years ago may demand quite major changes to wheel rate when modern tyres are employed.

Where the real interaction starts is between tyre stiffness, wheel rate and damping. Although I do not want to deal with damping yet we have identified two resonant conditions, one for the sprung mass (low frequency) and one for the unsprung mass (higher frequency). In the absence of damping both these conditions are disastrous, the first sending you into orbit and the second separating the tyre from the ground in a big way. The damper has to deal with these diverse requirements and that is a demanding task yet to be considered. Damping variation is usually the first adjustment to try in an established set-up and, as with stiffness, the rules, if there are any, depend on the make of tyre involved. Failure to succeed is then followed by experiments with different tyre stiffness and, if there are still problems, wheel rate changes need to be tried. I'm glad I never managed to go fast enough to worry too much about all this but it is essential stuff for GP riders.

These are some of the basic concepts relating to wheel rate. The general idea is to use a wheel rate that is just above the practical minimum for the available travel. Many riders will prefer the feel of somewhat higher values but only the individual can decide. There are two other aspects that need

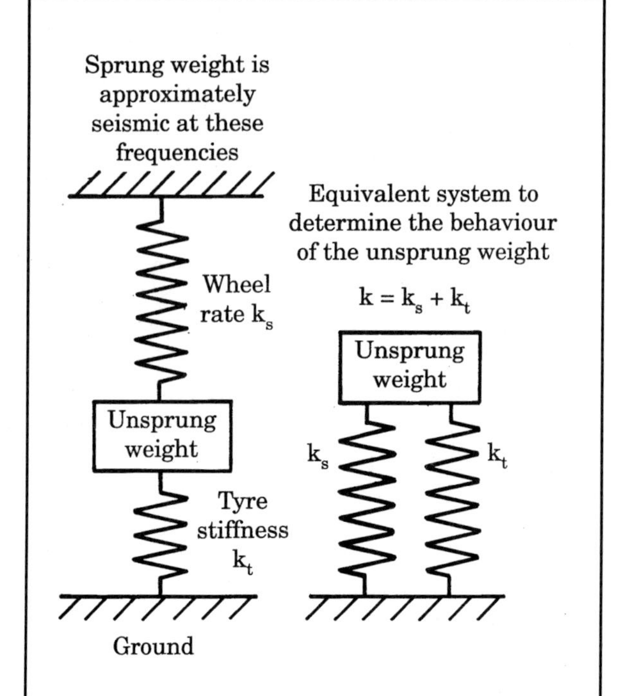

If $k_t = 10k_s$ the unsprung mass sees a stiffness that is roughly 10% higher than the tyre stiffness. Note that we are only dealing with small movements here, ie the movement of the unsprung mass under tyre deflection.

Above. Fig 5.15 *Because the tyres are relatively stiff the natural frequency at which the unsprung mass vibrates is relatively high compared to that of the sprung mass. At these frequencies the sprung mass cannot respond (see Fig 5.10) and it is effectively static or 'seismic'. This means that the unsprung mass movements see a stiffness that is equal to the sum of the tyre and suspension values.The wheel rate produced by the suspension therefore slightly increases the effective tyre stiffness. See also Chapter 5.3 on springs.*

to be considered. These are the distribution of wheel travel and preload. Neither of these affect the wheel rate you are using but both are crucial to making it work well.

Distribution of wheel travel

A fundamental requirement of suspension is that the wheel is able to move up to cope with bumps and down to cope with hollows. This means that the total wheel travel chosen has to be shared out in some way, either side of the normal laden position. The greatest requirement is for upward movements of the wheel since these are generated by all the major motion changes, however the ability to move down into hollows and 'track' the road surface is also vitally important. If this cannot happen the suspension 'tops out' and the tyre leaves the ground, even on very minor irregularities. The amount of travel allocated to hollows varies according to the type of bike and rider preference but it is typically 20-30% of the total travel available. Small differences are significant and I will come back to this shortly.

If you want to find a suspension fault on an existing bike then this is a good place to start since many bikes are set up to cope with bumps alone. To check existing set-ups, refer to Fig 5.16.

- First, determine the total suspension travel at front and rear (refer to notes that follow).

- With the bike normally laden measure vertically from the rear wheel spindle to some convenient point on the seat. This is the rear ride height. Make sure the bike is fully laden, ie no weight on your feet. Get someone to hold the bike upright and bounce it up and down a few times to settle the suspension.

- At the front, measure from the top of the fork slider to the bottom of the yoke when the bike is laden. On upside down forks, measure from the spindle to the fixed leg.

- Now get off the bike, lift it clear of the ground so the wheels hang free and repeat the measurements with the suspension fully extended.

Fig 5.16 *Checking the distribution of suspension travel. Compare the dimensions shown when the suspension is fully extended with that obtained under normal laden conditions.*

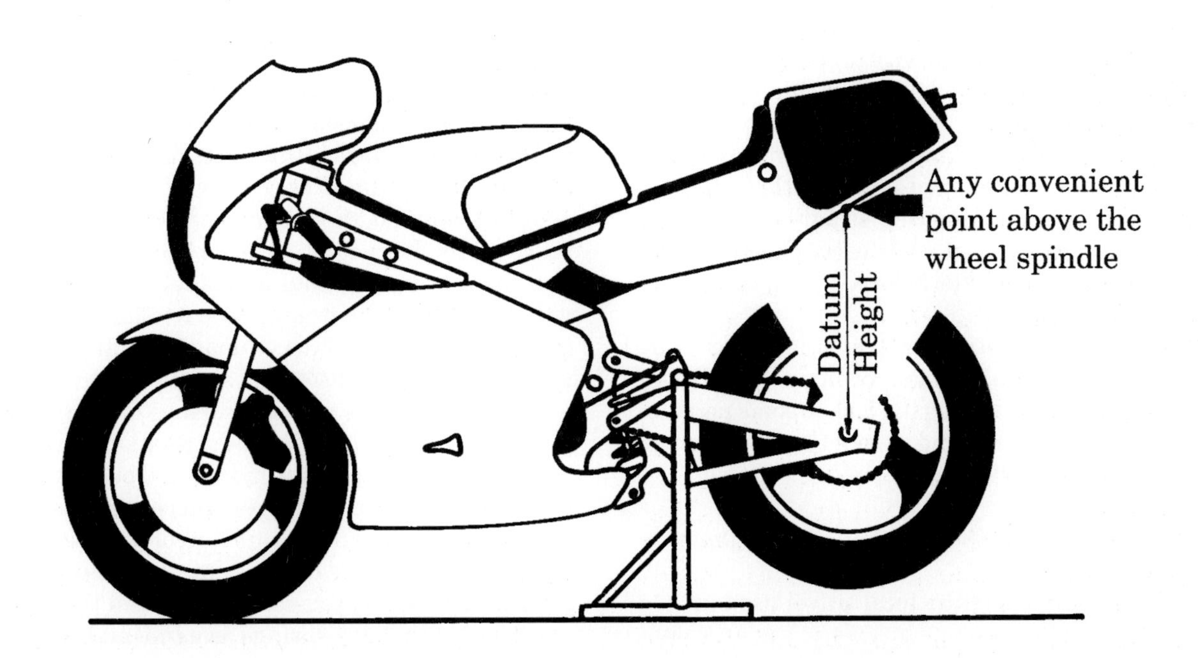

At the rear of the bike take all measurements vertically at the wheel spindle. To find the total travel it is best to remove the spring(s) and move the system by hand until it seats on the bump stop. Now follow this example.

Example. The total rear wheel travel is found to be 120mm. In the fully laden position the datum distance measured to some point above the spindle is 500mm and when the rear wheel hangs free it is 534mm.

The travel for hollows is 534 - 500 = 34mm

The percentage of the total travel used is,

$$\frac{\text{Travel for hollows x 100\%}}{\text{Total travel}} = \frac{34 \text{ x}100}{120}$$

$$= 28.3\%$$

This is a reasonable starting point, possibly slightly high on tarmac according to your preference.

At the front of the bike things are slightly different because there is not usually a convenient point to measure to vertically above the wheel. This does not matter. Although movements along the fork are different, providing we stick to them in all cases the percentage of travel used will be the same as if measurements were done vertically.

First, check out the total travel measured along the fork leg. Remove the spring caps to do this. It is not unknown for the springs to become coilbound before full travel is reached but at this stage I will assume that this does not happen. Having found the total travel, determine the distance between the slider and some fixed point on the yokes for both laden and 'hanging free' situations. Measure along the fork legs in each case. Calculate the percentage allocated as before.

Example. The total fork travel is found to be 90mm. In the fully laden position the datum distance measured along the fork to some point on the yoke is 300mm and when the front wheel hangs free it is 320mm.

The travel for hollows is 320 - 300 = 20mm

The percentage of the total travel used is,

$$\frac{\text{Travel for hollows x 100\%}}{\text{Total travel}} = \frac{20 \text{ x}100}{90}$$

$$= 22\%$$

The best allocation at the front end is more variable than at the rear and rider preference seems to vary significantly. When the available travel is relatively short, it is common to allocate rather less travel to hollows so that more travel is available to deal with braking loads. Overdoing this idea can increase the likelihood of losing the front end and a more sensible solution is to use progressive fork springs or obtain a bit more travel. 22% may be rather low for dealing with hollows but it is a reasonable point to start experimenting with.

If, having done this test on existing bikes, you find that the values are a long way out then you might assume that the wheel rate, and hence the current spring rates, are unsuitable. This might well be true but it is by no means certain because there is another factor involved called preload. The combined effect of preload and wheel rate can be very confusing so it is worth spending some time explaining what happens when preload is applied to the suspension.

Preload

Preload is a term used to describe a load that is set up in a spring before any weight is applied to it. It is achieved by compressing the spring using some form of adjuster and then constraining it mechanically. The spring is trying to force the two ends of the suspension unit (or forks) apart but cannot do so because the unit has reached its stops at full extension. However, when an external weight is applied, the suspension will not begin to move until the weight exceeds the preload that has been set up. Without preload, the suspension will respond to any weight once friction has been overcome and this produces unacceptable compromises that will be discussed shortly.

Preload is what you alter using the adjuster ring or cam on conventional suspension units. In the case of forks, spacers are inserted between the fork caps and the springs. These preload the springs by a certain amount according to their length, though there can be some rather peculiar results in this respect, especially when the forks are fitted with extra springs as a top out bumper.

To discuss preload, I want to return to my hypothetical 'single shock' system originally shown in Fig 5.9. Remember that in this system the spring has a stiffness equal to the wheel rate. I appreciate that some readers will not like using abstract ideas and will much prefer to concentrate on a real system however this then means we have to cope with inclined forks and suspension units, swinging arms, linkages and so on. These are best covered separately once the general ideas have been discussed.

First and foremost, the adjustment of preload has no effect whatsoever on wheel rate. What it does is allow the suspension to support a certain amount of load before any of the available travel is used up. If there is no preload then we might assume that the suspension will 'sag' considerably, ie compress, under the laden weight of the sprung mass. Alternatively, if we have a ridiculous amount of preload then the suspension may fail to move at all. The system is heavily 'topped out' and in this condition the wheel cannot move down any further. Clearly there is no travel available to deal with hollows.

What this means is that when you measure the amount the laden bike sags to check travel distribution, the result will depend on both the wheel rate and the preload. Fig 5.17 shows what happens at a suspension unit when there is no preload. At a) we have the suspension strut and the spring which has a certain free length. In b) the spring is fitted to the strut and the preload adjuster is set to just hold the spring in place, ie the fitted spring length is still the free length. Finally, in c), a force is applied to the strut. This causes it to compresses such that, compression = load applied/wheel rate. If we ignore friction, any appliedload will cause a movement. For example, if the spring stiffness, which is assumed equal to wheel rate in this case, is 2kgf/mm then every 2kgf applied will produce 1mm of compression. If the unladen bike load on this unit is 80kgf then the unit will compress 40mm. If the laden value is 140kgf then in this case it will compress by 70mm assuming it does not bottom. Note how both situations are inextricably linked by the wheel rate concerned.

Fig 5.17 *A suspension system with no preload. The fitted spring length is equal to the free length and the compression that is produced by a load W is given by (load / spring stiffness). In this illustration the single vertical spring has a stiffness equal to the wheel rate.*

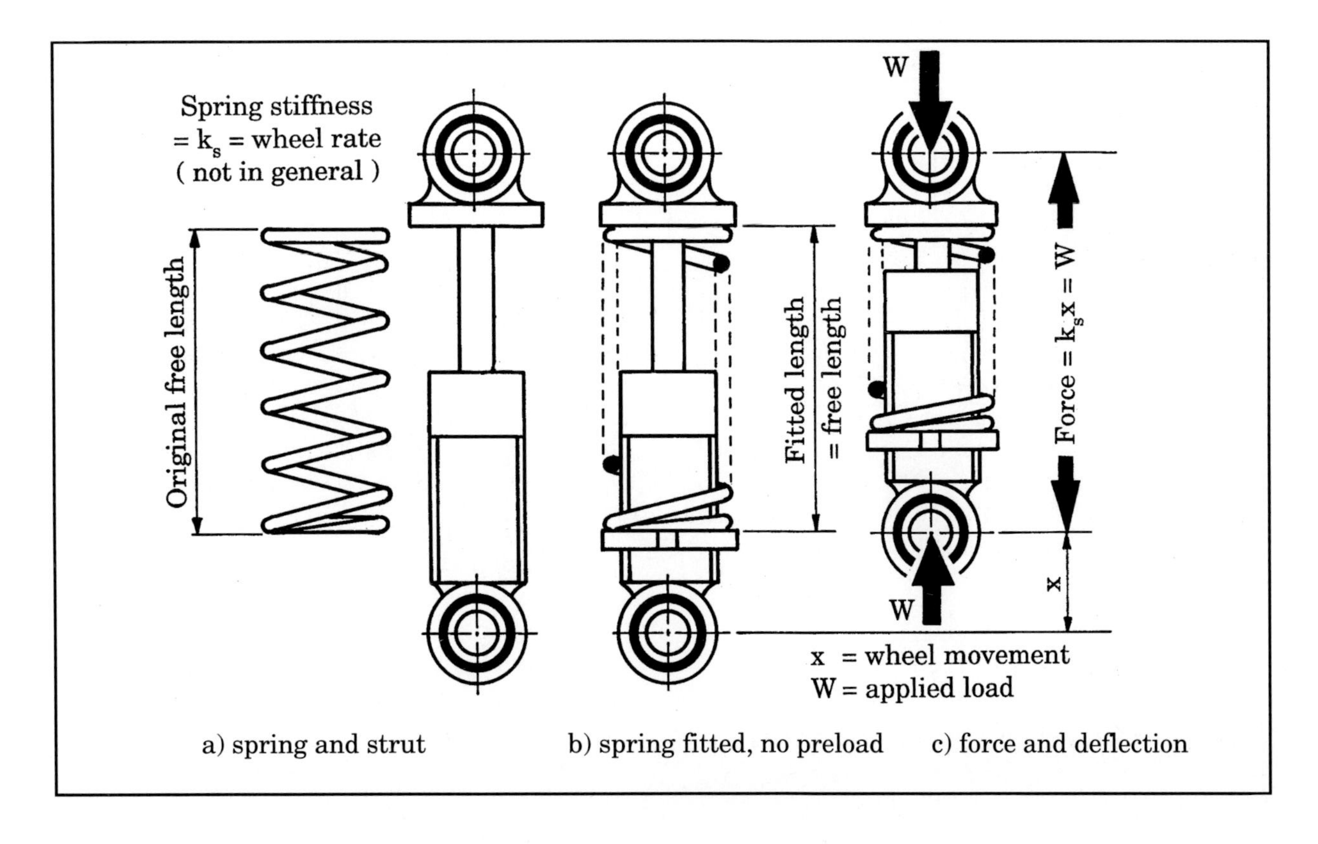

Fig 5.18 illustrates what happens when preload is present. At a) the spring is fitted as before but in b) the preload adjuster is wound up to compress the spring by amount x_p. As a result of this there is a force pushing the two ends of the strut apart. This force is equal to (wheel rate x preload compression of the spring). Until a load exceeding this value is applied to the strut, it will not move. In c) a load greater than the preload is applied and the sag produced is now less than before since it is only due to the difference between the load applied and the preload.

For example. If the preload is 40kgf then when the unladen load discussed previously is applied (80kgf), only 40kgf will cause compression. This would give only 20mm of compression instead of the previous 40mm, assuming the same rate of 2kgf/mm. In the laden case, a load of 140kgf no longer gives 70mm of compression but 50mm, ie (140kgf - 40kgf)/(2kgf/mm). By including preload, the direct link between compression and load has been modified but note that the wheel rate, or stiffness, remains the same. Once the preload has been overcome, a given change in load will give exactly the same compression as it did in the case with no preload. By far the best way to investigate this is by using a load/compression graph as shown in Fig 5.19 . With no preload and a constant rate the graph is a straight line that passes through zero. The wheel rate is found from the slope of the graph which in the example shown is about 3500N/200mm, ie 17.5N/mm.

When there is preload involved, external loads below this value do not cause movement so the graph rises vertically initially and forms a sort of step. In the example this indicates a preload of about 500N. Once this is overcome, the graph has the same slope as before and therefore the same wheel rate.

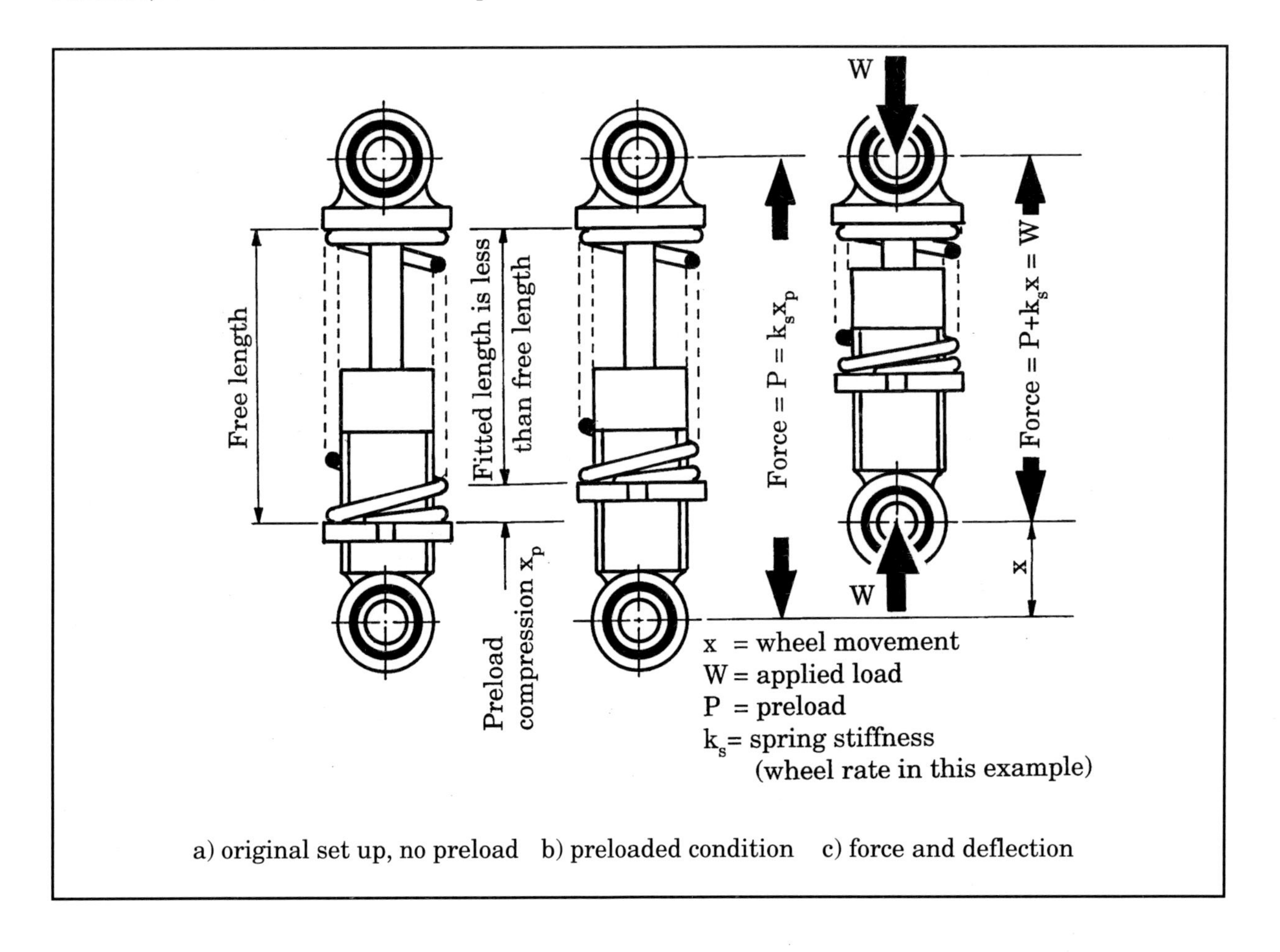

Fig 5.18 *A suspension system with preload. The net result is no deflection until the load applied is equal to the preload. The wheel rate is unchanged.*

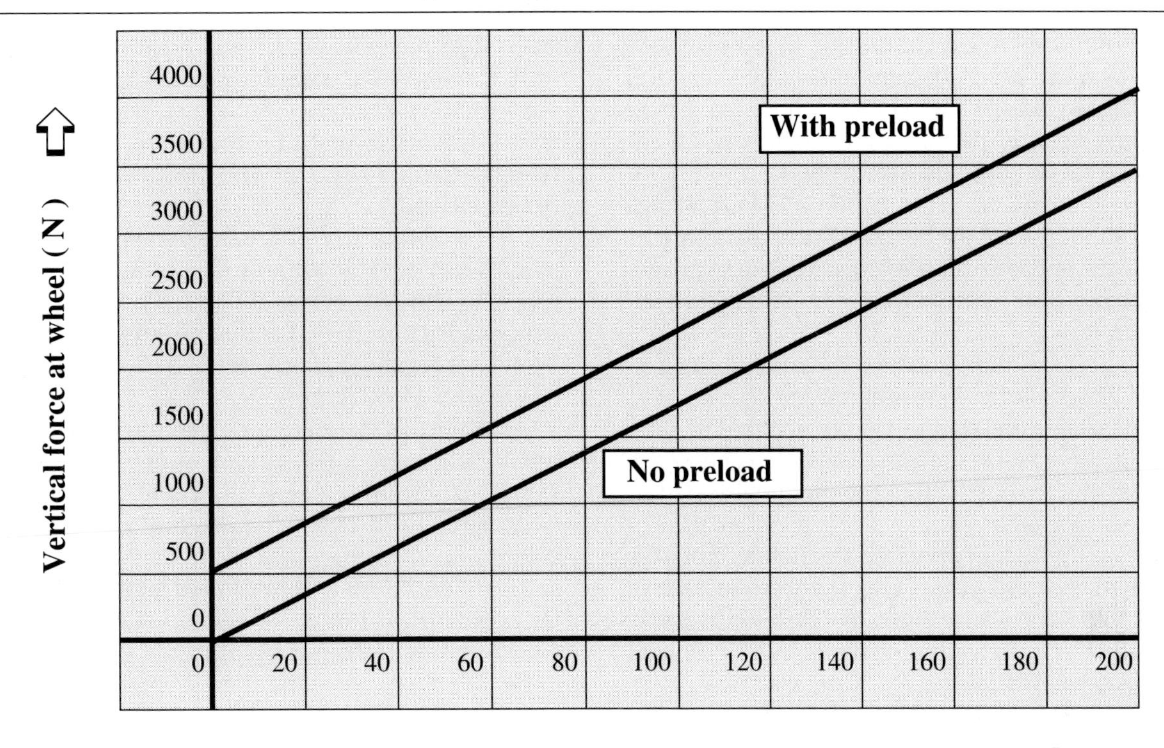

Fig 5.19 *Force vs wheel movement for systems with and without preload. Any preload produces a step in the graph at zero wheel movement and all forces up to this value are transmitted directly to the sprung mass. The greater the wheel rate the steeper the graph and a given wheel movement requires more force than for a lower wheel rate.*

Using preload, we can effectively remove any portion of the compression that the laden bike produces and thereby achieve the required distribution of wheel travel, eg 25% for hollows. This can be particularly important with linkage systems that have a high rising rate because if the system is not set up correctly you could be operating on a very different wheel rate to that intended. Clearly, preload can provide some compensation for variations in rider weight, or, in the case of road bikes, to allow for passengers.

If the system was set up correctly for you and a passenger is added then the bike will sag even further. This changes several things.

- The travel available to deal with bumps has reduced.
- The travel available to deal with hollows has increased.
- The cg is lowered.
- The squat geometry has changed.
- The steering geometry is altered.

Preload will allow you to reset the bike to the required position, provided the wheel rate is reasonable and the loads are not excessive.

However, this is not an ideal way of doing things and as you might expect there is a lot more to this than I have suggested so far. If you attempt to make every bike suit every rider via preload adjustment then you will not achieve the sort of results that can be obtained by a more thorough approach.

The first point to make is that adjusting preload alters the ride height of the bike and hence all the things just listed. If these were correct in the first place then adding or subtracting preload to cope with a different rider will alter them. Some bikes have separate ride height adjustment on the suspension units or you can make your own adjustable mountings to get round this problem. Leaving this aside, we still have to consider how the wheel rate and preload combine because racing bikes need rather more thought than how far you can twiddle the preload adjusters!

To illustrate what happens it is best to use some realistic numbers because the relative weight of the bike and rider determines what is required. I shall however stick with my hypothetical suspension unit.

As a first example, consider a light bike such as a 125. The unladen bike weighs 78kgf and I will assume this is distributed 50/50, ie 39kgf at each end. The unsprung components at each end weigh 17kgf so the sprung load in the unladen condition is 39 - 17 = 22kgf.

With a light rider on board the laden figure for the sprung weight at the wheel concerned rises to 50kgf and the total weight of bike and rider is 134kgf. We will assume there is only 70mm of wheel travel available.

The graphs in Fig 5.20 show how everything interacts. Firstly, if we allocate 25% of the travel to hollows then the laden sag at the wheel will be 0.25 x 70mm = 17.5mm. This occurs when the load is 50kgf so we have a point on our graph. With no preload, we can draw a line through this point and the origin to determine the required wheel rate as shown in graph ①The result is 2.86kgf/mm (160lbf/in) and that is extremely stiff, much stiffer than anyone would use. A clue to this is the situation at full suspension travel.

We could suggest that the maximum load the suspension will have to support is something near to that of the total laden weight (134kgf). It does not actually have to support the wheel assembly that is still on the ground when braking or accelerating but as a rough guide the total weight will suffice for illustration at this stage. Our non-preload suspension can support far more than this at full travel so it is clearly much stiffer than necessary. If we lower the wheel rate to suit the full travel requirement, the laden sag increases to about 37% of the total travel so there is insufficient travel to deal with bumps and the suspension is still very stiff - graph ②.

A solution is found by using preload. In graph ③ the line passes through the required laden sag point and supports the total weight at full travel. To do this a preload of about 22kgf is required and, since the bike applies a load of 22kgf when unladen we note that the suspension is just topped out in the unladen condition. It is no coincidence that a typical suspension set-up for a 125 requires that this is the case and hopefully you can see that by specifying what the sag is laden and unladen we tie up both the wheel rate and preload in a suitable combination.

The second set of graphs show what happens when a heavier rider gets on the same bike. In this case the changes are as follows. The total laden weight becomes 154kgf while the laden load at the wheel concerned rises to 59kgf. The unladen figure remains at 22kgf.

As it stands the bike now has more laden sag (about 22.5mm) and cannot support the total weight of bike and rider at full travel. At this point it is common to reach for the preload adjuster. Adding another 9kgf of preload solves the laden sag problem but note that the full load still cannot be supported at full travel. Unladen, the suspension is now significantly topped out - graph ④.

On a rainy day at some airfield this compromise would no doubt be tolerated. If the suspension bottoms ten times a lap then adding even more preload will cure it until you get home. A better solution lies in increasing the wheel rate somewhat as shown by line ⑤because this now supports the maximum load using less preload.

Although preload is clearly essential, any excess preload is a bad thing because wheel forces up to this value are transmitted directly to the sprung mass, which includes you! The bike is effectively rigid up to this point.

The important thing to note is that the system is now only just topped out again when unladen so perhaps we can ignore all of this and seek to meet the following conditions for any rider, whatever their weight, on a very light bike.

- The laden sag amounts to about 25% of the total travel available.
- In the unladen condition the bike is lightly topped out.

Right. Fig 5.20 *Graphs showing the conditions described in the text for a light bike. The graphs at the top apply to a light rider and show what happens with and without preload. The lower graphs show what happens with a heavy rider on the same bike. A change in wheel rate gives a better result than simply adding more preload.*

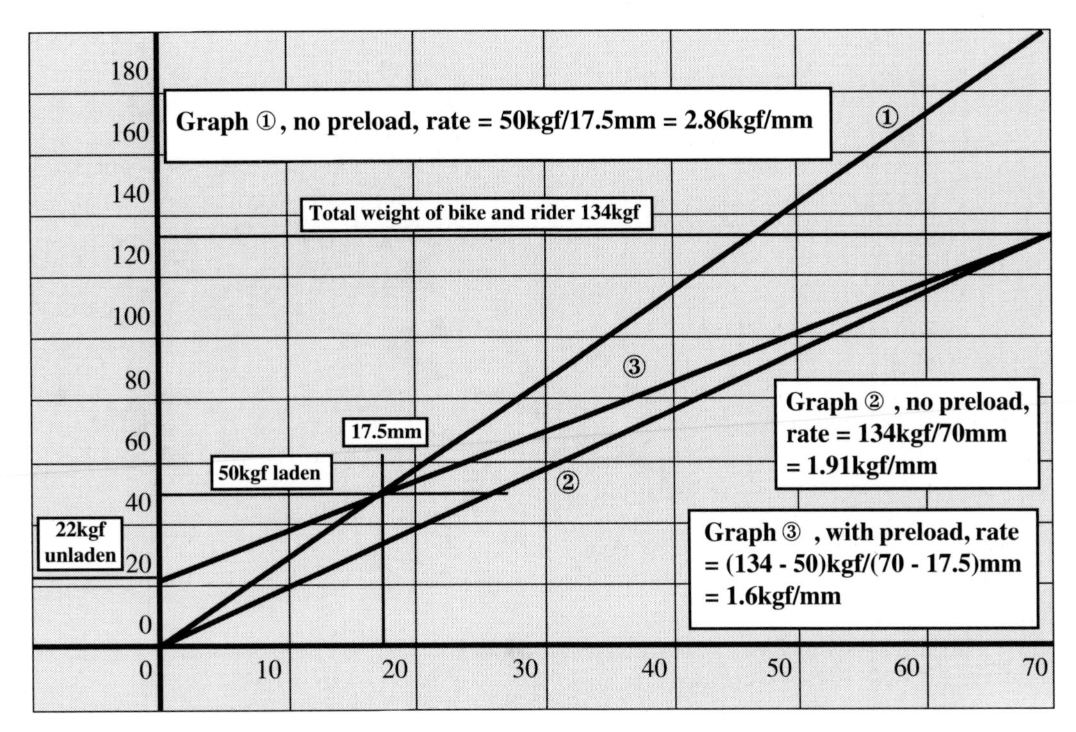

Suspension movement (mm) 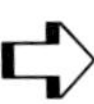

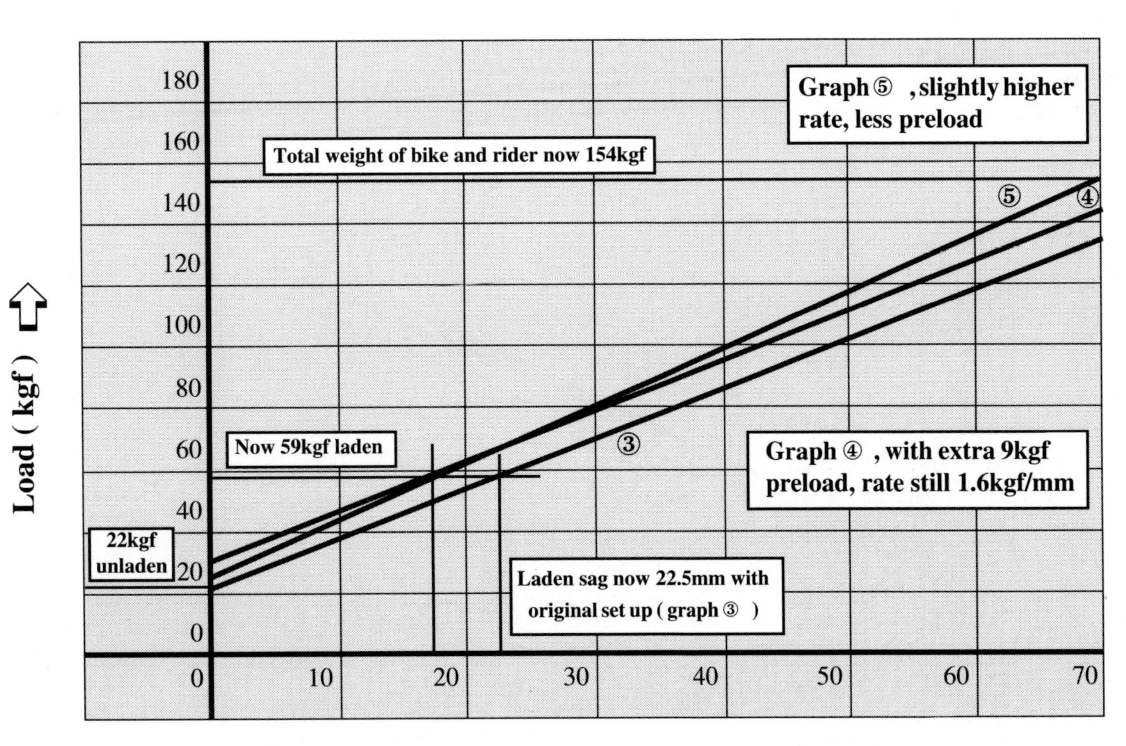

Suspension movement (mm) 

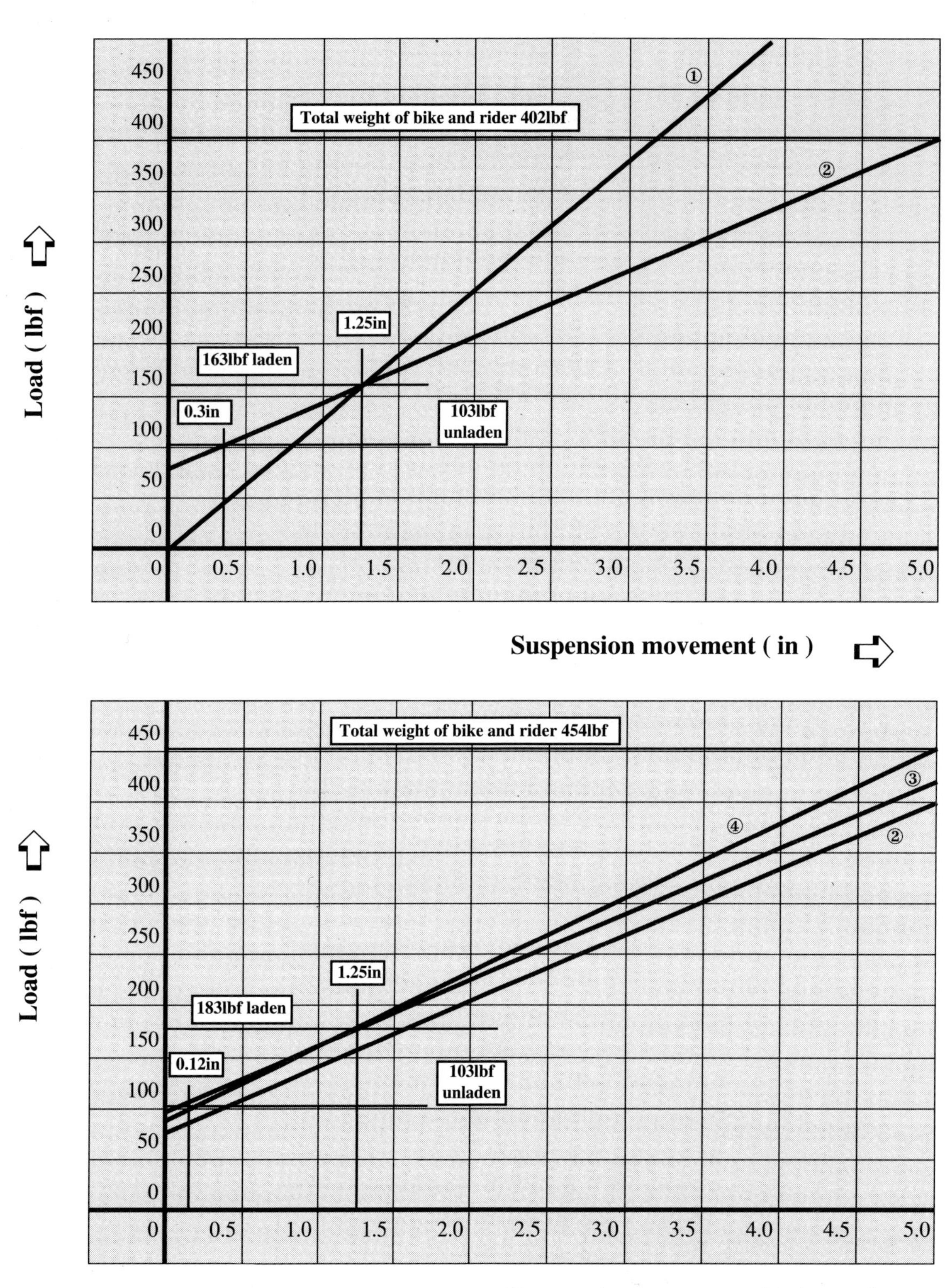

Total weight of bike and rider 402lbf
①
②
1.25in
163lbf laden
0.3in
103lbf unladen
Load (lbf)
Suspension movement (in)
0
50
100
150
200
250
300
350
400
450
0.5
1.0
1.5
2.0
2.5
3.0
3.5
4.0
4.5
5.0
Total weight of bike and rider 454lbf
③
④
②
1.25in
183lbf laden
0.12in
103lbf unladen
Load (lbf)
Suspension movement (in)

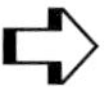

This corresponds to practical settings but you will not be suprised to learn that heavier bikes are rather different and there are many practical problems as well. To illustrate the difference between light bikes and heavy ones I will now consider a 500, again using the simplified suspension system. Fig 5.21 uses exactly the same principle as the previous one but is based on weights taken from a 500cc single cylinder bike that is heavier than the previous example. I have used Imperial units in this case. The figures involved are as follows.

- Total weight of bike and light rider = 402lbf.
- Laden wheel load (sprung) with light rider = 163lbf.
- Unladen wheel load (sprung) = 103lbf.
- With a heavy rider these figures become 454lbf, 183lbf and 103lbf respectively.

There is 5in of wheel travel so if 25% is allocated to hollows the laden sag will be 1.25in. This occurs at 163lbf for the light rider. Using no preload yields a wheel rate of 109lbf/in and it is stiffer than we need - graph ①

If the rough and ready idea of supporting the total weight of bike and rider at full travel is used, graph ② results with a much lower wheel rate of 64lbf/in. Note however that there is an unladen sag of about 0.35in (9mm).

Using the heavy rider instead gives the same problem as before (graph ②, repeated in lower picture). Increasing the preload solves the laden sag problem but fails to offer sufficient force at full travel unless further preload is added. Unladen, the bike is now almost topped out - graph ③ and it will be heavily topped out if the full weight can be supported at full travel. A better solution than adding yet more preload is to increase the wheel rate slightly as shown in graph ④. This provides the extra force at full travel and meets the laden sag requirement with less preload. As a result, the unladen bike now has a sag of about 0.15in (about 4mm) and requires a wheel rate of 72lbf/in.

Left. ***Fig 5.21*** *Another preload / wheel rate example, this time for a heavy bike. The graphs at the top relate to a light rider while those below are for a heavier rider on the same bike. Refer to text for details.*

Again, although this example is simplified, it yields the general idea. Heavier bikes should be set up with some unladen sag at the rear, unlike the very light ones that need to be topped out when unladen. The unladen situation is fixing what we will get in conjunction with the laden sag specification, ie satisfying the two conditions simultaneously defines the balance of wheel rate and preload.

In reality life is not this simple and you need a lot of experience to find the best set-up. You either have to spend years sorting things out or go to someone like Ron Williams who has spent their life dealing with such problems. I can only comment on the bikes I have been involved with and even those show many variations. 125's are normally topped out unladen, 250's are sometimes topped out or have a small amount of sag, perhaps 1-2mm. 500's and 750's have more unladen sag, up to around 12mm according to weight. Some people go to 15mm but I think this may be excessive. Large single/twin cylinder classic racers seem to like rather less unladen sag than their weight implies, perhaps just 1-3 mm at the rear.

Front forks can demand almost anything according to the style of riding and preferred damping characteristics but in general there is more unladen sag than for the rear, perhaps 10 - 15mm on 100mm of travel. There are other complications here and further details are given in Chapter 5.4.

It should be noted that 'spring preload' is not the only form of preload present. Front forks often have a compressed air load and the gas load on monoshock damper rods at the rear can be very significant in some cases. These aspects need to be checked out for individual products along with several other problems that I will deal with later.

Estimating wheel rate

This is of course the $64000 question. When you are dealing with existing bikes you can measure everything, but with a new special that is yet to be completed and ridden, you need some rough guide to get started. Based on the ideas just covered, you can of course calculate a wheel rate to suit any particular pair of conditions, eg the laden and unladen sag or the laden sag and the load supported at full travel. Although this appears simple I have experienced many problems when trying to use this method. The main reasons are as follows. Firstly, the use of a full travel load figure is difficult. If rising rates are employed then the data cannot be used to determine the initial wheel rate because the graph is not a straight line. Even when the rate is constant it is difficult to decide on a load figure. I used the full weight of the bike for illustration but suddenly applied loads create very different figures.

This leaves us with using data for the laden and unladen sags (measured vertically at the wheel). In principle the calculation is simple and a suitable formula is given on the right. Because the top line is a load difference, you do not need to find the sprung weight figures. Some of the difficulties are discussed in a moment but here are two examples for those who wish to pursue this method further.

Example. A new bike weighs 195kgf unladen and has a 55%/45% front to rear weight distribution. With a rider weighing 77kgf the distribution is 50%/50%. Estimate a wheel rate at the rear to suit 120mm total travel if 25% is allocated to hollows.

1) The unladen load at the rear is 45% of 195kgf = 0.45 x 195 = 87.75kgf.

2) The laden load at the rear is half of (195kgf + 77kgf), ie 136kgf.

3) The travel for hollows is 25% of 120mm = 0.25 x 120 = 30mm.

4) This is a heavy bike so assume 10mm unladen sag for illustration.

thus,

$$\text{Wheel rate} = \frac{136\text{kgf} - 87.75\text{kgf}}{30\text{mm} - 10\text{mm}}$$

$$= \frac{48.25\text{kgf}}{20\text{mm}}$$

$$= 2.4\text{kgf/mm} \quad (134\text{lbf/in})$$

$$\textbf{Wheel rate} = \frac{W_L - W_{UL}}{TH - US}$$

where

W_L = the laden load between the tyre and ground at the wheel concerned

W_{UL} = the unladen load between the tyre and ground at the wheel concerned

TH = the vertical wheel travel allocated to deal with hollows at the wheel concerned

US = the vertical unladen sag of the bike at the wheel concerned

Example. A 500cc classic racer is to have 4in of vertical travel at the rear wheel. If the unladen weight at the rear is estimated to be 144lbf and the laden value is assumed to be 260lbf estimate a wheel rate if the desired set up requires 0.1in of unladen sag and 1in is to be allocated to hollows.

$$\text{Wheel rate} = \frac{260\text{lbf} - 144\text{lbf}}{1\text{in} - 0.1\text{in}}$$

$$= \frac{116\text{lbf}}{0.9\text{in}}$$

$$= 129\text{lbf/in}$$

(2.3kgf/mm, 22.6N/mm)

Although this appears straightforward, some of the practical problems I have found are as follows. Firstly, the formula is only valid if the suspension sags when unladen. If it is just topped out unladen then that is acceptable but beyond this, ie with more preload, it is invalid. Since many people with light bikes seem to prefer a fair degree of topping out when unladen the formula is of no use to them. It also seems that everyone's idea of 'just topped out' is different.

Assuming there is some unladen sag, which is the case for the majority, then the result is very sensitive to the unladen sag value. Change it by one or two millimeters and you get a very different answer, especially if the total travel is short. This is to be expected, but unless you have state-of-the-art suspension, particularly at the front end, you will find it difficult to get repeatable results on existing bikes. Ten attempts will yield ten different answers especially on simple, run-of-the-mill front forks and there are other factors affecting what happens. For example, Fig 5.22 shows the characteristics of one set of forks (as raced) and you can see that the graph is somewhat different to those given earlier at small compressions. This will influence the unladen set-up if the bike is close to topped out and can cause confusion. The reasons for this are explained in Chapter 5.4, together with the practical influence of the tyres.

Not everyone can afford components costing vast sums of money and for these reasons I have always preferred to use the concept of natural frequency to estimate wheel rates. This method also has its problems and is perhaps rather more abstract but I have found it works very well once you have established the values you prefer.

Fig 5.22 *Load / compression graph obtained for a set of forks. The behaviour during the initial travel is explained in Chapter 5.4.*

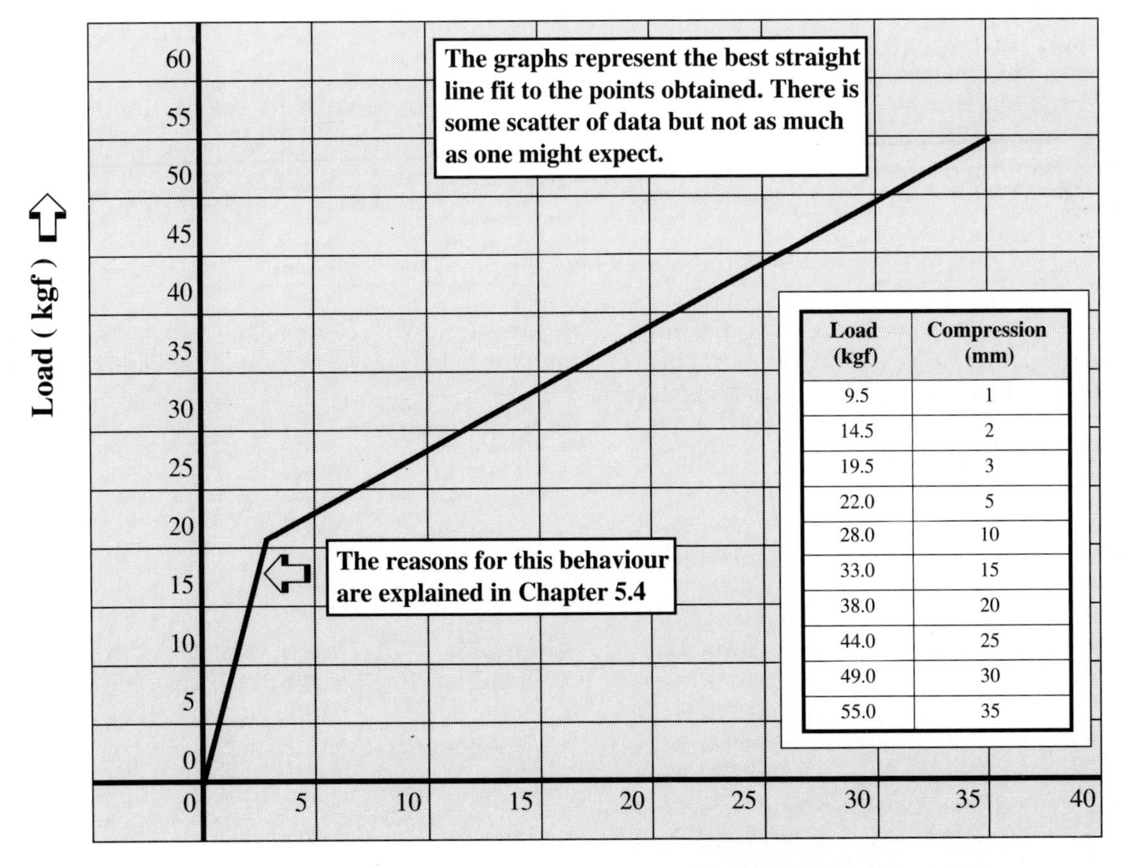

Load (kgf)	Compression (mm)
9.5	1
14.5	2
19.5	3
22.0	5
28.0	10
33.0	15
38.0	20
44.0	25
49.0	30
55.0	35

Use of natural frequency

I have outlined the previous method to estimate a new unknown wheel rate because it relates directly to things that most people understand, ie ride heights, sag etc. This provides some 'feel' for the subject and does not involve anything that may be deemed abstract by some.

However, I now want to look at another method that is often used by suspension specialists to estimate wheel rate. It is based on the frequency at which the sprung mass would vibrate when supported by a suspension system, ie the frequency at which it would move up and down, assuming that the suspension is neither coil bound or topped out.

It will become apparent that such frequencies are a sort of common denominator in suspension since they indicate how the wheel rate is matched to the sprung mass. Once you have established frequencies that suit you it is very easy to estimate the wheel rate required for a new bike.

The concept of resonant frequency was introduced earlier and what I am about to discuss is closely related to it. When a mass is supported by a stiffness it has a frequency at which it will vibrate up and down freely once excited by suitable forces. If there is a considerable amount of damping present then the vibration will not take place but as we reduce the damping the tendency to oscillate becomes clear.

The frequency at which the movement occurs depends on the sprung mass at the wheel concerned, the wheel rate and the amount of damping. Since you are unlikely to know how much damping there actually is, it is not possible to calculate the frequency of the damped oscillations, however it is possible to calculate what the frequency would be if there were no damping. This value is just as useful as a basis for comparison. It is called the natural frequency of free vibration and is normally calculated in Hertz (Hz).

Since 1Hz is one cycle per second then, if the rear suspension has a natural frequency of 1Hz, the sprung mass at the rear of the bike would move from a low position (say), up to a high position and back down to the starting point in one second. In practice this would apply only to small suspension movements about the laden position when no damping were present. These limitations do not make the idea any less useful. Natural frequency is calculated as follows.

$$\textbf{Natural frequency (Hz)} = 15.77\sqrt{\frac{k}{W}}$$

where

k = wheel rate in kgf/mm

W = laden sprung weight acting at the wheel concerned in kgf

This is also valid if the wheel rate is given in N/mm and the weight is in N

or

$$\textbf{Natural frequency (Hz)} = 3.13\sqrt{\frac{k}{W}}$$

where

k = wheel rate in lbf/in

W = laden sprung weight acting at the wheel concerned in lbf

Example. Wheel rate at the rear = 1.6kgf/mm and the laden sprung weight at the rear = 130kgf.

$$\text{frequency} = 15.77\sqrt{\frac{1.6}{130}}$$

$$= 15.77\sqrt{0.0123}$$

$$= 1.75\text{Hz}$$

Example. Wheel rate at the rear = 12N/mm and the laden sprung weight at the rear = 700N.

$$\text{frequency} = 15.77\sqrt{\frac{12}{700}}$$

$$= 15.77\sqrt{0.0171}$$

$$= 2.06\text{Hz}$$

Example. Wheel rate at the front = 90lbf/in and the laden sprung weight at the front = 180lbf.

$$\text{frequency} = 3.13\sqrt{\frac{90}{180}}$$

$$= 3.13\sqrt{0.5}$$

$$= 2.2\text{Hz}$$

The lower the frequency is, the softer the suspension, so it follows that in general a bike with a lot of suspension travel can use a lower frequency. Motocross bikes, with very long travel, eg 300mm, generally have frequencies below 2Hz. I have not had much experience of them but those I have looked at seem to correspond to about 1.8-2.0Hz. The low frequency is indicative of the isolation necessary for this application.

On most road bikes and roadracers, the figure is nearer to 2.2-2.3Hz reflecting the reduced travel, which is typically 100-130mm, and the need to avoid excessive pitching. Most road bikes are set on the soft side in racing terms, ie low frequency. Even a small reduction in frequency gives a much more bump free ride but on the race track the front end dive may be too much to tolerate. If this is the case you have no choice but to stiffen things up a bit, ie go for the slightly higher frequency.

If the travel is very short, less than 75mm, then the frequency will have to be higher still in most cases, perhaps 2.6Hz. If you prefer a very harsh ride you can go even higher. I believe that Formula One cars are set at about 7Hz but they have virtually no suspension movement at all, other than the tyres! Once you have got some feel for this, the wheel rate required on a new bike in order to achieve a desired natural frequency is calculated using the formulae on the right.

When using this method you have to know the sprung laden weight rather than the total laden weight. Again, working out an exact equivalent sprung weight is not as simple as it might appear but this does not really matter provided you are always consistent in the way you do things. I would suggest the method given in the previous chapter once the bulk of the bike exists. Briefly, this was as follows. Determine the laden weight at each wheel. These are total values. Support the bike with a box under the engine so that the wheels still just touch the ground. Remove the front fork caps and the rear suspension spring(s).

$$\textbf{Wheel rate (kgf/mm)} = \frac{Wf^2}{248.5}$$

where

W = laden sprung weight at the wheel concerned in kgf

f = desired natural frequency in Hz

This is also valid if the weight is in N but the wheel rate will now be in N/mm, not kgf/mm

or

$$\textbf{Wheel rate (lbf/in)} = \frac{Wf^2}{9.8}$$

where

W = laden sprung weight at the wheel concerned in lbf

f = desired natural frequency in Hz

Now place scales under each wheel so they are supporting everything that moves with the suspension. The scale readings are an approximate unsprung weight which you can subtract from the total values in order to obtain the nominal sprung values. Perfectionists will tell you about all the approximations here but in reality the extra work involved in pursuing all the mathematical detail is ridiculous in relation to the difference it will make. In many cases it will be adequate to simply weigh the complete wheel/tyre/brake assembly to find a reasonable approximation of the unsprung weight. Once you are happy to determine wheel rate in this way then the balance of wheel rate and preload is found by simply including enough preload to meet the laden sag specification. You can then determine the unladen sag and hence compare the two different methods of specifying what you require.

Example. A new single cylinder roadracer has 104mm of travel at the rear. The laden weight at the rear is 118kgf and the unsprung parts weigh 18kgf. Estimate an initial wheel rate.

The sprung weight is 118kgf - 18kgf =100kgf.

Using 2.3Hz at the rear,

$$\text{Wheel rate} = \frac{Wf^2}{248.5}$$

$$= \frac{100 \times 2.3 \times 2.3}{248.5}$$

= 2.13kgf/mm (119lbf/in)

Example. A new bike weighs 195kgf unladen. With a rider weighing 77kgf the weight distribution is 50%/50% and the vertical travel of the rear wheel is 120mm. Estimate a wheel rate if the unsprung parts at the rear weigh 20kgf.

Total weight = 195 + 77 = 272kgf

Weight on wheel is 50%, ie 136kgf

Sprung weight = 136 - 20 = 116kgf

Using 2.3Hz at this travel,

$$\text{Wheel rate} = \frac{Wf^2}{248.5}$$

$$= \frac{116 \times 2.3 \times 2.3}{248.5}$$

= 2.46kgf/mm (138lbf/in)

Example. At the front of the bike above there is 127mm of travel and the net sprung load is 78kgf. In this case,

The sprung weight is 78kgf

Using 2.2Hz because the travel is now somewhat longer,

$$\text{Wheel rate} = \frac{Wf^2}{248.5}$$

$$= \frac{78 \times 2.2 \times 2.2}{248.5}$$

= 1.52kgf/mm (85lbf/in)

Example. A motocross bike has 12in of travel. If the sprung load at the front wheel is 139lbf estimate a suitable wheel rate.

The sprung weight is 139lbf

At this length of travel 2Hz should be suitable, possibly 1.8Hz.

Using 2Hz,

$$\text{Wheel rate} = \frac{Wf^2}{9.8}$$

$$= \frac{139 \times 2 \times 2}{9.8}$$

= 57lbf/in (1kgf/mm)

Using 1.8Hz,

$$\text{Wheel rate} = \frac{Wf^2}{9.8}$$

$$= \frac{139 \times 1.8 \times 1.8}{9.8}$$

= 46lbf/in (0.82kgf/mm)

Example. A new 125 roadracer has 2.75in of vertical travel at the front. The laden weight at the front is 141lbf and the unsprung parts at the front weigh 27lbf. Estimate an initial wheel rate.

The sprung weight is 141 - 27 = 114lbf.

This is a small amount of travel which requires a higher frequency than normal, say 2.5Hz.

$$\text{Wheel rate} = \frac{Wf^2}{9.8}$$

$$= \frac{114 \times 2.5 \times 2.5}{9.8}$$

= 73lbf/in (1.3kgf/mm)

To convert	to	multiply by
kgf/cm	kgf/mm	0.1
kgf/cm	lbf/in	5.592
kgf/mm	kgf/cm	10
kgf/mm	N/mm	9.81
kgf/mm	lbf/in	56
N/mm	lbf/in	5.71
N/mm	kgf/mm	0.1019
N/mm	kgf/cm	1.0194
lbf/in	N/mm	0.175
lbf/in	kgf/mm	0.01786

Table 5.1 *Stiffness conversion factors. The units used by manufacturers vary greatly. WP Suspension use N/mm. Hagon quote kgf/cm, most motocrossers use kgf/mm and many people still much prefer lbf/in. I have chosen to use kgf/mm because this book is aimed at bike builders rather than scientists. N/mm is more correct but few people in sheds will see the point of multiplying every scale reading by 9.81!*

These examples should at least provide a starting point. The topic is discussed again in Chapters 5.4 and 5.5. My own preference for this method is based on several things. Firstly, although you are not finding the exact sprung weights using the methods described, you are using a simple method that is repeatable. Once you have the nominal sprung weight at the wheel concerned then the only other variable is frequency. The wheel rate formula is extremely sensitive to frequency and you may well disagree with what I, or anyone else, have suggested. This is of no consequence. Once you have adjusted the value to suit you then it will be reasonable for different bikes that have a similar amount of suspension travel.

Using the combination of laden and unladen sag to estimate wheel rate requires high quality components and very accurate measurement if it is to be repeatable. I have never been able to spend three figure sums on GP type forks and, as many of you will know, the cheaper alternatives are somewhat different to deal with.

Use the correct combination of formula and units. Table 5.1 can be used for conversions. The most important thing to remember at this stage is that you are not calculating the required spring stiffness. This will depend on the mechanism involved and I will deal with it later.

You can of course obtain data from existing bikes if you consider the set-up to be satisfactory. This is the way to build up your database of ideal frequencies. Since the front and rear suspension require rather different approaches, I will discuss this aspect in Chapters 5.4 and 5.5 respectively.

Rising rates

The wheel rate we have estimated is an initial value, an average based on the first 25 - 40% of travel. It is possible this may need to change as the travel increases. When the wheel rate is not constant then by definition it either increases or reduces, possibly both, at different points in the wheel travel.

If the wheel rate increases as the suspension is compressed then the suspension is said to have a rising rate. If the wheel rate reduces as the suspension is compressed then the system is said to have a falling rate. A system with a rising rate feels soft initially and becomes progressively harder with increasing wheel travel. The falling rate system becomes softer and can collapse if the change is excessive.

Any changes in wheel rate that occur come from two sources. Some changes are produced by suspension units that are fitted with springs of variable stiffness (commonly called progressive rate springs) or multiple springs. Others are produced by changes in the geometry of the mechanism as the swinging arm rotates. These changes alter the leverage between the suspension unit and the wheel. Linkage systems are designed to capitalise on the second method by producing specific changes in line with the designer's requirements. Combinations of both methods may be used in the search for a particular form of wheel rate variation. Forks use changes in spring rate (plus the forces produced by compressing the air column) but rear suspension may use either, or both, methods.

The variation in wheel rate achieved by a particular system can be illustrated in various ways. Firstly, if a vertical force is applied to the wheel and the wheel movement is measured then a graph of force vs wheel position can be drawn. If the graph gets steeper then the system has a rising rate. If the slope reduces there is a falling rate - Fig 5.23a.

Alternatively, it may be more convenient to consider the compression of the actual suspension unit in relation to the movement of the wheel. Note that this will only give a true result if the actual spring(s) have a constant stiffness. Assuming this is the case, then, because the spring(s) exert a force proportional to their compression, a graph of suspension unit compression vs wheel movement will be a straight line if the wheel rate is constant. If the compression of the suspension unit becomes greater for a given wheel movement as the travel increases then the system has a rising rate - Fig 5.23b. There are some errors in this method for certain systems but the general trend is clear enough.

Finally, we might consider the ratio of the force exerted by the suspension spring(s) to that produced at the wheel. Just to confuse you, some manufacturers use the value of (force exerted by suspension unit/ force at wheel) and, for a rising rate system, this produces a graph like Fig 5.23c. I have only discussed all these options because you could encounter any one of them. In terms of developing your own systems it is usually easiest to work with the relative movements of the wheel and spring(s) but bear in mind that this will not account for any stiffness variation built into the springs.

The case for rising rates

For many years, suspension systems had nominally constant wheel rates. Some increased slightly, others fell slightly but overall the changes were not dramatic. Conventional twin shock layouts are limited in the rate rise they can create without progressive springing.

Motocross systems have no choice but to use rising rates on modern circuits. Even with the high travel available the range of conditions is too wide. The problem is impact. A suddenly applied load from zero height gives a transient peak load that is higher than the value produced when the load is applied gradually. The practical implication is that if you suspended the bike just clear of the floor and then cut the support the suspension would momentarily sink further than the normal position it returns to. On top of this we have to add height. Using typical motocross wheel rates and a 3m jump the load is about 400% greater and could be much more depending on how the wheels land. To cope with such situations there has to be a

Fig 5.23 *Different representations of changing wheel rates. a) shows both rising and falling rates as a graph of force at the wheel vs wheel movement. b) uses wheel travel and suspension unit travel while c) plots the force ratio against wheel travel. If this is done using spring force / wheel force the graph slope reduces. Note that the three rising rate cases are not all for the same data.*

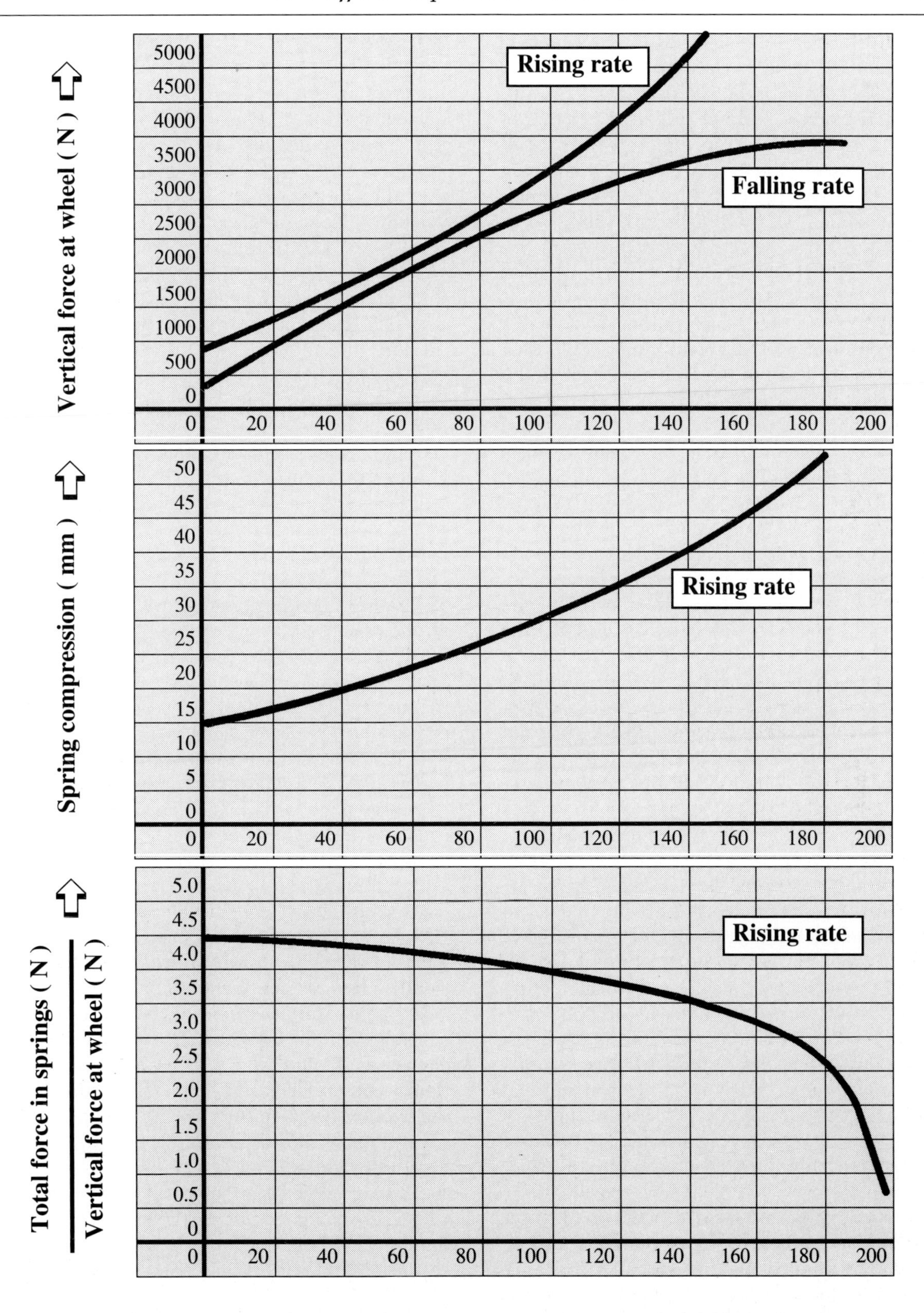

Vertical force at wheel (N)
5000
4500
4000
3500
3000
2500
2000
1500
1000
500
0
Rising rate
Falling rate
0
20
40
60
80
100
120
140
160
180
200
Spring compression (mm)
50
45
40
35
30
25
20
15
10
5
0
Rising rate
Total force in springs (N) / Vertical force at wheel (N)
5.0
4.5
4.0
3.5
3.0
2.5
2.0
1.5
1.0
0.5
0
Rising rate
Vertical wheel movement in mm (all three graphs)

rising rate that stiffens the suspension considerably. The rate usually rises at a slow rate for perhaps 75% of the travel and then starts to go up much more rapidly, perhaps spanning a change of 7:1 from the initial rate. The high rate near to full travel then 'leads' the system into the bump stop which, in a modern system, is designed as a high stiffness element with a progressive rate.

Clearly roadracing is different but there are still problems. Heavy braking and acceleration put loads on the suspension that may bottom it when using the wheel rate that is best under normal conditions. At this point some people start raising the preload but, while it may reduce the problem, it only creates a lot more. Similarly, increasing the (constant) wheel rate may not give exactly what you want, especially when there is very limited travel. The bottoming problem may be solved but perhaps the normal ride is inferior. In such cases there is a possible requirement for using some degree of rising rate that restores the normal ride quality while preventing bottoming.

However, even this is not without its problems. Cornering hard uses up lots of travel as explained previously, as does braking. If the rate rise is significant, both these events are conducted with the suspension well compressed and therefore relatively stiff if the rate is rising. Stiff suspension is not what you want if you now encounter bumps and ripples.

You should note that the majority of GP bikes use constant rate fork springs and the rear linkages only have very slightly progressive characteristics. On 125cc and 250cc GP bikes, a linkage ratio that varies from about 1.8:1 up to 2.0:1 is typical (wheel travel/damper travel) according to the WP Suspension Grand Prix engineers. This is considerably different from the needs of motocross but it will still produce a 23% rise in the wheel rate imparted by a particular spring. Since GP bikes have the highest levels of acceleration and retardation, most constructors would find it hard to justify even these levels of rate increase. It is very easy to get carried away by all the discussion of these matters that appears in the press, much of which is incorrect.

There are no absolute rules. You can only decide what you like best by experiment. Personally I prefer a constant rate for most of the travel, only using a rate rise as a lead into the bump stop, and only using enough to do the job. It probably stems from being brought up on short wheel travel!

Summary

In this chapter I have identified some of the most basic suspension stiffness requirements. The subject is vast and there are many technical books available that cover it in much more detail. However they do not, in my experience, actually tell you how to do something. I have tried to overcome this, not by identifying some specific wheel rate you should seek, but by showing how the wheel rates you prefer can be identified either by using a natural frequency or from the way the bike is set up laden and unladen. I have always found the use of natural frequency to be the more reliable of the two if it is combined with preloading to achieve a 25% travel when laden. In particular, note that a change of rider can alter the load figures considerably and therefore demand a change in wheel rate. You will not get the best behaviour by simply winding on more and more preload.

Although one can specify numerous theoretical goals, only two seem to have universal acceptance. The first is the improvement in suspension compliance when the unsprung mass is small in absolute terms and small compared to the sprung mass above it. The second is avoiding excessive preload in the system. Opinions vary regarding almost everything else so you need to find out what suits you. There is a minimum constant wheel rate that can be used in any situation but once the rate is increased above this or made a variable quantity then anything is possible.

As far as wheel rates are concerned, the advantages of low wheel rates in terms of ride quality have to be offset against the practical limits of travel and the changes that long travel creates in terms of cg position and steering geometry. Even if such changes are acceptable, there are many riders who simply do not like the feel of soft suspension and long travel. If you don't like it you don't trust it and that inevitably means slower lap times. Only a rider can make the final choice in relation to the tyres they are using.

Starting with a wheel rate is the only sensible way to view the springing requirements. Although the spring stiffness required to achieve a given wheel rate will vary considerably according to the final mechanism, the range of wheel rates which a rider prefers is relatively narrow. Since you can now identify this using the methods described it is possible to consider any type of mechanism as a means of achieving it.

5.3 Suspension springs

Introduction

Virtually every motorcycle built in recent years relies on coil springs to provide the 'stiffness' element in the suspension. If the springing system consisted of just one vertical spring above the wheel then the spring stiffness required would be equal to the desired wheel rate.

This is rarely the case. Front forks normally have two springs and they are not vertical. Most rear suspension involves one or two springs which again are rarely upright. Some twin shock bikes use four springs, two on each suspension unit. In virtually every case a swinging arm is used, the actual wheel motion is not vertical, and the mechanism provides varying leverage between the spring(s) and the wheel. We have to start somewhere and I am going to look at the springs first because they are the common element in all these systems.

Coil springs

Coil springs are generally regarded as standard parts, ie you are more likely to buy them than to make them. Since it is almost certain that you will use standard dampers the springs have to fit these and a number of standard sizes have evolved to suit. The main questions to be answered are what stiffness do you need and, in the case of existing springs, what stiffness have you got? The first question cannot be answered until we have looked at the mechanism involved but the second one is reasonably straightforward.

Spring stiffness is no different from the other stiffness related aspects already discussed. It defines the relationship between a change in load and the deflection produced. If a spring has a stiffness of 10N/mm then it will compress by one millimetre for every ten newtons applied. A load of 100N would give 10mm compression and so on until the spring becomes coilbound, ie solid. Similarly, a spring with a stiffness of 70lbf/in would compress one inch under 70lbf, two inches under 140lbf and so on - Fig 5. 24.

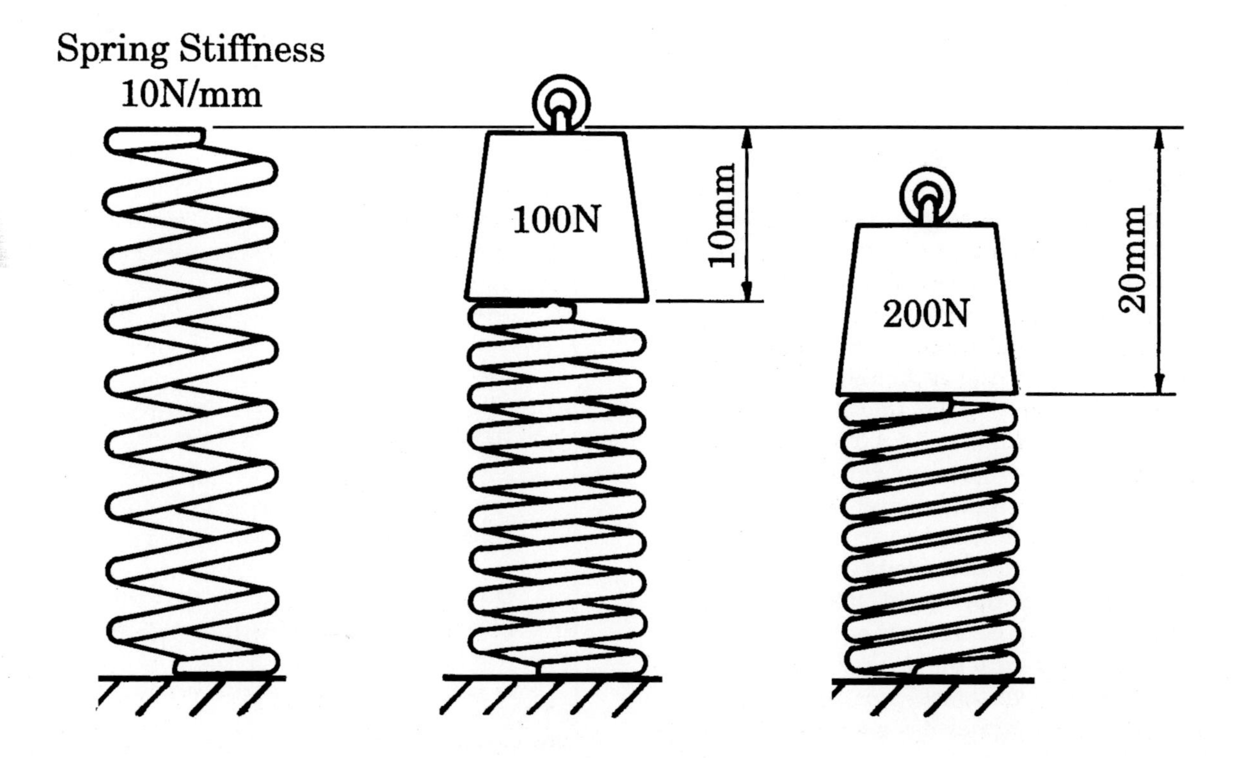

Fig 5.24 *Relationship between stiffness, load and deflection within the working range of the spring.*

Springs with constant stiffness

The key feature of coil springs is the relatively large amount of elastic deflection they produce for a given load. Assuming the spring is correctly designed and heat treated it is capable of being loaded up thousands of times before some of the elastic deformation becomes plastic and a permanent shortening of the spring takes place.

Coil springs provide this large deflection by arranging the wire in a form where it is twisted by the load. The more wire there is to twist the greater the total deflection will be for a given load. More coils (number n) will therefore give a lower stiffness as will a greater mean diameter (D).

The cross-section of the wire offers a resistance to being twisted that will increase as the wire diameter (d) becomes greater and different materials offer differing degrees of elasticity for the same cross-section. Putting these observations together more formally, the general expression for coil spring stiffness in compression is,

$$\text{Stiffness} = \frac{Gd^4}{8D^3n}$$

where
G = shear modulus of the material
d = wire diameter
D = mean coil diameter
n = number of coils being twisted

This formula shows that the stiffness is particularly sensitive to changes in wire diameter and mean coil diameter. The modulus is a property of the material that describes its elastic behaviour and you should note that it does vary from one steel to another. Mass-produced compression springs for 'general engineering' are made from a variety of preconditioned steels specially developed for the purpose. Although there are many options, the value of the modulus is normally taken as 79289N/mm^2 (11.5 x 10^{6}lbf/in^2)

However, top quality suspension springs need to be made from slightly better materials for two reasons. Firstly, if a higher strength material is employed then it is possible to use a thinner wire and hence reduce the weight. Reductions are not particularly great because other factors need to be changed to reinstate the desired stiffness with a thinner wire. Nevertheless, it is a consideration in these days of optimal design. The second and generally more important aspect concerns fatigue. The coil spring is continually subjected to the conditions that cause fatigue failure and the fatigue resistance of the more general spring steels is marginal for our applications when the spring design is optimal.

For these reasons suspension springs are generally made from steels which contain significant amounts of alloying elements (see Volume 2), in particular chromium-vanadium or chromium-silicon alloys (eg AISI6150 and AISI9254 respectively). In general, the Americans, who make lots of alternative suspension springs, tend to favour the chromium-silicon alloys while many British springs are chrome-vanadium. Both alloys are acceptable for our applications provided they are properly heat-treated. This is the really important factor. The silicon variant does have slightly higher strength but the vanadium alloy is more forgiving in terms of heat treatment. For either of these materials, the most accurate modulus figure I can offer is 79354.8N/mm^2 (11.509434 x 10^{6}lbf/in^2). Inserting this figure into the general formula given earlier produces the following working formulae for spring stiffness.

$$\textbf{Stiffness (N/mm)} = \frac{9919.35d^4}{D^3n}$$

where

d = wire diameter in mm
D = mean coil diameter in mm
= outside dia. - wire dia.
n = number of active coils

(multiply by 0.1019 to get kgf/mm)

or

$$\textbf{Stiffness (lbf/in)} = \frac{1438679d^4}{D^3n}$$

where

d = wire diameter in inches
D = mean coil diameter in inches
= outside dia. - wire dia
n = number of active coils

Be careful with stainless spring steels. Martensitic types can use these formulae but with Austenitic types the modulus could be up to 13% less, thereby reducing the constants given by the same amount. It all depends on the specific steel used.

These formulae allow you to estimate the stiffness of existing springs but, although they look innocent enough, there are a number of things that can lead to significant errors in use.

Firstly, when springs are wound on a mandrel they invariably show a slight taper and therefore to find the mean coil diameter you should,

- Measure the outside diameter a few coils from each end and find the average value (add readings then divide by number of readings).
- Measure the wire diameter (d) at several coils. This should show little variation but average if necessary.
- Subtract the wire diameter from the outside diameter to obtain the required mean diameter (D).

The second problem concerns the number of active coils (n). This is the number of coils actually being twisted and it is less than the total number of coils. Begin by finding the total number of coils noting that the manufacturers normally work in quarter turn increments, ie the number need not be a whole number.

To do this follow the example in Fig 5.25. Start at the lower free end of the wire and count the number of times the wire goes round in a circle making sure that when you get to the top you account for any fractions of a turn. Once you have found the total number of coils in the spring the number of active coils can be determined.

Fig 5.25 *Finding the total number of coils in a spring. Manufacturers usually work to a one quarter of a coil and it is important not to ignore any fractional turns when determining the total. The method depicted here is as follows. a) Start at the lower free end and count the number of complete revolutions the wire makes. Each one is shown by a black dot in the examples. c) When you arrive at the top of the spring ensure that any fractional turns are accounted for.*

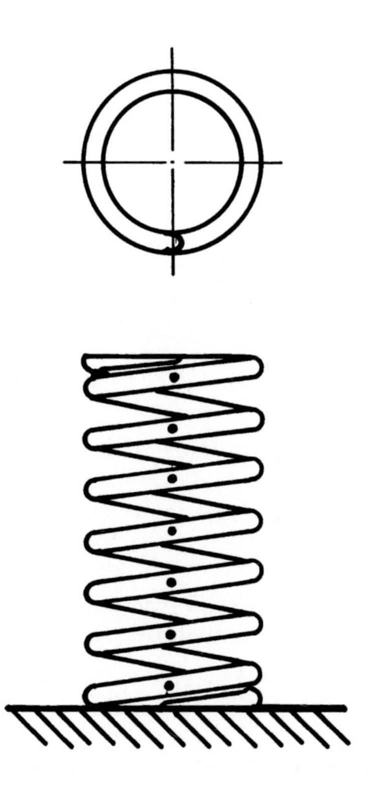

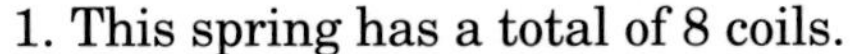

1. This spring has a total of 8 coils.

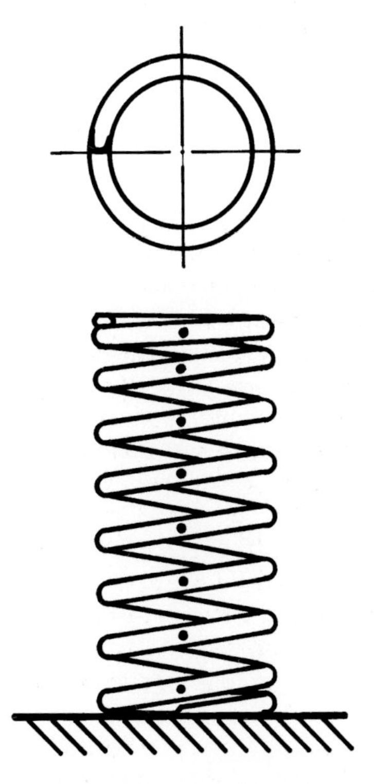

2. This spring has a total of 8.75 coils.

This depends on the end preparation of the spring. Fig 5.26 gives examples and in 99% of cases you will be dealing with closed and ground ends.

Active coils = total coils - 2

(closed and ground ends only)

Even this simple relationship can vary and it is possible that in some cases (total coils - 1.5) may be closer. The reason is that when the spring is made its stiffness is often fine tuned by closing up the end coils a bit. Unless you have a lot of spring experience you will have to stick to the basic formula given.

Example. A steel suspension spring with closed and ground ends has a wire diameter of 10mm and a mean coil diameter of 70mm. There are 8 coils in total.

Active coils = 8 - 2 = 6

$$\text{Stiffness(N/mm)} = \frac{9919.35d^4}{D^3 n}$$

$$= \frac{9919.35 \times 10^4}{70^3 \times 6}$$

= 48.2N/mm (275lbf/in)

Example. A steel suspension spring is made from 0.375in diameter wire. The outside diameter is 3.25in and there are 10.25 coils. The ends are closed and ground.

The mean diameter is 3.25in - 0.375in = 2.875in

Active coils = 10.25 - 2 = 8.25

$$\text{Stiffness(lbf/in)} = \frac{1438679d^4}{D^3 n}$$

$$= \frac{1438679 \times (0.375)^4}{(2.875)^3 \times 8.25}$$

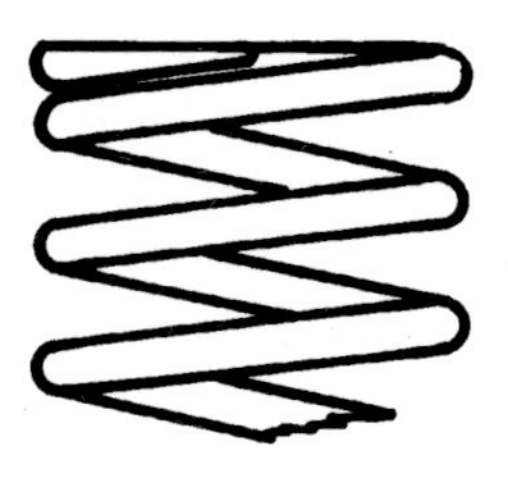

a) Closed and ground end.

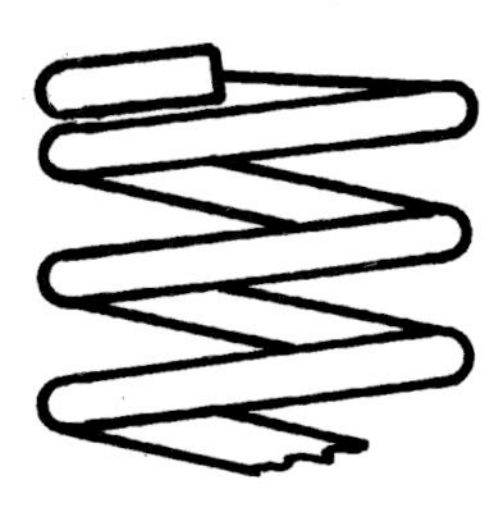

b) End closed but not ground.

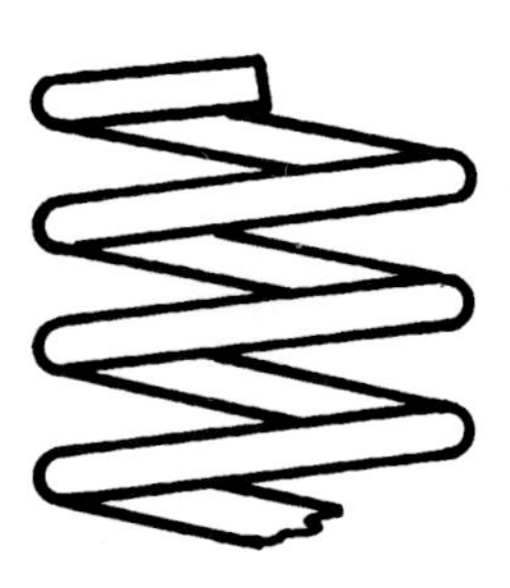

c) Open end.

Fig 5.26 *Spring end preparation. At the top is the closed and ground end that is normally used for suspension springs.*

$$= \frac{28450.4}{196.05}$$

=145lbf/in (25.4N/mm, 2.59kgf/mm)

Table 5.2 can be used for conversions to other units.

Tolerances

You may think that all these details do not matter but they most certainly do. Spring stiffness is a problem for many reasons. Firstly, when springs are manufactured a stiffness value is the hardest quantity to achieve on a repetitive basis, indeed of the four application categories used in the trade only Class 4 specifies a stiffness value. In most cases only specific load and length data is adhered to. If a spring has to be in Class 4 as ours do then for a spring of normal proportions tolerances of +/-3% are possible on the stiffness but this is the minimum. Long or very short springs require greater tolerance. The only way you are going to do better than this is if the manufacturer makes a whole batch and you select the best of the batch. This is expensive. Furthermore, the specified tolerance will only be held over 10 - 85% of the total compression, ie the first 10% and last 15% of compression are grey areas in which no stiffness will be specified.

These tolerances are significant. If a monoshock spring is designed to give a stiffness of 60N/mm (342.6lbf/in) then the actual stiffness could be anything from 58.2N/mm to 61.8N/mm (332.3-352.9lbf/in). If you decide from track tests that this is too soft then you should go for an increase which is not less than 20%. If you go for smaller changes, say 10%, then the difference between a new spring on bottom tolerance limit and an old one on top tolerance limit will be negligible.

Similarly, if you are unable to have the spring stiffness properly checked and have to estimate it using the calculation described then you will be lucky to get any closer than +/-10% so the rule for changes is the same, don't go up or down in less than 20% increments initially.

If you get into very fine changes then you can of course use smaller intervals but only based on a number of springs that have been precisely calibrated. Such finesse is most unlikely to be necessary at the rear of the bike because the effect on wheel rate is reduced by the suspension mechanism, often quite dramatically. Front forks are not affected in the same way and fine tuning at the front end may pay big dividends in some cases.

To determine the actual stiffness, the spring has to be compressed while measuring applied load and deflection. Twin shock springs and fork springs are reasonably soft but fairly long. This requires some form of insert to prevent the spring buckling under load. If it buckles it always manages to fly out in your direction! You can get a very good idea of stiffness by compressing springs on to scales but don't just use a couple of figures. Take several readings, plot a load vs compression graph, and find the slope of it. Monoshock springs are usually too stiff for you to do this manually. Most technical colleges will have a suitable hydraulic testing machine in the engineering department and this is one way forward. Failing that, contact a spring manufacturer or supplier.

To convert	to	multiply by
kgf/cm	kgf/mm	0.1
kgf/cm	lbf/in	5.592
kgf/mm	kgf/cm	10
kgf/mm	N/mm	9.81
kgf/mm	lbf/in	56
N/mm	lbf/in	5.71
N/mm	kgf/mm	0.1019
N/mm	kgf/cm	1.0194
lbf/in	N/mm	0.175
lbf/in	kgf/mm	0.01786

Table 5.2 *Stiffness conversion factors.*

Solid height

You need to ensure that any springs you select do not become coilbound before you want them to. For closed and ground ends a general formula for solid height is,

Solid ht. = wire dia(total coils - 0.5)

Again, minor variations are possible due to manufacturing tolerances and techniques.

Example. A suspension spring with closed and ground ends has a wire diameter of 10mm and 10 coils. If it has a free length of 180mm how far can it be compressed before it is coilbound?

Solid height= 10mm(10 - 0.5)

= 10 x 9.5 = 95mm

Max. compression = 180mm - 95mm

= 85mm

Progressive springs

The possibility of using a rising rate has been discussed in the last chapter. Rate changes can be achieved either through the mechanics of a mechanism or by building them into the springs. Both methods are employed for rear suspension but front forks have to achieve these changes via the springs or by air compression characteristics.

When springs have a stiffness that varies with deflection they are generally called progressive rate springs. To achieve the rate changes the pitch of the coils is altered thus placing more or fewer coils in different regions of the spring - Fig 5.27.

When a load is applied the close coils have the lowest stiffness and so they close up first. Once the coils touch each other they become inoperative and so the stiffness is now due to a smaller number of coils which effectively makes the spring stiffer (see formula). The result is a rising spring rate as described previously.

Progressive springs are a simple way of achieving a low initial wheel rate which then rises to prevent bottoming. Until recently most progressive springs for twin shock bikes had just two or three fairly obvious rate changes and the groups of coils having different pitches could be clearly seen. This situation has improved and Hagon's in particular offer a very wide range of springs which have a nice gradual rise in stiffness over most of the travel, followed by a more rapid rise near full travel. However, there are some problems. The main problem is space. This is often restricted and once you decide that several coils will be out of action early on it becomes difficult to achieve all the different requirements, ie sufficient compression, desired rate and required rate change. The use of progressive rates for short monoshock units is somewhat limited by this but there is massive scope for most twin shock units and even more for front forks where the long spring length is well suited to this type of design.

Suppliers will generally specify these springs in one of two ways. Either they will quote an average stiffness , ie the spring will start off softer than the quoted figure and finish up harder, or they will quote two figures, in which case the first figure is normally the lowest stiffness and the second figure is the highest stiffness.

For general use an average stiffness figure makes sense but you have to be careful with such data when you are seeking specific wheel rates. If the spring is designed to give a very substantial increase in stiffness at some point in order to prevent bottoming, then the sooner in the travel this occurs the more the average stiffness will differ from the initial value. As such you may not be buying exactly what you expect.

As usual the solution is simple enough. Talk to the manufacturers and explain exactly what you want to achieve. Ideally you want a load/compression graph for the spring concerned. Note that very few GP bikes use progressive fork springs and the progression at the rear, if any, is also extremely mild for the reasons outlined earlier.

Right. Fig 5.27 *Progressive springs. The spacing of the coils is not equal and the close coils become coilbound first. With fewer active coils the stiffness rises. This is evident from the increasing slope of the force vs stiffness curve (only first 100mm of compression shown).*

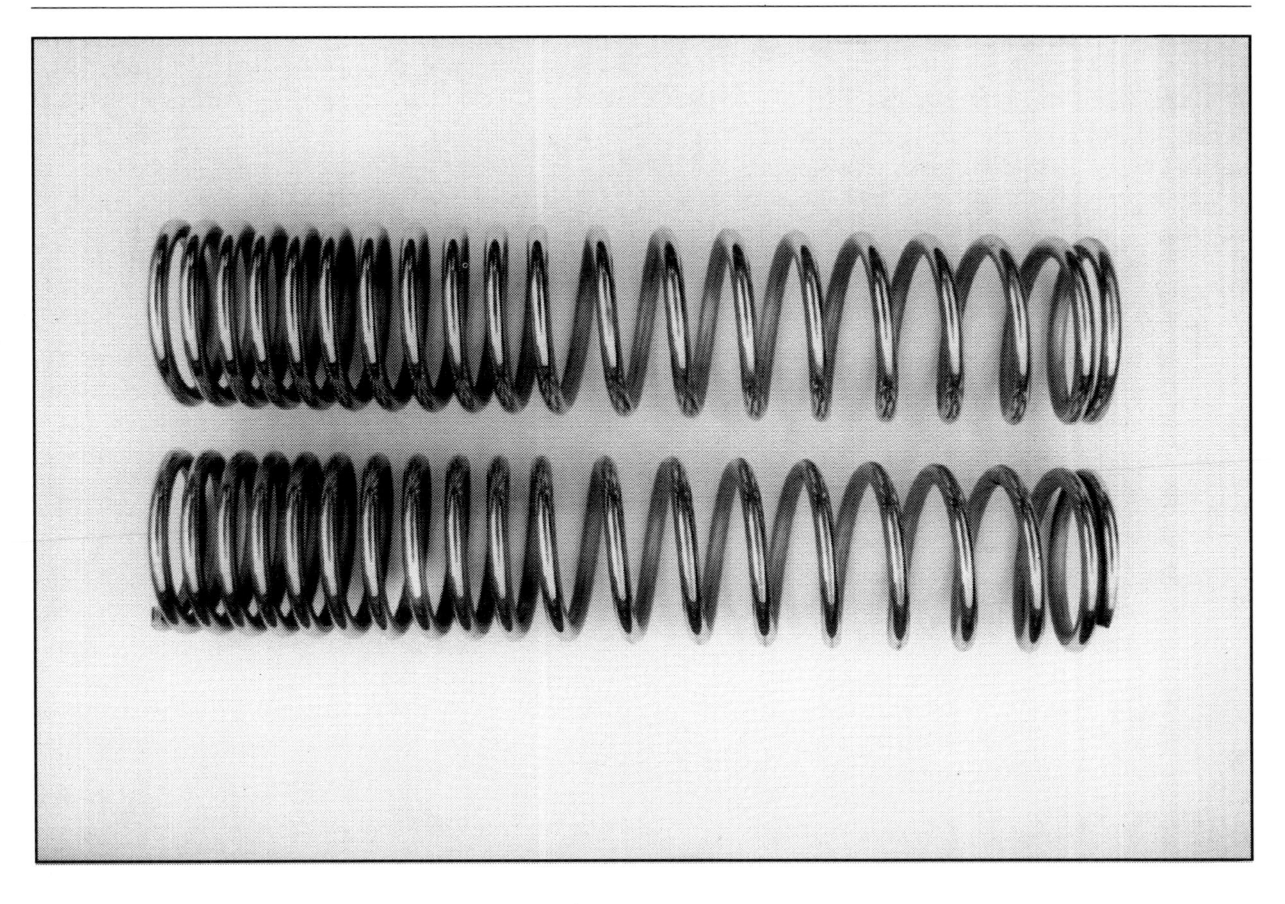

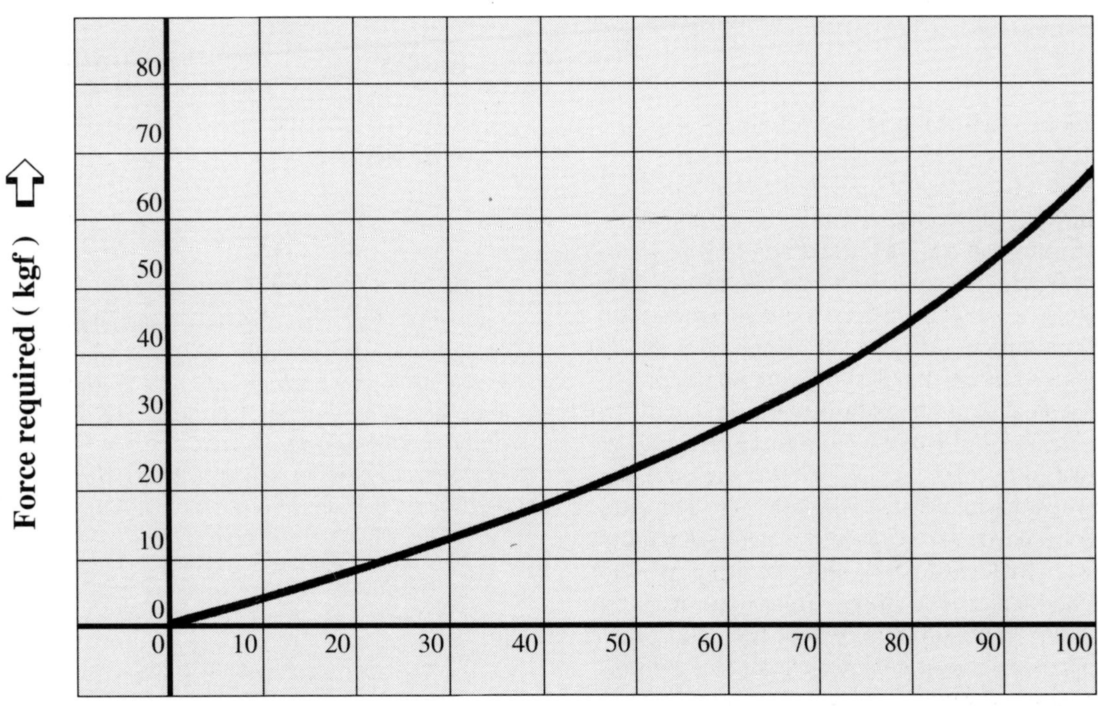
80
70
60
50
40
30
20
10
0
0
10
20
30
40
50
60
70
80
90
100
Force required (kgf)
Spring compression (mm)

Spring sources

The first point of contact is the supplier of the damper or forks that the springs have to fit though in some cases little choice may exist and the cost may be very high. For general experimenting the following companies have good stocks at reasonable prices.

- For a wide range of twin shock springs (including progressive types) and some monoshock, Hagon Products, Hainault, Essex. Tel. 0181 - 502 - 6222. Hagon will check the stiffness of your existing springs.

- For a wide range of twin shock and monoshock springs as well as progressive rate fork springs, M.R.Holland, Spalding, Lincs. Tel. 01775 - 766455. They will supply virtually any monoshock spring made to standard dimensions.

There are of course many others. If you cannot obtain what you want off the shelf then you will have to have the springs made. Again there are many companies but I can recommend the following,

- Suspension Supplies, Sheffield. Tel. 0114 - 275 - 3723.

This company will make virtually any suspension spring from good quality materials and produce many of the springs you will buy elsewhere. If it becomes necessary to produce a special spring you should avoid trying to be too clever about it. Don't try to design the spring, just provide all the physical space details and explain what you want to achieve in terms of stiffness and compression. Let them design it, it's their job! This is particularly important for progressive rate springs. The rate effectively changes in steps and to get best results the points at which the rate changes occur need to be matched to several things. This is one of many reasons why you should only deal with specialist manufacturers of suspension springs, not general industrial suppliers.

Finally, for general up to date information on anything to do with springs, eg local manufacturers, materials, standards etc contact,

- The Spring Research and Manufacturers' Association, Henry Street, Sheffield S3 7EQ (0114 2760771).

Spring combinations

Springs can be combined in all sorts of ways to produce different stiffness characteristics. I will only deal with those situations commonly encountered on a motorcycle.

Springs in parallel

This is the general layout for twin shock suspension and front forks - Fig 5.28a. In both cases the total force is shared by the springs and each spring experiences the same deflection. Under these conditions,

Total stiffness = k1 + k2

where

k1 and k2 are the individual stiffnesses.

Right. Fig 5.28 *Springs in series and parallel. The springs in front forks and those on a normal twin shock bike represent parallel combinations. The total stiffness they present is the sum of the individual stiffness values so with identical springs the total stiffness is double that of each unit. Springs in series are more complicated. The combined stiffness is less than that of the softest spring. If one spring becomes coilbound the stiffness increases to that of the spring which is still active. This system was used by Girling to provide a rising rate and is now offered by Hagon Products.*

For more than two springs used like this (rather unlikely) just add together each stiffness. This arrangement can also be used to provide a simple rate rise in front forks to prevent bottoming. A short spring of small diameter can be fitted inside the main springs so that it only comes into play near full travel. The spring should be wound with the opposite pitch to the main springs otherwise they may become entangled. It also needs suitable guidance to prevent buckling.

Springs in series

Springs are said to be in series if each spring experiences the same load and the total deflection is the sum of the individual deflections as shown in Fig 5.28b. This arrangement gives a combined stiffness that is lower than that of the softest spring. For two springs with stiffnesses k1 and k2 the combined stiffness is,

$$\textbf{Combined stiffness} = \frac{k1 \times k2}{k1 + k2}$$

Example. Two springs are in series. One has a stiffness of 18N/mm and the other has a stiffness of 10N/mm.

$$\text{Combined stiffness} = \frac{10 \times 18}{10 + 18}$$

$$= \frac{180}{28}$$

$$= 6.43\text{N/mm}$$

Example. Two springs are in series. One has a stiffness of 140lbf/in and the other has a stiffness of 100lbf/in

$$\text{Combined stiffness} = \frac{140 \times 100}{140 + 100}$$

$$= \frac{14000}{240}$$

$$= 58.34\text{lbf/in}$$

These results may surprise you but they are correct. For example, if we use the springs referred to in the last example and apply a 100lbf load then the deflections are as follows,

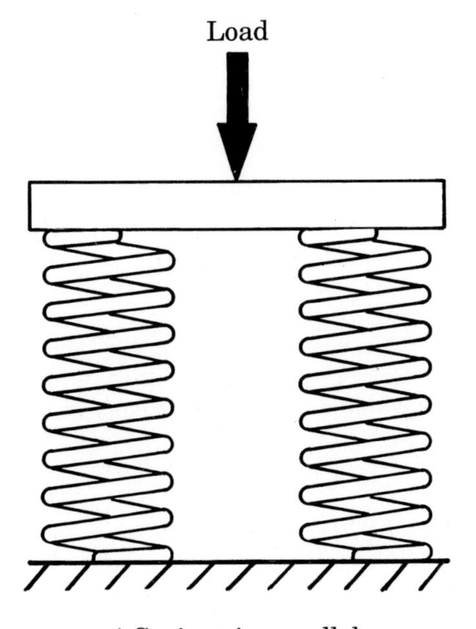

a) Springs in parallel.

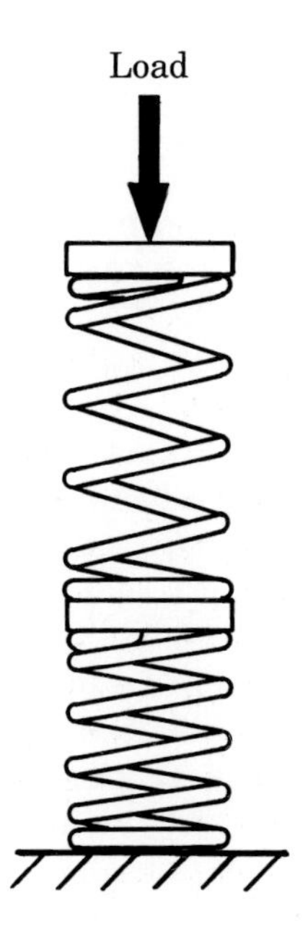

b) Springs in series.

- The 100lbf/in spring deflects by 1in under a 100lbf load.

- The 140lbf/in spring deflects by 100/140 = 0.714in.

- The total deflection is 1in + 0.714in = 1.714in.

- The combined stiffness is such that 100lbf gives 1.714in total deflection, ie stiffness = 100lbf/1.714in = 58.34lbf/in as stated.

In its most basic form this does not have a lot of use on a bike but it becomes extremely useful if the arrangement is such that one spring becomes coilbound during normal deflections. If it does then the stiffness will start off at the combined value which is lower than that of either spring. As soon as one spring becomes coilbound the stiffness will rise to that of the spring which remains active, ie we have a rising rate.

This system was used extensively by Girling on their 'twin rate gas shocks'. The manufacturing rights were bought up by Alf Hagon who now offers the same arrangement fitted to much improved dampers - Fig 5.29. The two springs are separated by a plastic collar and the short spring has a stiffness of 31.5N/mm (32kgf/cm,180lbf/in). Girling originally used square section wire for these short springs but Hagon have reverted to normal round wire. By combining the short springs with a range of other springs all sorts of combinations can be produced as I will now demonstrate.

Selection of 'twin rate' springs

The first thing you need to know when combining springs like this is the load that will render the short spring coilbound. In the case of the original Girling units and the new Hagon ones this figure is 1093.8N (111.5kgf, 245.9lbf). This load produces a compression of 34.7mm (1.366in). The procedure I will describe first assumes that you are using these springs. Since Hagons specify their stiffnesses in kgf/cm I will use the same units.

- Fig 5.30 shows the combined rate of the Hagon/Girling short spring with other springs. Use this graph to select the spring required to combine with the short spring.

- Divide the load required to render the short spring solid (111.5kgf) by the combined spring stiffness. This gives the compression of the combined springs required to render the short spring coilbound.

Example. An initial spring stiffness of 15kgf/cm is required. Select a spring to combine with the Hagon short spring and determine the point at which the rate will rise. What will it rise to?

> Using Fig 5.30, to achieve an initial rate of 15kgf/cm you need a main spring with a stiffness of 28kgf/cm.
>
> To find the compression to render the short spring coilbound, divide 111.5kgf by the combined stiffness in kgf/cm, ie 111.5/15 = 7.4cm.

Fig 5.29 *Hagon 'twin rate' spring system based on an earlier Girling design.*

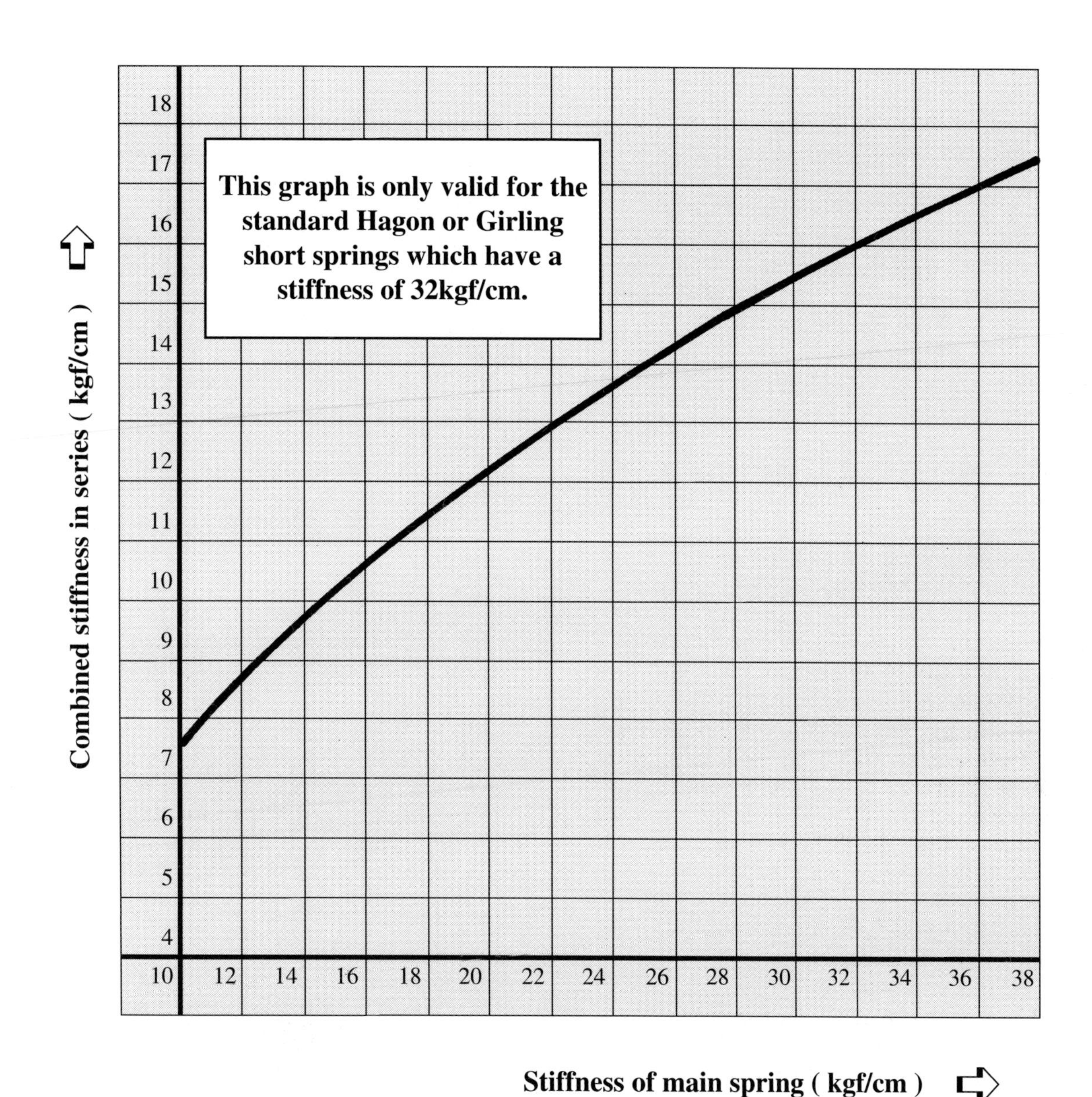

Above. Fig 5.30 *This graph allows you to determine the combined rate produced by any normal main spring in series with the standard Hagon / Girling 'short' spring. The graph is based on the formula given for springs in series and assumes a stiffness of 32kgf / cm for the short spring.*

So, in this example we use a 28kgf/cm main spring in series with the 32kgf/cm short spring. The result is an initial stiffness of 15kgf/cm which will change to 28kgf/cm when the combination has compressed by 7.4cm. Note that the 7.4cm includes any preload compression.

Since many people will prefer to work in imperial I have produced Fig 5.31. The method is the same.

Example. An initial stiffness of 85lbf/in is required. Select a spring to combine with an original Girling short spring and find the point at which the rate rises. What does it rise to?

From the graph we require a 160lbf/in main spring

The coilbound load for the standard short spring is 245.9lbf thus,

Compression to render this spring coilbound = 245.9/85 = 2.89in

In this example the combination of the 180lbf/in short spring with a 160lbf/in main spring gives the required initial rate of 85lbf/in. This will change to 160lbf/in after 2.89in of compression (includes any preload compression).

This system is excellent for many applications and is particularly favoured by riders of twin shock trials bikes. The only criticisms we could make are as follows.

- The change in stiffness takes place suddenly. This is perhaps the greatest criticism.

- In some cases the higher stiffness may be more than you would like. It is always equal to that of the main spring.

- The desired combined stiffness is linked to the point at which the stiffness changes. The lower the initial stiffness required the greater the travel before the stiffness changes. This in itself may not be a problem but there is no choice in the matter.

The first problem can be overcome by using a main spring that is progressive. This is virtually standard on current Hagon units. The situation is now more complicated and can only be considered in relation to specific progressive rate characteristics. Talk to the manufacturer.

Even with a fixed main spring stiffness this is a simple means of obtaining a rise in rate. It is easy to experiment with and it is very cost effective. In practice you will not be able to buy any stiffness that you might come up with so if you intend to experiment get a current list of the standard springs available. Don't forget that the free length must suit your dampers or you will not be able to obtain a suitable preload.

You can of course use any short spring and do not have to employ the standard ones. This gives even more flexibility but you cannot use the graphs given to find the combined rates. Use the formula originally given for springs in series. You also need to know the load that renders your short spring coilbound. Do not use my figures (1093.8N, 111.5kgf, 245.9lbf).

At the circuit where you may not have these graphs to hand and cannot remember the correct formula, a reasonable approximation to the combined stiffness can be found by adding together the two stiffness values and dividing the total by four. For example, a 28kgf/cm spring in series with a 32kgf/cm spring gives a combined stiffness of (28 + 32)/4 = 15kgf/cm. This approximation works for common combinations but becomes poorer as the main spring gets softer.

Right. Fig 5.31 *Imperial graph showing the combined stiffness of various springs in series with the standard Hagon / Girling short spring. The short spring is assumed to have a stiffness of 180lbf / in.*

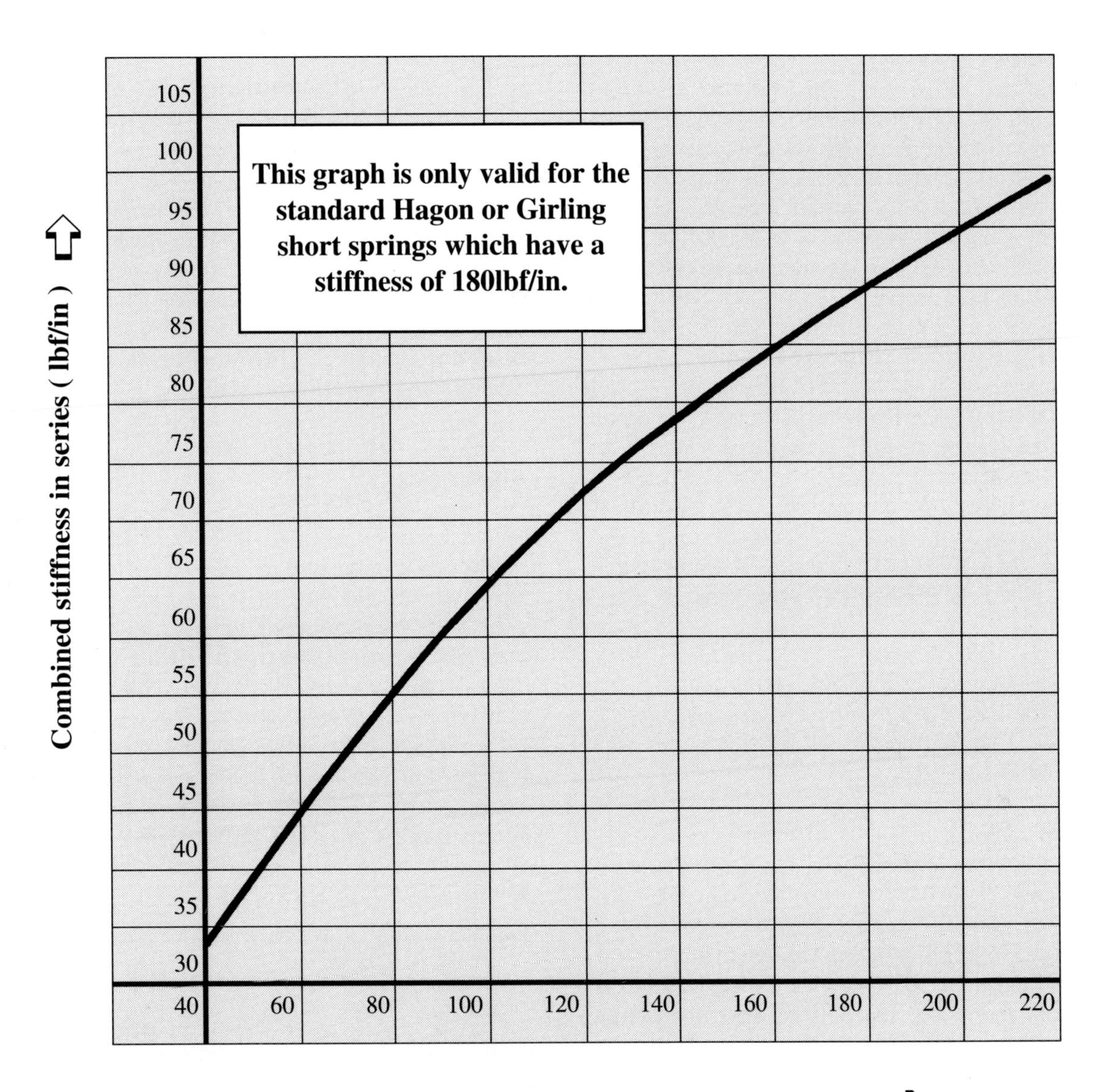
105
100
95
90
85
80
75
70
65
60
55
50
45
40
35
30
40
60
80
100
120
140
160
180
200
220
This graph is only valid for the standard Hagon or Girling short springs which have a stiffness of 180lbf/in.
Combined stiffness in series (lbf/in)
Stiffness of main spring (lbf/in)

Plunger systems

It is unlikely that you will be producing anything with plunger suspension but I want to discuss the arrangement of the springs because it may have implications for something you are building. Fig 5.32 shows the system and the springs seem to be in series. In actual fact they are not in series but in parallel and the stiffness is the sum of those associated with the individual springs.

The key element here is the fact that the loads are applied between the springs, not on the end of them. It is also important that neither spring reaches its free length under normal conditions. To illustrate the point Fig 5.32 assumes that both springs have stiffness 'k' and the preload produced by initial compression during fitting is 'P'. With no external load the spindle clamp has a load P on either side of it.

When a load 'W' is applied at the spindle it moves up by some amount 'x'. At this point the upward force is W + (P - kx) and the downward force is (P + kx). Equating the two gives,

$$W + (P - kx) = P + kx$$

$$W = P + kx - P + kx$$

$$W = 2kx$$

but W /x is the effective stiffness
and therefore $W/x = 2k$

Thus the effective stiffness is the sum of the individual spring stiffnesses. I have to admit that this particular situation caused me a great deal of confusion for many years and I was not happy about it until I tried it out in practice. You may have similar reservations and if that is the case then you need two soft springs off rear suspension units, a threaded rod long enough to hold the springs together and three pieces of plywood.

Begin by checking the individual spring stiffness using a graph plotted from load and compression readings. Then bolt up the springs as shown using one piece of ply between them and one at each end. Start with zero preload and, pressing on the top of the combination, confirm that the spring stiffness in series is half that of each spring.

Now tighten the nuts to compress both springs by something like 25mm, ie 50mm total and apply loads via the plywood in the middle. Measure the loads on the scales; the compression of the lower spring, and plot a graph. It will start off at twice the spring stiffness and then drop to that of one spring once the upper coil reaches its free length, ie after about 25mm.

The fact that this situation only exists while both springs remain compressed is important. If at some point one of them reaches its free length it will cease to have any influence and the wheel is then restrained by the action of just one spring. As such the effective stiffness has dropped (by 50% if the springs have equal stiffness) and you have a falling rate system! This situation occurred on some plunger units. If you adopt anything along these lines, make sure both springs stay in contact if you need the combined stiffness.

Summary

Springs can be coupled in series, parallel or a combination of both. Parallel connection gives an effective stiffness that is the sum of the individual values. Series connection gives an effective stiffness that is lower than that of either spring until one of them becomes coilbound. The stiffness is then equal to that of the spring which is still working. If you have two suspension units, each with two springs in series, sort out the stiffness for a single unit first. When you have found that, double it to get the total stiffness.

Fig 5.32 *An arrangement that can be very confusing.*

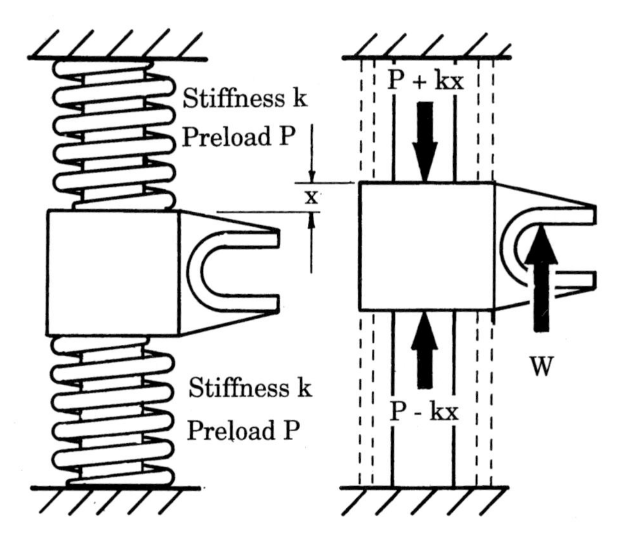

5.4 Front fork springing

Fork structure

There are many interesting topics we could discuss in relation to the front forks but this whole section is specifically about the suspension itself, rather than the structure of the forks. The only thing I would like to say at this stage is that the suspension will only feel right if the forks are comparatively rigid and the basic telescopic fork layout makes this difficult unless the forks are of high quality. Most fast riders are aware that fork flexing can be a problem but all such problems are relative. You get what you pay for and at GP level some of the fork structures are deemed to be too stiff, taking away the feel that the rider needs.

With normal forks this is not the case and the rules for minimising flexure are very simple. You need short, large diameter stanchions constrained by deep section yokes. The wheel spindle needs to be as large as possible (hollow), it needs to fit into a reamed hole and the spindle clamps need to be substantial. Upside down forks offer a better starting point from a structural point of view. Larger sections imply more weight and you therefore have to employ the lightest high quality materials. Slider/leg clearance must be maintained at all leg positions. The bores have to be truly circular and free from taper. Small changes bring large rewards. A 10% reduction in length gives a 27% reduction in deflection at the wheel for a given bending load and, if the sliders were rigidly clamped to the stanchions, the structural stiffness of many older forks would almost double! Clearance is therefore critical.

Apart from structure, the other crucial aspect is stiction. You need to ride very hard to have problems with flexure on modern forks but the tendency to stick then slip, especially when side-loaded, affects everyone to some extent. Reducing stiction is the best thing you can do to a pair of forks and it will make setting up much easier.

You only have to look at modern high quality forks like the WP Suspension units in Fig 5.33 to see these principles in action. You can normally make significant improvements to older forks simply by re-engineering them in terms of limits, fits, bushes etc. It is not always necessary to change the basic design of sliders, yokes or stanchions though you will usually be faced with a re-design of the damping mechanism. Many only have rebound damping and most are very poor compared to modern standards. If you cannot sort this out for yourself, take the forks to someone who can, eg Ron Williams.

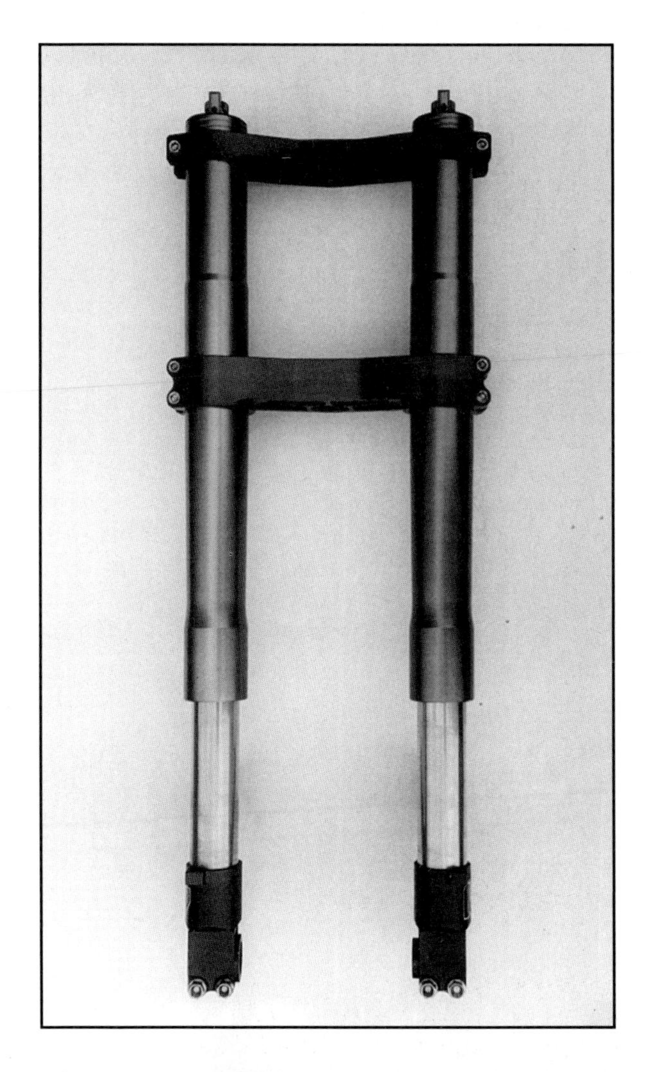

Fig 5.33 *These WP front forks are at the pinnacle of modern motorcycle engineering. This set is for the 1996 Honda NSR250. The inherent layout of telescopic forks is not ideal as a structure but forks like this overcome most problems by using high quality materials and good design. Although many alternatives have been proposed, conventional forks have an enduring aesthetic appeal that is hard to match.*

Fork spring stiffness

Taking the overall situation first, the general objective is to achieve a desired wheel rate. The method I use for estimating wheel rate was covered in Chapter 5.2 and I will give extra examples shortly. The first observation is that the forks have two parallel spring elements and therefore each leg will only have to provide half of the total stiffness required. We also note that there is normally an element of pneumatic springing due to compression of the air above the fork oil but I will discuss this aspect later.

However, the fork legs are not vertical, they are inclined at the castor angle - Fig 5.34. We want to achieve a certain wheel rate k such that when the vertical force at the wheel changes by some amount F the wheel will move vertically upwards by amount x where x = F/k. In doing so the fork springs have to move further than the value x and they actually compress by x/CosØ where Ø is the castor angle. For a typical castor angle of 24 degrees the distance is about 10% more than the vertical move.

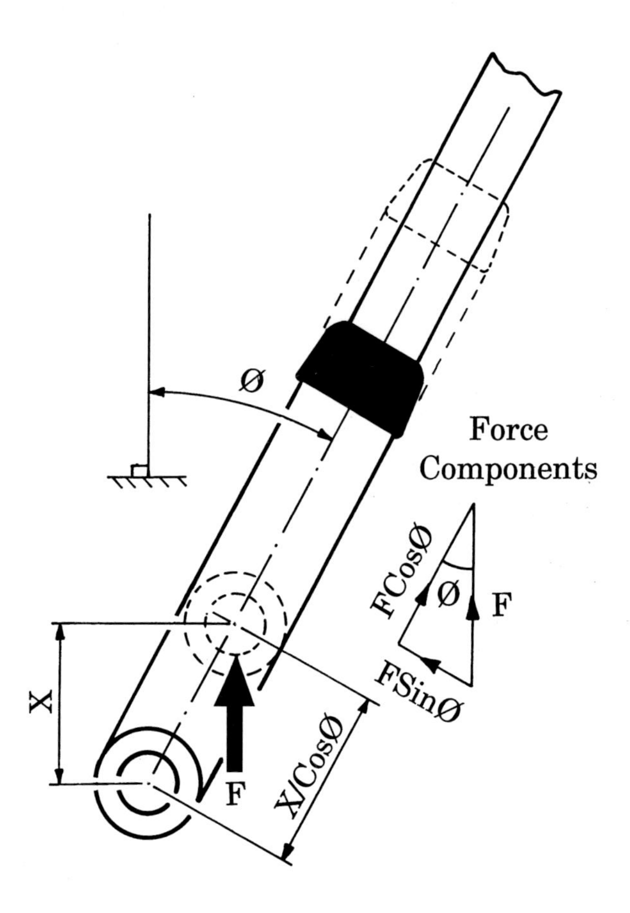

Furthermore, the compression of the springs is not driven directly by force F because it does not act along the spring axis. Only part of the force is available to compress the springs, the rest of it is used to bend the fork legs and help the sliders stick! The actual component of force compressing the springs is FCosØ. To achieve this, the stiffness of the fork springs must be such that the force FCosØ produces deflection x/CosØ thus,

$$\text{Spring stiffness (total)} = \frac{F\text{Cos}Ø}{x/\text{Cos}Ø}$$

$$= \frac{F\text{Cos}^2Ø}{x}$$

but F/x is the wheel rate thus

$$\text{Total spring stiffness} = \text{wheel rate x Cos}^2Ø$$

Assuming both springs are similar we finally obtain,

Spring stiffness = Const. x wheel rate

where

Stiffness = that required for each leg

Constant = 0.5Cos²Ø

and Ø is the castor angle

Table 5.3 gives values of the constant for a range of castor angles. The calculated stiffness is of course that from all sources, ie both springs and air compression but it is usually convenient to assume that it is all related to the springs. Air compression can then be used to help overcome any bottoming problems.

Fig 5.34 *Fork spring stiffness is not the same as wheel rate. Firstly, because the two springs are in parallel each one has to contribute half the total wheel rate. Secondly, the forks are not vertical so the wheel force is not applied directly to the springs. This reduces the required spring stiffness for a given wheel rate.*

Table 5.3 shows that for the sort of castor angles normally used on road racers, the stiffness of each fork spring needs to be about 40-42% of the desired wheel rate. For example, if you estimated a wheel rate of 1.6kgf/mm (90lbf/in) using the ideas in Chapter 5.2, then the fork springs required will have a stiffness of about 0.64kgf/mm (36lbf/in). Here are some more formal examples.

Example. A wheel rate of 12N/mm is required at the front of a bike with a 22° castor angle. What is the required spring stiffness?

Using **Table 5.3** the constant is 0.430

Thus spring stiffness = 0.430 x 12N/mm

= 5.16N/mm

Example. A wheel rate of 10kgf/cm is required at the front of a bike with a 24° castor angle. What is the required spring stiffness?

Using Table 5.3 the constant is 0.417

Thus spring stiffness = 0.417x 10kgf/cm

= 4.17kgf/cm

Example. A wheel rate of 70lbf/in is required at the front of a bike with a 25° castor angle. What is the required spring stiffness?

Using Table 5.3 the constant is 0.411

Thus spring stiffness = 0.411x 70lbf/in

= 28.7lbf/in

These are of course initial rates assuming that the wheel rate was determined as described in Chapter 5.2. The following examples include the determination of wheel rate.

Example. A Seeley G50 classic racer has a laden front wheel load of 211lbf and the unsprung weight is 39lbf. Estimate a suitable fork spring stiffness if the head angle is 63 degrees and the travel 5ins.

Sprung load = 211 - 39 = 172lbf.

From Chapter 5.2,

Angle Ø°	0.5Cos²Ø
20.0	0.442
20.5	0.439
21.0	0.436
21.5	0.433
22.0	0.430
22.5	0.427
23.0	0.424
23.5	0.420
24.0	0.417
24.5	0.414
25.0	0.411
25.5	0.407
26.0	0.404
26.5	0.400
27.0	0.397
27.5	0.393
28.0	0.390

Table 5.3 *Values of 0.5Cos²Ø for different castor angles. Multiply these by the desired wheel rate to give spring stiffness.*

$$\text{Wheel rate (lbf/in)} = \frac{Wf^2}{9.8}$$

Using f = 2.3Hz for 5in of travel,

$$\text{Wheel rate} = \frac{172 \times 2.3 \times 2.3}{9.8}$$

= 93lbf/in

Castor angle = 90 - 63 = 27deg

From Table 5.3, constant = 0.397 hence,

Spring stiffness = 0.397 x 93 = 37lbf/in

Example. A 125cc motocross bike weighs 87kgf unladen. With a rider who weighs 68kgf the weight distribution is 50%/50%. Fork travel is 300mm and the castor angle is 26deg. Estimate a suitable fork spring stiffness if the unsprung front end weighs 14kgf.

Total laden weight = 87kgf + 68kgf = 155kgf

Weight at front = 50% of 155kgf = 77.5kgf

Sprung weight = 77.5 - 14 = 63.5kgf

From Chapter 5.2,

$$\text{Wheel rate (kgf/mm)} = \frac{Wf^2}{248.5}$$

Using f = 1.9Hz for 300mm of travel,

$$\text{Wheel rate} = \frac{63.5 \times 1.9 \times 1.9}{248.5}$$

$$= 0.922\text{kgf/mm}$$

From Table 5.3, constant = 0.404 hence,

Spring stiffness = 0.404 x 0.922 = 0.37kgf/mm

Example. A 125cc roadracer weighs 170lbf unladen. With a rider who weighs 8stones (112lbf) the weight distribution is 48%/52% front to rear. Fork travel is 2.7ins and the castor angle is 26deg. Estimate a suitable fork spring stiffness if the unsprung front end weighs 27lbf. When a 14stone (196lbf) rider is on the bike the weight distribution becomes 45%/55%. Suggest a new spring rate.

Total laden weight = 170lbf + 112lbf = 282lbf

Weight at front = 48% of 282lbf = 135lbf

Sprung weight = 135 - 27 = 108lbf

From Chapter 5.2,

$$\text{Wheel rate (lbf/in)} = \frac{Wf^2}{9.8}$$

Using f = 2.6Hz for 2.7in of travel,

$$\text{Wheel rate} = \frac{108 \times 2.6 \times 2.6}{9.8}$$

$$= 75\text{lbf/in}$$

From Table 5.3, constant = 0.404 hence,

Spring stiffness = 0.404 x 75 = 30lbf/in

When the heavy rider gets on the bike the sprung weight changes from 108lbf to 138lbf and the stiffness needs to go up in proportion. Work it out again or use,

$$\text{New stiffness} = \frac{30 \times 138}{108}\ \text{lbf/in}$$

$$= 38\text{lbf/in}$$

This is quite a substantial change bearing in mind that there are two springs and it demonstrates the need to account for the weight of the rider. Compensation of this order via preload alone is not a good idea.

There is no point in getting too wrapped up in these calculations because they are all approximations and you will not be able to obtain the exact springs you require. Initial experiments should involve a change of at least 10% or you may not even notice the difference. Most standard springs on offer come in steps of around 0.1kgf/mm, 1N/mm or 5lbf/in but GP riders use much smaller changes, typically 0.25N/mm (0.03kgf/mm, 1.4lbf/in) on 125cc and 250cc bikes. Remember that these bikes are already dialled in very accurately. Table 5.4 may be useful.

It is unlikely that you will get it right first time but you should be somewhere near. If not, try to find out why and alter your preferred frequency values ready for next time! For bikes ridden on tarmac, road or race, not many have fork springs softer than 0.4kgf/mm and few are above 1.2kgf/mm (roughly 22-67lbf/in). Most off-road bikes with

Right. Table 5.4 *Top. Maximum and minimum stiffness of Progressive Suspension (USA) fork springs for a variety of road bikes. Data supplied by M.R.Holland, tel 01775 766455. Bottom. Typical spring variations for several Grand Prix bikes. These are constant stiffness springs and the changes reflect both rider preference and track condition. Data from WP Suspension.*

Motorcycle	Fork spring stiffness (progressive rate)			
	Minimum		Maximum	
Make and model	kgf/mm	lbf/in	kgf/mm	lbf/in
BMW R80	0.54	30	0.81	45
Honda XR250	0.36	20	0.54	30
Honda VT500	0.54	30	0.81	45
Honda XR500	0.45	25	0.63	35
Honda CBR600	0.63	35	0.89	50
Honda CB750	0.63	35	0.89	50
Honda VFR750(92)	0.72	40	1.16	65
Kawasaki Zephyr 550	0.63	35	0.89	50
Kawasaki GPZ600	0.63	35	0.89	50
Kawasaki GPZ900	0.63	35	0.89	50
Kawasaki ZZR1100	0.72	40	1.16	65
Norton Commando	0.45	25	0.63	35
Suzuki RG500 Gamma	0.63	35	0.89	50
Suzuki GSXR750J	0.72	40	1.16	65
Suzuki GSXR750G	0.63	35	0.89	50
Suzuki GS1000	0.63	35	0.89	50
Triumph Bonneville	0.45	25	0.63	35
Yamaha RD350	0.45	25	0.63	35
Yamaha XJ550	0.45	25	0.63	35
Yamaha FZR600	0.63	35	0.89	50
Yamaha YZF750SP	0.63	35	0.89	50
Yamaha FJ1200	0.63	35	0.89	50

Motorcycle	Variation to suit rider and conditions (constant spring rates)			
	Minimum		Maximum	
Make and model	kgf/mm	lbf/in	kgf/mm	lbf/in
Honda RS125 GP 1996	0.56	31.3	0.64	35.8
Yamaha TZ125 GP 1996	0.56	31.3	0.64	35.8
Aprilia 125 GP 1996	0.61	34.1	0.66	36.9
Honda NSR250 GP 1996	0.61	34.1	0.71	39.8

long travel are in the range 0.35-0.5kgf/mm (roughly 19-28lbf/in).

Tyre changes

Only at the highest level of racing are you likely to fine tune the fork spring stiffness to suit the tyres that are fitted. Variations are slight once the rider likes a particular setting and damping is more critical. Sometimes the tyre pressures, which contribute to tyre stiffness, can be used as a means of adjustment, particularly for slight chattering.

For most people, the bike will be built with some fork springs that are a first estimate and this will be refined during track tests. If the forks do not bottom and do not feel excessively bouncy that will probably be the last time you change them.

However, experiment can bring great rewards and there is no doubt that changing tyres has an effect on the overall wheel rate that exists, ie springs plus tyres.

Tyres reduce the wheel rate that would exist due to springs alone. The natural frequency of the sprung mass is therefore reduced. Although not exact, an approximate expression for the actual wheel rate is useful for considering how much influence the tyres will have.

$$\text{Actual wheel rate} = \frac{WRS.Kt}{WRS + Kt}$$

where

WRS = wheel rate due to springs alone

Kt = tyre stiffness

WRS and Kt must have the same units

This assumes that the tyres and suspension behave like springs in series as far as the sprung mass is concerned. The reduction in wheel rate due to the tyres depends on the relative values of tyre and suspension stiffness.

Example. Wheel rate due to springs alone = 1.6kgf/mm, tyre stiffness = 22kgf/mm.

$$\text{Actual wheel rate} = \frac{1.6 \times 22}{1.6 + 22}$$

$$= 1.49\text{kgf/mm}$$

(7% softer)

Example. Wheel rate due to springs alone = 1.6kgf/mm, tyre stiffness = 13kgf/mm.

$$\text{Actual wheel rate} = \frac{1.6 \times 13}{1.6 + 13}$$

$$= 1.42\text{kgf/mm}$$

(11% softer)

The greatest reduction comes from a high wheel rate (implication: stiff springs, heavy bike and rider) combined with a change to tyres with a lower wall stiffness, eg wets. In practice, although the compound of the wets is much softer (which affects the damping), the carcase is not as different as you might think. It has to be capable of transmitting the power involved and, if the carcase is too soft, the rain clearance slots close up and the tyre loses grip.

There are various ways of accounting for this but it is easy to give the wrong impression. For example, if you switch to a set of wets then the wheel rate will drop and it is easy to calculate the increase in spring rate necessary to restore the original overall wheel rate.

However, you will not want the original wheel rate you had in the dry now that the track is wet, indeed it may be necessary to actually soften the rear spring slightly so that the tyre grips better on the bumps. Similarly, if you switch from soft tyres to stiff tyres, you can only reduce the spring stiffness to compensate if it is already above the practical minimum that prevents the forks bottoming. GP engineers tell me this is often a problem. Many riders like the front end so soft that it bottoms out on braking and they lose the front end going into the corner.

There are thus two things to consider.

- How to account for tyre stiffness.
- Typical changes in spring rates to suit various tyres and conditions.

The first aspect is simple sums but the second requires substantial experience at the highest level. To incorporate the tyres into your initial estimate of the required wheel rate use the following.

$$WRS = \frac{WR.Kt}{Kt - WR}$$

where

WRS = wheel rate due to springs alone

WR = actual wheel rate required

Kt = tyre stiffness

WR and Kt must have the same units

Example. A wheel rate of 1.6kgf/mm is required on a bike with 24° of castor. Estimate a suitable spring rate for tyres with a stiffness of a) 20kgf/mm, b)14kgf/mm.

Case a)

WR = 1.6kgf/mm, Kt = 20kgf/mm

$$WRS = \frac{1.6 \times 20}{20 - 1.6}$$

$$= 1.74\text{kgf/mm}$$

For 25° castor, $0.5Cos^2Ø$ = 0.411 (Table 5.3)

$$\text{Spring stiffness} = 0.411 \times 1.74 = 0.72\text{kgf/mm}$$

Case b)

WR = 1.6kgf/mm, Kt = 14kgf/mm

$$WRS = \frac{1.6 \times 14}{14 - 1.6}$$

$$= 1.8\text{kgf/mm}$$

For 25° castor, $0.5Cos^2Ø$ = 0.411 (Table 5.3)

$$\text{Spring stiffness} = 0.411 \times 1.8$$

$$= 0.74\text{kgf/mm}$$

The last figure is roughly 12% higher than you would have calculated if the tyres had been neglected.

Example. A wheel rate of 70lbf/in is required on a bike with 27° of castor. Estimate a suitable spring rate for tyres with a stiffness of 1100lbf/in

WR = 70lbf/in, Kt = 1100lbf/in

$$WRS = \frac{70 \times 1100}{1100 - 70}$$

$$= 74.8\text{lbf/in}$$

For 27° castor, $0.5Cos^2Ø$ = 0.397 (Table 5.3)

$$\text{Spring stiffness} = 0.397 \times 74.8$$

$$= 29.7\text{lbf/in}$$

As far as fine tuning the springs to the tyre is concerned, everything seems to depend on the make of tyre and rider style/preference. At WP Suspension I was shown data relating to a GP tyre that was provided in 16 different stiffness values and 11 different compounds. Despite all the knowledge obtained from testing such a vast number of combinations, another make of tyre experiencing the same problems required a totally opposite approach to get the best results. Given this situation, any general guide could be very misleading but it is useful to incorporate the tyre stiffness into your initial spring estimates.

Preload

Virtually all fork springs will have some significant degree of preload. This is usually first discovered by unscrewing the fork cap and watching it spring off leaving the last two threads in the top of the leg! A very small amount of preload is essential to make sure the springs are bedded down. Any greater requirement is determined by the set-up you have specified for the laden condition. It is achieved by inserting tubular spacers on top of the fork springs or by using a suitably threaded adjuster as shown in Fig 5.35. Indeed, even if you have solid fork caps it pays to obtain a spare set and drill and tap them to take an adjuster that you can use initially to find the correct preload. If you intend to retain the adjusters for normal use you will need to design them so that they do not leak compressed air from the inside of the forks or your air springing will be non-existent. This should be avoided because the air springing element can be extremely useful.

It is possible to calculate the required preload to meet the set-up specification but my experience suggests that this is a waste of effort for the following reasons. Firstly, when you have calculated a suitable spring stiffness you will almost certainly find that such a spring is not available and you will have to take the nearest you can get or have special springs made. Even if you have the springs made, the tolerances on spring rate discussed previously will almost certainly ensure that the stiffness is not exactly what you thought.

Fig 5.35 *Spacers provide spring preload but adjusters are much better to experiment with. Permanent adjusters must be air tight at high pressures.*

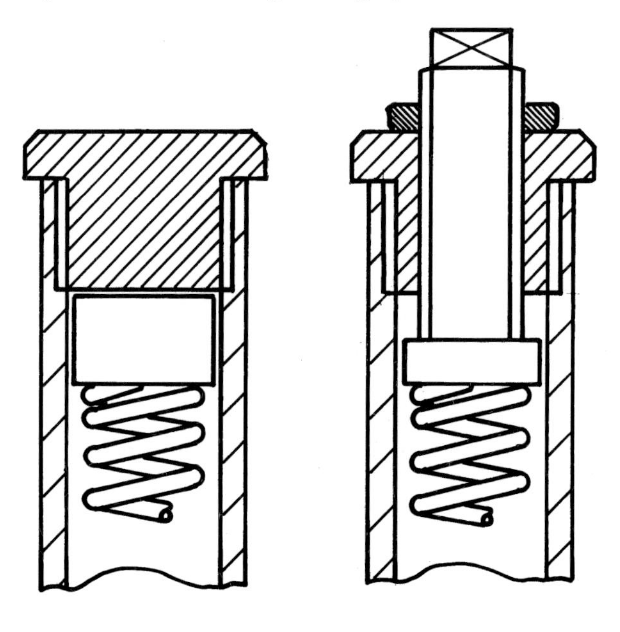

For these reasons it is pointless to calculate the length of the preload spacers and it is much better to obtain the correct length by experiment, preferably via adjusters.

To find the correct preload spacer length for your proposed set-up it is the laden sag that you should use, ie with you sitting normally on the bike and someone else keeping it upright. Start with no preload and measure the laden sag of the forks. Gradually add preload until the sag meets your laden specification, eg 25% of the total travel available. If you estimated the spring stiffness using the method described then a reasonable combination of stiffness and preload should result, provided the frequency chosen was realistic. Once you have done this, check the unladen sag and keep a record of that as well. You must have some unladen sag in the forks (see end of chapter).

Things can get very confusing here, especially on existing bikes. If you follow the procedure described and adjust the preload on the fork spring until the laden sag is correct then when you check the unladen sag it will almost certainly be different from what you intended.

If the unladen sag is too small then, ironically, it means that the springs are too soft to achieve the set-up you require with your weight on the bike. What has happened is that in order to achieve the correct laden sag you have had to provide much more preload than that which would be correct with the right spring. As a result of this excess preload, which you need to compensate for the soft spring, the unladen bike has too little sag. It may well be heavily topped out and will often do so with a resounding bang when the forks are unloaded despite the soft springs - Fig 5.36.

Right. Fig 5.36 *a) Ideal spring rate gives correct unladen sag when the preload is adjusted to give the correct laden sag. b) With a stiffer spring, less preload is required to reach the required laden sag and the unladen sag increases. c) With a softer spring, more preload is required to reach the required laden sag and the unladen sag is reduced.*

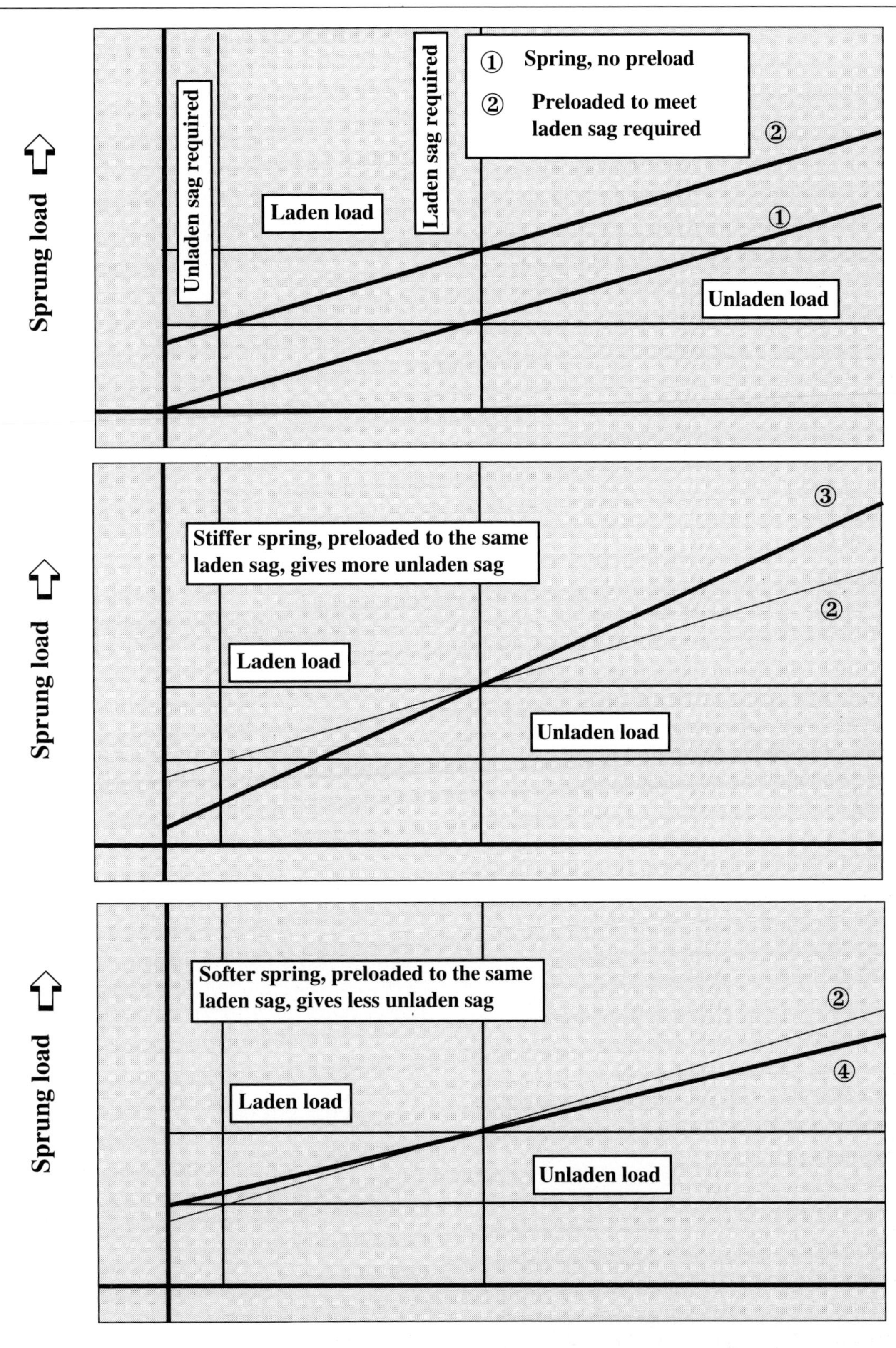
① Spring, no preload
② Preloaded to meet laden sag required
Unladen sag required
Laden sag required
Laden load
Unladen load
②
①
Sprung load
Stiffer spring, preloaded to the same laden sag, gives more unladen sag
Laden load
Unladen load
③
②
Sprung load
Softer spring, preloaded to the same laden sag, gives less unladen sag
Laden load
Unladen load
②
④
Sprung load
Suspension travel

If, after setting up the correct laden sag, the unladen sag is too great, then the springs are too stiff. In this case a relatively small amount of preload has been applied in order to comply with the laden sag. In the unladen condition there is insufficient preload to support the sprung mass where it should be and it therefore sags excessively. The basic rule is always to determine the set-up in the following order.

- Find the fully extended suspension position and determine a datum distance along the forks.

- Check the laden situation first. Start with zero preload and measure the new datum distance. The difference between this measurement and the original one is the laden sag as measured along the fork axis. Now gradually increase the preload until the laden sag is correct.

- Finally check the unladen sag value. If it is too small then the springs are too soft. If it is too great the springs are too hard but make sure the figures are reliable - see below.

To progress further than this you will need to finish the bike and test at the track. Don't abandon everything because the settings fail to tally with your ideal. Test it first.

Checking existing front wheel rates

In previous chapters I mentioned some of the problems relating to the unladen condition, especially if one is dealing with very light bikes, small suspension travel and heavier riders.

When trying to check out existing wheel rates etc, I much prefer to take the forks off the bike and then test the forks themselves in several stages. Once you are sure of the current spring stiffness you can then calculate the wheel rate produced. The alternative is to load up the bike and take measurements but simple forks do tend to stick quite a lot, especially if they are soft, and it is not easy to get repeatable results.

To illustrate some of the things that you may encounter along the way here is an example. The fork components shown in Fig 5.37a are a simple set of non-adjustable Marzocchi's.

- Strip the forks completely and remove the main springs. Note the short top-out (rebound) springs in the photograph.

- You can either calculate the approximate spring stiffness from its dimensions (Fig 5.37b using formulae from Chapter 5.3) or better still test them.

- To test the springs use a pair of sliding tubes to prevent them buckling (17g tubes slide inside each other) and apply a load by hand onto a set of bathroom scales. Measure the compression and plot a load - compression graph as shown in Fig 5.37c.

- Calculate the spring stiffness from the slope of the graph. If your calculated value does not match within 10%, check everything again, especially the sizes of wire and mean diameter.

- In theory the forks have a total stiffness that is twice that for one spring. Test the other spring and you might be suprised!

Right. Fig 5.37 *a) Components of a simple fork leg used in the example. b) Spring stiffness estimated using the method suggested in Chapter 5.3. c) Graph produced by compressing a single spring onto a set of bathroom scales. Use sliding tubes to prevent buckling and zero the scales with the spring resting on them. Draw the best line you can through the points and find the slope as shown. Forces should be in Newtons but 99% of domestic scales show kg. Progressive springs will give a curve but you may not be able to compress them sufficiently by hand to find out the behaviour near full travel.*

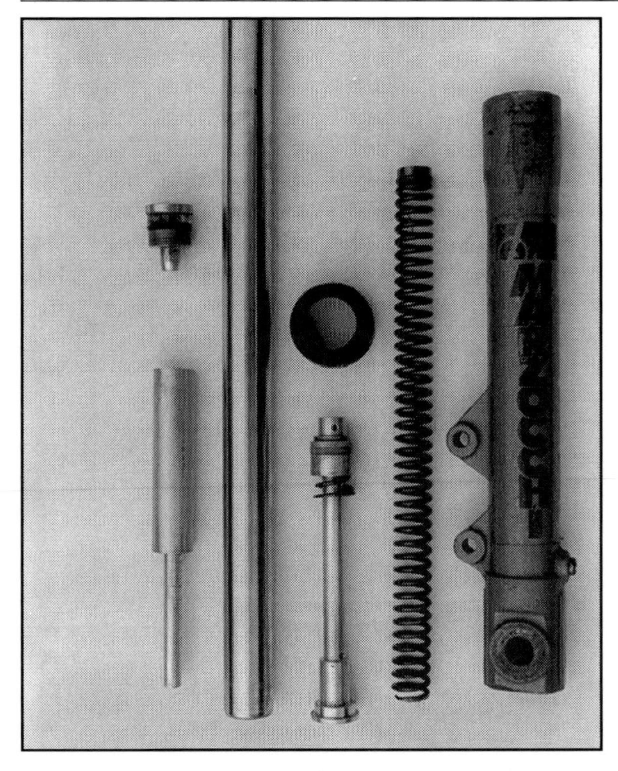

a)

From Chapter 5.3,

$$\text{Stiffness (N/mm)} = \frac{9919.35d^4}{D^3 n}$$

d = 3.4mm, D = 19.4mm, n = 38.75

giving,

$$\text{Stiffness} = \frac{9919.35 \times 3.4^4}{19.4^3 \times 38.75} \text{ N/mm}$$

Stiffness = 4.69N/mm

= 4.69 x 0.1019 kgf/mm

= 0.48kgf/mm

(0.1019 conversion factor from Table 5.2)

b)

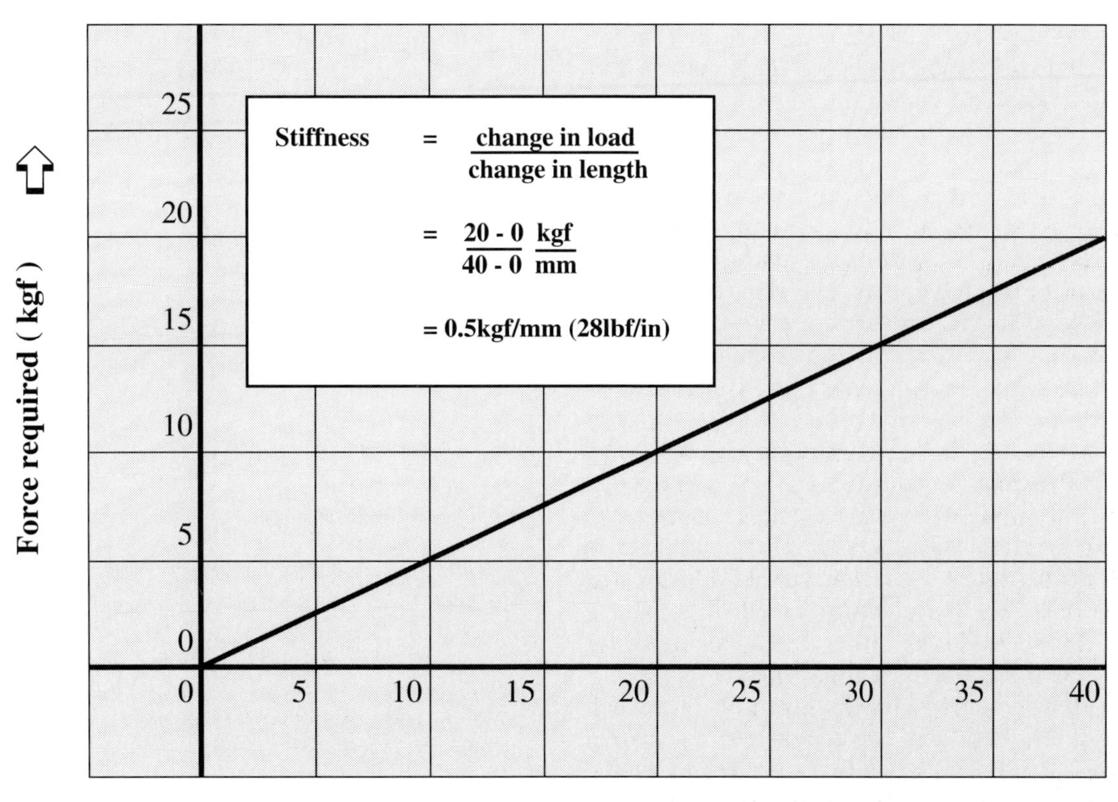

- You can now assemble the forks, preferably cleaned, lightly oiled and without seals. Now try loading these onto the scales. It is most unlikely that you will manage to test more than 50% of the travel but this will still allow an initial wheel rate to be found. Zero the scales before you start.

There are several things that may confuse you at this stage. Fig 5.38a shows the result for the forks used (initial 35mm out of 70mm total travel).

The first thing to note is that when the preload spacers are installed, the force is applied to two springs in series, ie the main spring and the top-out or rebound spring as it is commonly called - Fig 5.38b. This means that the main spring is not compressed as much as you thought. In the example, an 'apparent' preload compression of 23mm is in fact only 17mm, the rest being taken up by the very stiff top-out springs . This will not alter the effect of preload when the bike is laden because the top-out springs will have lost contact but it may well confuse you if the bike is topped out unladen and there is a lot of preload.

Once you apply a wheel load to the forks another confusing thing happens. The moving leg is initially resisted by both the top-out spring and the main spring acting together like plunger suspension - Fig 5.38c. As a result, the forks begin to move against a very high stiffness initially and this situation continues until the top-out spring loses contact and normal operation resumes. This occurs after about 3.5mm of travel in the example shown opposite. This is very important, because it means that when the front end is lightly loaded the suspension is much more rigid. It can lead to pattering and chattering problems when exiting the corners. At GP level, the selection of the rebound springs is critical.

Despite these 'interesting' events that you may encounter, the basic aim is simple enough. Once you are fairly sure of the 'normal' total fork rate, divide it by $\text{Cos}^2\text{Ø}$ to obtain the effective wheel rate. To obtain $\text{Cos}^2\text{Ø}$, either use a calculator or use Table 5.3 and double the value given.

Do this for every bike that you are satisfied with, then check out the laden and unsprung weights at the front. Use these figures to determine a frequency and add this to your list of useful numbers!

$$\textbf{Wheel rate} = \frac{\textbf{Total spring rate}}{\textbf{Cos}^2\textbf{Ø}}$$

where Ø = castor angle (deg)

Example. The total fork stiffness is found to be 1kgf/mm and you like it! The laden load at the front wheel is 65kgf and the unsprung weight is 13kgf. Castor angle is 26deg with 80mm of travel.

Using Table 5.3, $\text{Cos}^2\text{Ø} = 0.404 \times 2 = 0.808$

$$\text{Wheel rate} = \frac{1\text{kgf/mm}}{0.808}$$

$$= 1.24\text{kgf/mm}$$

From Chapter 5.2,

$$\text{Wheel rate (kgf/mm)} = \frac{\text{Wf}^2}{248.5}$$

Sprung weight W = 65 - 13 = 52kgf

thus,

$$1.24 = \frac{52 \times f^2}{248.5}$$

$$f^2 = \frac{1.24 \times 248.5}{52}$$

$f^2 = 5.93$, thus $f = 2.43\text{Hz}$

(record for 80mm travel and tyres used)

Fig 5.38 a) Load - compression graph obtained by pressing the forks onto scales and measuring the compression. b) Preload is applied via springs in series so the main spring does not compress as much as you think. c) When the fork leg first starts to move, it does so against two springs in parallel (like plunger suspension). This is why the graph has a steep slope rather than being vertical initially. As soon as the moving leg clears the top-out spring normality returns.

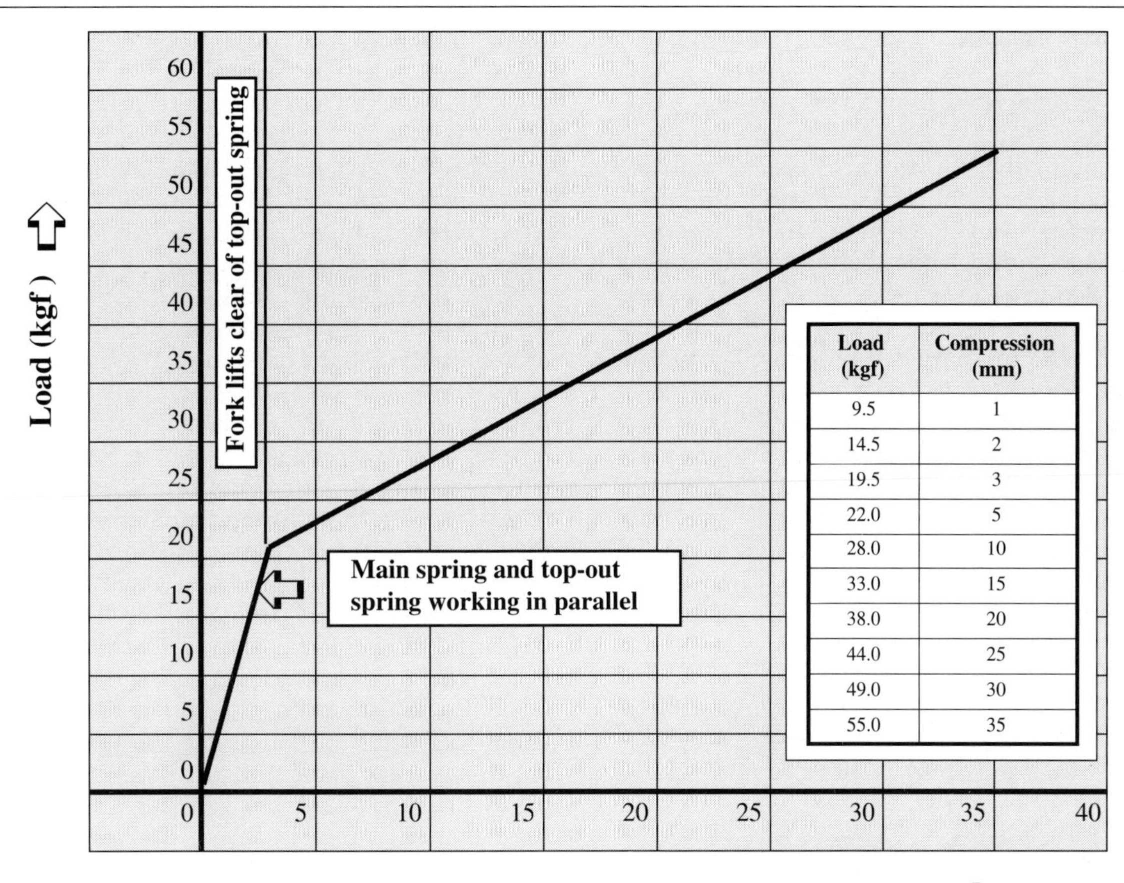

Load (kgf)	Compression (mm)
9.5	1
14.5	2
19.5	3
22.0	5
28.0	10
33.0	15
38.0	20
44.0	25
49.0	30
55.0	35

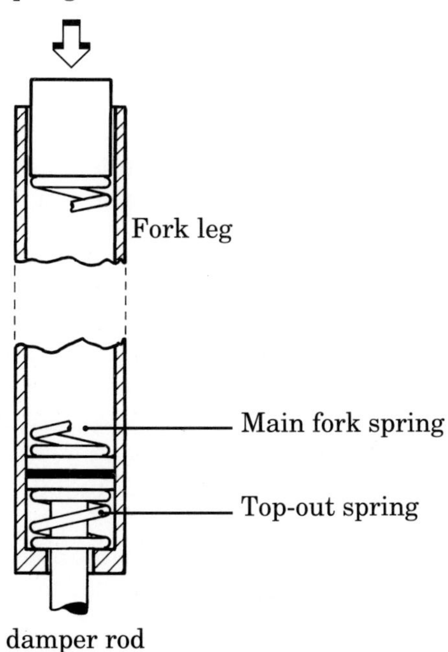

b) Preload is applied to both springs.

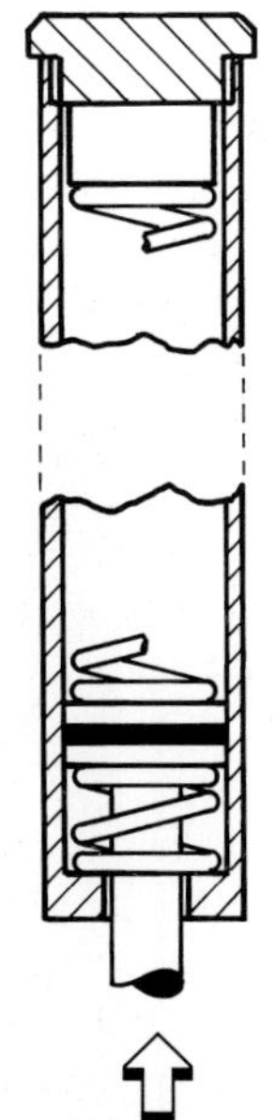

c) Wheel force sees both springs in parallel until the damper rod lifts clear of the top-out spring.

Air compression

The other element in front fork springing is the compression of air in the space above the damping oil. Assuming that the seals are in good condition this effect is very significant during the latter part of the fork travel and it plays an important role in preventing the forks from bottoming out under heavy braking. As a general approach, it seems best to spend some time sorting out the springs and preload to suit normal conditions. The result is usually on the soft side and there will be a tendency to bottom out under heavy braking. Air compression can then be used to just prevent this.

Fig 5.39 shows the basic situation. The oil level forms the boundary of a sealed chamber. With the forks fully extended it has some volume V_1 and is at pressure p_1. The initial pressure p_1 is frequently atmospheric though if valves are fitted it can be raised. In general the initial pressure cannot be raised very much or the events that follow will either blow the seals or render the forks virtually solid at full travel. If you intend using significant amounts of air springing you must employ special seals. Normal seals tend to stick when the pressure on them is high and in this book I am only considering 'air assistance'.

Fig 5.39 *Provided the sealing is satisfactory, forks have an element of pneumatic springing that is produced by compression of the air above the fork oil.*

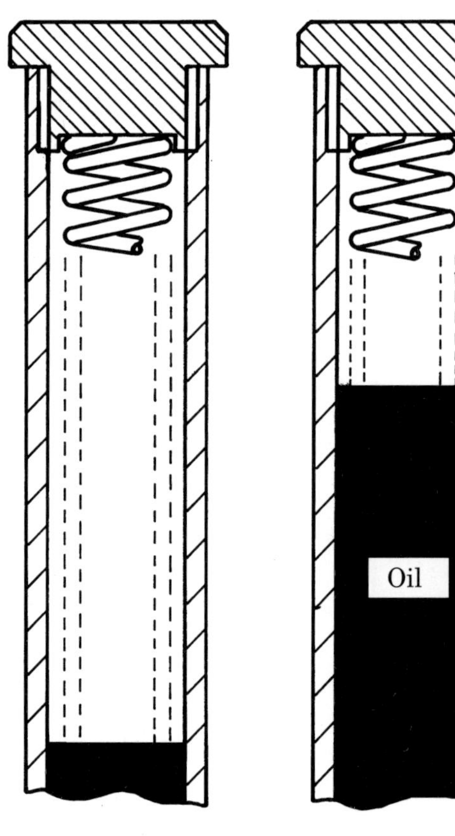

a) Leg extended. b) Leg compressed.

When the forks are compressed the volume of the air chamber is reduced thus compressing the air it contains. As the air is compressed its pressure will rise. The pressure generates an increasing force on top of the damper rod piston. This force assists the springs.

The manner in which the pressure rises depends on the way heat energy transfers during the process. If the temperature remained constant during the actual compression itself then the product of pressure and volume would also remain constant. This would cause the pressure to double if the volume was halved. This is nice and simple but somewhat unrealistic. A more reasonable assumption is that the compression is fairly quick and that during the actual compression no heat energy has time to transfer from the air. Note that this is not the same as saying the temperature remains constant. In this case, called adiabatic compression, the new pressure is given by the formula on the right and it produces a somewhat higher pressure when the volume reduces.

If we halve the volume in this case, the pressure increases 2.6 times instead of simply doubling. The truth lies somewhere in-between these cases and varies. This is one of the problems with using air on its own. The characteristics will vary somewhat with changes in temperature. In practical terms there is nothing to gain from pursuing this further because the sums become very complicated if you want to find out exactly what happens. We only need a general idea that shows us the way air can assist our existing fork springs. The formula given on the right is more than adequate for this purpose. The index of 1.4 may be somewhat high but you will never know. Fig 5.40 shows how the pressure changes under one particular set of conditions. Note how rapidly the pressure increases as the compression becomes substantial. The force generated on the damper rods is proportional to this pressure increase and we therefore have a rising rate system.

One of the problems we now face is the fact that there are several variables to contend with. Briefly, these can be summarised as follows.

- Initial volume. This is determined by the oil level which must be sufficient to submerge completely all the damping elements at any position.
- Final volume at full travel. This can be reduced by using various forms of spacer or increased by adding extra chambers on top of the existing fork caps.
- Starting pressure. This is normally atmospheric but it can be increased if valves are fitted.

$$p_2 = p_1 \left[\frac{V_1}{V_2} \right]^{1.4}$$

where

p_1 = original pressure at volume V_1

p_2 = new pressure when the volume is reduced to V_2

Fig 5.40 *Pressure changes in a chamber as the volume is reduced. The variables are discussed in the text and the figures are calculated using the formula above.*

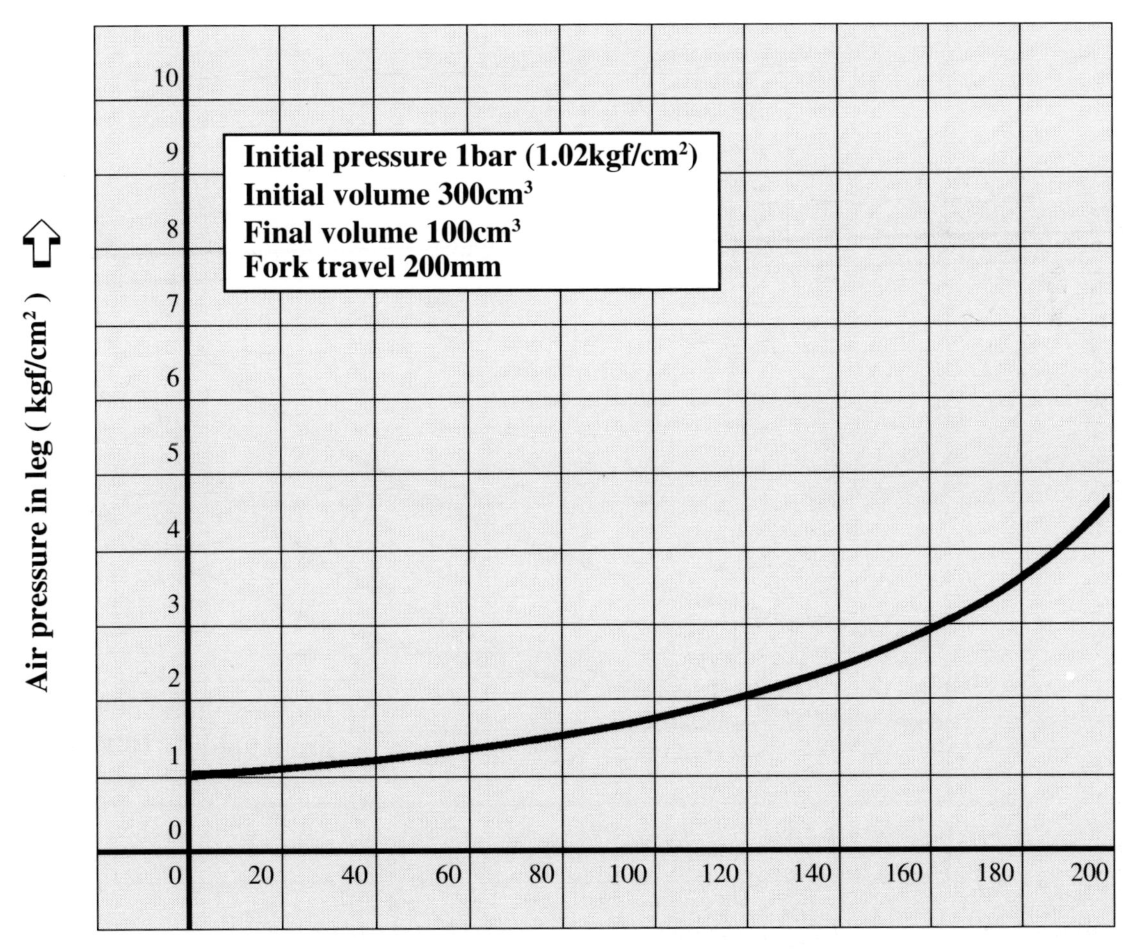

Changes can be made to any of these values but their effects are different as Fig 5.41 shows. Altering the initial starting pressure has a proportional effect on the values all the way through the range. To alter the pressures you will need suitable valves. In the early 70's when we had to make these things for ourselves Austin Allegro hydrolastic suspension valves were the thing to use but these days purpose-made valves are fitted to many forks. Whatever the case, seal damage is a real possibility so conduct experiments in small steps. Volume changes are rather different. The simplest change you can make is to alter the level of damping oil in the leg. As this is increased above the normal amount the way in which the volume ratio V_1/V_2 changes is modified.

Fig 5.42 gives an example. Under existing conditions, the volume of air above the oil at full fork extension is 360cm^3. At full compression it is 120cm^3 and so the volume ratio at full travel is 360/120 = 3. If you now add an extra 30cm^3 of oil, the initial volume reduces to 330cm^3 and the final volume becomes 90cm^3. This increases the volume ratio to 330/90 = 3.67, a change of 22%. However, now add another 30cm^3 of oil. With 300cm^3 of air now compressed into 60cm^3 the volume ratio is 5.

Fig 5.41 *The pressure characteristic can be altered by changing the starting pressure or by adding oil to alter the initial and final volumes. The results are different.*

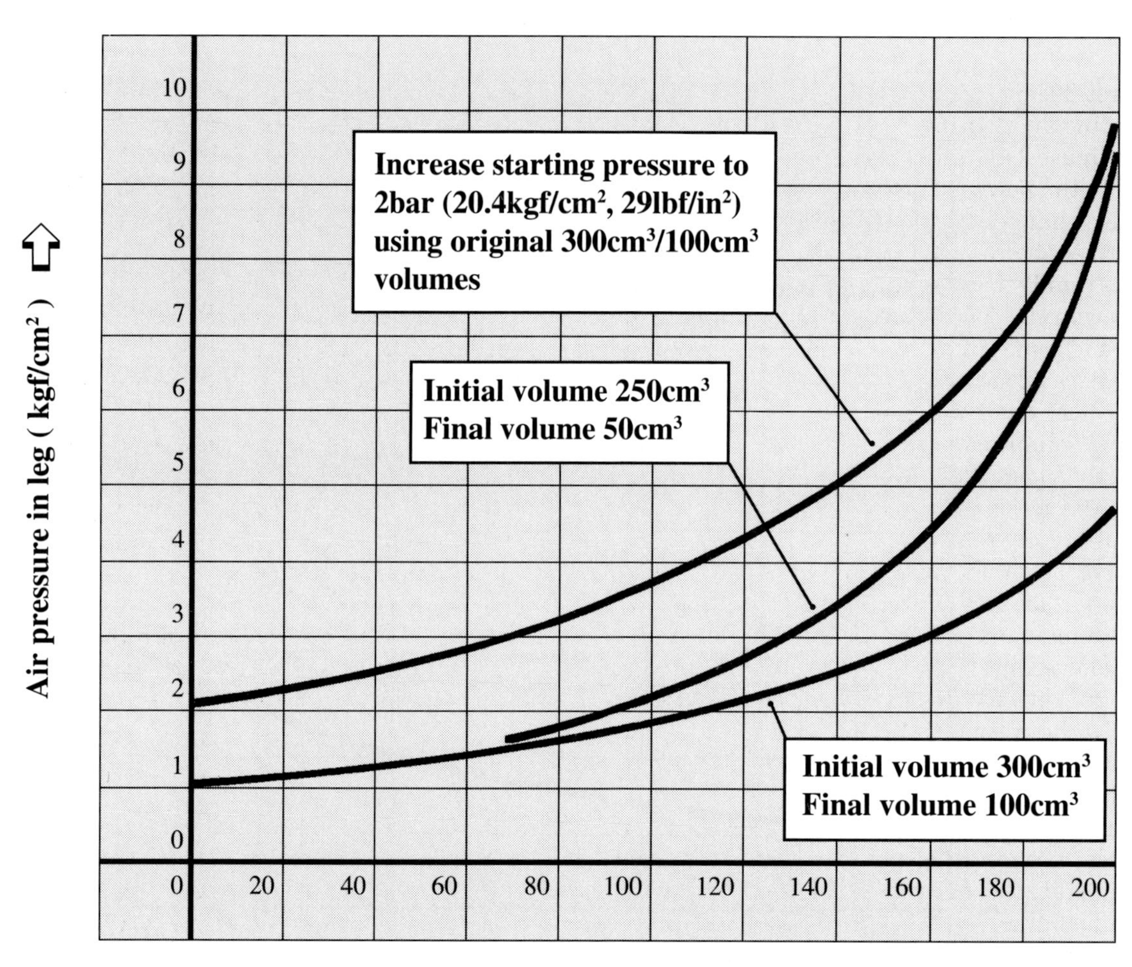

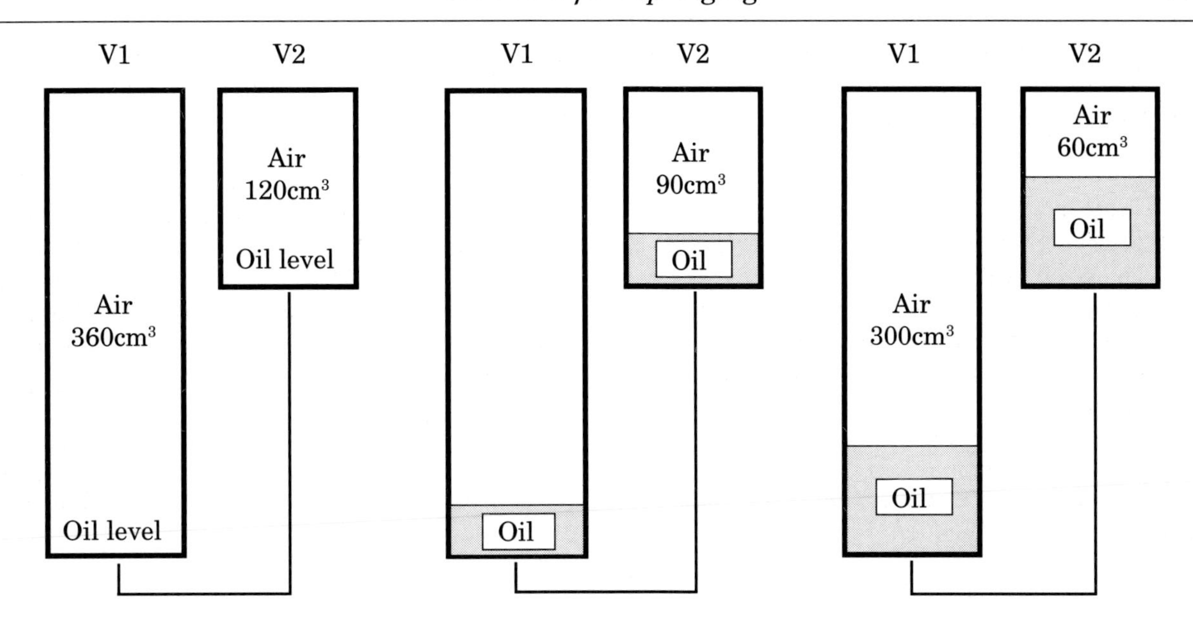

Fig 5.42 *Volume changes are particularly influential. When you add extra oil, although the initial and final volumes are equally affected, the volume ratio at full compression increases quite rapidly. The changes are further increased by the power of 1.4.*

The first $30cm^3$ altered the volume ratio by 22% but adding another $30cm^3$, $60cm^3$ in total, gives a 67% increase. On top of this, the volume change is raised to the power of 1.4. This makes the actual pressure changes 33% and 105% respectively so you can see that pressure changes start off gradually but rapidly increase as more oil is added. This is why you can often add some oil, observe no effect, add some more, and find the forks are solid near full travel. You need to consider specific cases because various combinations of starting pressure and volume can yield a wide range of characteristics. When the pressure is high near full travel, the forks will become very bouncy, then solid, assuming the seals hold out.

I have never found any forks where the air volume was too small when using the manufacturer's recommended oil level. If this does happen you can try lowering the oil level slightly but you are in danger of affecting the damping mechanism when the forks are well extended. A typical symptom is pattering at the front end when accelerating out of corners. There are only two sensible solutions. First, try softer springs. Second, add some air chambers or machine out the fork caps and reinstate the oil level to the manufacturer's minimum value.

I obviously cannot provide specific guidelines here because everything depends on the dimensions and initial pressure. You will have to investigate individual forks and work it out from there.

It is easy to get confused between measurements if you are doing sums relating to this. Manufacturers usually quote an oil volume and a level figure. This level is normally measured from the top of the fork legs when the legs themselves are fully compressed and no springs are fitted. Somewhat different data is required for any springing calculations. To find the volumes you need for calculation I suggest the following.

- After bleeding the forks with the right amount of oil in, fully extend them and put the springs in.
- Fill the leg right to the top noting the volume of oil involved.
- Measure the fork cap depth and syringe out oil until you reach the actual level to the bottom of fitted fork caps.

(continued)

Travel	Vol. change	Volume V2	V1/V2	$(V1/V2)^{1.4}$	Pressure	Force
mm	cm^3	cm^3			N/mm^2	N
0	0	300	1.00	1.00	0.100	113
25	25	275	1.09	1.13	0.113	128
50	50	250	1.20	1.29	0.129	146
75	75	225	1.33	1.49	0.149	169
100	100	200	1.50	1.76	0.176	200
125	125	175	1.71	2.12	0.212	240
150	150	150	2.00	2.64	0.264	299
175	175	125	2.40	3.41	0.341	387
200	200	100	3.00	4.66	0.466	528

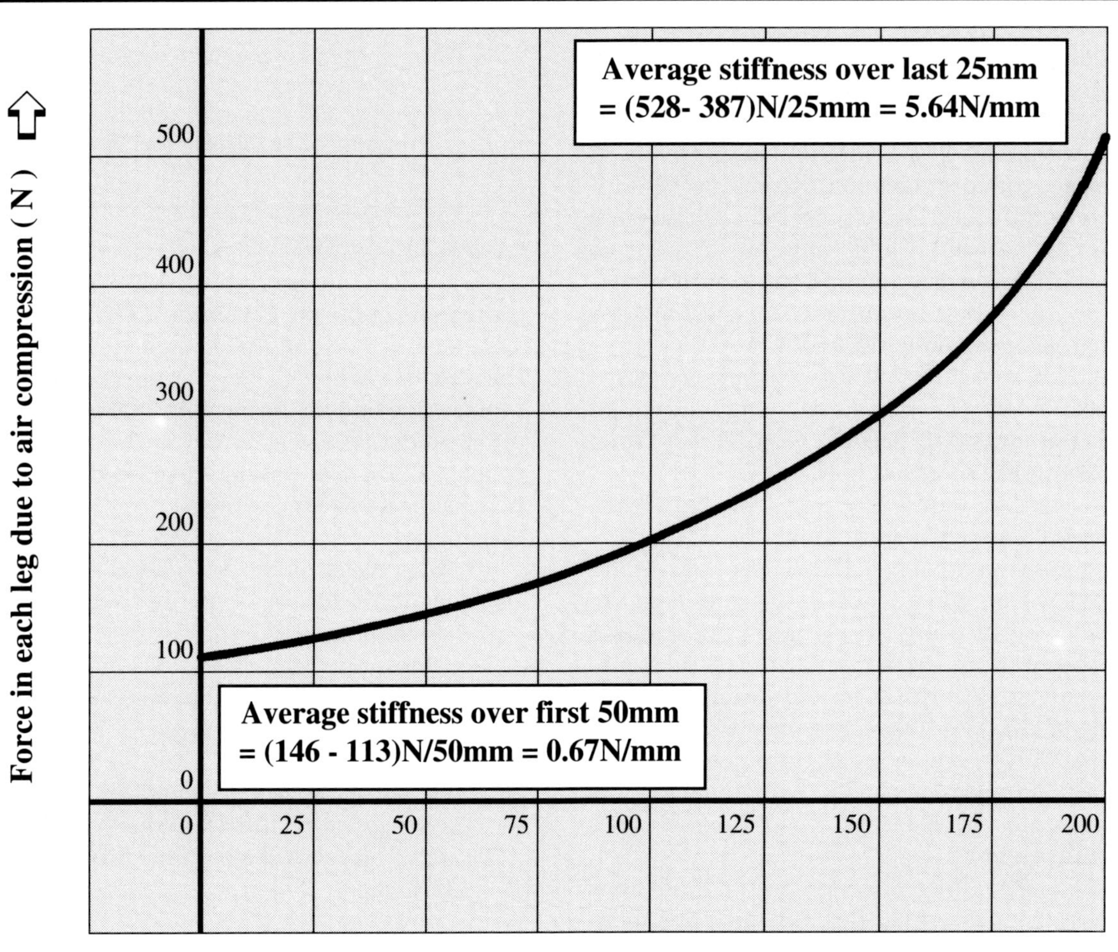

- Subtract what you syringed out from the excess volume needed to fill completely the extended leg and this gives you the air column volume at full extension. If the springs stick up a long way above the legs when the caps are off there will be errors but nothing to worry about.

- Fully compress the leg remembering to catch the oil! When the oil is level with the top of the leg, syringe out enough to lower it to the fitted fork cap level.

- Now syringe out whatever is necessary to reach the correct level. This figure gives the air volume at full compression.

These figures will allow you to calculate the maximum pressure, assuming a known starting pressure. The volume at intermediate positions will be approximately proportional to the travel.

Converting pressure to force also has pitfalls. The extra force is only that due to the pressure rise above atmospheric since atmospheric values on the inside are balanced by those on the outside.

Example. The air pressure in a set of forks when they are fully extended is nominally atmospheric (1bar, $0.1N/mm^2$, $14.7lbf/in^2$). The initial volume is measured as $300cm^3$ and the final volume at full compression is $100cm^3$. Fork travel is 200mm and piston area is $1134mm^2$.

The maximum pressure is,

$$p_2 = 0.1(300/100)^{1.4}\ N/mm^2$$

$$= 0.1(3)^{1.4}$$

$$= 0.1 \times 4.65$$

$$= 0.47N/mm^2$$

Top left. Table 5.5 *Calculated values for the example in the text.*

Bottom left. Fig 5.43 *Forces produced by air compression in each leg of the forks considered in the text.*

The change in volume as the forks compress is $300cm^3 - 100cm^3 = 200cm^3$. This is produced by 200mm of travel so the volume reduces by $1cm^3$ for every mm of travel. This allows us to produce Table 5.5 and Fig 5.43. The force is found from pressure x area but note that the first figure, 113N, is due to atmospheric pressure and this is balanced both inside and outside the fork leg. It is only the changes from this value that will assist the springs. This fact does not affect the use of the graph shown for calculating the stiffness.

Graphs like that in Fig 5.43 allow the stiffness due to air compression to be calculated. This acts in parallel with the springs so the total stiffness is the sum of that due to both springs and air. Don't forget there are two fork legs. For the example given, the stiffness associated with each fork leg is nominally 0.67N/mm (3.7lbf/in) during the first 50mm of travel. However, taking an average over the last 50mm of travel gives 5.6N/mm (32lbf/in) which would be highly significant on virtually any bike. Volumes can be adjusted to change this as desired.

Will it bottom?

You now have some idea of the actual spring stiffness and preload compression required to meet your preferred set-up. The force available from air compression can also be estimated for specific forks though experiment is the only real answer here. In theory we could now work out the maximum loads and determine whether or not the suspension will bottom. In practice I have found this to be unreliable for several reasons.

Firstly, the likelihood of bottoming the suspension depends on how hard you brake. Although it is easy to put numbers in and say that changes are necessary this may not prove to be the case. If you are not braking hard enough to demand changes there seems to be little point in compromising the normal ride by using stiffer springs that you possibly do not need.

Secondly there is the variation in riding style. Some riders are smooth brakers and others are very aggressive. This interacts with the compression damping to give a variety of effects. If the compression damping at high damper speeds is significant then the rider who slams on the brakes will find that the damping force is suddenly very high. It will off-load the springs as long as the fork is compressing and may therefore prevent bottoming that would otherwise occur. People who ride like this can have problems with sorting the damping out to suit other conditions and should experiment with forks that automatically increase the compression damping as a form of anti-dive. A lot depends on the low-speed damping as well because the damper movement will be retarded by the extra force presented.

Given the infinite range of riding styles, damping characteristics and damper settings that are possible, any simple calculation is not very representative of reality and to me seems to be a case of trying to solve a problem that may not exist. I think that once you have got as far as achieving your desired set-up the answer is to wait until the bike is ready to test. Even then you should not make early judgments. Wait until the damping is sorted out. Given that some of the best settings leave the forks almost on the limit of bottoming perhaps once or twice a lap, I think this is the only sensible way to do it.

If bottoming is a serious problem and you are satisfied with the level of compression damping (see Chapter 5.6) then obviously something has to change. If you are satisfied with the basic ride (and you defined the set-up!) then the first thing to experiment with is the air chamber. The basic possibilities have been outlined but I would start off by having the chambers at atmospheric pressure initially and experimenting with reduced volume (higher oil level). There are limits to this because when the forks are fully compressed the oil level cannot be above the top of the stanchions! However, you should reach either a lockout or a seal disaster well below this point. Reducing the air volume at the same starting pressure has little effect on the early stages of travel which, if you are happy with the normal ride, is what you want. It then increases the stiffness dramatically near to full travel. Once you have found that bottoming can be prevented in this way it is worth spending some considerable time looking for an optimum combination of starting pressure and volume because, although higher start pressures will increase initial stiffness, the effect is usually small compared to the springs until considerable travel has taken place.

Provided the fork sealing is good this is the method to use first because it does not corrupt your normal ride. Any other changes will involve a compromise of the original settings. First, you can try very small preload changes. This is not always the best way forward but it is the simplest thing to do and you might be right on the limit so that very minor changes do the trick, especially if your original specification included a lot of laden sag. For example, during heavy braking, the highly progressive nature of the air springing may make the forks too bouncy. In such cases, adding a few more millimetres of preload and lowering the front ride height to restore the steering geometry can work very well when combined with slightly increased air space. Failing this the only answer is to alter spring stiffness either by using a higher constant rate spring or by changing to progressive springs. Personally I think that the latter course of action should be a last resort because you then add another infinite range of possibilities that you have to sort out. When the situation is marginal, ie bottoming is only a minor problem, I always seem to have success by simply adding some extra very short springs inside the main springs to increase the stiffness slightly at the very upper limits of travel. There is simply no substitute for experiment as far as these matters are concerned.

Although I have suggested using frequency to estimate the spring stiffness, you must ensure that the final result does give some unladen sag on the forks. This is different from the rear where light bikes will be close to topped out when unladen.

If the forks do not have any unladen sag then when the front end is lightly loaded on the track the combination of the main springs and the top-out (rebound) springs creates a high stiffness that will seriously compromise the roadholding as discussed earlier. The unladen sag requirement is very variable according to rider preference but 10mm-15mm (0.39in-0.59in) is deemed to be about right for a fork travel of 100mm (3.94in).

Always add the preload slowly and check the laden and unladen sags at several preload settings. Both sags will reduce as the preload is applied. Once you have reached a laden sag of 30% it is worth testing the combination. Then up the preload to give 25% (laden) and test again. If, before you reach this point, the unladen sag has reduced to zero, then you need to change the spring rate and amend your frequency values. If the forks are too crude to get repeatable unladen sag figures, just make sure there is something there and set about trying to improve the forks you are using. Alternatively, save up for something that is better engineered.

5.5 Rear suspension springing

Introduction

Rear suspension springing is somewhat more complicated than that associated with front suspension because the mechanisms usually produce substantial leverage between the wheel and spring(s). Because of this the spring forces are normally very different from the wheel forces and spring travel may be substantially less than wheel travel.

When these two aspects are combined the general result is a wheel rate that is not the same as the total spring stiffness. Furthermore, as the wheel moves this relationship changes so, for a constant spring stiffness, the wheel rate will usually vary somewhat.

The manner in which the wheel rate varies with suspension travel is as diverse as the systems themselves. Conventional twin shock layouts can produce wheel rates that rise by perhaps 60%. They can also produce wheel rates that fall to zero if the geometry is ridiculous. In such cases the suspension will collapse under heavy loads and one or two examples did so when people first experimented with laid down shocks and long wheel travel. Virtually any situation between these extremes can be achieved. It all depends on the geometry used. Similar observations apply to monoshock cantilever systems.

Modern linkage systems offer a means of producing wheel rate changes that cannot be achieved from normal twin shock/monoshock-cantilever mechanisms. It is possible to produce all sorts of characteristics on twin shock bikes by using a combination of the mechanism and specially designed springs but linkage systems offer unrivalled flexibility in these matters at the expense of complexity and, sometimes, excessive friction.

Not all linkage systems capitalise on this aspect and many yield either a constant wheel rate or a mildly rising one. In such cases you have to balance the considerably increased complexity and engineering requirements against the reduced advantages that remain. Only the individual can decide.

Fig 5.44 *A state-of-the-art rear suspension unit. Most of the development relates to damping. Springing is still achieved by a coil spring with adjustable preload but stiffness requirements vary considerably according to how the rear suspension mechanism is laid out.*

The implications of leverage

There are two aspects of leverage to be considered.

- The relationship between spring force and wheel force.
- The relationship between wheel movement and spring movement.

Force ratio

To get things started, consider the situation presented in Fig 5.45a. In this example a vertical spring force F_s acts on a horizontal swinging arm at some point other than the wheel spindle. This produces a clockwise turning effect on the swinging arm which is equal to $F_s \times L_s$ where L_s is the moment arm shown in the diagram.

The vertical force this would produce at the wheel can be found by determining the force F_w that would be needed at the spindle to balance the turning moment. If the two turning effects are equal then,

$$F_s \times L_s = F_w \times L_w$$

thus $F_w = (F_s \times L_s)/L_w$

or $F_w = F_s/n$

where $n = L_w/L_s$

The value n is commonly called the leverage ratio. If the spring force is applied at the wheel then n equals one but as we move the springs towards the swinging arm pivot the value of n increases and the force produced at the wheel reduces. For example, if the spring(s) act half way along the swinging arm then the wheel force produced is only half the actual spring force.

In general the spring force is unlikely to be vertical, indeed its direction will alter as the swinging arm rotates. Fig 5.45b shows the spring force inclined at some angle. As a result of this the turning effect is reduced because the effective leverage has changed. Distance L_s, which must be measured at right angles to the force, is less than it was originally and the greater the inclination of the units the greater the reduction in length. The practical outcome is that inclined units create less force at the wheel for a given spring stiffness so the suspension becomes softer.

Finally, we must acknowlege that the swinging arm itself will rotate and is therefore not always horizontal. In such cases the same reasoning must be applied to length L_w, ie it must be measured from the pivot to the point where it meets the line of action of force F_w at 90°. This force will always be assumed vertical since we are interested in wheel rate. Fig 5.45b illustrates both these situations and the dimensions involved.

To conclude, we can always relate the spring and wheel forces using the formula given provided we employ appropriate values for the lengths L_w and L_s. The practical outcome of all this is that the force ratio will vary when the lengths vary. Such changes can produce either rising or falling wheel rates but to see the final effect we need to look at the movement ratio as well.

If the suspension springs were located at the wheel spindle then, in nominal terms, the spring movement is equal to the vertical wheel movement. In practice this is rarely the case and the spring force is applied somewhat nearer to the pivot as shown in Fig 5.46. This makes the spring movement less than that of the wheel. For the specific case shown (horizontal arm, vertical spring force), we obtain,

$$\text{Tan}\varnothing = x_s/L_s = x_w/L_w$$

hence $x_w = x_s L_w/L_s$

or $x_w = n x_s$ where $n = L_w/L_s$

So, for this specific case we find that the force ratio and the movement ratio are both determined by the same value n. As far as force is concerned, the wheel force reduces when the value of n increases but it has the opposite effect on wheel movement.

For example, if the value of n is two then the wheel force is only half the spring force but the wheel travel is twice that of the spring. Both aspects determine the effective wheel rate. In this specific case the spring force would need to be double that required at the wheel and it would have to be produced by a spring compression that is only half the wheel movement. The final result

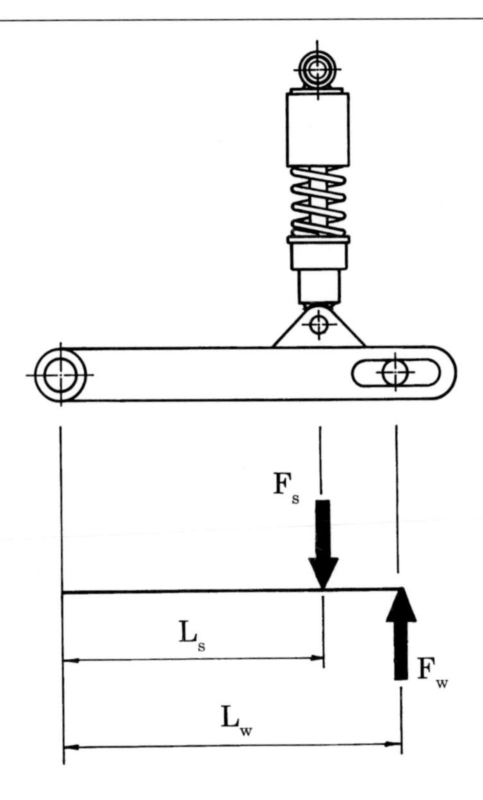

a) Spring vertical, arm horizontal.

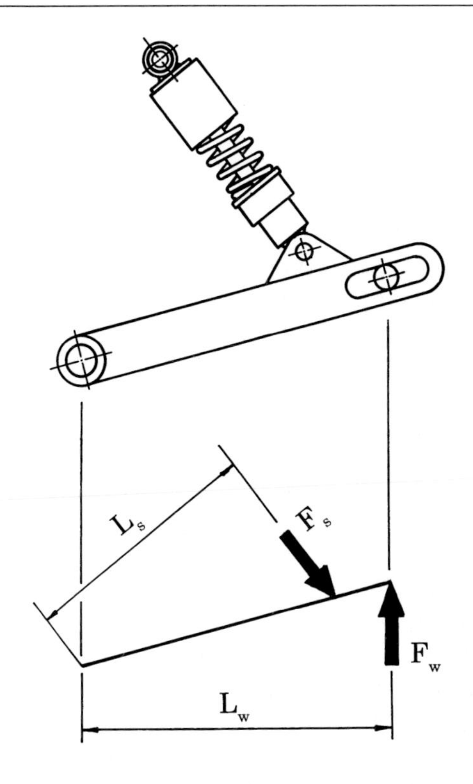

b) Spring and arm inclined.

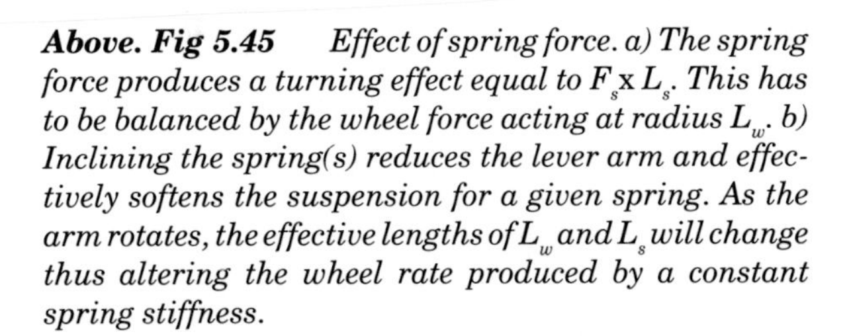

Above. Fig 5.45 *Effect of spring force. a) The spring force produces a turning effect equal to* $F_s \times L_s$*. This has to be balanced by the wheel force acting at radius* L_w*. b) Inclining the spring(s) reduces the lever arm and effectively softens the suspension for a given spring. As the arm rotates, the effective lengths of* L_w *and* L_s *will change thus altering the wheel rate produced by a constant spring stiffness.*

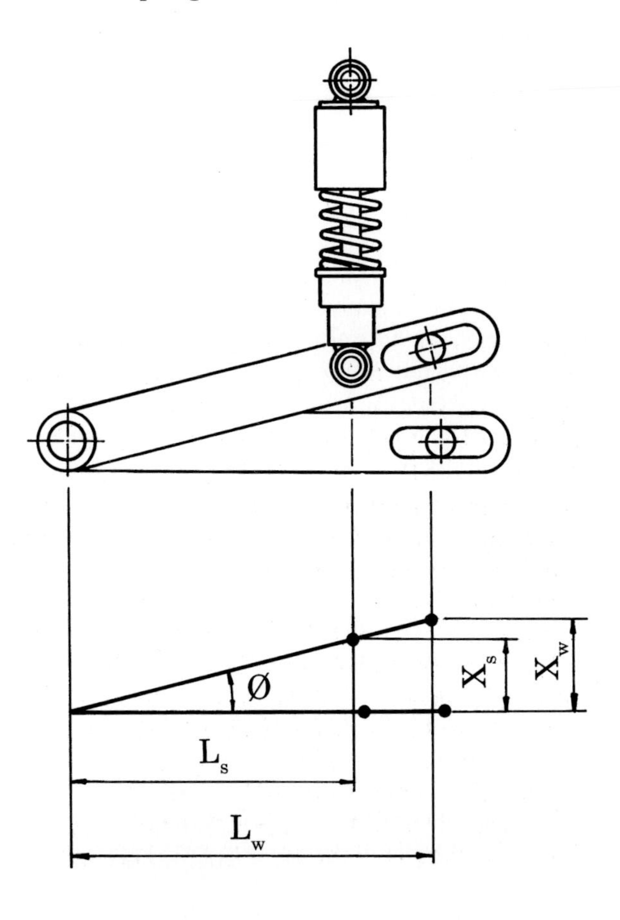

Right. Fig 5.46 *Relationship between wheel movement and spring movement for an arm that is initially horizontal and a spring that is vertical. If the spring is moved nearer to the pivot, the spring movement associated with a given wheel movement is reduced. This requires a stiffer spring to create the same force at the wheel. Since the wheel then has greater leverage over this force a further increase in spring rate is required to overcome this aspect. The combined effects require that the spring stiffness is (*n^2 *x the desired wheel rate) where n = leverage ratio.*

is a spring stiffness that needs to be four times that required at the wheel. In effect, the stiffness has had to double to account for the force ratio and double again to account for the movement ratio. In general terms,

$$\textbf{Wheel rate} = \frac{\textbf{total spring rate}}{\mathbf{n^2}}$$

or

Total spring rate $= \mathbf{n^2}$ **x wheel rate**

where

n = leverage ratio (see text)

$$= \frac{\textbf{wheel movement}}{\textbf{spring movement}}$$

$$= \frac{\textbf{Lever arm to wheel}}{\textbf{Lever arm to spring}}$$

Leverage and movement ratios

There are several things we must note about the value of n. Firstly, it is going to alter with suspension travel. If it reduces the wheel rate will increase. If it increases the wheel rate will fall.

Secondly, we note that the n^2 term was generated by two separate n values, one for force and one for movement, which were assumed to be equal. In the case of linkage and monoshock/ cantilever systems this is, fortunately, a very reasonable assumption and we would always utilise a value of n calculated using n = (wheel movement/spring movement) because this is easy to measure.

For many twin shock systems this is not a reasonable assumption, especially if the shocks are steeply inclined and the travel is long. You have to remember that the relationships were derived using simplified layouts, eg horizontal swinging arms, and the analysis is therefore limited. Large inclinations of the suspension units lead to inequality between the two supposedly equal values of n and it is necessary to deal with them separately. This may seem to invalidate some basic laws of science but it does not. Once the job is finished you will find that the work put into the spring is equal to the work done on the wheel by moving it vertically.

From a practical point of view this will have little effect on spring selection. Although you might do the sums to a few decimal places you will arrive at a spring stiffness that you cannot buy and will no doubt take the nearest value which is probably 15% higher. However this is not the full story and the differences can have a considerable impact on how the wheel rate changes. On some twin shock mechanisms, using the n^2 value based on movement will produce errors of 30% when compared to those obtained using separate force and movement ratios. For these reasons it is best to treat this whole business on two separate levels.

- If you simply want to find a nominal spring stiffness to obtain your desired wheel rate then use the formula given and obtain the n value by either method. The result will be more than adequate.

- If you are also interested in how the wheel rate will alter as you move through the whole range of travel then it is best to use a drawing and determine the n value associated with force separately from that associated with movement. This is much more work!

Since many people will simply want to select suitable springs I will deal with this aspect first. Provided you specify an initial wheel rate and stick to the first 30% or so of wheel movement, the results will be useful.

Estimating spring rates

The general method is the same for all types of system. Calculate leverage ratios using any of the following methods.

- Measure the vertical wheel travel and the corresponding compression of the suspension spring. It is easiest to do this with the spring removed by measuring the travel of the damper! Only cover the first 25% or 30% of wheel travel.
- If the mechanism does not exist, take values off a drawing. It only needs to be a simple line drawing showing what moves where.
- Lever arms can be measured on a bike but it is difficult to do it accurately. Again, a simple drawing is useful.

Example. On a twin shock bike, the first 18mm of vertical rear wheel movement causes the springs to compress by 15mm. Estimate suitable spring rates to achieve an initial wheel rate of a) 22N/mm, b) 2.0kgf/mm, c) 120lbf/in.

$$\text{Leverage ratio } n = \frac{\text{wheel travel}}{\text{spring travel}}$$

$$= \frac{18\text{mm}}{15\text{mm}}$$

$$= 1.2$$

$$\text{Thus } n^2 = 1.2 \times 1.2 = 1.44$$

$$\text{Total spring rate} = n^2 \times \text{wheel rate}$$

$$\text{For each spring, rate} = \frac{n^2 \times \text{wheel rate}}{2}$$

a) For 22N/mm

$$\text{Spring rate} = \frac{1.44 \times 22\text{N/mm}}{2}$$

$$= 15.8\text{N/mm}$$

b) For 2.0kgf/mm

$$\text{Spring rate} = \frac{1.44 \times 2\text{kgf/mm}}{2}$$

$$= 1.44\text{kgf/mm}$$

c) For 120lbf/in

$$\text{Spring rate} = \frac{1.44 \times 120\text{lbf/in}}{2}$$

$$= 86\text{lbf/in}$$

Example. On a bike with monoshock/rocker suspension, the first 50mm of vertical rear wheel movement causes the spring to compress by 28mm. Estimate a suitable spring rate to achieve an initial wheel rate of 110lbf/in.

$$\text{Leverage ratio } n = \frac{\text{wheel travel}}{\text{spring travel}}$$

$$= \frac{50\text{mm}}{28\text{mm}}$$

$$= 1.79$$

$$\text{Thus } n^2 = 1.79 \times 1.79 = 3.2$$

$$\text{Total spring rate} = n^2 \times \text{wheel rate}$$

$$= 3.2 \times 110\text{lbf/in}$$

$$= 352\text{lbf/in}$$

Example. A monoshock unit has a spring stiffness of 7kgf/mm. During the early travel the spring compresses 25mm while the wheel moves up 45mm. What is the wheel rate?

$$\text{Leverage ratio } n = \frac{\text{wheel travel}}{\text{spring travel}}$$

$$= \frac{45\text{mm}}{25\text{mm}}$$

$$= 1.8$$

$$\text{Thus } n^2 = 1.8 \times 1.8 = 3.24$$

$$\text{Wheel rate} = \frac{\text{Total spring rate}}{n^2}$$

$$= \frac{7\text{kgf/mm}}{3.24}$$

$$= 2.16\text{kgf/mm}$$

If you do several examples you will realise how sensitive the answers are to your value of n. While n is very close to unity, n^2 is also close to unity but as soon as n gets above about 1.1, n^2 takes off rapidly. Small errors in the value of n then have a big effect as this example demonstrates.

Example. On a bike with monoshock/rocker suspension, the first 50mm of vertical rear wheel movement causes the springs to compress by a) 28mm, b) 30mm. Estimate suitable spring rates to achieve an initial wheel rate of 2kgf/mm.

$$\text{Leverage ratio } n = \frac{\text{wheel travel}}{\text{spring travel}}$$

Case a) $n = \frac{50\text{mm}}{28\text{mm}}$

$= 1.79$

Thus $n^2 = 1.79 \times 1.79 = 3.2$

Total spring rate $= n^2 \times$ wheel rate

$= 3.2 \times 2\text{kgf/mm}$

$= 6.4\text{kgf/mm}$ (358lbf/in)

Case b) $n = \frac{50\text{mm}}{30\text{mm}}$

$= 1.67$

Thus $n^2 = 1.67 \times 1.67 = 2.78$

Total spring rate $= n^2 \times$ wheel rate

$= 2.78 \times 2\text{kgf/mm}$

$= 5.56\text{kgf/mm}$ (311lbf/in)

ie the 2mm changes makes a 15% difference.

These calculations, in conjunction with the topics covered in the last chapter, will generally suffice for initial spring rate estimates. For convenience, a summary of all the relevant information is given opposite.

Example. A classic racer has 110mm of rear wheel travel and twin shocks. The laden load at the rear is 120kgf of which 19kgf is unsprung. The laden sag is 28mm and during this movement the dampers compress 23mm. Estimate a suitable spring rate for the rear suspension of this bike.

Sprung weight $= 120 - 19 = 101\text{kgf}$

Using frequency of 2.3Hz, and the formula given opposite for wheel rate in kgf/mm,

$$\text{Wheel rate} = \frac{101 \times 2.3 \times 2.3}{248.5}$$

$= 2.15\text{kgf/mm}$

Leverage ratio $n = \frac{28\text{mm}}{23\text{mm}}$

$n = 1.217$

Thus $n^2 = 1.48$

Total spring rate $= n^2 \times$ wheel rate

$= 1.48 \times 2.15\text{kgf/mm}$

$= 3.19\text{kgf/mm}$

For each spring, rate $= \frac{3.19}{2}$

$= 1.6\text{kgf/mm}$ (90lbf/in)

This particular bike actually uses 85lbf/in springs so the estimate is reasonable. At one stage it was fitted with 100lbf/in springs and still performed reasonably well. 2.3Hz is rather high for comfort but if you have only limited travel, as in this case, you have to accept this. It does give a taut feel which many riders like.

Summary of spring rate calculations at the rear

1. Estimate a suitable wheel rate

a) From experience

b) By using either of the following

$$\textbf{Wheel rate (kgf/mm)} = \frac{Wf^2}{248.5}$$

where W = sprung weight at rear in kgf
f = frequency in Hz

or

$$\textbf{Wheel rate (lbf/in)} = \frac{Wf^2}{9.8}$$

where the weight is now in lbf

c) Or by using

$$\textbf{Wheel rate} = \frac{W_L - W_{UL}}{TH - US}$$

where W_L = laden tyre load at rear

W_{UL} = unladen tyre load at rear

TH = travel for hollows (vertical laden sag)

US = vertical unladen sag

2. Estimate the spring rate using

Total spring rate = n^2 x wheel rate

where

n = leverage ratio (see text)

$$= \frac{\text{wheel movement}}{\text{spring movement}}$$

Divide total stiffness by number of springs to obtain the stiffness of each spring

Suggested data (guide only)

1. Frequencies

a) Short travel road race, 75mm or less, eg on an 80 or 125: 2.6Hz

b) 75 - 90mm travel: 2.5Hz

c) 100 - 130mm travel: 2.2 -2.3Hz

d) 200mm travel: 2Hz

e) Off road, 250 - 300mm: 1.8 - 2Hz

2. Laden and unladen sags

a) Laden sag about 25% of total travel

b) Unladen sag (measured vertically)

1) 125: zero (topped out)

2) 250: 0 - 2mm

3) 500/750: 9 -12mm

Preload

Add preload to achieve the required laden sag value. More preload will reduce both the laden and unladen sag figures. If you preload a spring which is too soft so that you meet the laden sag specification, the unladen sag will be too small. If the spring is too stiff, then when preloaded to meet the laden sag the unladen sag will be too great.

These ideas are all that most people need to use however those with more interest in the design will want to know how the wheel rate changes with travel. This is best done by using full size drawings and taking measurements from them.

Obviously I cannot reproduce drawings at full size in this book and have therefore used CAD to create small scale versions. At full size, or even half size, hand drawn pictures are more than adequate. To emphasise this I compiled the tabulated data from my original hand drawn diagrams. Even if you hate anything metric a ruler graduated in millimetres is the most convenient one to use for length measurements. The resolution is about as good as you can work with and it is difficult to buy long rulers calibrated in thirtyseconds of an inch over the whole length. For drawing arcs use a modified pair of metalworking trammels or a beam compass. Failing either use a pencil held at the required radius by a tensioned thread pivoting on a nail!

Twin shock systems

This 'classic' form of springing can offer more than adequate suspension for the majority of riders provided a sensible design is combined with good quality dampers.

Depending on the design, the initial wheel rate may reduce, increase or stay constant. The variations achieved by normal layouts are not great but you can achieve a very worthwhile rise in rate by designing it correctly. The rise is nothing like that which can be achieved with linkages but it is nevertheless very useful for preventing bottoming.

Fig 5.47 gives a brief summary of the general situation. In the early days units were virtually upright and close to the wheel spindle (a). This gives an initial wheel rate nominally equal to the total spring stiffness. It looks somewhat unattractive, requires a long subframe and produces a falling rate during the latter part of the travel in most cases. The exact behaviour depends on the initial angle of the swinging arm. The main problem is that wheel movement is restricted to that of the dampers which in the past was fairly short. One advantage of this layout is the very low loads it imparts at the swinging arm pivot.

Moving the shocks away from the spindle and inclining them somewhat offers several improvements (b). Allowable wheel travel is increased and

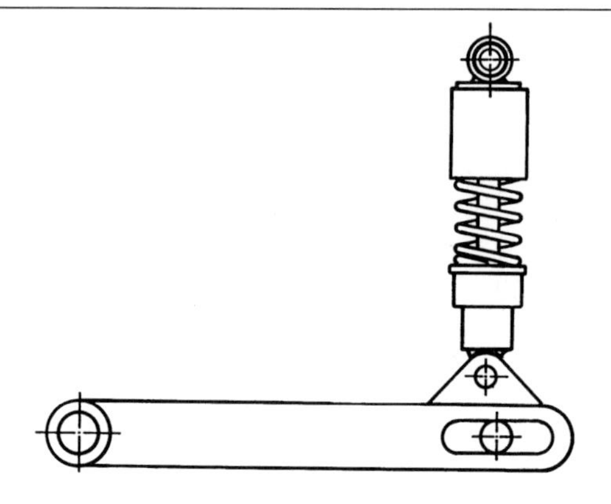

a) Upright units/small leverage.

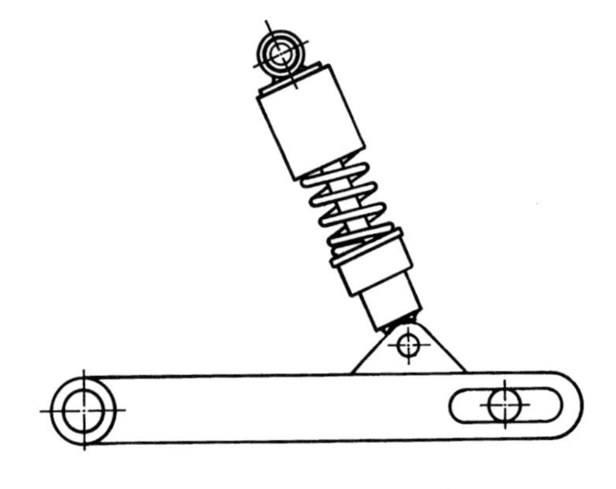

b) Moderate inclination/leverage.

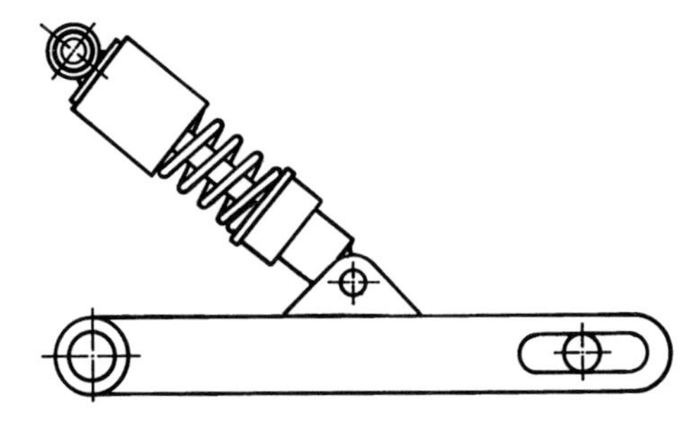

c) High inclination/leverage.

Fig 5.47 *Twin shock layouts. a) Upright units give a slightly falling rate near full travel, restrict wheel movement and look out of date. b) Moderate inclination and leverage improves things and can produce a useful rise in rate if the correct geometry is used. (c) Overdoing the inclination and leverage causes several problems.*

the falling rate can be made to stay constant or rise by a useful amount. Taking this to the extreme (c) negates any gain. The wheel rate falls dramatically, the pivot loads increase and the swinging arm suffers serious bending. Not a wonderful situation.

For most applications the best results will be achieved from a mechanism that gives maximum rate rise. I say this because the increases we can obtain are nothing like those that are possible with linkages and the pros and cons of vast rate rises are not involved here. At best, we just have a gradual rise that may, at full travel, achieve a value which is some 60% greater than the initial stiffness, less if you so desire.

To achieve this situation the distance from the swinging arm pivot to the lower shock mounting needs to be the same as that from the pivot to the top mounting - Fig 5.48a. This means that longer dampers will need more inclination than short ones. Modern high quality dampers are available with substantial travel so they do not need to be too far away from the wheel to obtain sufficient leverage. However, long damper travel means a long overall damper length which may imply increased seat height. In such cases it is best to position the lower damper mounting below the pivot - spindle centreline as shown in Fig 5.48b.

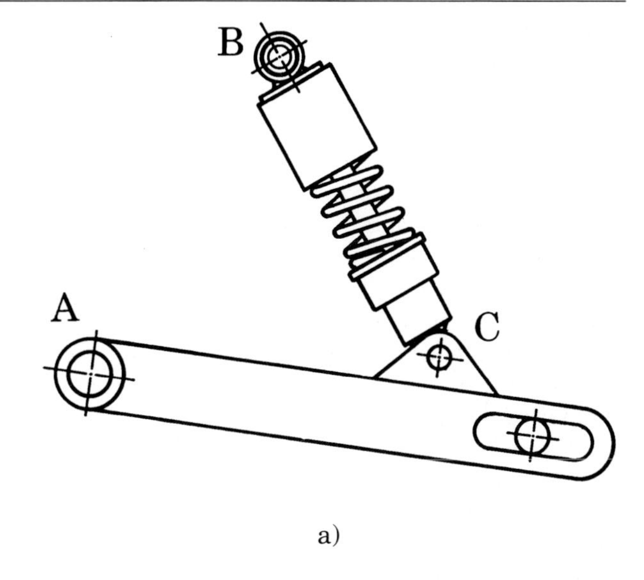

A = Swinging arm pivot
B = Damper top mounting
C = Damper lower mounting

For maximum rise in rate make distance AB equal to distance AC

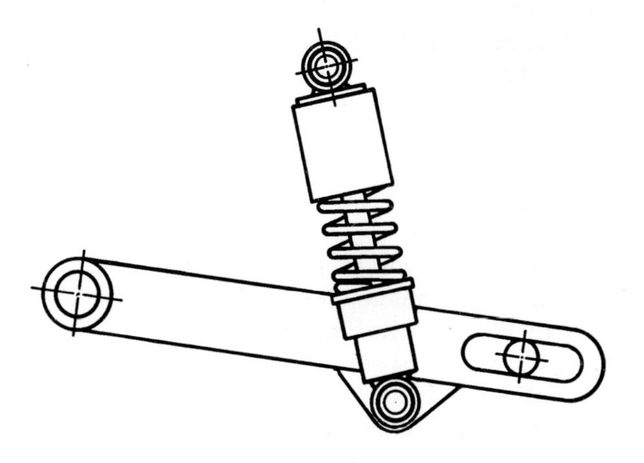

b)

Right. Fig 5.48 *a) To obtain the maximum rise in wheel rate the distance from the pivot to the two unit mountings should be equal. With long units use the arrangement shown in diagram b). This gives the same result but a lower overall height.*

Changes in wheel rate

If you produce a simple line drawing showing how the swinging arm and springs move throughout the full travel, then you can calculate the leverage ratio n previously described. If you do this for the first 20mm of wheel movement, it is unlikely to be the same as for the last 20mm. Furthermore, if you start to measure the lever arms and calculate n from them then they too will alter. Finally, if you compare values of n calculated by the two different methods then they will not be the same either!

The results depend on the specific layout but if you can see that the values are very different then in order to investigate how the wheel rate alters with travel it is best to work with two separate n values. Instead of finding n from wheel and spring movement, then squaring it, you should find one n value in this way and another from the lever arm distances. The following method will allow you to check out the wheel rate at any point in the travel, whatever the geometry. If you only want a rough idea, just use the first and last 20mm of travel.

- Draw the centrelines of the swinging arm and dampers corresponding to full suspension extension.
- Repeat for every 20mm or so of movement up to full travel.
- Determine the lever arms L_s and L_w together with the damper length at each position. Calculate values of L_s/L_w at each point.
- Find the spring compression at each position and note the initial value of (wheel travel/damper travel).
- Use the initial travel ratio to estimate the spring stiffness required to achieve the desired initial wheel rate.
- Find the wheel force = $F_s(L_s / L_w)$ at each position.
- Plot a graph of wheel force vs wheel movement.
- Determine the variation in stiffness.

Example. The twin shock layout shown in Fig 5.49 has been proposed (it is deliberately ridiculous!). Estimate the spring stiffness to give an initial wheel rate of 1.3kgf/mm and investigate the variation in wheel rate up to 200mm of travel.

Fig 5.45 shows the drawing involved. I have done this for every 20mm of movement. The original was full size. It is clear that this system will collapse completely near full travel because the springs are almost horizontal.

Table 5.6 details the figures involved. During the first 40mm of movement the springs compress by 21mm so the ratio of wheel travel to spring travel is 40/21 = 1.905 from which n^2 = 3.63. Since spring stiffness = n^2 x wheel rate the total spring stiffness required is 3.63 x 1.3kgf/mm = 4.72kgf/mm, say 5kgf/mm. However there are two springs so each one will be 2.5kgf/mm.

- Column 1 gives vertical wheel travel.
- Column 2 gives the lever arm of the wheel at each position. Always measure horizontally.
- Column 3 gives the lever arm of the spring. The measurement must be at 90deg to the spring's line of action.
- Column 4 calculates Ls/Lw at each position. (note this is not the leverage ratio, n, which is Lw/Ls)
- Column 5 gives damper length BC.
- Column 6 subtracts damper length at each position from the initial value to obtain spring compression.
- Column 7 gives the total spring force at each position. It is obtained by multiplying the spring compression by the total spring stiffness which is 5kgf/mm. You can ignore preload in this calculation.
- Column 8 multiplies the spring force by the ratio Ls/Lw in column 4 to find the vertical force at the wheel.

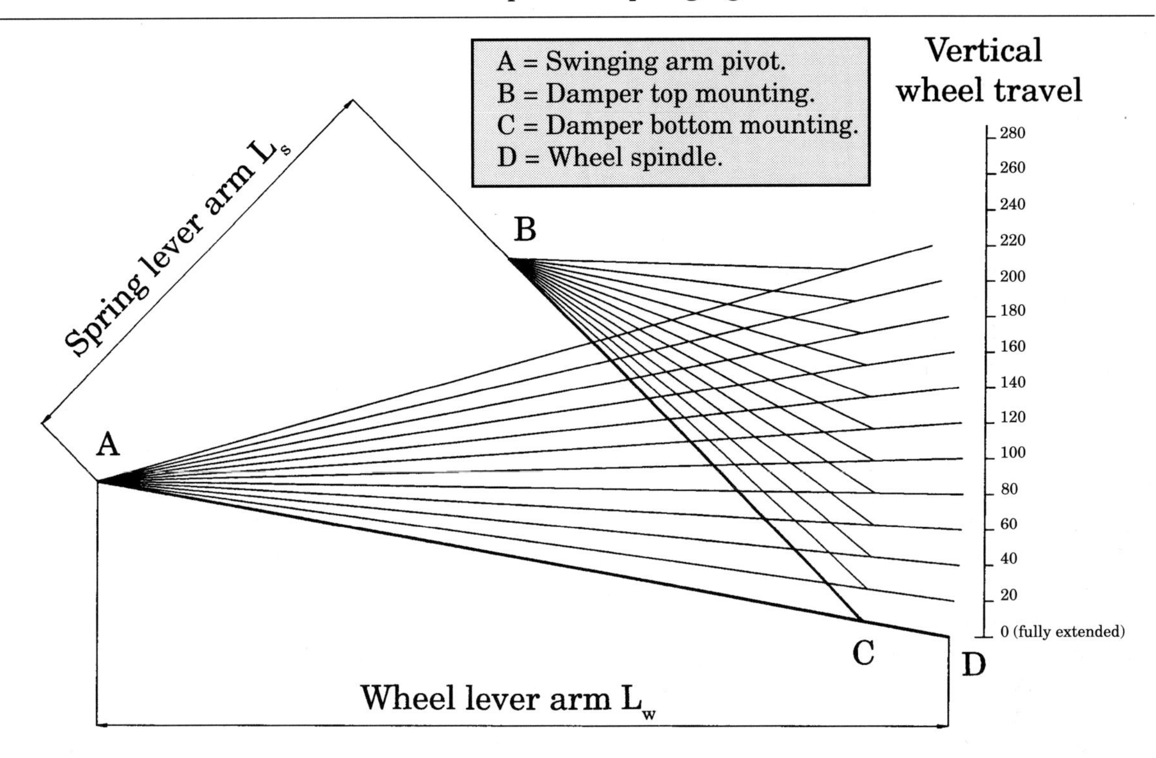

Above. Fig 5.49 *The proposed twin shock layout used in the first example. Centre lines of swinging arm and spring are shown at 20mm increments of wheel movement. The layout is deliberately ridiculous to show how the falling wheel rate is analysed.*

Below. Table 5.6 *Measurements taken from the full size version of the drawing and calculated values used to plot wheel force vs wheel travel.*

Wheel travel	Wheel lever arm Lw	Spring lever arm Ls	Ls/Lw	Damper length BC	Spring compression	Spring force Fs = comp x 5kgf/mm	Wheel force Fs x(Ls/Lw)
(mm)	(mm)	(mm)		(mm)	(mm)	(kgf)	(kgf)
0	492	258	0.524	289	0	0	0
20	495	253	0.511	279	10	50	26
40	497	247	0.497	268	21	105	52
60	499	240	0.481	259	30	150	72
80	500	232	0.464	249	40	200	93
100	500	223	0.446	240	49	245	109
120	499	212	0.425	231	58	290	123
140	497	200	0.402	222	67	335	135
160	495	185	0.373	215	74	370	138
180	492	169	0.343	207	82	410	141
200	487	150	0.308	201	88	440	136

Finally, a graph of wheel force vs travel is produced using values from the first and last columns in the table. This is shown in Fig 5.49 and the slope of the graph is wheel rate. It starts off at nominally 1.3kgf/mm as required but gradually reduces. It eventually falls to zero and the suspension therefore collapses as predicted. In use it would collapse well before full travel because the low rates cannot support normal loads.

You can use this method for any layout. I have chosen something rather silly to illustrate a significant rate change. Having said that, you do sometimes see layouts that are in danger of collapsing but they are not to be recommended. The method suggested earlier to achieve maximum rise is probably as good as anything.

To get the general idea and save a lot of work, just use a movement at the start of travel and a movement at the finish. Note that even if you change the spring stiffness you only need to plot one graph. The form of rate variation will be unaltered and the actual values simply change by a multiplying factor of (new stiffness/original stiffness). These methods can be applied to any layout. When starting from a blank sheet of paper I would suggest the following.

Fig 5.49 *Wheel force vs wheel travel for the first example. Note the falling wheel rate which eventually becomes zero. This system is unsatisfactory but was chosen to illustrate the general method. If you prefer imperial spring rates, ie lbf/in, but find measuring lengths in mm convenient, make sure you calculate the spring compression in inches before multiplying it by the stiffness to get wheel force. lbf/in x mm does not give lbf!*

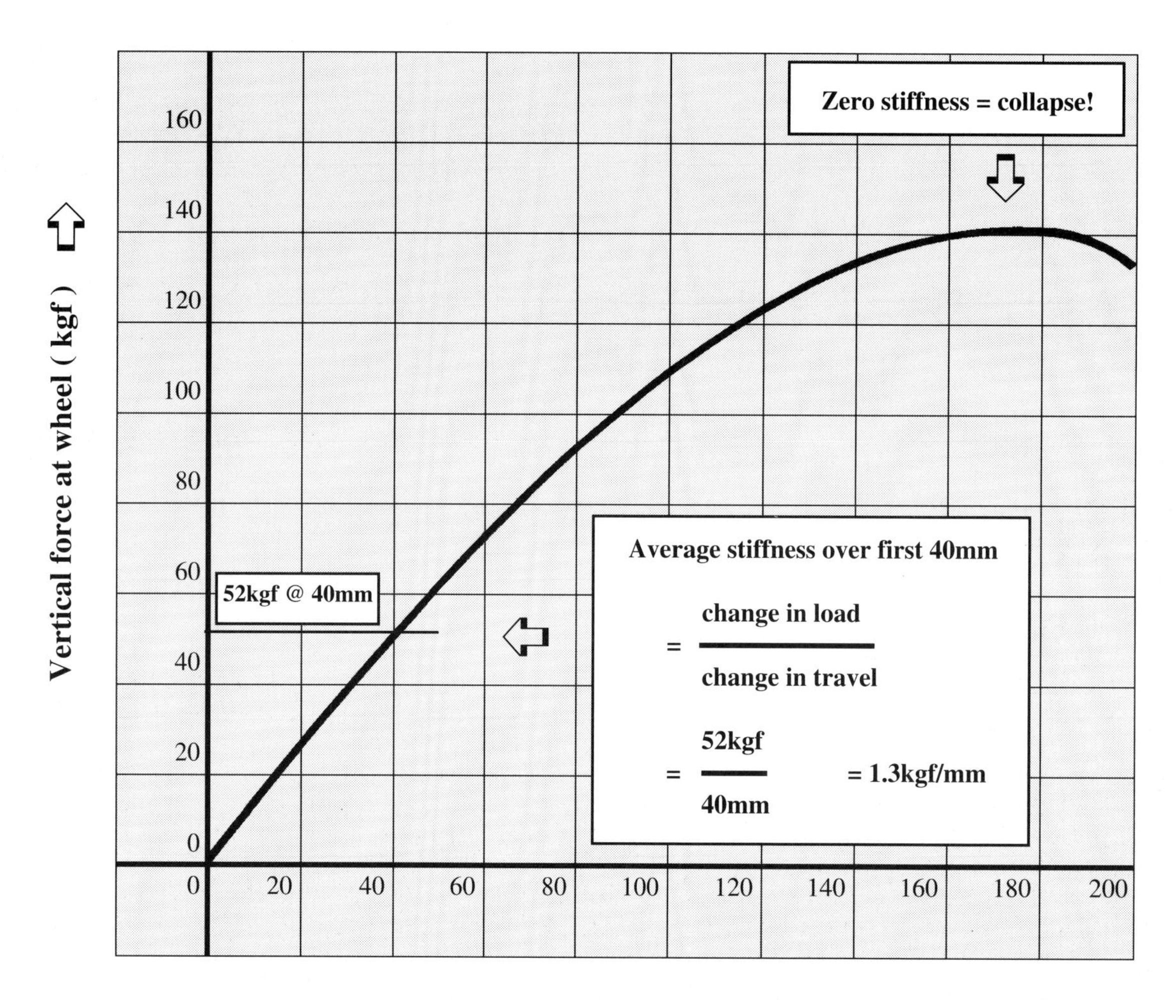

- Determine swinging arm length.
- Decide on wheel travel.
- Select suitable dampers and a nominal leverage using wheel movement/damper travel.
- Use the leverage to find a lower suspension mounting point.
- If the dampers are tall, consider mounting them below the arm.
- Fix the top mounting point. The conditions for maximum rate rise were given earlier.
- Draw it out as shown, find suitable springs and check out the changes in wheel rate.

Fig 5.50 *The early Yamaha cantilever monoshock layout had a long suspension unit that was located at the headstock. The long unit provided space for complex damping mechanisms but short units have caught up.*

Cantilever monoshock

This layout, which was originally employed by Vincent and others, was brought back to life by Yamaha in the late 1970's. One of the main objectives was to retain the high leverage of laid down shocks without the drastically falling rate. This allowed significant amounts of wheel travel without the previous problems. Added bonuses included a stiffer swinging arm layout and the use of a single suspension unit, thereby avoiding the need for closely matching two units.

On the debit side, the spring loads are now carried at one point and the loads on the pivot can be high if the leverage is large.

Yamaha adopted a large, long suspension unit that went right up to the headstock as shown in Fig 5.50 but the majority of current systems utilise much shorter units as did Vincent and BSA in the 1950's.

Personally I am not totally convinced by all of the arguments for or against this system when compared to twin shock. There is less unsprung inertia but beyond that I think either system can be made to do the job and if the twin shock swinging arm is a bit flexible it can be triangulated like the cantilever one, though not as effi-

ciently. It is really a matter of personal preference and having designed both systems and won races on them I think it is all down to the individual design and construction.

One thing is certain. Once monoshocks took hold, most of the serious damper development went into them and I think this was more influential than most people think. In most cases you were trying to compare monoshocks using the latest dampers and twin shocks using much more crude devices. Today you can buy very high quality, very adjustable twin shock racing units and so both systems can be made to work well.

As far as analysis goes the methods are identical to twin shocks. Having done that already I will simply make some general observations. A rising rate will be achieved if the value of n falls with increasing travel. This happens when the lever arm L_w reduces or the lever arm L_s increases.

The ratio of these lengths also ties in more closely with travel ratios because the angular oscillation of the monoshock is usually quite small. The less droop the swinging arm has when laden the more the rate will rise but squat and chain requirements may restrict this.

A typical design would make the angle between the spring and the pivot 90° at full travel. Prior to this the value of L_s will be less so the wheel rate will rise due to the combination of reducing L_w and increasing L_s. Here is an example using imperial stiffness data but with lengths measured in mm because that is usually convenient.

Example. A swinging arm 400mm long (centres) is to give 130mm of wheel travel from a monoshock unit having 60mm of travel. The initial wheel rate required is nominally 90lbf/in. Design a cantilever system that gives a rising rate and estimate a suitable spring stiffness.

Fig 5.51 is the drawing for this example. The value of wheel travel / spring travel is nominally 130 / 60 = 2.167 so use $n^2 = 2.167 \times 2.167 = 4.69$ as a starting point to give a spring stiffness of 4.69 x 90lbf/in = 422lbf/in. This is a lot of travel to base the stiffness on but it will do as a starting point.

The arm radius to the damper mount is nominally 400mm x (60/130) = 185mm.

Following Fig 5.51, draw out the arm movement and the arc travelled by the damper mount on the swinging arm. Identify the point where the suspension unit will meet the small arc at 90° when an acceptable top suspension mounting position is used. Join this point to the pivot to obtain the basic arm layout at full travel. Now apply the same method as for twin shock systems, ie set out the positions at about 20mm intervals and compile the necessary data to complete the graph as shown. The data for the example is in Table 5.7. Note that the spring compression must be converted to inches before it is multiplied by the stiffness in lbf/in.

As expected this example gives a rise in wheel rate. You can plot a graph as before or simply take the first and last pairs of values as follows.

Taking the first 20mm,

$$\text{Wheel rate} = \frac{\text{change in wheel force}}{\text{change in wheel position}}$$

$$= \frac{(67 - 0)\ \text{lbf}}{(20 - 0)\ \text{mm}}$$

$$= 3.35\text{lbf/mm}$$

Since there are 25.4mm in one inch,

$$= 3.35 \times 25.4\text{lbf/in}$$

$$= 85\text{lbf/in}$$

Taking the last 20mm (to 140mm),

$$\text{Wheel rate} = \frac{\text{change in wheel force}}{\text{change in wheel position}}$$

$$= \frac{(525 - 433)\ \text{lbf}}{(140 - 120)\ \text{mm}}$$

$$= 4.6\text{lbf/mm}$$

Since there are 25.4mm in one inch,

$$= 4.6 \times 25.4\text{lbf/in}$$

$$= 117\text{lbf/in}$$

The initial rate is only about 85lbf/in because of the approximations but it rises to 97lbf/in in the first 40mm of travel. In the last 20mm of travel the wheel rate has risen to 117lbf/in.

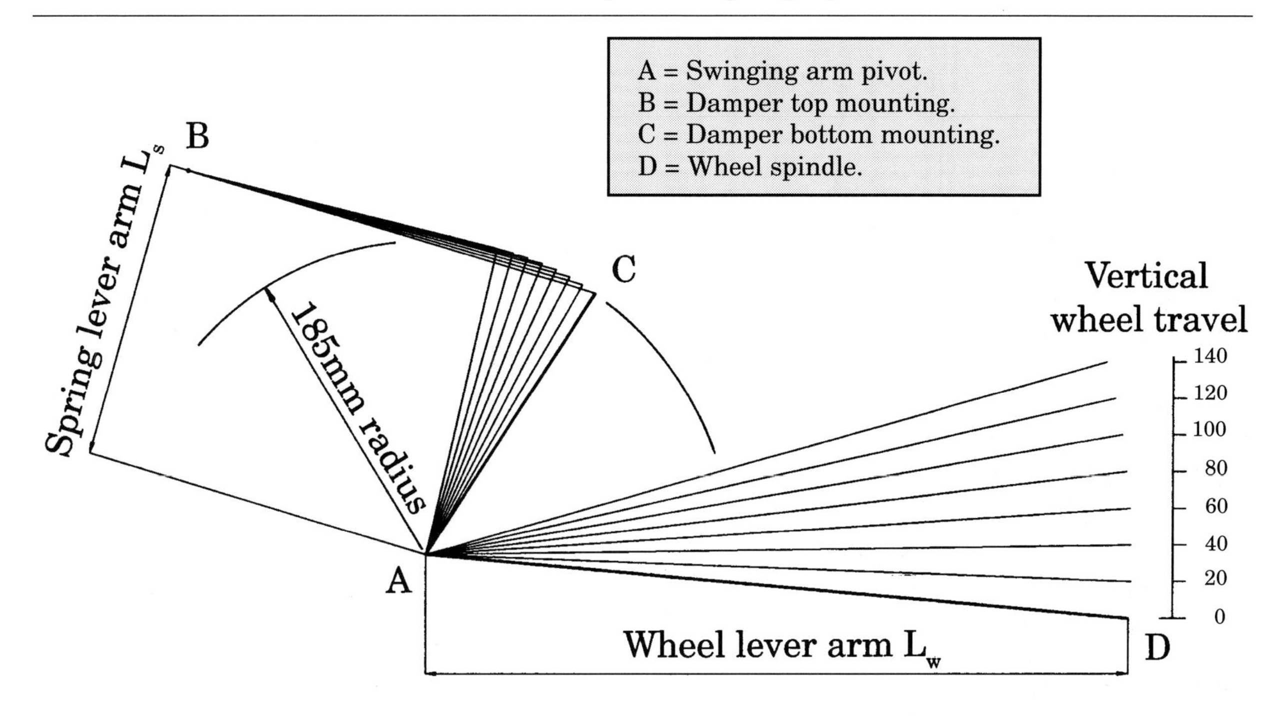

Above. Fig 5.51 *Drawing for the monoshock example showing how the swinging arm and damper move as the wheel travels through a vertical height of 140mm. Note that the variation in the spring's lever arm is relatively small and most of the change in wheel rate comes via the reducing lever arm of the wheel near to full travel.*

Below. Table 5.7 *Data taken from the full size version of the above drawing together with calculated values of wheel force vs wheel travel.*

Wheel travel	Wheel lever arm Lw	Spring lever arm Ls	$\frac{Ls}{Lw}$	Damper length BC	Spring compression	Spring force Fs = comp x 422lbf/in	Wheel force Fs x(Ls/Lw)
(mm)	(mm)	(mm)		(mm)	mm (ins)	(lbf)	(lbf)
0	398	177	0.445	240	0	0	0
20	400	179	0.448	231	9 (0.35)	149	67
40	400	181	0.453	221	19 (0.75)	316	144
60	398	182	0.457	213	27 (1.06)	449	205
80	397	183	0.461	203	37 (1.46)	615	283
100	394	184	0.467	195	45 (1.77)	748	349
120	390	185	0.474	185	55 (2.17)	914	433
140	386	185	0.479	174	66 (2.60)	1097	525

Linkage systems

Linkage systems pose some serious problems for the amateur.

- The variety of mechanisms and their dimensions is infinite.
- Envisaging new mechanisms can be satisfying but difficult.
- Analysing the behaviour of a mechanism can be extremely tedious if you do not have suitable Computer Aided Design facilities.
- The real aim of using linkages is to produce a specific type of rate change. Even if you actually know what this variation is, designing a linkage to produce it exactly is very difficult.

Firstly, unless you have some sort of sixth sense or little else to live for you will almost certainly finish up copying an existing linkage system. Several examples were given in Chapter 5.1. There is nothing wrong with this since I doubt if anything radically different from what has already been tried will yield any practical improvement.

Having made the decision to use a certain type of system you then have to sort out all the dimensions. Copying is of course a starting point but direct copies are rarely suitable. By far the best way to do things is to make a simple two dimensional working model out of thin plywood, aluminium or whatever. Use any sensible dimensions and then see what happens - Fig 5.52.

What you need to look at is the relationship between spring compression (damper travel) and vertical wheel travel. To do this, provide a small hole where the moving damper mounting(s) are and insert a sharp pencil or ball point pen so that the path traced by the mounting is drawn out as you move the model linkage. Mark off specific intervals of wheel movement and increase the pressure on the pencil at these points so that you finish up with a series of marks like those shown in Fig 5.52. From this the compression of the springs at each wheel position can be found and the n value calculated from (vertical wheel travel/ spring travel). With most linkages the spring articulation is small and you can use n^2 values based on movement alone. Use the initial value of n to estimate the required spring stiffness for a given wheel rate. Once the initial wheel rate has been found, the variation of wheel rate with travel can be calculated using the n^2 value at a number of linkage positions. Anything more exact is not a practical proposition. Data can be presented in any form you like and a number of options were given at the end of Chapter 5.2.

Having arrived at a working system of your choice you then need to experiment from there. It is impossible to say what constitutes an ideal rising rate profile and no amount of analysis will substitute for track testing. Remember that GP bikes only use very mildly progressive linkages, nothing radical like motocross. If you have decided to seek a change it will be necessary to go through the 'model' stage several times using minor variations to show what actually changes what in your configuration. There is no shortcut to this unless you want to get involved in some serious sums.

For those who prefer sums to metal bashing, the only methods of designing linkages to produce specific rate profiles I know of are the heuristic combinatorial techniques, though some of the advanced CAD animation packages can make a stab at it. If this is your scene read the following as a starting point. Personally, despite having a reasonable education, I think it is easier to make plywood models and drill a few more holes!

'Optimal design and dynamic simulation of a motorcycle with linkage suspension', E.Pennestri and A.Strozzieri, International Journal of Vehicle Design, Vol 9, No 3, 1988, pages 339 to 350.

'Heuristic Combinatorial Optimization in the Kinematic Design of Mechanisms', Parts 1 and 2. T.W.Lee and F.Freudenstein, Journal of Engineering for Industry, November 1976, pages 1277 to 1284.

Right. Fig 5.52 *A simple working model will prove far more useful for most people than trying to analyse the linkage mathematically. Use a suitable marker to plot the movement of wheel and spring from the model. This model, in plywood, has bushes to accept a pencil at most pivots. From these you can plot a graph as shown in the lower diagram and hence calculate the general variation in wheel rate using the methods already discussed.*

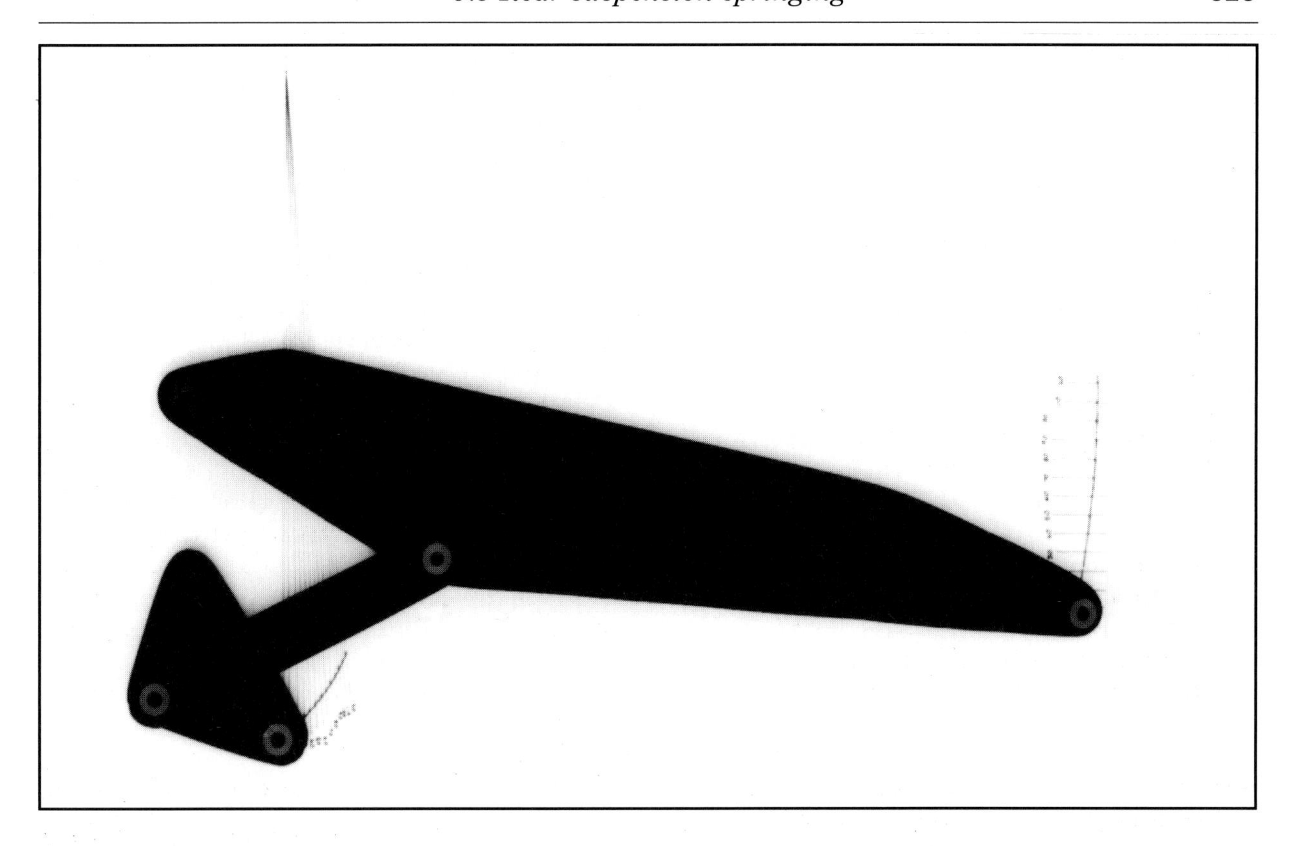

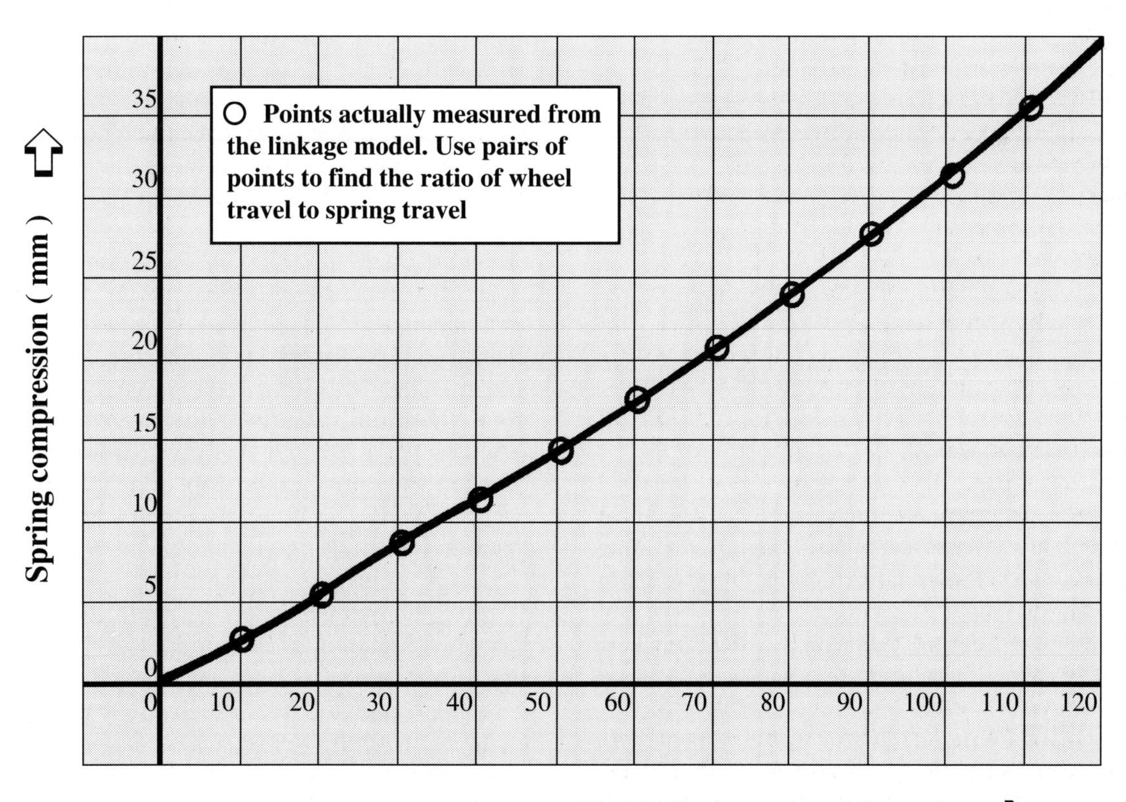
Points actually measured from the linkage model. Use pairs of points to find the ratio of wheel travel to spring travel
Spring compression (mm)
Vertical wheel travel (mm)
0
5
10
15
20
25
30
35
0
10
20
30
40
50
60
70
80
90
100
110
120

I appreciate that some readers will be expecting more on this subject but the linkages are such individual designs that I could do fifty examples and still not cover what you want. For my money the simplest method of making progress is,

- Make a model similar to the one shown.
- Find the initial value of n where n is (wheel travel/spring travel).
- Select a spring stiffness to give the initial wheel rate required using spring rate = n^2 x wheel rate.
- Determine the value of n throughout the range of travel and hence the variation in wheel rate. If it looks like what you imagine you need, make it!
- If tests show problems go through the obvious things first, eg if it bottoms too often try a touch more preload or a stiffer spring. If this compromises normal handling then experiment with the model to achieve a greater rise in rate. Go for a least 10% changes at first. You can always come back a bit once you know you are going in the right direction.
- If you can't make it work to your liking go and see a man who can.

Practical set-up

The methods outlined are primarily aimed at people making their own bikes. Once this is done, everyone faces the same problems of optimising the spring rates.

Remember how all this started. The key element was wheel rate and you effectively defined that from your chosen suspension set-up in terms of a natural frequency or the travel allocated to hollows combined with the unladen sag. If your assessment at this stage is ridiculous then everything else will be as well. Defining a suitable set-up requires a lot of experience and is, to a large extent, influenced by the rider's personal preference. I have outlined my own findings in previous chapters but you will need to establish what suits you. Everyone is different.

In practice the springing is much less sensitive to errors than damping and much easier to sort out. From the point of view of dealing with bumps there is no one stiffness that is correct since the response depends on the speed at which you hit the bumps. Furthermore, changes in unsprung mass will alter the requirements but no matter how much you look into these aspects you still finish up with the general idea of using suspension which is relatively soft, while trying to avoid bottoming out except under extreme circumstances.

If you decide to use a significantly rising rate then the initial stiffness can of course be lower and your set-up will reflect this. If the wheel rate is nominally constant, or only rises slightly, then you will be forced to increase the stiffness until it prevents bottoming. Once it does so, this is probably somewhere near the right value.

I have never read anything that suggests a general procedure for sorting this out so I can only describe my own findings. Firstly, I think it pays to try and sort out the fork springing first. I say this because when I first started racing on tarmac there were a number of occasions when I thought I had problems at the front end which subsequently turned out to be problems at the back end! Talking to people who knew more than I did indicated that this was not uncommon.

Once the front end is reasonable you can concentrate on the back using the same ideas as those discussed in the last chapter. Start with no preload and measure the laden sag. This should be too great. Gradually increase the preload until the laden sag is correct according to your specification. If you have made the bike yourself to a specific design then at this point the steering geometry and cg height should also be correct. Check them both to confirm this.

With the laden sag correct get off the bike and see what happens to the unladen sag. If it is too small you have had to use too much preload because the springs are too soft. If the unladen sag is excessive then the springs are too stiff and you have probably only needed a very small amount of preload to meet the laden specification. Whatever the case, don't abandon it because of small differences. You need to try things out first because who is to say that your proposed set-up data is the best for you. Experiment may lead you to alter completely the way you set your bikes up.

If you find that the steering geometry, ground clearance, or cg height is different from what you intended then you have to try various forms of correction. The simplest is to alter the preload or spring stiffness but this changes your suspension set up. Better alternatives include the use of longer or shorter suspension units as required and/or modifications to the suspension mountings. These changes also have implications for the chosen squat geometry. Moving the swinging arm pivot is not normally an option once the bike is finished unless suitable adjusters are included.

When building a special it pays to check all these things out before final painting and finishing. It is very easy to make mistakes that lead to a bike that is rather different from what you planned and it is easier to alter things while it is still bare metal. I always used to test my specials at an airfield before I painted or plated anything.

Suspension behaviour at the rear is further complicated by the transfer of power and the anti-squat/pro-squat characteristics of the swinging arm. This is particularly relevant to the problem of squat during hard acceleration. Most bikes do not have any adjustment of the swinging arm pivot so to change the squat at a given sprocket size you have to alter the length of the suspension units or change the mounting positions so that the inclination of the swinging arm is altered. This does not have quite the same effect and, as you have guessed, it will alter the steering geometry as well! This is an area where I don't think there are any short cuts and you need to experiment just to see what happens, even if you are satisfied with what you already have. The saving grace in all this is that you can experiment at the back end without going very fast. Maximum acceleration occurs at very low road speeds so, with a nominal amount of damping applied, a useful approach is as follows.

- Forget all about the squat geometry initially, just accept what you have created.

- Using your estimated spring stiffness, adjust the preload to give the correct laden sag. This is probably the most important thing. Too much preload will give a harsh ride and lots of jolting. It will also encourage dive at the front when braking. Try riding the bike on a bumpy stretch at various road speeds.

- Now try some full throttle starts and see what happens. If the rear end squat is excessive, experiment with a bit more preload but ideally look at stiffer springs or more rapidly rising rates until the behaviour is acceptable.

- Experiment with things that alter the degree of anti-squat. Major sprocket changes are an easy option, pivot adjustment if you have it. Changing suspension unit lengths or mountings will alter the steering geometry. Ignore this initially and concentrate on the behaviour of the suspension. You may well achieve a situation that does not bottom even with the original springs and might contemplate permanent changes so that these settings can be retained.

- The final decisions are individual ones. Soft suspension offers good compliance but allows the cg height and steering geometry to alter quite a lot. Some people use softer springs to smooth out the ride on bumpy tracks but, although the quality of ride is better, the pitch changes can be quite large.

Overall, most riders will easily find something suitable at this stage. Refinement for serious racing is a different aspect altogether and fine tuning is circuit specific in conjunction with the damping. You do not need any of my sums to get this far but sums will help you get somewhere near in the absence of vast experience. They can also save you money. Whether it is as good as it could be is difficult to decide but it is certainly easier to sort out the springing on paper than the damping. Since final decisions are influenced by the damping, that is the next topic to consider.

5.6 Damping and suspension problems

The need for damping

Anything that involves a weight being suspended by springs has inherent problems and motorcycles are no exception. The basic cause of these problems is the ability of the spring and weight to retain most of the energy that is put into them by virtue of external forces.

If the wheel is moved up relative to the sprung weight then the work done goes into the spring where it is stored as strain energy. As soon as it is free to do so, the spring extends again and in doing so it transfers energy to the sprung weight. This accelerates further above the wheel than it was originally. The weight then falls down again beyond its original position thus causing the spring to compress more than it does due to the sprung weight alone. The whole process then repeats itself with remarkable efficiency.

How long this type of behaviour can persist, and how violent it can become, is controlled by what we call damping. Damping is the dissipation of energy and all mechanisms have some damping, even when a purpose-built damper unit is not fitted. Typical sources are air resistance, internal friction in materials which are deforming and friction between the various moving surfaces, joints and bearings.

If there were no damping whatsoever (termed undamped and not a practical possibility) then any momentary force that puts energy into the spring will set the weight bouncing up and down indefinitely provided there are no constraints. The toys you see hanging from long thin springs in the shop window are almost like this but damping due to air resistance eventually stops them.

If the only damping associated with motorcycle suspension were that due to air resistance and material deformation, the result would be a disaster. Once disturbed, the bike would bounce up and down for some considerable time as shown below in Fig 5.53. Any large disturbance would send the

Fig 5.53 *With insufficient damping, any spring compression from the static position will set off a rise and fall of the bike that persists for some considerable time.*

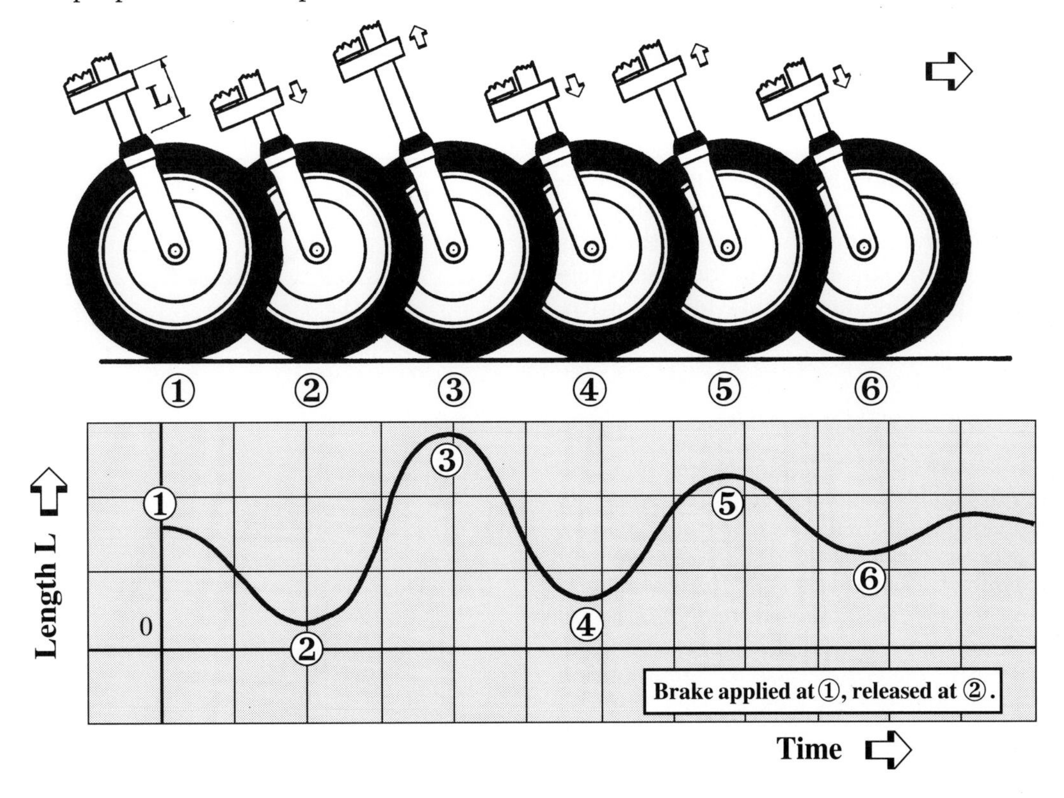

suspension crashing into the mechanical stops. Furthermore, if the bike receives even small force inputs at a rate that is close to the resonant frequency of the suspension, then the oscillation will rapidly build up to destructive proportions.

This is the fundamental reason why we have to have purpose-built dampers as part of the suspension. Their function is to limit the energy that is retained in the springs so that the behaviour of the bike is controlled. Without them, the motorcycle is virtually unrideable.

However, although we must have damping, it needs to be achieved in such a way that the resulting suspension characteristics are suitable for our purposes. This is where the real challenge lies and the design of modern dampers is highly sophisticated. They do far more than just meet the basic need of dissipating energy.

Whatever method we use, including more damping will extract more energy from the system and cause the oscillatory behaviour to die away more quickly. Fig 5.54 is rather idealised and relates to one specific type of damping but you can see the general idea.

With only a small amount of damping the oscillation is still very evident though it does die away. The suspension is underdamped. Increasing the damping eventually leads to the removal of all the oscillation and tendency to overshoot (which may not involve oscillation). If the suspension moves as quickly as possible without any overshoot in response to a sudden input, then the system is said to be critically damped.

Adding yet more damping slows up the movements considerably. The response is very sluggish and is said to be overdamped. This basic theory is all very well but the suspension of the motorcycle has two totally different weights to deal with.

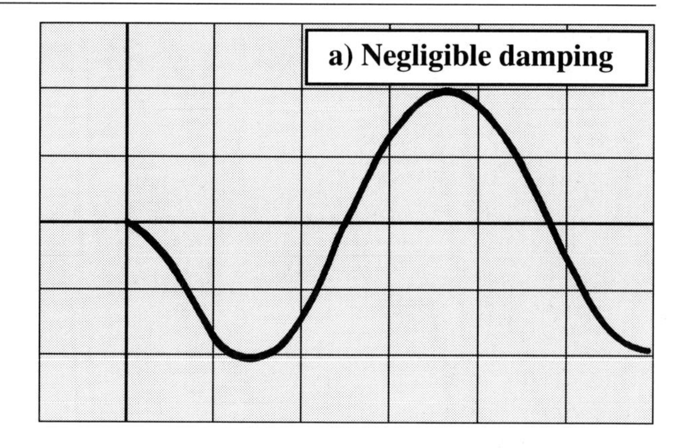

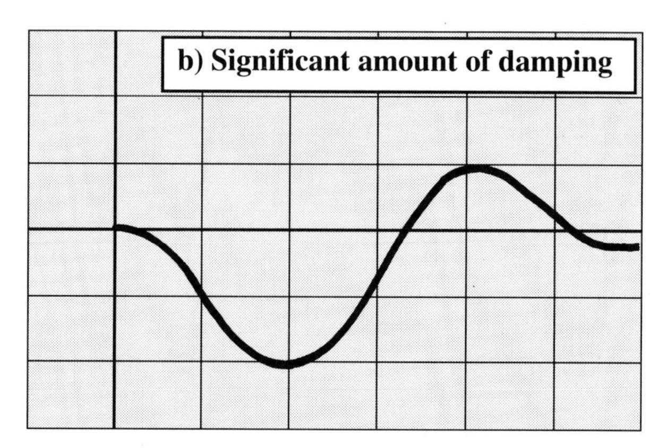

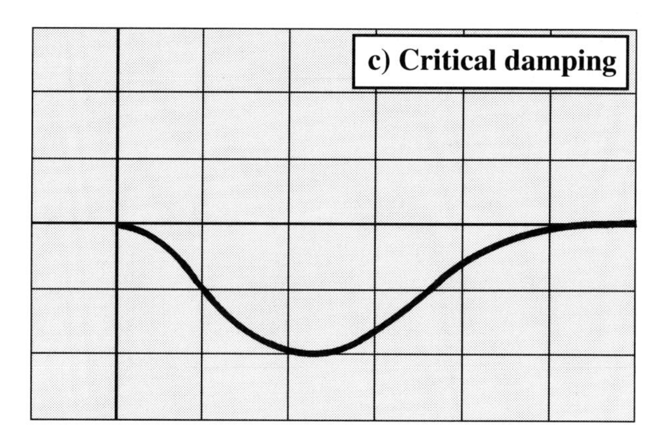

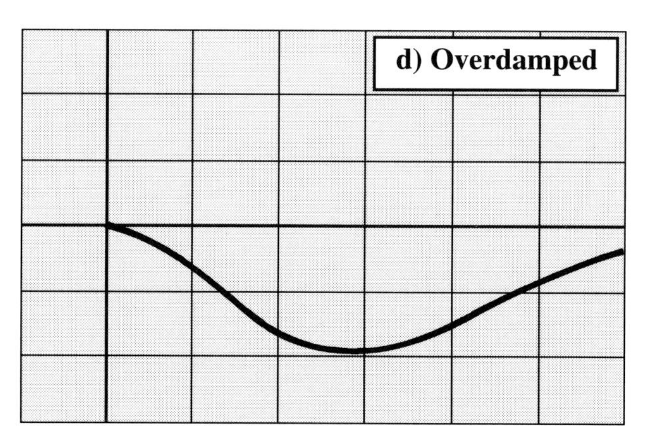

Fig 5.54 *General influence of damping. All graphs show sprung weight position vertically and time horizontally following braking. a) With negligible damping any small oscillations continue almost indefinitely. b) More damping makes the oscillations decay more quickly. c) At some point, the underdamped system becomes critically damped. There is just sufficient damping to prevent any overshoot. In d) still more damping is added and the movement becomes very sluggish or overdamped. Motorcycles have a problem because one damper has to control two different weights with different stiffness values involved.*

Sometimes the wheels sit still and the sprung weight moves up and down. Under different conditions, the sprung weight remains virtually still and the unsprung weight moves up and down. The conditions are very different so anything that controls both of them is going to be a compromise.

Damping systems

The obvious candidate to provide damping is friction. Friction converts the mechanical energy input into heat energy which can then be transferred to the atmosphere relatively easily. As such it fulfills the basic requirements of a damping system, but friction takes many forms.

When we talk about friction in general terms we usually mean Coulomb friction, the sort of friction you get when you try to push a heavy box across the floor. Damping pioneers soon realised this and many vintage bikes have friction dampers that are a sort of miniature disc brake as shown in Fig 5.55.

Although this form of damping certainly does the job we have described so far, it does it in such a way that the suspension behaviour is seriously impaired. The friction damper offers its highest resistance right at the very start of any movement. Until the resistance has been overcome, the damper fails to move and the suspension is effectively rigid. This is a serious problem. We are dealing with conditions where the suspension needs to be as free as possible so that it can comply with small road surface changes. Any tendency to stick like this will seriously impair the roadholding under many racing conditions.

Once the external forces overcome this initial 'sticking' the suspension will move. The weights are now gaining speed and this must be controlled or they will acquire large amounts of kinetic energy. Unfortunately, just as we are likely to need more damping, the friction damper responds with reduced resistance as shown in Fig 5.55. This 'stick-slip' type of response certainly provides damping but apart from that the behaviour is about as far removed from the ideal as you can get.

It is easy to forget that all the work put into the friction damper is converted to heat. If the heat is not transferred to the atmosphere effectively the damper gets excessively hot and its behaviour alters. Friction dampers can become very hot. Add to this the lack of repeatability, equal damping in both directions of movement, wear, etc and you can see that this method is not satisfactory even though it does provide the basic requirement of a damping system.

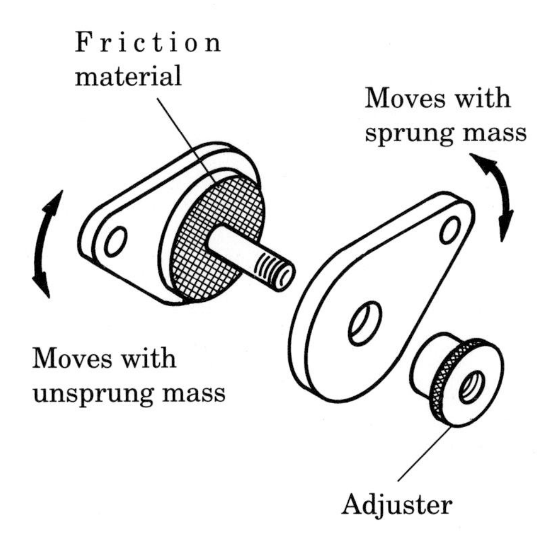

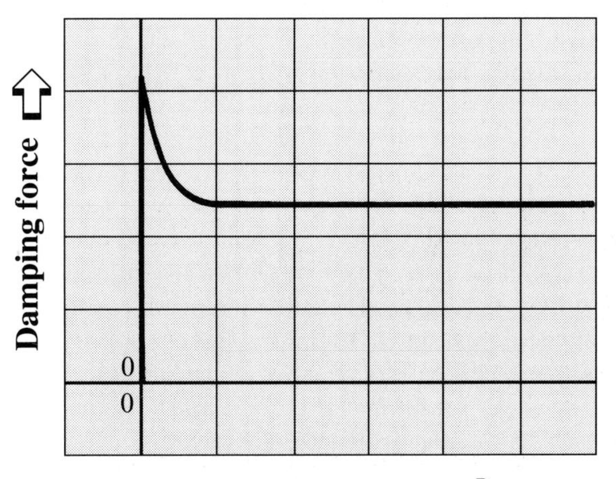

Fig 5.55 *Simple friction damper used on many vintage bikes and the characteristics produced. This system certainly provides damping but the results are far from consistent and are not at all suited to our needs.*

Modern dampers overcome most of these problems by using the excess energy to force oil through various forms of valve and orifice. It is easy to forget that the energy still has to be dissipated as heat, which is always difficult to do repeatably, but the basic characteristics are considerably better for our purposes than those offered by the friction damper. Designs vary greatly but the fundamental principles, and problems, are the same.

Damper movements

The force required to move a hydraulic damper is related to the speed at which the piston inside it is moving through the oil contained within the damper. I will obviously have a lot more to say about this later in the book but it is important to establish this idea very early on. The position of the damper is not generally important, assuming that the damper is working within its normal range. Some sophisticated dampers may utilise position for making alterations to the way the damper behaves but, fundamentally, the damper is a speed sensitive device (damper speed not road speed).

One end of the damper is fixed to the sprung weight and the other end is fixed to the unsprung weight. The damper then responds to the relative speed of the two ends as shown in Fig 5.56.

The two ends of the damper that are mounted on the bike can only do one of two things. They can move towards each other, ie the damper compresses, or they can move away from each other, ie the damper extends.

In most cases the movement is fairly obvious and the terminology reflects common conditions. During braking the forks compress. They have the same action when the bike first hits a bump so the terms compression damping and bump damping are both used for the force generated when the damper is getting shorter.

When the brakes are released the forks extend. The sprung weight rebounds so the terms rebound damping and extension damping have similar meaning, ie the force generated when the damper is getting longer. Similarly, the rear damper compresses on acceleration and extends during initial braking. However, these are not the only conditions that might exist. For example, at some point both the sprung weight and the unsprung weight could be moving upwards. This will happen when the bike leaves the ground. In situations like this the damping may be due to compression or extension. It all depends on the relative speed of the two ends of the damper. It is also perfectly feasible that no damping force is generated even though the bike is leaping about. This would occur if the sprung weight and unsprung weight are moving in the same direction at the same speed. It is most important to remember this basic idea. The damper will always respond to the relative speed of the sprung and unsprung weight that it is fixed to.

The greater the force required to operate the damper, the more energy you need to do it. This means that to extract a lot of energy from the suspension we would need a damper that generates quite high forces. This presents several conflicts. We need to remove the energy but we may not want the high forces.

In the early days, the general opinion was that all damping functions should be carried out during the rebound period and the compression movements should be undamped. The logic of this seems perfectly reasonable. Bumps in the road will normally compress the damper and if this offers a lot of resistance the wheel will not be able to move quickly enough to comply with the road surface.

Unfortunately, if you only apply damping during the rebound period, leaving the compression undamped as suggested, then the force you need to remove a certain amount of energy will be greater than that which is necessary if the damping is equally shared over both periods. This does of course assume that the compression and rebound activity is the same.

Modern dampers generally offer a compromise. Damping is provided during both compression and rebound but the bulk of the damping is done during rebound. The provision of compression

Right. Fig 5.56 *Racing dampers generally respond to both compression and rebound though the bulk of the energy dissipation is done during rebound. The force generated depends on the relative speed of the sprung and unsprung weights that the damper is attached to.*

damping turns out to be very necessary because when the compression damping is negligible the wheels or sprung weight actually move further than they need to. This stores yet more energy in the spring than is necessary and therefore demands even more damping to control it. Furthermore, the provision of compression damping provides the rider with a very sensitive 'feel' of the track surface. Racers tend to use this much more than road bike riders because, although it provides feel, it seriously impairs comfort. Nevertheless, all serious applications generally share out the damping function between both rebound and compression movements.

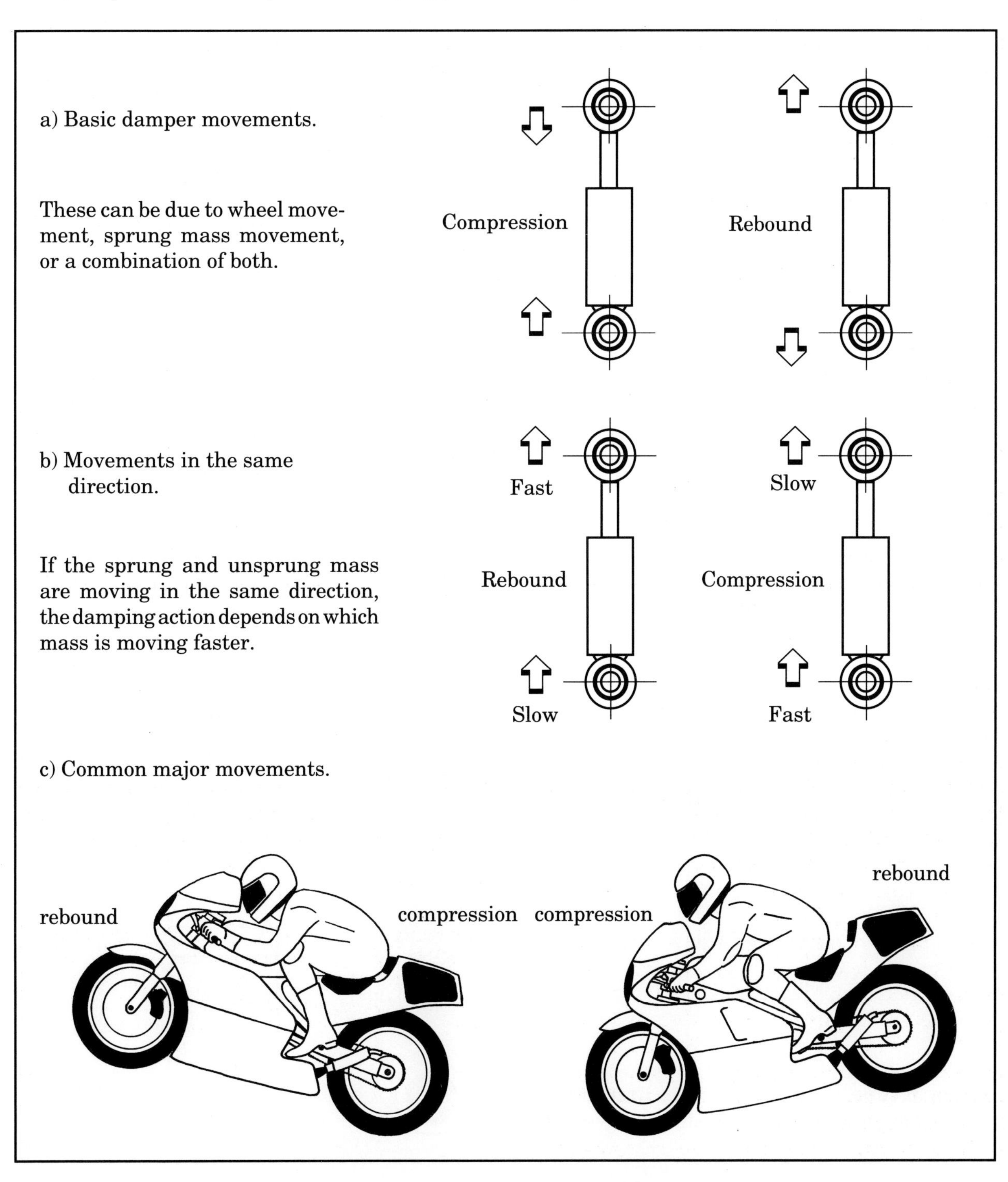

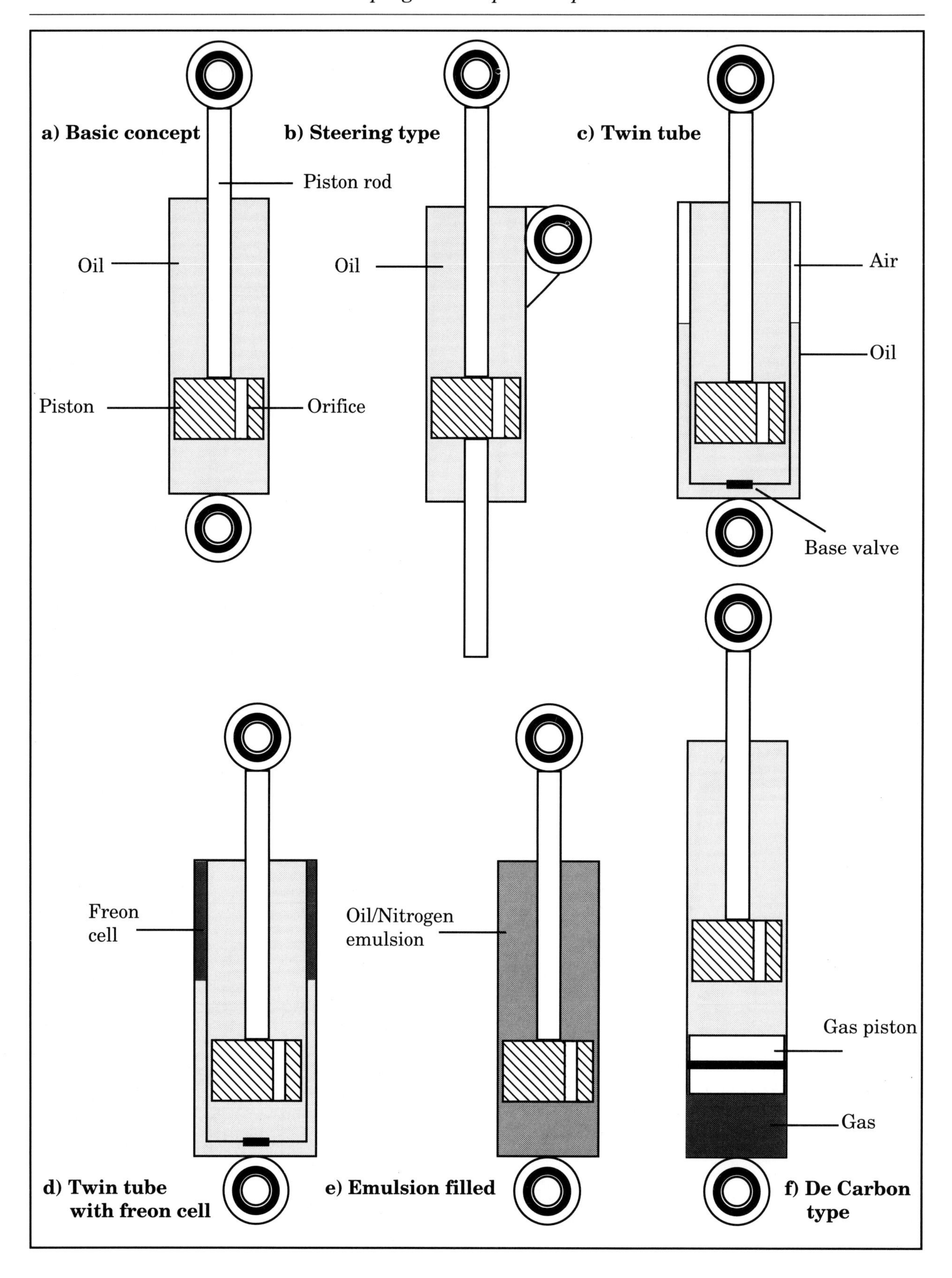
a) Basic concept
Piston rod
Oil
Piston
Orifice
b) Steering type
Oil
c) Twin tube
Air
Oil
Base valve
d) Twin tube with freon cell
Freon cell
e) Emulsion filled
Oil/Nitrogen emulsion
f) De Carbon type
Gas piston
Gas

Types of hydraulic damper

Fig 5.57 shows some of the basic stages in the evolution of modern dampers. The basic idea consists of a piston that has a hole in it moving through a suitable fluid, eg thin oil. Moving the piston requires a force so if the piston and body are moved by the suspension, some of the energy associated with the suspension activity is used to move the piston. If the hole in the piston is small and the oil is thick a lot of force is required. Thin oil and large holes need less force so the degree of damping can be controlled by hole size, oil viscosity, or both. As drawn, movements that extend the damper generate the same forces as those which compress it so this is a basic two-way damper.

This is simple in theory but there are many practical problems. The piston has to attach to the suspension via a piston rod and the piston rod inside the damper has a variable volume. It is zero when the damper is fully extended and a maximum when the damper is fully compressed. If the damper is completely filled with oil at full extension there is no space for the incoming piston rod!

If the damper is only partially filled with oil then the space is full of air. In use, the oil and air tend to mix and form a foam that has nothing like the viscous properties of the oil and no consistent characteristics whatsoever. This will cause the damping force to vary in an uncontrollable manner. Unless they are cartridge forks, most front forks are in this sort of situation. Problems can be minimised by keeping the damping mechanism well below the surface of the oil and using specially developed oils. In a sense the deficiencies of this system did us a lot of favours because they forced the oil manufacturers to produce damping oils with high resistance to foaming and many other desirable properties. More of this later.

The modern solution to this problem takes several forms. The simplest is to make the piston rod pass straight through the damper so that its volume inside the damper is constant - Fig 5.57b. This is used for steering dampers but is somewhat impractical for suspension units because of the overall length it implies.

Suspension dampers, including forks, have used several solutions. Most of the early efforts were directed at conventional rear dampers but modern forks incorporate many of the lessons learned.

The first adaptation was to use a twin tube system in which the gap between the tubes acted as a reservoir for the oil. Oil can transfer to and from the reservoir as required via suitable valves in the base of the damper so the free surface of the oil is totally removed from the main piston and its orifice/valve system - Fig 5.57c. This is the basic concept of cartridge forks.

Under arduous conditions this system can still cause problems though it is rear dampers which suffer most. There is still an air space and it is possible for air to find its way into the oil (called aeration) of the outer reservoir. If this coincides with a rebound action the air can then be drawn into the main working cylinder where it lowers the effective oil viscosity. As a result, the damping reduces or 'fades' due to the presence of the air.

There are three common solutions to this problem. The first is to contain the 'air' inside a plastic bag. In practice freon gas is used. This is sold under numerous trade names in the UK including Arcon, Iscon, and Genitron. The bag behaves like a balloon and all the remaining space is filled with oil - Fig 5.57d. Volume changes are accommodated by compressing the bag and this system was used by Girling for early twin shock units though I am told that assembly was a rather slow process as one can imagine.

The second solution, as shown in Fig 5.57e, is much more simple. The outer tube is discarded and the inner is filled completely, not with oil but with an oil/nitrogen emulsion at a pressure of about 10bar (146lbf/in^2). Although this is an emulsion, ie the gas and air are mixed, it is a much more consistent medium than oil with air added at random. The emulsion has a lower viscosity than oil but that is not a major problem if the valves/orifices are reduced in size to suit. The varying volume requirements associated with the piston rod movement are handled by compression of the gas bubbles. This system is very common and relatively inexpensive. Some excellent emulsion-type rear dampers are available for road bikes. Finally, in Fig 5.57f we have the most common

Left. Fig 5.57 *The basic principle of a hydraulic damper together with common solutions to the problem of piston rod displacement. a) Principle of a two-way damper. b) Steering type damper has a constant internal volume but is long. c) Twin tube damper can draw in air. d) Use of a sealed freon cell to replace the air. e) Damper filled with a controlled emulsion. f) De-Carbon type uses nitrogen gas at high pressure, separated from the oil by a movable piston.*

solution for competition dampers. This system is a more practical version of the freon cell. Instead of a plastic bag a lightweight piston is used to seal the oil from nitrogen gas at high pressure. The nitrogen can compress to accommodate volume changes as the piston rod enters or leaves the oil chamber. The actual damping mechanism is pure oil in a sealed chamber. There is no access for air if the seals are sound. This type of unit was originally called a De Carbon unit after the inventor but the idea is now universally adopted. In principle the design has to be rather long for a given stroke because of the gas and piston but this is easily overcome, either by using a separate gas/piston reservoir connected by a suitable hose, or by arranging the reservoir in a different way as shown in Fig 5.58.

Despite its elegance, even this type of construction has problems. The whole unit is pressurised by the gas load and when the damper is stationary the pressure on either side of the damping piston is equal but the areas are not since one side has the piston rod attached. The area on this side is less than that on the opposite side so a net force is produced that drives the unit to full extension, a form of internal preload if you like. The force produced depends on the gas pressure and the piston rod area. Reducing the rod size will reduce

Fig 5.58 *WP Suspension competition dampers using a gas chamber separated from the oil by a movable piston. A separate gas reservoir allows the main strut to be shorter.*

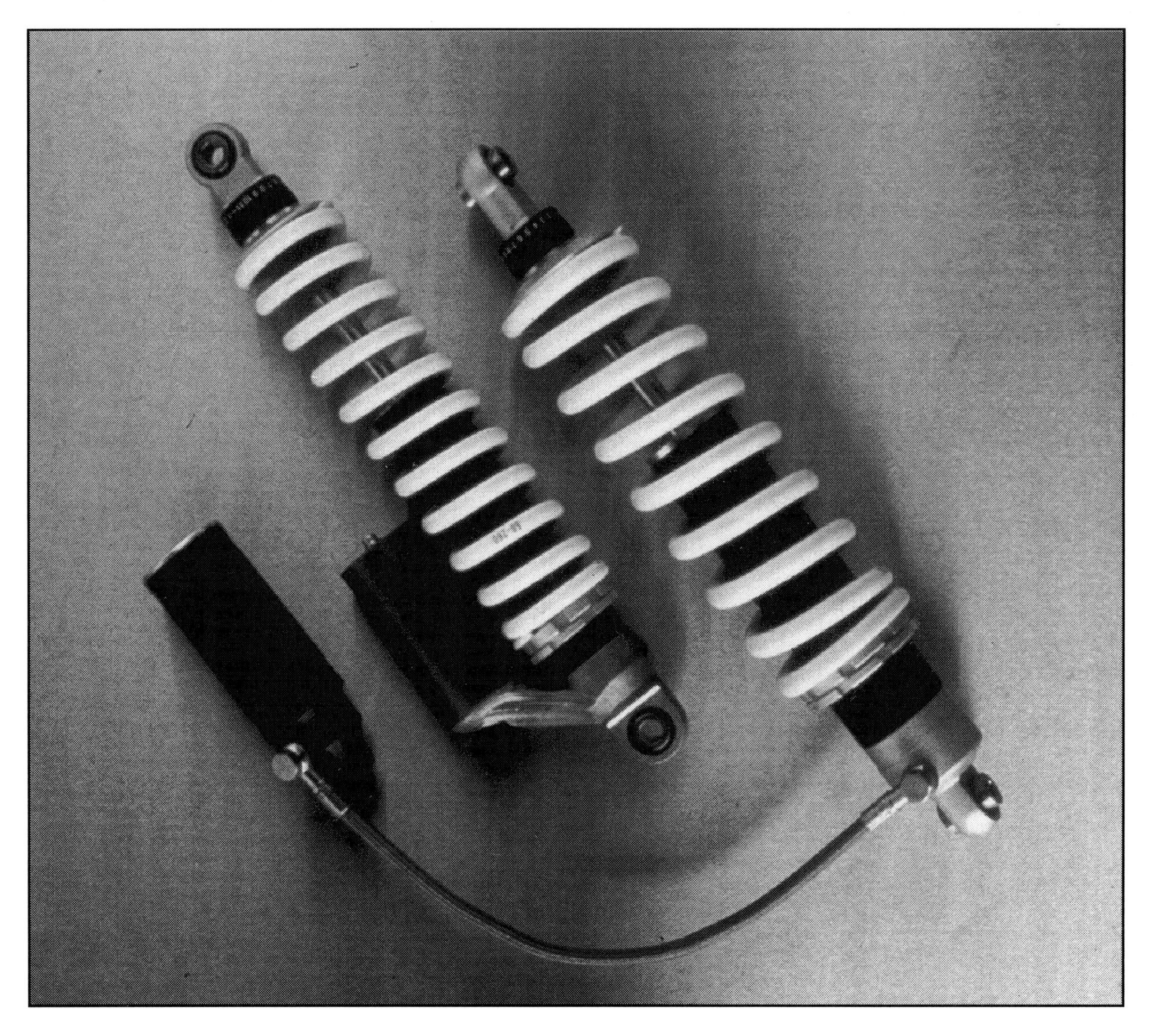

the force but it also weakens the rod and so quite high forces have to be tolerated. On WP Suspension race dampers the force is typically 153N-214N (34lbf-45lbf) but some makes of damper generate much higher forces.

Lowering the gas pressure too much in order to reduce the force is fraught with problems. A formal analysis of damper operation would show that the gas pressure plays a key role in preventing what is called cavitation. This is a fairly complicated situation in which the pressure of the oil can fall to zero during rapid piston movements leaving an 'air pocket' that is compressible. As a result of this the damping reduces, ie it fades. The gas pressure has to be high enough to prevent this at any level of applied force and pressures of around 14bar (203lbf/in^2) are typical. Bear this in mind if you are dabbling with the unfamiliar!

These then are the basic forms of construction and all stem from the problems of accommodating the moving piston rod while trying to maintain a constant damping medium.

Damper characteristics

Whatever the type of construction used, the main practical requirement is obtaining suitable damping characteristics that remain as consistent as possible during the course of a race. The ability to adjust them at will is a major bonus but I will discuss this aspect later.

On the face of it, damping can be achieved by no more than a hole in a piston. Anyone who has taken a quality damper apart will know that this is not the case and the performance of modern dampers is only achieved via great complexity.

The first important characteristic of any damper is that it cannot support any constant load, except when there is a force due to gas pressure and the external load is below this figure. In general, any constant load on the damper will cause it to change length as oil passes through the piston. This is important. The damper cannot function as a spring.

Once normal operational loads are applied and the damper is moving, the resistance it offers is determined by the speed of movement of the piston relative to the oil. A wide range of speeds is possible because the two ends of the damper may be moving in the same direction at different speeds or in opposite directions. For a constant size of orifice, the resistance offered by the damper rises rapidly as the speed is increased - Fig 5.59. This rise is so great that the basic idea is not really practical. The force rises as the square of the damper speed so any orifice size that provides a reasonable amount of damping to slow movements will virtually lock up the suspension when a large impact arrives and demands a very fast movement. This is actually demonstrating the prime function of the damper but we have to get acceptable results over a wide range of damper speeds. As we stand, the basic idea cannot meet our requirements under low speed and high speed conditions (damper speed not road speed). Also note that if the oil has to pass through the same hole during compression and rebound then the damping force will be the same in both directions.

Fig 5.59 *If a simple constant area orifice is used in the piston, the force required to move it is proportional to (speed)^2. This is not a practical proposition because a size that gives reasonable low speed damping offers far too much resistance at high speeds.*

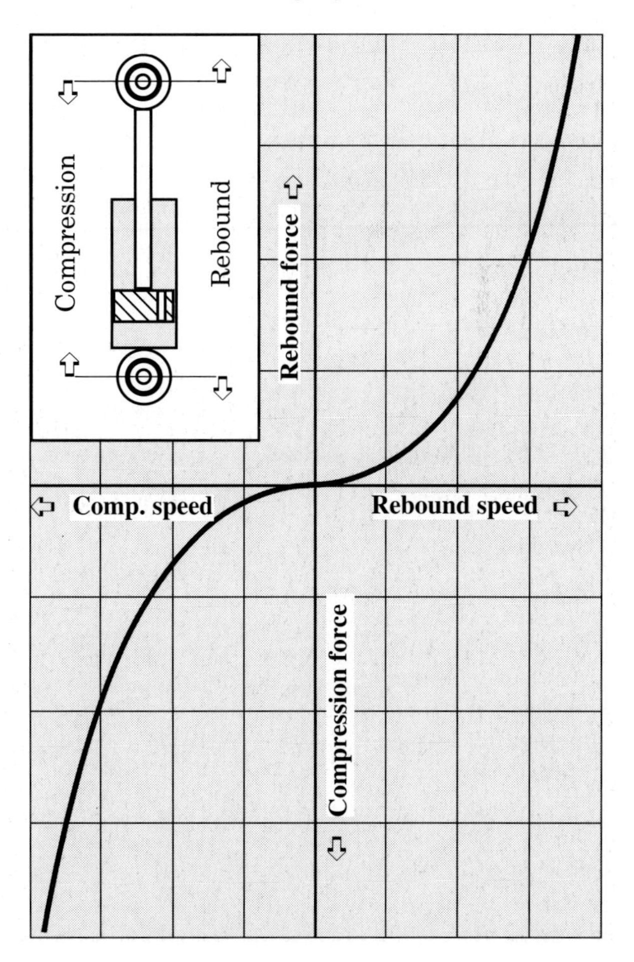

To obtain something more useful, the simple orifice has to be supplemented by a variety of valving arrangements. At the most basic level we could provide different holes for the oil to pass through on compression and rebound. By using different orifice sizes the forces generated can be varied independently. This requires one-way valves on each orifice but even so the original highly progressive characteristic is retained.

To change this, more complex valves are required. These vary greatly in detail. Most manufacturers use a system of spring steel shims but others use combinations of poppet valves and coil springs or needle valves. Irrespective of the details, the general idea is shown in Fig 5.60.

At low damper speeds the flow passes through some fixed orifice or 'bleed' circuit. As damper speeds increase the resistance gets higher as described previously but this time a point is reached where another, larger, orifice is opened via the oil pressure acting on a valve or shim. Once this happens the resistance is controlled by the size of this new orifice and the lift of the valve. There is of course a region of transition where the valve is just starting to open but, at high damper speeds, the valve lifts off fully and the damper's resistance, though still rising with speed, is much less dramatic. The precise force values and shape of the curve can be adjusted by altering orifice sizes, changing spring/shim stiffness and structure or varying the oil viscosity. These ideas are applied to both the compression and extension characteristics independently.

Fig 5.60 *To reduce the rapid rise of force with velocity the basic orifice is supplemented by a suitable valve or shim stack. Once oil pressure causes the valve to begin to open, the flow area is increased so the force does not rise as rapidly. Eventually, full flow is achieved and the force starts to rise more rapidly again but an acceptable compromise can now be reached.*

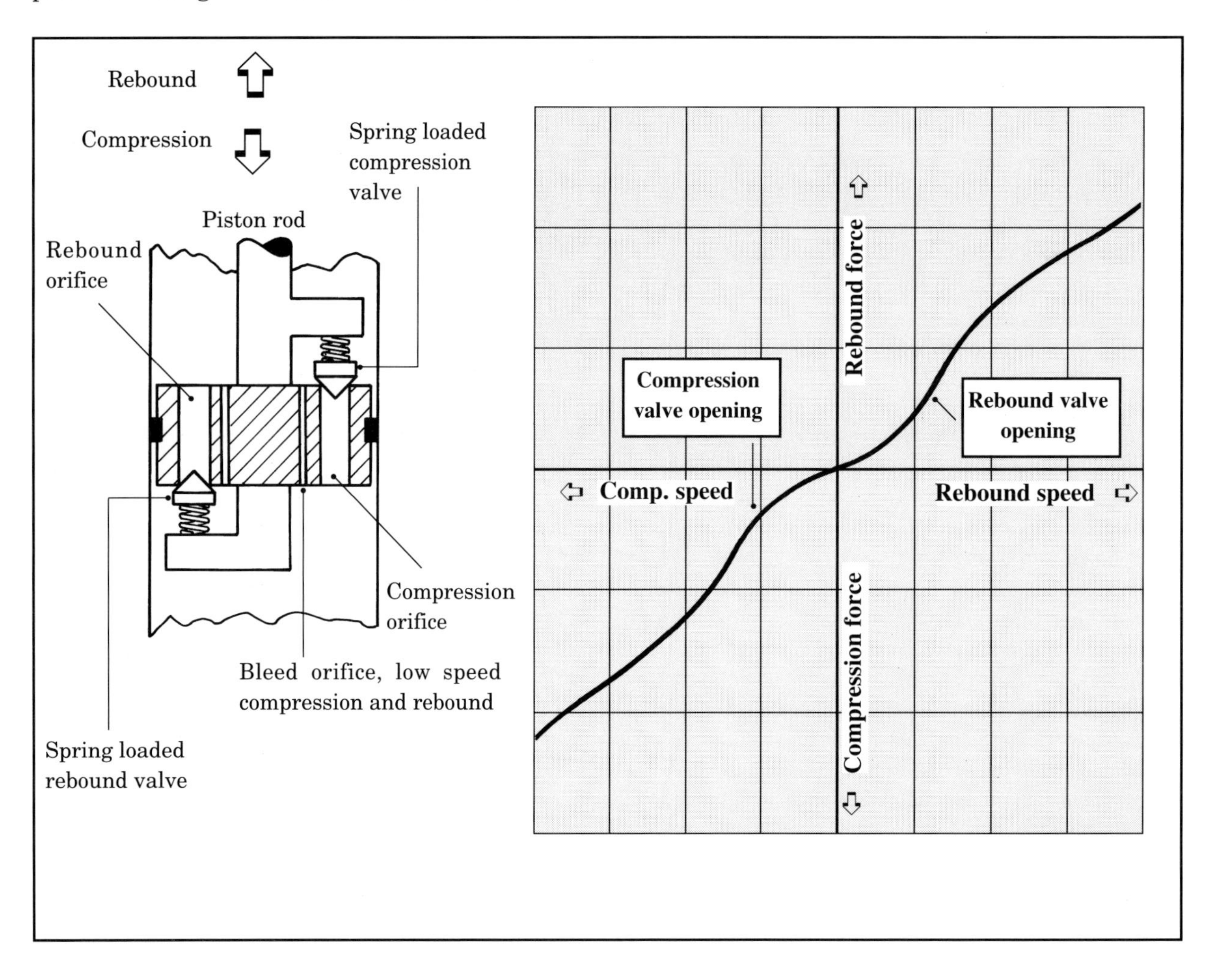

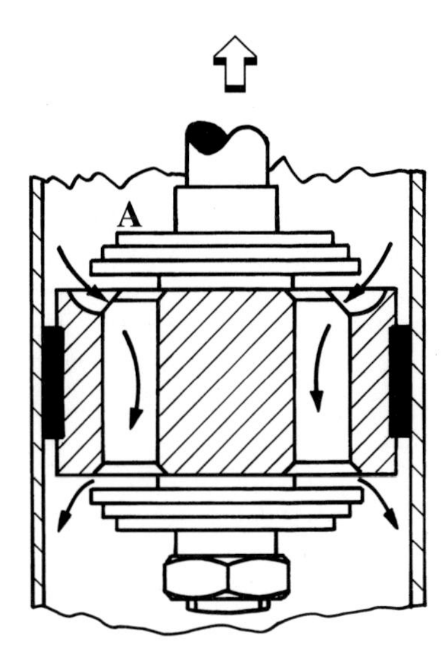

Low speed rebound

Oil flows past the compression shimstack at A and there is sufficient clearance at entry not to restrict the flow. On reaching the rebound shimstack, the low speed flow is controlled by the design of the shimstack near the piston. At higher speeds, the increased oil pressure deflects the stack as shown (right) and the flow is determined by the way the stack deflects at different speeds.

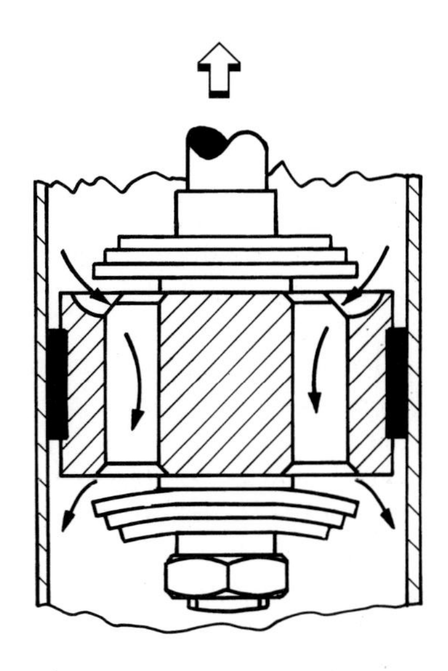

High speed rebound

Fig 5.61 *Principle of a simple shim stack. Only rebound control is shown. Compression control using the upper shim stack is via another set of holes in the piston. The number of variables is vast and includes shim diameters, thickness, number, preload on the stack, orifice shape etc. The stack may be further supplemented by other valves of different types.*

The most common arrangement is basically a shim stack like that shown in Fig 5.61. The original fixed orifice or bleed circuit is provided by using some shims that do not cover the holes in the piston completely. This allows the oil to get past without having to lift the shim. By modifying the design of the shim stack, it is possible to alter the shape of the damping force vs speed characteristic. In modern racing dampers, the shim stack design can be very complex in order to produce the desired characteristics which vary considerably according to the application.

Adjustment

Adjustment is basically divided into internal and external. The range of internal adjustment possible is virtually unlimited because you can completely revalve the damper. However, you cannot defy the basic laws of fluid flow that apply! The manufacturer will have provided the characteristics they consider best for the application concerned. These vary enormously and even a small change in the progression of rear linkages can demand totally different characteristics for both compression and rebound damping. I was fairly certain that it is impossible to determine theoretically what the best characteristic will be. It has to be done by experiment. I put this to a number of different damper manufacturers, including those working with cars as well as motorcycles, and everyone agreed that the only reliable method is to experiment. Obviously with a large test program a lot of data emerges and guidelines for something new are thus established. Even so, most manufacturers admitted to getting it wrong sometimes when building a new damper and there are clearly no shortcuts to success.

Once a reasonable characteristic has been established, it is then necessary to provide a range of external adjustment. On racing dampers the adjustment has to cover both the rebound and compression. Although it does most of the work, it is usually adequate to provide the rebound damping with a general adjustment that influences the whole range of damping speeds, ie it increases or decreases the force throughout the range of damper speeds. Compression damping requires a lot more finesse and quality damping systems will often provide independent adjustment of both the low speed and high speed compression characteristics. This applies to both forks and rear dampers.

Adjustment can be achieved in various ways. One way is to use a coil spring to compress the shim stack and then allow the preload on this spring to be adjusted externally. Less preload allows the shims to deflect more easily and lowers the damping force.

The other common method of adjustment is needle valves and these are sometimes used instead of shim stacks for the entire rebound function. It is also possible to make the needle valve self-compensating for temperature effects. To do this, the needle sits in a chamber that contains a suitable liquid - Fig 5.62. When the oil temperature rises it becomes thinner and produces less damping force. However, the liquid behind the needle will expand when the temperature rises and this moves the needle out slightly from its mounting thus reducing the oil flow area. With less flow area, the thinner oil can be made to produce the same damping force so the user does not detect the fade that would occur without this rather neat feature.

Fig 5.62 *Needle valves are commonly used for damper adjustment. By placing the needle in a chamber filled with suitable liquid, compensation for the loss of oil viscosity with temperature can be achieved.*

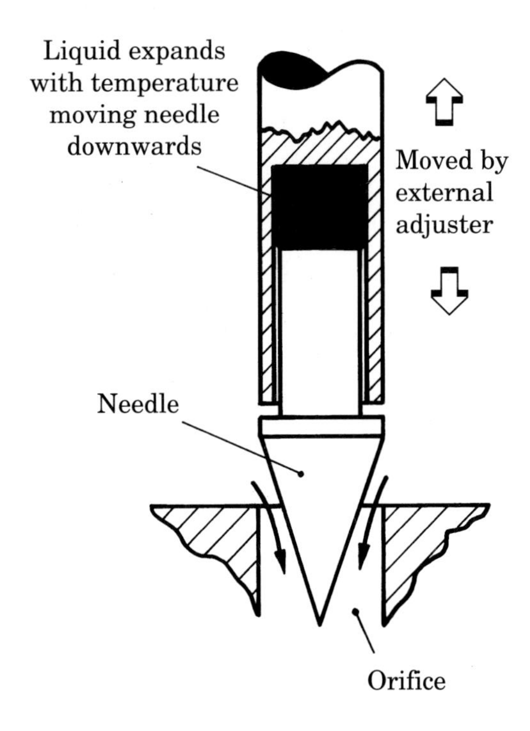

It is pointless describing particular dampers in detail because they are all different but the illustrations that follow should help to convey the general ideas.

Fig 5.63 shows the internals of two road bike dampers. The one on the left uses a coil spring (top of picture) to preload the rebound shim stack and this is controlled by the adjuster at the bottom. More load makes the shims harder to deflect and increases the damping. Compression adjustment is done by a valve in the reservoir (not shown).

The other example, on the right, has a fixed preload on the rebound shim stack and employs a needle valve within the piston to achieve adjustment. Again, the actual adjuster is the black 'dial' at the bottom of the unit.

Fig 5.64 is a section through one type of rear damper manufactured by WP Suspension. In this example both the compression and rebound damping are controlled by shim stacks. These are designed to achieve the mean level of damping required in each direction. External adjustment is provided in two different ways. The rebound adjuster, at the top of the damper, uses the technique of preloading the shims with a spring. On compression, the oil faces an additional restriction in the form of an adjustable orifice at the base of the reservoir. The combination of this and the compression shims determine the level of damping present. Overleaf, in Fig 5.65, there is an exploded view of another type of WP Suspension rear damper showing various options. There are several different mountings, some with adjustment for damper length and hence ride height. A hydraulic spring preload adjuster is also shown.

Both rebound and compression damping are nominally set by shim stacks and there is provision for up to 52 shims in total! In this example the rebound adjustment uses a needle valve operated by the adjuster at the top of the unit. Compression adjustment is again by a valve in the base of the oil reservoir. This is a 1996 race damper.

Finally, Fig 5.66 overleaf shows a pair of high quality race forks. With these, both fork legs are equipped with the same degree of 'nominal' compression and rebound damping but the adjustment is then split between the two legs. The left

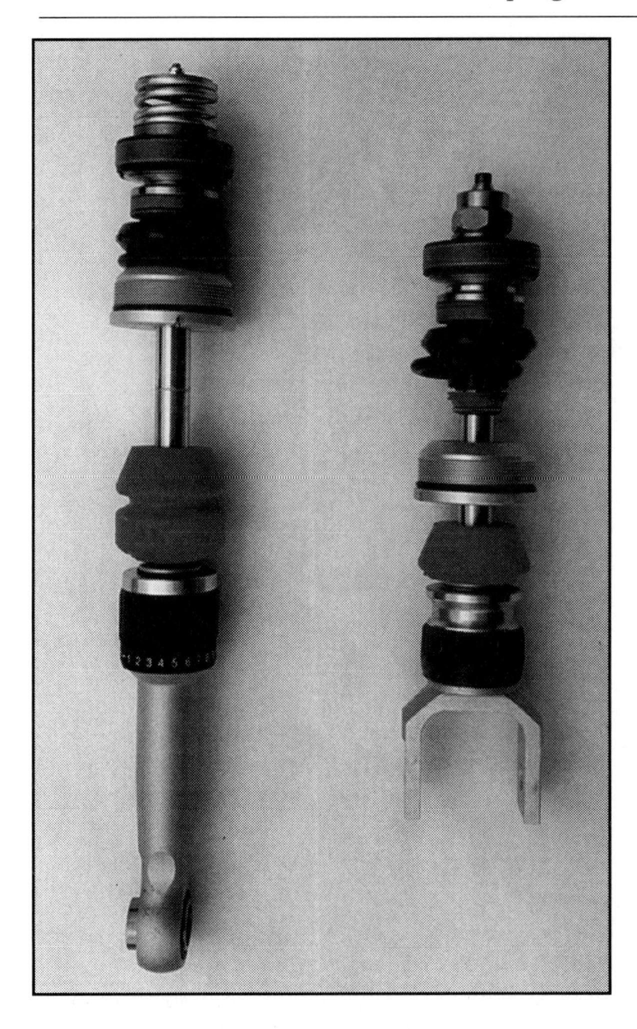

Above. Fig 5.63 *Examples of different damper internals described in the text.*

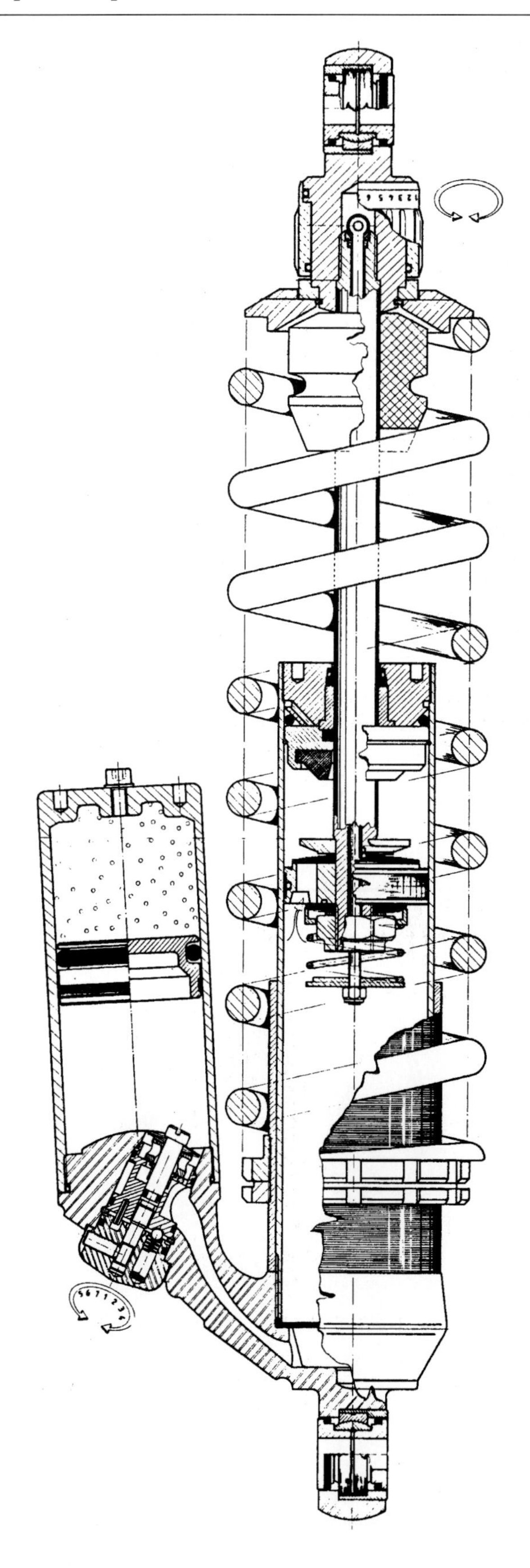

Right. Fig 5.64 *Cross-section showing the construction of a rear damper manufactured by WP Suspension.*

fork leg contains the rebound adjustment and the right leg has the compression adjustment.

Rebound adjustment affects the whole range of damper speeds and is achieved via the adjuster on the top of the left fork leg. It operates a needle valve, part No 205 (left leg). For compression, there is a general adjuster on top of the right hand fork leg which again operates a needle valve in the piston. However, in this case there is also an independent low-speed adjuster at the base of the leg. If you are currently racing on a pair of classic-type forks, the complexity of these 'state-of-the-art' equivalents may come as something of a shock. The ones shown are for the 1996 Honda NSR250.

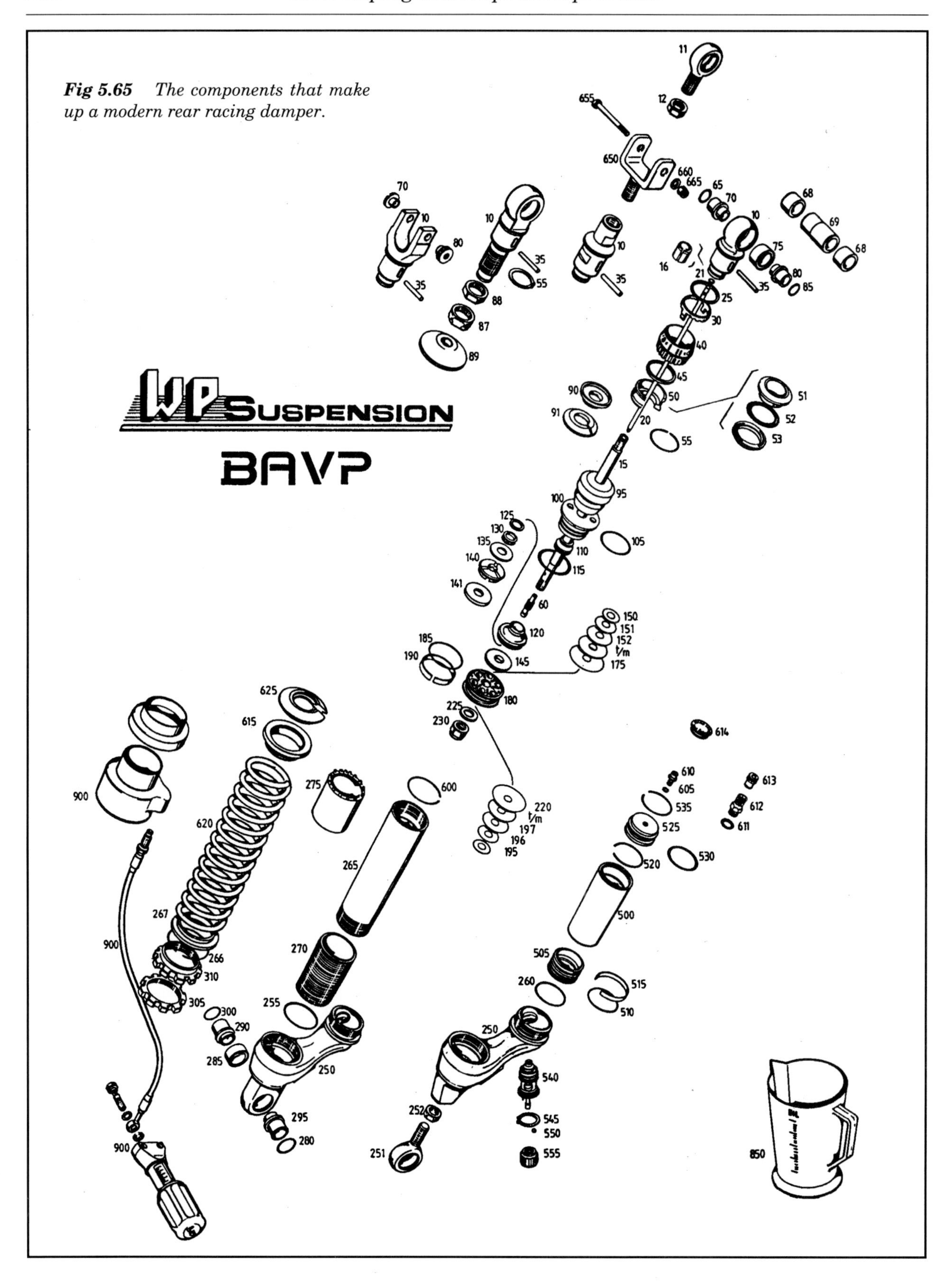

Fig 5.65 *The components that make up a modern rear racing damper.*

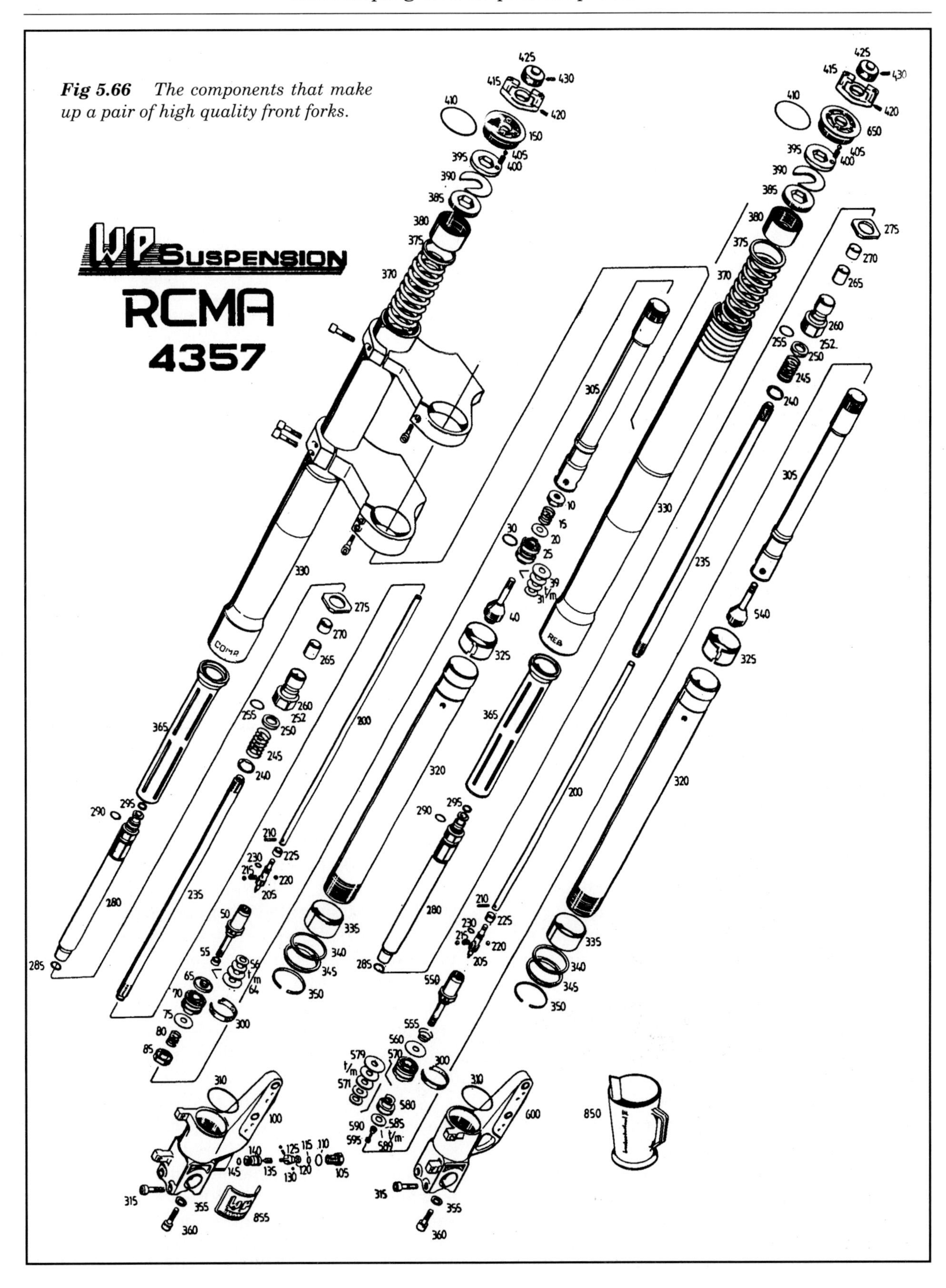

Fig 5.66 *The components that make up a pair of high quality front forks.*

Damper speed and leverage

The whole business of damper characteristics is fairly complex but some level of understanding can be very useful. The most important factor is damper speed because everything stems from this. As far as I know, the motorcycle industry does not have a standard scale of vertical wheel speeds but the European car industry does. Since they drive on similar surfaces the list in Table 5.8 is informative.

Basically, unless you hit kerbs or potholes the list suggests that vertical wheel speeds encountered on tarmac are normally less than about 600mm/s (23.64in/s). Off-road conditions are totally different. The car industry tests at 1.5m/s (4.9ft/s) routinely, Landrovers prove at speeds up to 4m/s (13.1ft/s) and WP can test their off-road forks at up to 5m/s (16.4ft/s). All these higher speeds are strictly related to impact and safety so they are not usually relevant to normal tarmac racetrack activity.

The automotive data turns out to be a useful guide. To find out exactly what does happen on the race track you need access to reliable data logging and I am deeply indebted to the WP Suspension GP engineers for allowing me to use their data.

The example in Fig 5.67 is taken from a top 250cc factory bike. Believe me, this is about as high up the ladder as you can go in terms of both bike and rider. The data covers entry to the first corner at Jerez in 1996. Three traces are shown in the top diagram. These come directly from sensors mounted on the bike and indicate road speed, rear damper movement and front fork movement. The lower trace gives acceleration and this is a calculated value based on the road speed data. Other data including exhaust temperatures, engine speed etc appear in the middle box. These values are specific to the cursor position chosen (vertical dotted line).

There is so much to learn from this data that it is easy to get carried away. I will therefore stick to the task in hand and will discuss the other aspects later on. The most obvious feature as far as damper speed is concerned is the fork dive on braking which begins at time = 360.5sec and is indicated as portion A to B on the diagram. The movement is such that, during the fastest period of compression, the forks compress by about 46mm in a time period of 0.167sec giving an average damper speed of about 46mm/0.167s = 275mm/s. Taking exact

Term used	Test speed (mm/s)	Conditions
Leak	52	General control, cornering, braking on smooth roads
Leak	131	
Blow off	262	Very heavy braking, control on unmade roads up to the severity of cobbled streets
Blow off	393	
Blow off	524	
Orifice	1000	Limiting for safety, applies to potholes, impacts, accidents etc
Orifice	1500	

Table 5.8 *Damper speeds used by the car industry for dampers mounted close to the moving wheel.*

values from the data shows that it is actually 278mm/s. This is typical of a rapid sprung mass movement. GP engineers tell me that 300mm/s is about the maximum they see on braking but unsprung mass movements as the bike negotiates bumps can reach 600mm/s, measured along the forks. High-sides can throw up figures around 800mm/s but this is hardly normal activity. There are many fork actions that take place at lower speeds but it is important to note that the speed variations can apply to any length of travel, ie movements can be at similar speeds even though one movement is just a few millimetres while another uses up most of the travel. Do not confuse the speed and the travel.

As far as the rear damper is concerned there are several differences. The main one is the fact that the damper is operated via the suspension linkage and therefore it does not move at wheel speed in this example. The damper would move at wheel speed, or close to it, if it were mounted directly at the wheel spindle. On this particular bike the leverage ratio of the linkage is nominally 2:1 and so the damper moves at only half the wheel speed. This is illustrated overleaf in Fig 5.68.

Accepting this, we find that on heavy braking the rear damper extends by about 21.7mm in 0.167s giving an average speed of 130mm/s. This is equivalent to that which would be generated by a wheel speed of about 260mm/s, ie it is of the same order as the dive rate at the front end. Again, the speed we see is largely due to the sprung mass

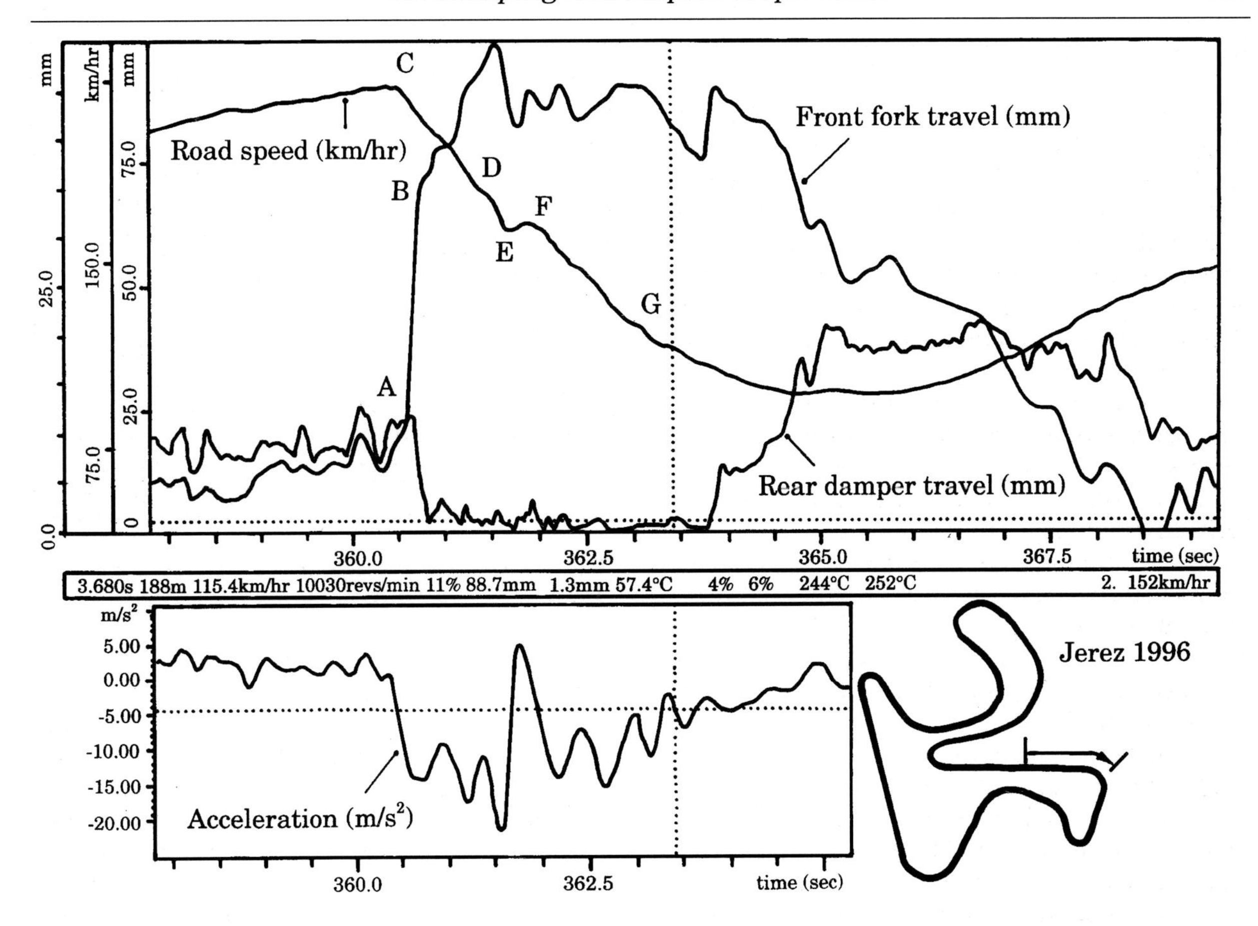

Fig 5.67 *Data logger output from a 1996 250cc GP bike as it enters turn one at Jerez during the 1996 Grand Prix. The top three traces show fork travel, rear damper travel and road speed. Note that the point 0.0 on the movement scales corresponds to the fully topped-out suspension positions. The details relating to damper speeds are discussed in the text (source WP Suspension).*

lifting at the rear rather than the wheel moving. In general, the rear wheel activity (unsprung mass) shows a lot of high speed movements that are of short duration and travel. These reflect the search for grip on a surface that is not perfectly smooth and, as with the front end, wheel movements up to 600mm/s cover most situations.

Note that during the braking period, the rear suspension is topped-out for some of the time. This is not desirable and GP engineers are extremely skilful at preventing it, however this rider is actually over-braking at one point. Referring to the road speed graph and the corresponding acceleration data at the bottom, the rider initially slows down at an average rate of about 12m/s^2 (1.22g), period C to D. This is absolutely on the limit, even with GP tyres, skill and suspension. During the period D to E he over-brakes slightly. Figures approaching 2g are not sustainable and the rider has to correct this in the period E to F. He does so in the space of a mere 250ms and, not only that, but his correction is so good that he continues his braking at around 11m/s^2 (1.12g) as if nothing has happened (period F to G). There is not much you can say about this level of skill. Few people have it and I am certainly not one of them!

Sidetracking slightly, do not be deceived by the high peak deceleration figures. There are several factors that can be misleading. Firstly, the speed sensor is mounted on the front wheel and this tends to squirm about under heavy braking. It is not a perfect reflection of the bike's forward motion but it is more than adequate in most cases.

Secondly, the values are calculated by differentiating the speed data. This process is inherently 'noisy', ie it accentuates very small changes. Obviously many of the sudden changes are important but the mean level of deceleration during this frantic braking effort is somewhere around 1.1g. Some of the claims you read in the press make you think that these bikes slow down at a constant 2g or more but they do not.

From this discussion it is clear that a range of 0-600mm/s (0-23.6in/s) represents the common order of wheel speeds and twin shocks can operate close to these figures. Monoshock dampers operate at much lower speeds determined by the leverage but up to 350mm/s (13.8in/s) covers most of them. If you hit a solid object the figures are somewhat greater!

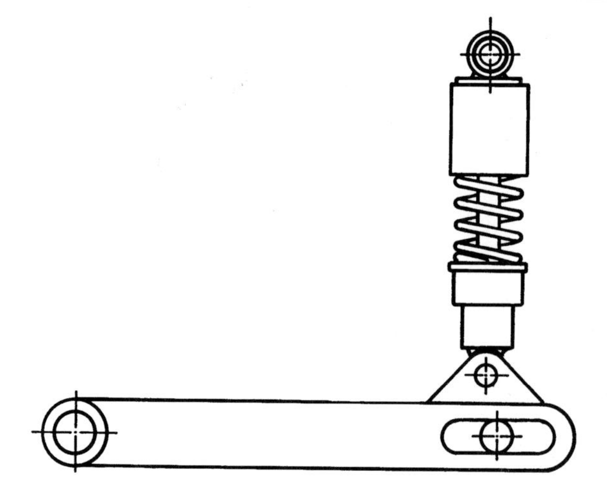

a) High damper speed.

Damping force

Now that we have some idea of the speed at which the wheel moves, it is possible to look at the damping forces again. From a practical point of view the most important point to come out of the discussion so far is that a change in leverage at the rear will demand very different damping characteristics so it is no good fitting any old damper, even if it is a good one in terms of consistency etc. Manufacturers are of course aware of this and I have noticed that in recent years certain manufacturers have provided a much greater range of adjustment. This has gone down particularly well with the amateur constructor who may not be aware of how influential the leverage can be at the rear. He buys a damper that, when fitted with a suitable spring, has a range of adjustment that is so wide that he is almost guaranteed to find something suitable. This is particularly true of certain makes of after-market road bike dampers.

GP engineers do not work like this. The damping characteristic is so finely tuned to the bike, tyres, rider and circuit that adjustment is more a

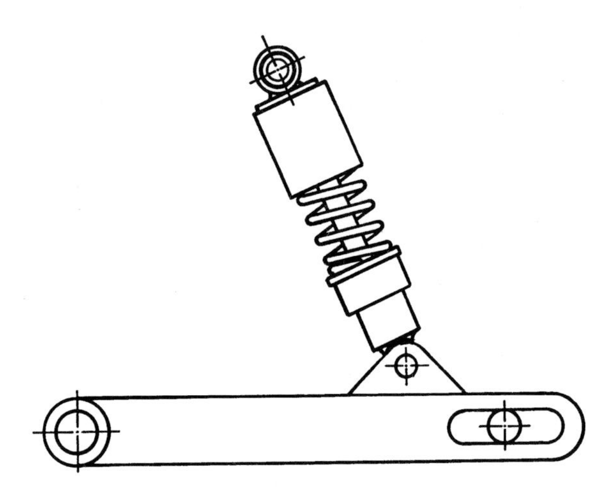

b) Slightly lower damper speeds.

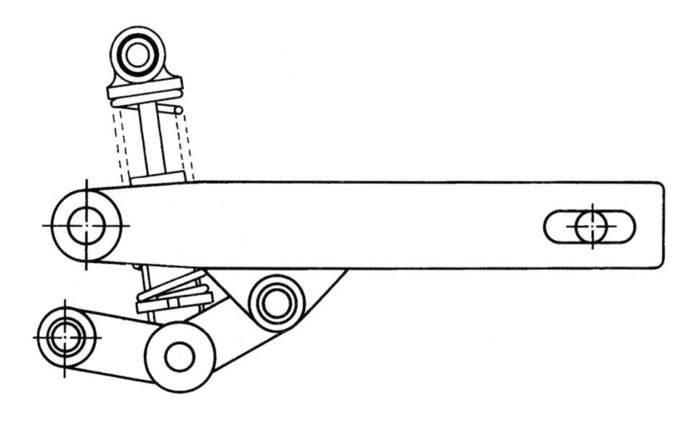

c) Much lower damper speeds.

Fig 5.68 *When leverage is involved, the damper moves a shorter distance than the wheel in the same time. It therefore has a lower average speed which is determined by the leverage ratio. Since the leverage varies with travel, so does the speed ratio. a) This damper moves at roughly wheel speed. b) This damper moves more slowly, about 78% of wheel speed for small movements. c) This damper moves at considerably less than wheel speed.*

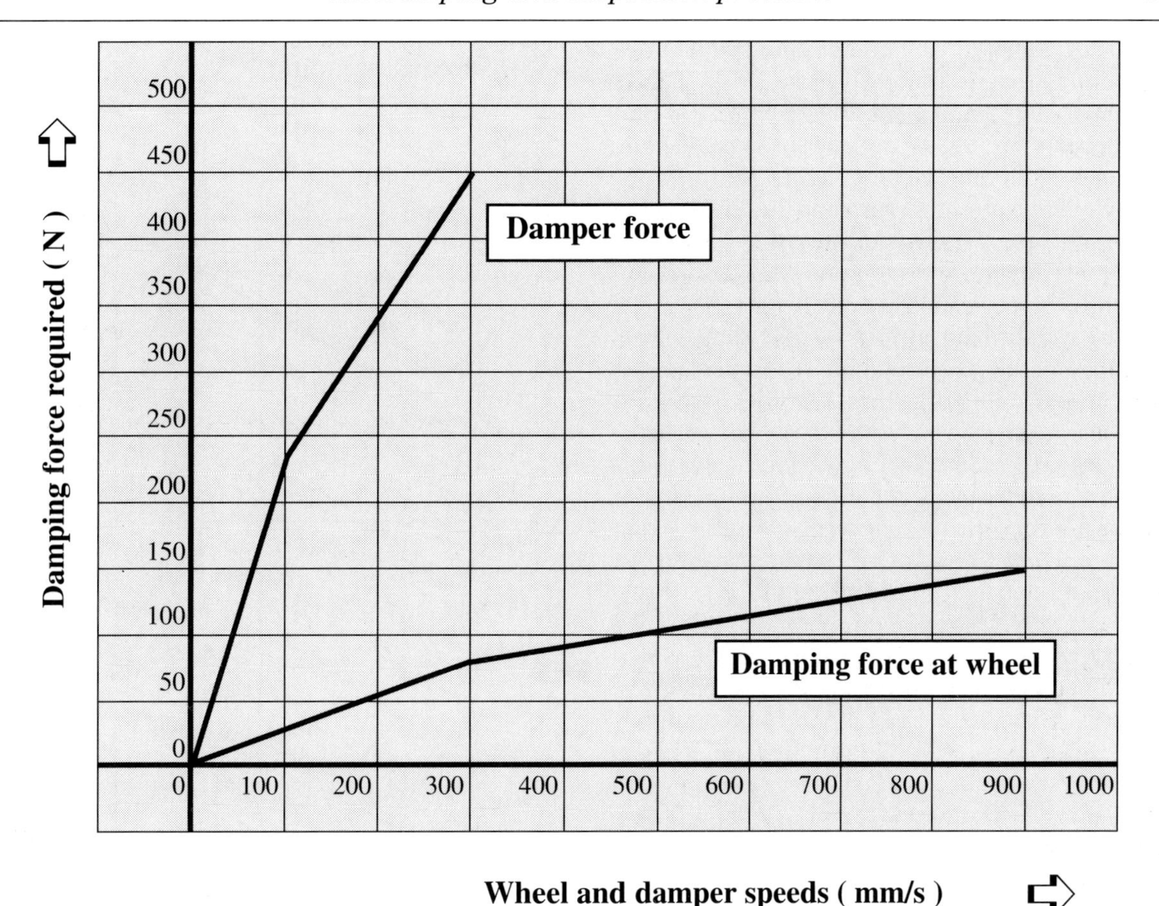

Fig 5.69 *Required damping characteristic at the wheel and the necessary damper characteristic to provide it when the value of (wheel travel / damper travel) is nominally 3.*

case of a nudge here and there rather than a global change of 50%! The following example illustrates how influential the leverage can be. Everything is simplified but it still makes the point.

Example. In Fig 5.69 there is a graph showing the total rebound damping force proposed at a wheel vs speed of wheel movement. A straight-line approximation is used. The value of (wheel travel/damper travel) = n = 3 and it is assumed that this is also the value of n relating the forces (see Chapter 5.5). At 900mm/s the force required at the wheel is 150N. To achieve this the damper force will have to be 3 x 150N = 450N.

However, the damper speed will be less than that of the wheel, specifically 900/3 = 300mm/s so the damper must provide 450N at this speed. This gives a point on the graph for the actual damper. Similarly, the wheel requires a force of 80N at 300mm/s so the damper must produce an actual force of 240N (3 x 80) at100mm/s (300/3). Joining the points gives the final graph for the damper itself. If there were two dampers each must provide half of this. If the system has a significant rate rise, ie the value of n reduces, then the damper will need to produce an increase in force (at all speeds) that is proportional to the change in leverage.

Note what has happened. The force required has gone up n times but the damping coefficient, which is the force per unit velocity, has gone up by a factor of 9, ie n^2. For example, during the low speed region, the wheel force changes by 80N over a speed of 300mm/s. The damping coefficient is therefore 0.267Ns/mm, ie 80N divided by 300mm/s. To provide this, the damper force changes by 240N over 100mm/s which gives a damping coefficient of 2.4Ns/mm, ie 9 times the value at the wheel. Similarly, for the higher speed region the damping coefficient at the wheel is (150N - 80N) / (900mm/s - 300mm/s) = 0.117Ns/mm. To provide this the damper needs to produce a coefficient value of 1.05Ns/mm which is again n^2 times the wheel figure. Note however that the area under the wheel force graph and the area under the damper force graph are the same. The significance of this will be explained shortly.

These simplified examples clearly show why a change of leverage requires quite dramatic changes to the actual damper's characteristics. To some extent we can short-circuit the complexity of looking at leverage in detail and say that the damping has to be matched to the springs, though this is just one aspect. The more leverage the wheel has over the springs, the stiffer the springs have to be and dampers need similar treatment.

For example, Hagon's supply twin-shock units in three grades of damper as standard. Soft dampers are normal for springs up to 16kgf/cm, medium damping covers 18-20kgf/cm and hard damping goes with springs stiffer than 23kgf/cm. This is ideal for everyday use but fast racers tend to want damping to suit their style of riding and preferred bike set-up.

Damping technology has now reached art form proportions as well as the obvious technical requirements. Fast riders rely heavily on the low-speed compression damping for feedback on what the tyres and road surface are doing. This can cause problems because on the one hand the rider is extremely sensitive to the shape of the force vs speed curves while on the other the basic requirements of energy extraction have to be met.

Fig 5.70 illustrates some of the problems. In the first diagram the relationship between force and speed is a straight line. This is called viscous damping. It is difficult to obtain this exact relationship from normal valving but some of the data I have for current GP bikes shows damping characteristics that are extremely close to this.

The steeper the graph the greater the damping coefficient, ie the change in force produced by a given change in damper speed. A steeper graph implies heavier damping and the area under the graph represents the power of the damper, ie the rate at which it is absorbing energy from the suspension. The most basic requirement is that the total area provided, ie compression + rebound, gives sufficient damping to control the suspension. To do this with viscous damping you have to

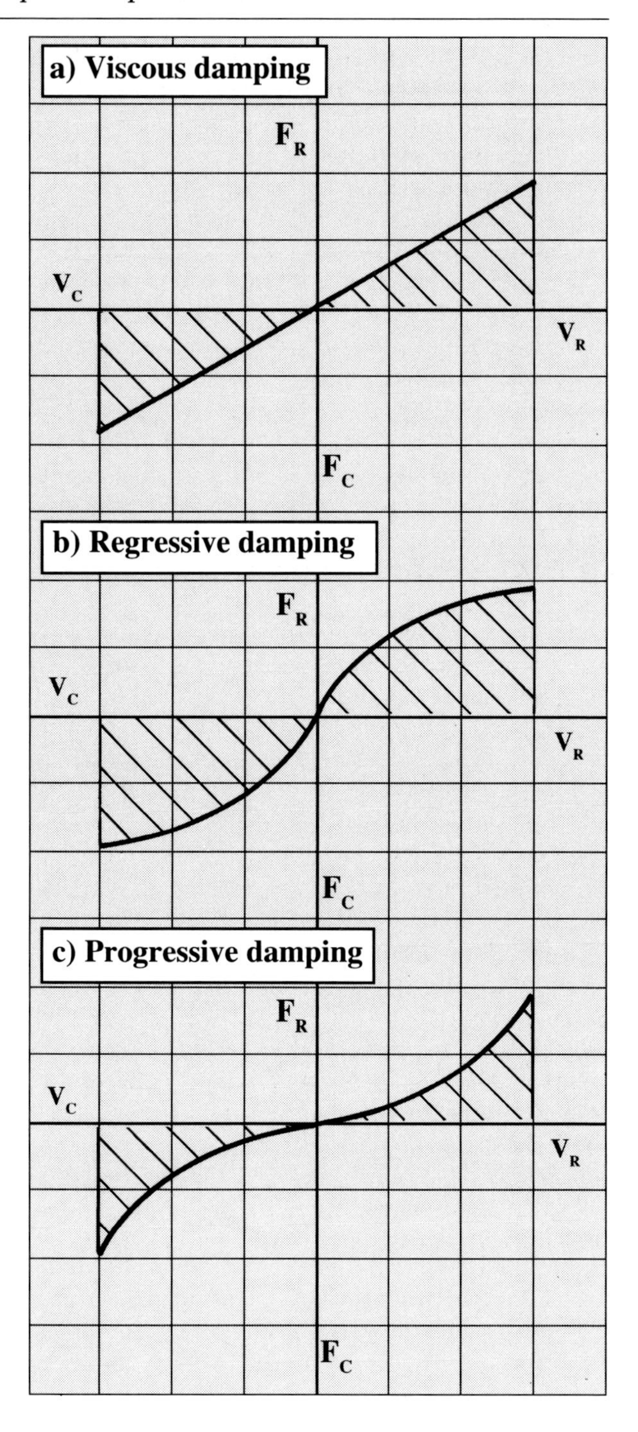

Fig 5.70 *a) With viscous damping the force is proportional to damper speed. The area under the graph represents the power of the damper. b) A regressive characteristic provides a high level of overall damping for a given level of damping force. c) With a progressive damper characteristic the area, and hence mean level of damping, is low, even though the force is the same at high damper speeds in this example.*

increase the slope of the graph, possibly developing too much force at high damper speeds. The alternative is to depart from the true viscous form by introducing more low speed damping and pushing the graphs up the force axes.

Heavily applied, this creates diagram b), and the damping now has a regressive characteristic. This produces a lot of area under the graph so the mean level of damping is relatively high for the forces produced. Low speed damping is increased and the rider will be very aware of this.

Finally, in diagram c) the damping is highly progressive, not as dramatic as a simple orifice but still rather radical. In this case everything is different. For the same peak high-speed damping force, the area, and hence the mean level of damping, is much lower, as are the low-speed damping forces that the rider feels. If the required area is achieved, the high-speed damping presents extremely high forces and will respond by locking up the movement when it is rapid.

There are thus three requirements. One is to ensure that the total area under the compression and rebound curves is about right. This will give a suitable mean level of damping. The second requirement is to achieve this using a curve shape that suits the conditions and rider preference. Finally, the total damping must be shared out between the compression and rebound periods. Any general adjustments should alter the area by raising or lowering the whole characteristic rather than altering the shape of the graph.

Sums will not get you very far in this unless you are a specialist manufacturer. The only part worth calculating is the mean level of damping required and this is not simple. The calculation will provide a viscous damping coefficient with identical compression and rebound graphs. From this the total area can be obtained.

In practice the compression and rebound areas will be different with compression usually less than half that found on rebound. This is not a problem. If you reduce the area under the compression graph you have to increase that under the rebound graph to retain the mean level of damping required.

How the total area needs to be shared out depends on your springing philosophy. You can go for stiff springs and lots of rebound damping or soft springs with extra compression damping and no amount of theory will decide this. Most people do use more rebound area than compression but racers generally like the compression area fairly high, particularly in the low speed region, so that they can use softer springs. Once the balance between the areas is decided, the shape of the graph can be fine tuned by experiment. In general, the rebound period has to do most of the work and therefore needs a regressive characteristic to obtain sufficient area - Fig 5.71. If the linkage progression is very mild, the compression damping can offer a very slightly progressive characteristic, not much removed from viscous damping.

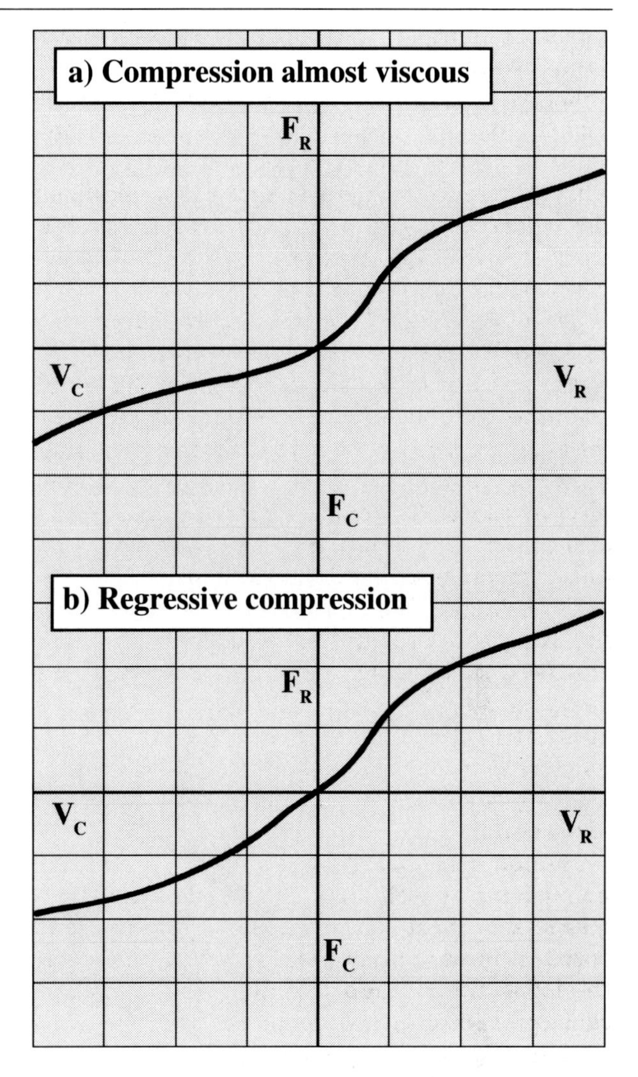

Fig 5.71 *a) If the suspension leverage is constant or only mildly progressive the compression damping curves can be very flat though the rebound needs to be regressive to get the area. b) If the linkage is relatively progressive, the compression damping will usually need to be regressive to obtain sufficient total area.*

However, if the linkage is more progressive then it may not be possible to achieve the mean level of damping necessary and the compression damping then has to offer a form of regressive characteristic as well, otherwise the rebound damping will have to be excessive. There is clearly an infinite number of possibilities and most of the work is going to be in the hands of the manufacturer and other suspension specialists.

Mean level of damping

The mean level of damping required in any application is determined by what the damping has to control in terms of mass and stiffness. With a simple mass on the end of a spring there is a resonance problem at a frequency determined by $\sqrt{(\text{stiffness/mass})}$ and the damping required to control this is related to $\sqrt{(\text{mass x stiffness})}$. The system can be critically damped with viscous damping if the damping coefficient is equal to $2\sqrt{(\text{mass x stiffness})}$.

Suspension is considerably more complicated because there are at least two resonant conditions to deal with, three if there is a lot of friction.

Firstly, there is the sprung weight which moves up and down on the suspension springs. Chapter 5.2 discussed this and a resonant frequency of around 1.5-3Hz is normal. The damper speeds this will generate if the wheels are not moving up and down is easy to calculate using,

Peak speed = 3.142fa

where f = the frequency in Hz
a = the total peak to peak movement

If the movement is in millimetres the speed is in mm/s. If the movement is in inches the speed is in in/s. So, if the sprung weight is moving up and down 30mm at say 2Hz, the peak damper speed will be,

Peak speed (mm/s) = 3.142 x 2 x 30

= 189mm/s

Thus in this case the damper needs to control a resonance at about 2Hz while moving at speeds up to a peak of 189mm/s. To do this with viscous damping it needs a damping coefficient that is proportional to $\sqrt{\text{sprung mass x wheel rate}}$. Unfortunately, this is not the only requirement. The unsprung mass has a much higher resonant frequency. We are now dealing with small movements that the wheels make against a stiffness that is equal to (tyre stiffness + spring stiffness). This occurs as the tyre walls deflect and the tread tries to stick to the road. If it is not controlled, the tyres will chatter and hop about. Ultimately, adhesion is lost.

Fig 5.72 shows this happening on a GP bike, mid-corner at Assen. In this specific case the problem was cured by altering the tyre pressures slightly, thus changing the tyre stiffness.

Although these movements are very small, they occur at high frequency, say 12-15Hz. This means that small movements still generate high damper speeds. For example, if the frequency is 14Hz and the total movement is 4mm then, using the formula just given, the peak damper speed is,

Peak speed (mm/s) = 3.142 x 14 x 4

= 176mm/s

This is almost identical to the peak damper speed imposed in the sprung mass example. We clearly have a problem. The damper produces a force that relates to its speed of movement. The speed of movement produced by the sprung mass and the unsprung mass can be almost identical but the masses and stiffnesses involved are very different. They therefore need different levels of damping to control them! I do not think it is worthwhile dredging through all the arithmetic that relates to this but one important conclusion, apart from the obvious one that says everything is a compromise, is that the unsprung weight must be as light as possible.

Right. Fig 5.72 *This data logger output, taken from a 250cc GP bike at Assen in 1996, clearly shows both tyres chattering in mid-corner. The effect is to move the rider off line. We know it is the tyres, even though the trace records total damper movements, because the sprung weight is too great to change position at these frequencies (data source WP Suspension GP engineers).*

If the unsprung weight is relatively high, then in combination with the high stiffness imposed by the tyres it will need a lot of damping to control it. The level of damping required will be excessive as far as the sprung weight is concerned. Put another way, if the damping is set up for ride quality, the roadholding will be poor. Racers need the road holding and have to tolerate the jolting that the necessary damping imposes. If you want it all to get a lot better, reduce the value of unsprung weight compared to sprung weight. Yes, this has been said before, but for different reasons.

It is possible that there is a third resonance problem for the damper to deal with but this is unlikely to be the case on a racing bike. If the suspension is full of friction then the whole bike is effectively rigid for small loads. The total weight, ie sprung and unsprung, is then sitting on top of the tyres where it acts as a simple mass/spring system having yet another set of characteristics. If the damper has to meet these as well, you don't have a chance of making it work correctly. There has probably been sufficient discussion of this in recent times to inform all concerned. Not much was said in the old days and many riders used to provide most of their damping via really tight swinging arm bushes! If you still do this you will never obtain the quality of suspension that is possible with modern dampers no matter how much you spend on them.

Given all these conflicting requirements it is easy to see why damping is probably the most frequently adjusted quantity on the bike. Some of the conflicts are obvious. Heavy braking causes the sprung weight to dive rapidly and it can generate damper speeds, in the forks, of about 240-300mm/s. If we get this damped as we would like, the wheel chattering up and down a few millimetres will generate similar speeds and it will have to cope with the same damping force

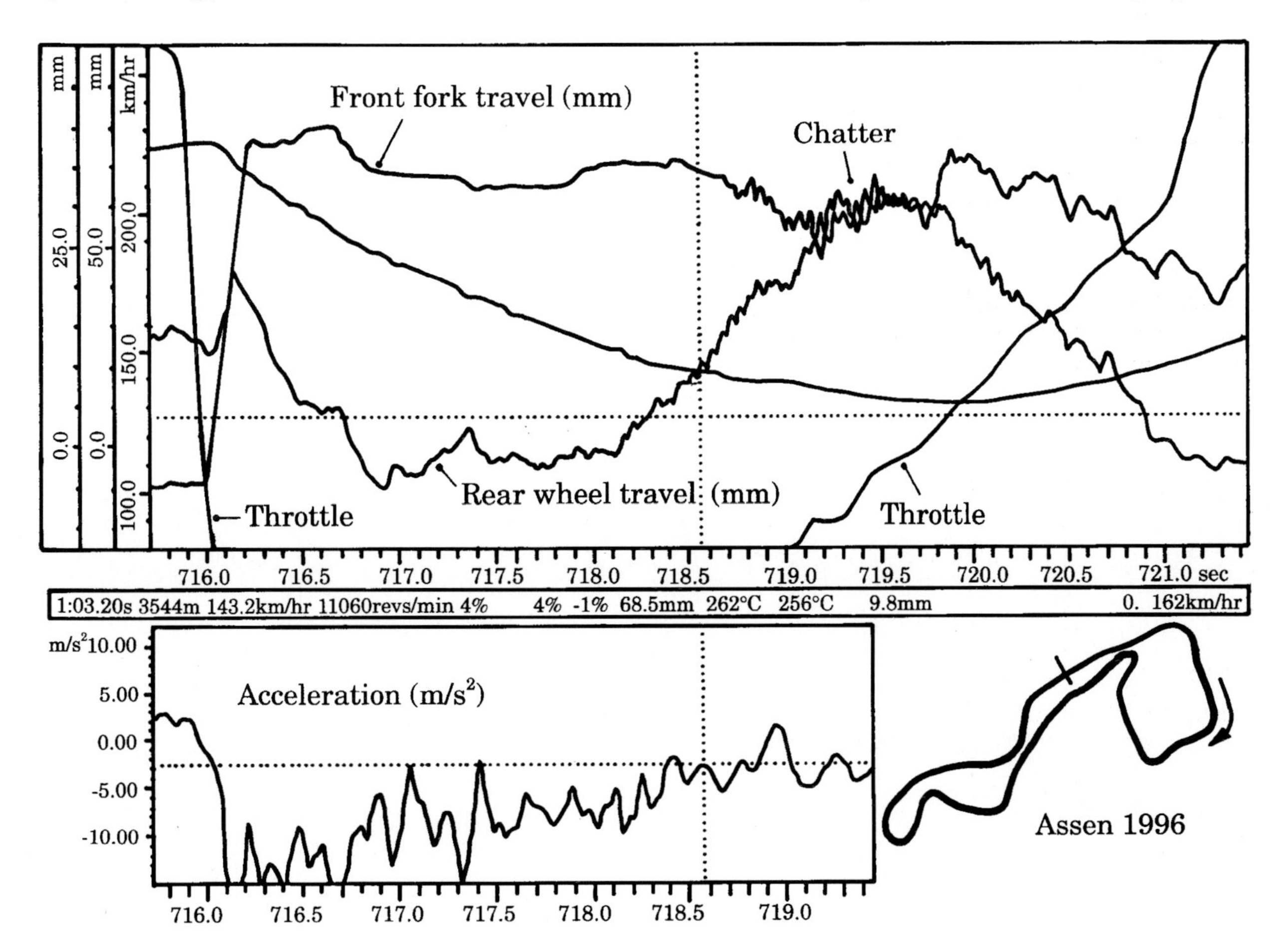

since there is only one damper to do both jobs. For most people none of this will matter. Damping is very specialised and, outside the GP world, few people will order a damper with specific characteristics. You rely heavily on the knowledge and experience of the suspension manufacturers to provide something that will work well. Any specialist in this area needs to be as much of a psychologist as an engineer because the type of characteristic that suits one rider will not suit another, even if the mean level of damping is the same. I do not have this knowledge and can only provide the general guide that is given at the end of this chapter.

As far as the mean level of damping is concerned this is only really of interest to people designing or re-valving dampers. The ability to test the operation of the damper is essential and only the specialist will have suitable equipment.

For these people the following may be of interest. My industrial background relates quite closely to damping since much of my work has been with control systems for robots and the like, all of which need their motion controlling very carefully. With an interest in bikes as well, I was always curious about how suitable levels of damping could be estimated and for many years I never found anything that was a reasonable compromise between pure theory and actual practice.

Finally, I obtained a paper by A.G.Thompson, University of Adelaide, entitled 'A simple formula for optimum suspension damping'. Thompson is very well respected in the field of automotive suspension analysis and this paper develops a relatively simple method of finding the mean level of damping required to minimise the average tyre deflection, ie the analysis relates to optimum roadholding, not comfort (which would require much less damping).

Fig 5.73 gives the formula Thompson derived, slightly modified to cope with different units. It determines a suitable damping coefficient, from which the total compression and rebound area can be estimated as shown. Specialists may find this interesting to play around with. The effect of increased unsprung mass is easily demonstrated as is the influence of different tyre stiffness. The paper was originally published in the Journal of Automotive Engineering, The Institution of Mechanical Engineers, April 1972. Any I.Mech.E. Member can obtain copies through the Institute library.

Right and below. Fig 5.73 *Specialists may wish to experiment with this formula for the mean level of damping required to achieve optimum roadholding. The values are higher than those required for a comfortable ride! Follow the example to determine the coefficient C. This gives the slope of a viscous force vs velocity graph which can then be drawn, eg if C = 1.2N s / mm then at 800mm / s the force is 960N. Draw a line through this point and the origin then calculate the total area to determine the mean level of damping required. This is the total damping at a particular wheel. If there are two dampers each has to provide half of this. Adapted from a paper by A.G.Thompson, as detailed in the text.*

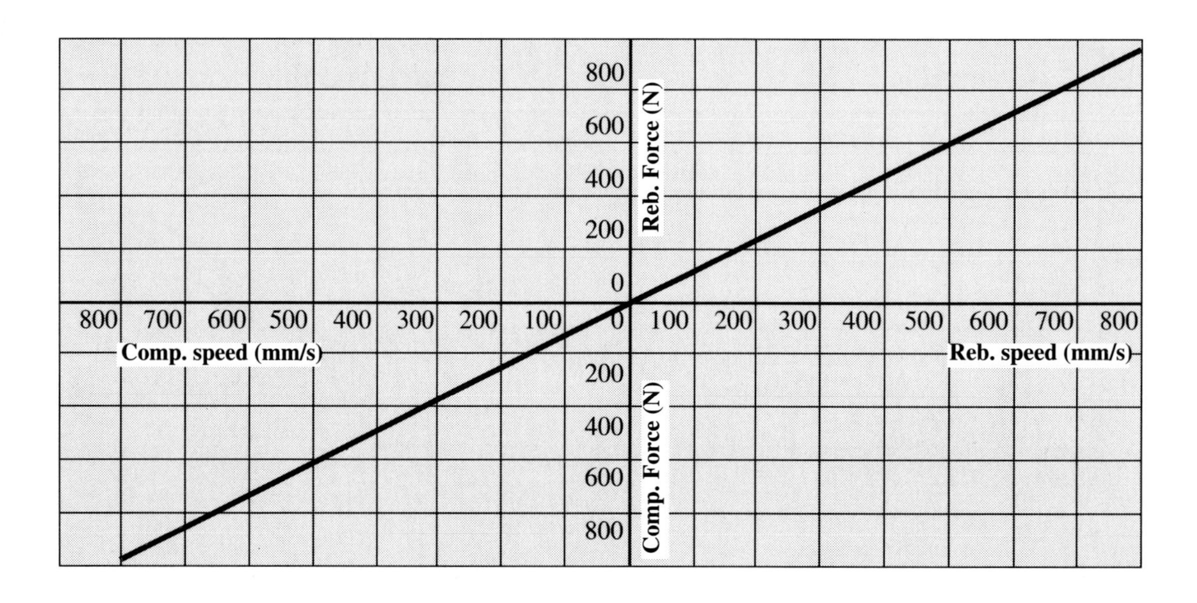

- Calculate the required damping coefficent to give minimum mean squared tyre deflection using one of the formulae on the right.

- The units for each value must be correct and the rules of algebra must be adhered to.

- Example.

M_s = 96kg, M_{us} = 17kg,
K_t = 140N/mm, K_s = 12N/mm

$$C = \sqrt{\frac{140 \times 17}{1000}\left[\left[\frac{96}{96+17} - \frac{12}{140}\right]^2 + \frac{96}{17}\left[\frac{12}{140}\right]^2\right]}$$

$$C = \sqrt{2.38\left[\left[0.849 - 0.086\right]^2 + 5.65\left[0.086\right]^2\right]}$$

$$C = \sqrt{2.38\left[0.582 + 0.042\right]}$$

$$C = \sqrt{1.486} = 1.218\text{N.s/mm}$$

- This is the slope of a graph like the one shown opposite. Draw out the graph for your range of damper speeds. The total area underneath it, ie compression and rebound, is the theoretical area required, hence the damping power. Defining this up to 800mm/s should cover all normal needs. Above this you are dealing with safety valving.

$$C = \sqrt{\frac{K_t M_{us}}{1000}\left[\left[\frac{M_s}{M_s + M_{us}} - \frac{K_s}{K_t}\right]^2 + \frac{M_s}{M_{us}}\left[\frac{K_s}{K_t}\right]^2\right]}$$

where

C = damping coeff in N.s/mm
K_t = tyre stiffness in N/mm
K_s = wheel rate in N/mm
M_{us} = unsprung mass at wheel concerned in kg
M_s = sprung mass at wheel concerned in kg

or, in imperial units use,

$$C = \sqrt{\frac{K_t M_{us}}{386.4}\left[\left[\frac{M_s}{M_s + M_{us}} - \frac{K_s}{K_t}\right]^2 + \frac{M_s}{M_{us}}\left[\frac{K_s}{K_t}\right]^2\right]}$$

where

C = damping coeff in lbf.s/in
K_t = tyre stiffness in lbf/in
K_s = wheel rate in lbf/in
M_{us} = unsprung mass at wheel concerned in lb
M_s = sprung mass at wheel concerned in lb

- If you find this satisfactory, try to maintain this total area under the real curves, ie when the characteristics are non-linear and bump and rebound are not equal.

Testing of dampers

A big problem with dampers is that useful tests can only be carried out on the track or by using specialist equipment. Attempting to test a damper by hand is a relatively meaningless activity that will not endear you to suspension specialists.

The inability to gain meaningful results in this way is simply due to the damper characteristics. It may help when dealing with thirty year old dampers at the local autojumble but as far as quality dampers are concerned you will not be able to move the dampers fast enough. Indeed, you may even confuse yourself.

For example, if the damper has a lot of low-speed damping then you will feel it, even though the damping at 'real' speeds may be relatively low. Similarly, a damper that virtually locks up in normal use may feel relatively soft when you attempt to pull it or push it by hand.

Manufacturers test dampers using a variety of specially built machines. These are commonly called 'shock dynos'. Modern machines are purely electro-hydraulic and operate under computer control. Earlier machines were mechanical and used a crank and connecting rod mechanism. An electro-hydraulic example is shown in Fig 5.74.

Using the modern machine it is possible to compress or extend the damper at any chosen velocity within the capability of the machine while simultaneously recording the force involved. This allows a force vs damper speed graph of the type discussed already to be produced directly.

However, most testing tends to follow the format devised for the original mechanical machines. With these, the crank rotates at a constant speed and the damper is continuously stroked through a compression and extension cycle. This is more representative of actual use and the rig can be left to run for a period of time, after which the initial and final results can be compared to see how much the performance has deteriorated. Fade shows up immediately as a lower damping force.

Fig 5.74 *Left. General view of an electro-hydraulic damper testing system. The force vs position loops can be seen on the computer screen. Right. A close up showing the hydraulic actuator that moves the damper and the load cell that records the force required.*

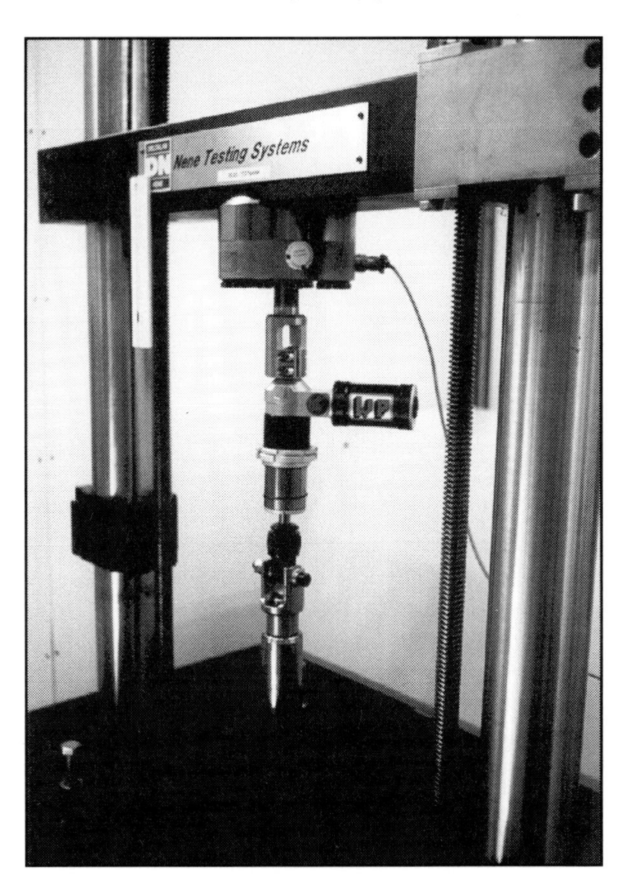

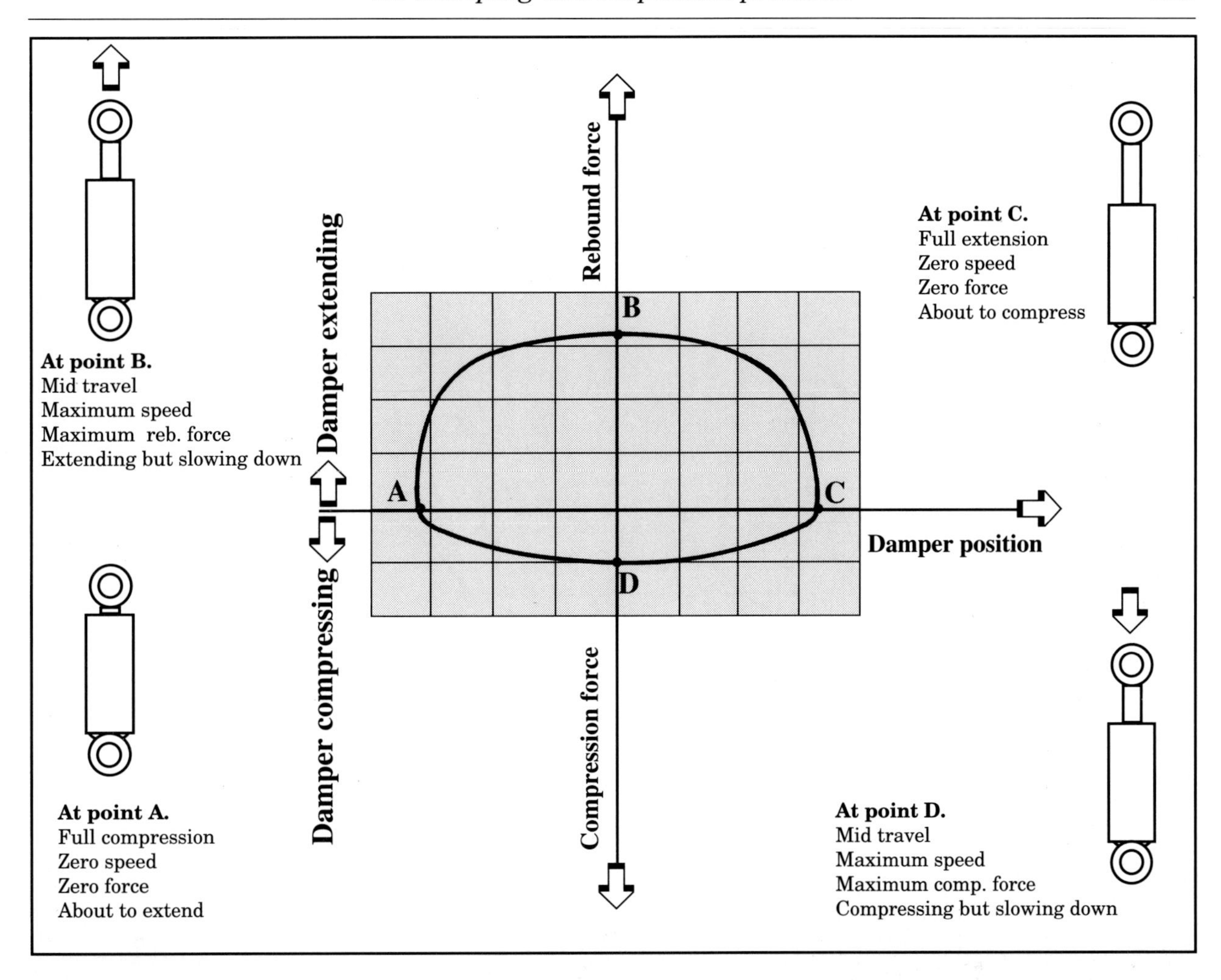

Fig 5.75 On a 'shock dyno' the damper is continuously cycled through its compression and rebound strokes. The test is such that the speed of the damper is zero when it is fully extended or compressed and varies up to some maximum value at or near to mid-stroke. The tester plots the graph above automatically, showing how the force required to move the damper varies with stroke and hence speed. Stroke is the distance from A to C.

The results of these tests are generally portrayed in the form of a graph of damping force vs damper travel. These can be generated automatically if the machine has suitable instrumentation and an example is shown in Fig 5.75.

Damper test results

Some understanding is necessary to interpret these 'egg-shaped' graphs and an electro-hydraulic machine will produce a slightly different shape from a mechanical one. The reasons for this are probably best left until after the basic idea has been explained.

The damper starts from one extreme position where it has zero speed. I will assume this is the point where it is fully compressed. This corresponds to point A on the diagram. It is then extended by the machine in such a way that it accelerates until it reaches maximum speed at roughly mid-stroke. This is point B. The damper then continues to extend but it is slowing down. At point C it is fully extended and the speed is momentarily zero. It then begins compressing at an increasing speed. Having reached the same maximum speed as before when about half way through the compression, it slows down to a momentary stop before repeating the cycle. Although the speed varies from zero to some maximum, the motion is continuous and, for the mechanical machine, is just like the motion of a piston in an engine.

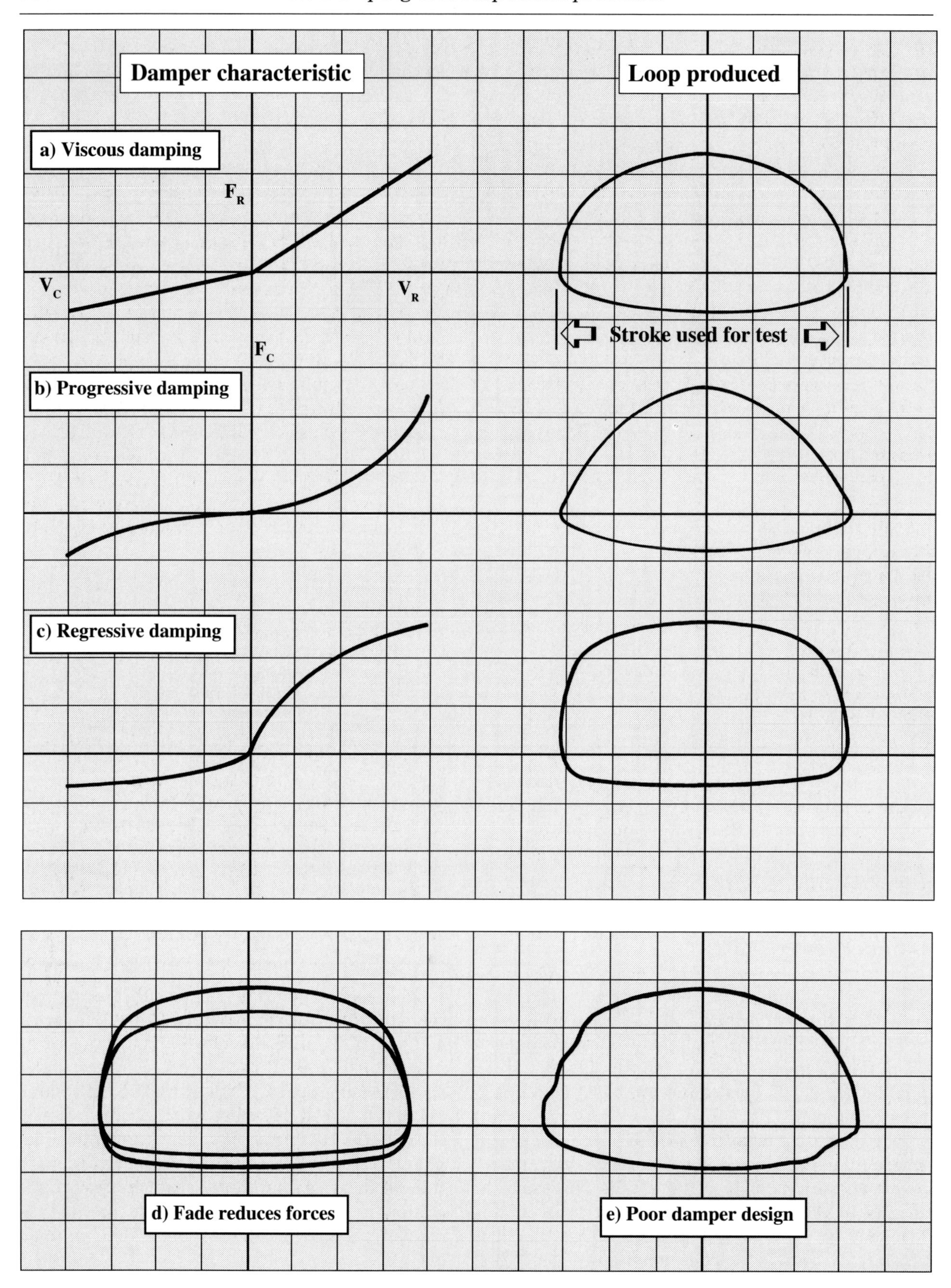
Damper characteristic
Loop produced
a) Viscous damping
F_R
V_C
V_R
F_C
Stroke used for test
b) Progressive damping
c) Regressive damping
d) Fade reduces forces
e) Poor damper design

The egg shaped graph is produced by plotting the force necessary to move the damper against the damper travel. How much you can tell from this graph depends on whether you know the speed at which the crank rotates. For the moment, I will assume we do not know this. In this situation, the actual force values are fairly meaningless because they could represent any particular damper speed. We can see what force the maximum damper speed produced, but we cannot determine what that speed is.

However, we can tell a lot about the general damper characteristics. Referring to Fig 5.76, the relative force values on compression and rebound show where the bulk of the damping is being done. In the examples given, the rebound damping lies above the axis, ie rebound is greater than compression. Be careful here because the graphs are often drawn the other way up or even on their side.

In each case the general shape of the 'egg' indicates what type of damping characteristic there is, though, since changes are relative, you do need a bit of experience here. If the shapes are roughly elliptical (diagram a), then the force vs velocity characteristic is close to being linear, ie viscous damping. If the curves are more pointed, then it shows that the force at low speeds is relatively low so the characteristic is a progressive one as shown in diagram b. Finally, when the 'egg' has very upright sides, then the low speed damping is relatively high and the characteristic is therefore somewhat regressive, diagram c.

Other aspects can also be revealed without any sums. If the test is allowed to run for a period of time then the forces produced may fall as shown in diagram d. This is fade and there are several possible causes. Usually, the oil is getting too hot and losing some of its viscosity. You can partly confirm this by repeating the tests in a cool airstream though this will not solve the problem if the heat is not transferring effectively to the outside surface of the damper. The ability to do this depends on the design of the damper.

Finally, you may well encounter some very odd shapes of which diagram e is an example. These indicate all sorts of problems including sticking, cavitation and so on. The basic rule is to avoid dampers that show such effects. Any quality damper will produce a nice smooth curve.

The next feature you can assess is adjustment. Most modern dampers offer independent adjustment of the compression and rebound damping. These are normally 'general' adjusters, ie they will lift or lower the whole force vs speed characteristic. This causes the graph to enlarge or contract as shown in Fig 5.77. The shape is changed by this enlargement so it is often difficult to tell whether the adjustments are general or speed specific, eg low speed damping, unless you have all the relevant examples.

Left. Fig 5.76 *General interpretation of the 'egg-like' graphs produced from a damper tester. a) Viscous damping produces a relatively elliptical shape. b) Progressive damping gives less force at low damper speeds so the curves become more pointed. c) When there is a lot of low speed damping, the force changes quickly during the start and end of the stroke. This makes the sides of the 'egg' relatively steep. d) After testing for some time, the forces may reduce. This is fade. e) Any odd kinks and bumps show problems of the type you do not want on competition dampers. Avoid anything like this.*

Fig 5.77 *General adjustments, which affect the entire range of damping, cause the graph to change as shown.*

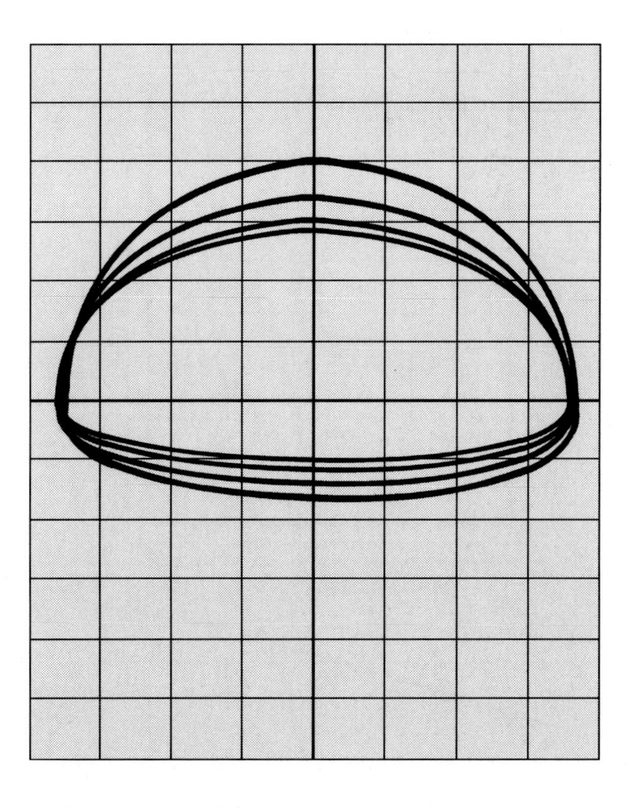

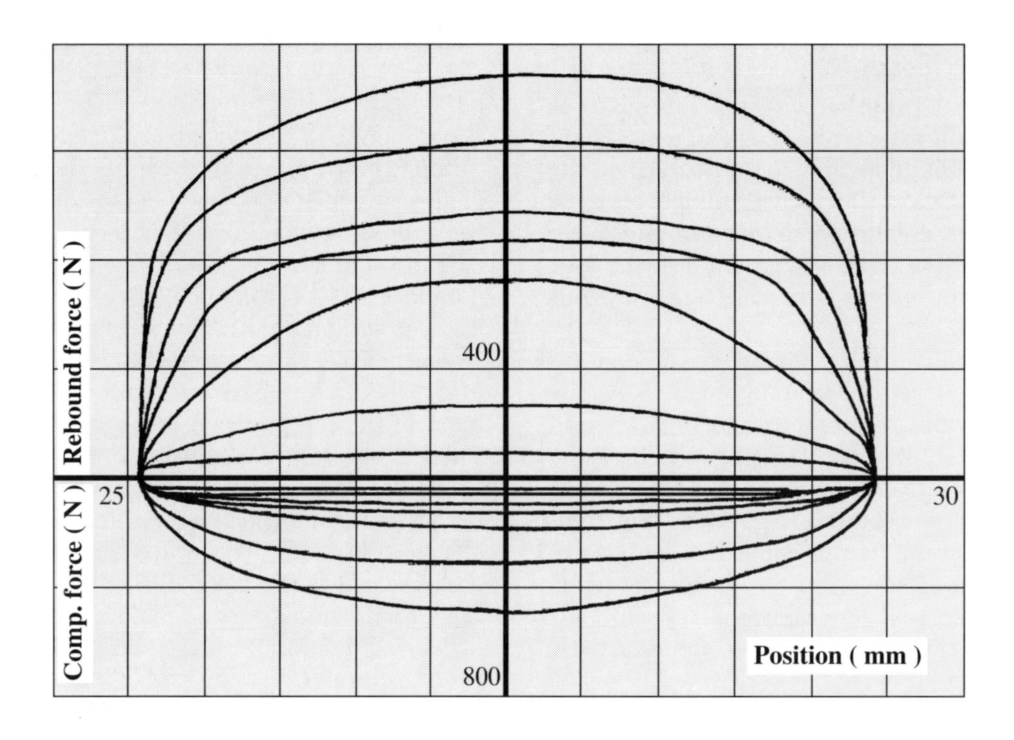

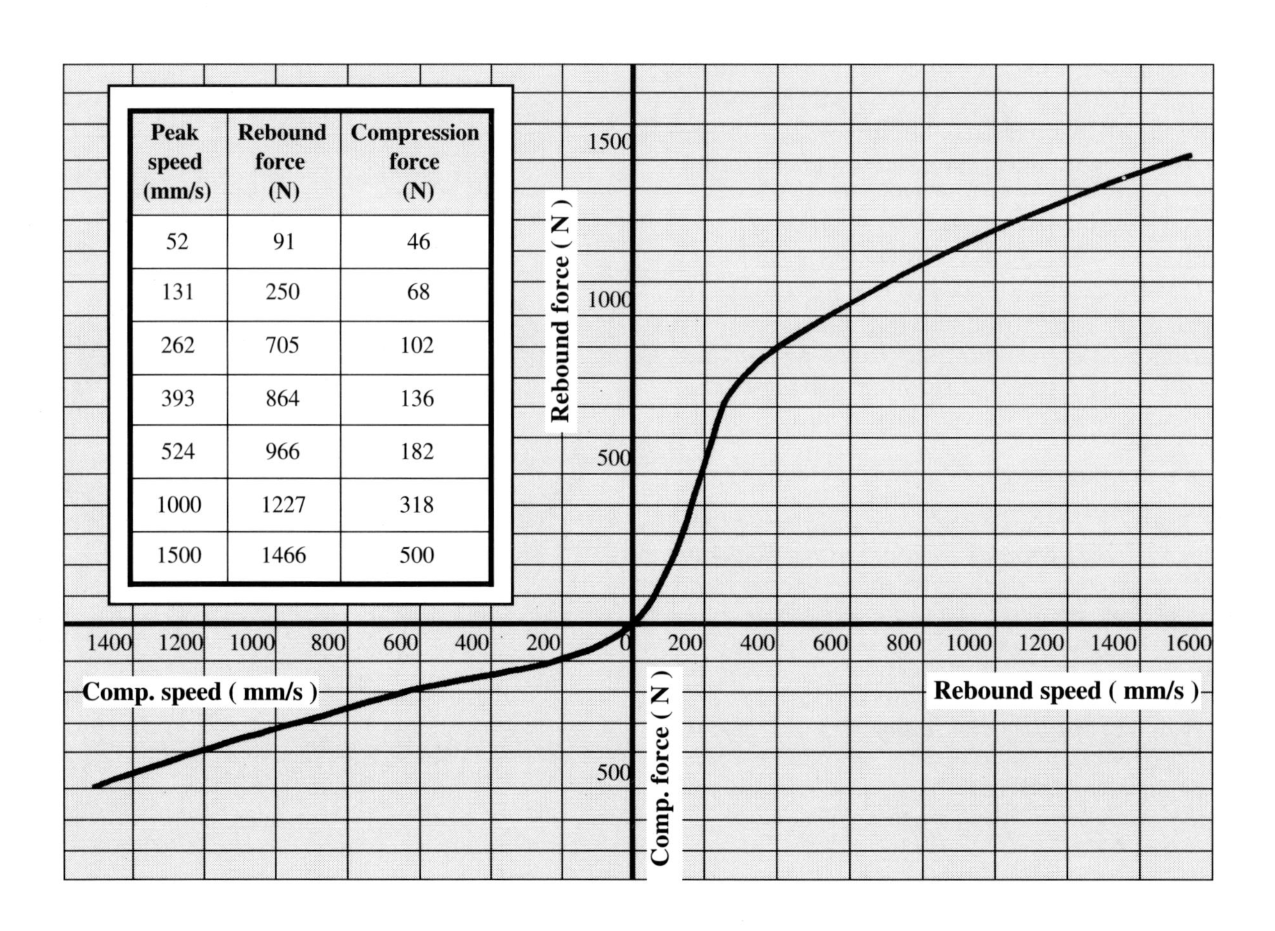

Peak speed (mm/s)	Rebound force (N)	Compression force (N)
52	91	46
131	250	68
262	705	102
393	864	136
524	966	182
1000	1227	318
1500	1466	500

Force vs speed data

If you actually want to evaluate the damper's force vs speed characteristics from the shock dyno data then you need to know the rate at which the damper is being cycled. This is effectively the crankshaft speed of the mechanical tester, eg 100revs/min. If you know this figure then, assuming that the motion is sinusoidal, the peak damper speed is given by,

$$\textbf{Max. Damper speed} = \frac{NS}{19.1}$$

where

N = cranking speed in revs/min
S = stroke used

If the stroke is in millimetres, the speed is in mm/s. If the stroke is in inches, the speed is in ins/sec

Example. A damper is tested at 100revs/min. The stroke (total extension or compression) is 50mm. What is the peak damper speed.

$$\text{Max. speed (mm/s)} = \frac{100 \times 50}{19.1}$$

$$= 261.8\text{mm/s}$$

Example. A damper is tested at 120revs/min. The stroke (total extension or compression) is 3in. What is the peak damper speed.

$$\text{Max. speed (in/s)} = \frac{120 \times 3}{19.1}$$

$$= 18.85\text{in/s}$$

Left. Fig 5.78 *Determination of damper characteristics from a shock dyno test at specific speeds.*

From this you can see that the force at different speeds can be found either by testing the damper at a constant crankshaft speed and varying the stroke, or by leaving the stroke fixed and varying the crankshaft speed. Fig 5.78 is a test carried out on an electro-hydraulic tester. In this case there is no actual crankshaft, the hydraulics simply cycle the damper in a similar way. This particular example has been carried out so that the peak damper speeds correspond to the standard test speeds given previously in Table 5.8. As such, we know both the peak speed and the force so the actual force vs velocity graphs can be produced as shown. The area under the graph can be determined to estimate the mean level of damping.

Finally, it is necessary to point out the difference between the mechanical and electro-hydraulic tests. In an ideal world, the damper is cycled using a perfectly sinusoidal motion like that shown in Fig 5.79. An electro-hydraulic tester can do this very accurately.

The mechanical mechanism of a crank and connecting rod does not generate a sine wave unless the connecting rod is infinitely long. In practice the connecting rod length is limited and

Fig 5.79 *A perfectly sinusoidal displacement of the damper produces a sinusoidal speed variation as shown. The mechanical crank / connecting rod system deviates from this slightly and the peak speed can be shifted a reasonable way from mid-stroke. This makes the test appear lop-sided as shown overleaf.*

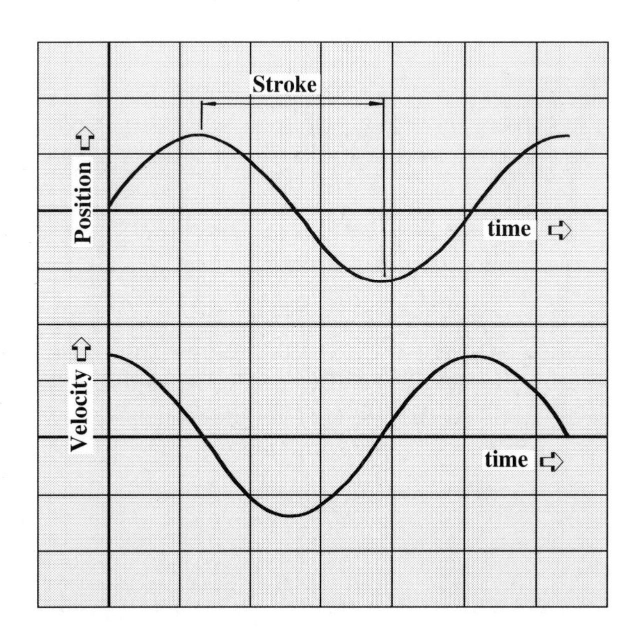

this leads to a speed variation that is not perfectly sinusoidal. The degree of error in damper speed depends on how much longer the connecting rod is than the stroke, but for most machines this error is less than 10% at its peak and is generally disregarded in favour of a simple sine wave.

One aspect that cannot be ignored is the fact that peak velocity will not occur at mid-stroke as it does with the electro-hydraulic machine. This means that some of the 'egg' traces will be a bit asymmetrical even when the damper characteristics are symmetrical - Fig 5.80. Again, the shift depends on the ratio of connecting rod length to stroke so some test results will look more 'lop-sided' than others. Anyone interested in the actual motion should read about normal engine crankshaft/connecting rod behaviour which is the same.

Fig 5.80 *Mechanical testers do not produce peak damper speed at exactly mid-stroke. The shift of peak speed, hence force, from mid-stroke, is determined by the value of L / r, ie connecting rod length / crank radius. The stroke of the damper is 2r so when tests are conducted at different strokes the shape of the graph alters. Electro-hydraulic testers do not have this problem.*

Damping oils

Although rear dampers are normally sealed and rebuilding them is highly specialised, most riders will experiment with different damping oils and oil levels in the front forks.

Modern damping oils are highly developed for their purpose and you should not be tempted to use any old oil that happens to have the desired viscosity (discussed shortly). The basic requirements of damping oils are as follows.

- The viscosity (thickness) must be suitable.
- A high viscosity index is required (a high index implies that the oil maintains its viscosity better when temperature rises).
- Suitable anti-foaming agents are used.
- The oil does not harden the seals or cause them to swell too much.

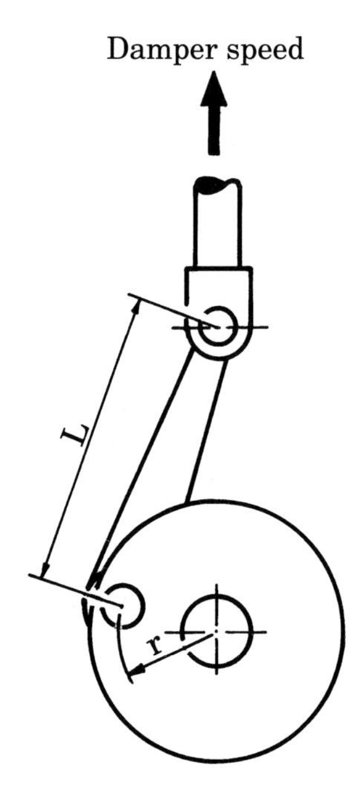

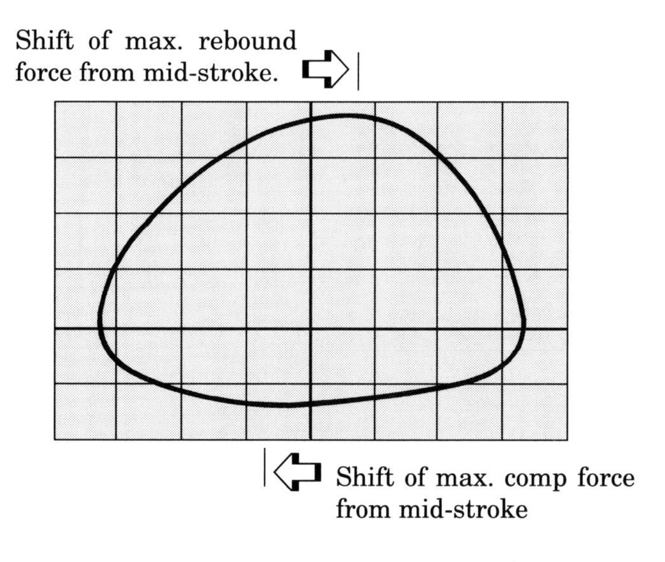

• The lubricating properties are acceptable.

All these requirements will be met by the leading brands but it is best to use oils specifically designed for the forks, especially if they are cartridge forks. The recommended oil will be compatible with all the materials used in the forks and this is becoming more important as the variety of sealing and bearing materials increases. You may feel that there are less expensive, equally suitable oils available but with state-of-the-art components there is certainly an element of risk involved in using a variety of oils.

Experiments can be carried out with both oil level and oil viscosity. Altering the level affects the air compression and was discussed in Chapter 5.4. It does not affect the damping unless you put in so little oil that the damper mechanism is starved at some point.

Viscosity changes do affect the damping very significantly but note that they will affect both compression and rebound damping since both mechanisms utilise the same oil. This can sometimes be a problem and if you cannot achieve the necessary balance there is no alternative to getting a specialist to revalve the forks. If you try this yourself, only alter orifice sizes in very, very small steps or you will have to weld them up and start again. Old fools like me learned all about this in the days when we had to make our own damping mechanisms for forks that were very crude in comparison to modern equivalents.

The higher the oil's viscosity, the thicker it is and the more the damping will increase, within limits. It is easy to reach a point where the thicker oils cannot get through the orifices and further increases in viscosity will not increase the damping, though they may damage the seals.

I will discuss viscosity in a moment but if you find yourself using thicker and thicker oils it is better to revalve the forks to suit a thinner oil. Thick oils are not really suitable because they are more likely to cavitate.

Cavitation will produce fade as will too low a viscosity index. Most damping oils have a viscosity index above 140 and this is usually fine in the forks which benefit considerably from the cooling airstream. The index is a number that is worked out from the oil's fall in viscosity with temperature, a higher number implying less reduction. Rear dampers, particularly monoshocks that work hard over a short stroke behind the engine, are more prone to fade caused by loss of viscosity with temperature. Most manufacturers use oils with a viscosity index above 250.

Viscosity

Viscosity is a very complex subject and viscosity values are specified in several forms using a large variety of units, some of which are very strange. The user is generally protected from this by the SAE system of grading oils but faces problems when any other system is used.

Since virtually everyone uses standard oils and sees viscosity specifications in the form of the SAE index, I will remark only briefly on the background to this. You may well come across some of the terms that follow and they can be very confusing. In general terms viscosity indicates how thick the oil is. Thin, runny oils have low viscosity and thick, sluggish oils have high viscosity.

Based on this general idea, one way to test for viscosity is to allow a certain volume of oil to flow through a hole while the temperature is kept constant. The time taken for all the oil to discharge is indicative of the viscosity. This test leads to two fairly common viscosity indicators, Redwood Seconds and Sabel Universal Seconds (SUS).

This idea is somewhat removed from the more scientific definitions of viscosity. A general definition is the ability of the fluid to resist a shear stress and other tests do exist which yield more formal values. The oil is placed between two concentric cylinders and the outer one is rotated. The oil then exerts a drag on the inner cylinder and that drag is a measure of the viscosity. By measuring the torque produced the viscosity can be calculated.

The basic value is called dynamic viscosity. It is a shear stress divided by a shear rate and that produces units such as Ns/m^2, otherwise written as Pa.s for Pascal seconds, the Pascal being $1N/m^2$. Many other units are used and one cP, the 'centipoise' is equivalent to 0.001Pa.s, or 1mPa.s. The Imperial unit 1lb/ft s is equal to 1488.16cP. I said you would find this confusing!

It is also useful to utilise the value of viscosity/density. You may recall this idea from Section 4. In this case the result is called kinematic viscosity and yields metric values that are usually given in mm^2/s. Centistokes (cSt) are also used and 1cSt = $1mm^2/s$. In Imperial, $1in^2/s$ is 645.16cSt. These are the basic units of viscosity and there are numerous standards that relate these 'scientific' values to more user friendly representations. Nevertheless, it is not uncommon to see the scientific units used directly.

The best known standards are the SAE (Society of Automotive Engineers) standard and the ISO (International Standards Organisation) version. These give a series of reference numbers and specify the viscosity conditions that apply. The ISO version uses the kinematic viscosity at 40°C. It quotes a nominal value and a limiting range for each case. This is shown in Table 5.9.

The SAE standard is rather more involved. It quotes a minimum kinematic viscosity value at 100°C and, for some oils, a maximum value. For others, it also quotes a maximum dynamic viscosity at low temperatures. This data is used to determine the influence on engine cranking when cold and the ability of the oil to flow to the oil pump inlet when starting. This data is also given in Table 5.9. If the SAE grade has a 'W' after it, then the oil is graded against all three conditions. If there is no 'W' then only the viscosity at 100°C applies.

Damping oils come at the lower end of the viscosity list. Commonly listed grades are given as 2.5, 5, 7.5, 10, 15, 20 and 30. The SAE list includes 5W, 10W, 15W, 20W and 30W but it does not define the intermediate grades. These are obtained by blending and in principle equal parts of 0W and 5W produce the 2.5 grade. Similarly, 5W and 10W can produce 7.5 grade. You can do this yourself but only do it with the same make and type of oil.

In general it is best to try and use oils in the range 2.5 to 7.5, ie the thin ones. On some dampers this will not produce adequate damping and the damper should be modified rather than using thicker and thicker oils. In some cases you may have little choice. Many classic forks which only have rebound damping need very thick oils unless the internals are re-designed. There are people out there performing well with engine oil in the forks but this does not mean it is ideal.

Finally, remember that viscosity is only one requirement. You can satisfy this using any old oil

ISO designation	Viscosity at 40°C (mm^2/s)	Viscosity limits (mm^2/s)	
		Min	Max
ISO VG 2	2.2	1.98	2.42
ISO VG 3	3.2	2.88	3.52
ISO VG 5	4.6	4.14	5.06
ISO VG 7	6.8	6.12	7.48
ISO VG 10	10	9.00	11.0
ISO VG 15	15	13.5	16.5
ISO VG 22	22	19.8	24.2
ISO VG 32	32	28.8	35.2
ISO VG 46	46	41.4	50.6
ISO VG 68	68	61.2	74.8
ISO VG 100	100	90.0	110
ISO VG 150	150	135	165
ISO VG 220	220	198	242
ISO VG 320	320	288	352
ISO VG 460	460	414	506
ISO VG 680	680	612	748
ISO VG 1000	1000	900	1100
ISO VG 1500	1500	1350	1650

SAE Grade	Max. low temp viscosity		Viscosity at 100°C in mm^2/s	
	Cranking	Pumpability		
	Pa.s @ °C	Pa.s @ °C	Min	Max
0W	3.25 @ -30	30 @ -35	3.8	-
5W	3.50 @ -25	30 @ -30	3.8	-
10W	3.50 @ -20	30 @ -25	4.1	-
15W	3.50 @ - 15	30 @ -20	5.6	-
20W	4.50 @ - 10	30 @ -15	5.6	-
25W	6.00 @ -5	30 @ - 10	9.3	-
20	-	-	5.6	9.3
30	-	-	9.3	12.5
40	-	-	12.5	16.3
50	-	-	16.3	21.9
60	-	-	21.9	26.1

Right. Table 5.9 *ISO and SAE oil grades in terms of their viscosity at certain temperatures.*

of the right grade but don't expect the suspension to be the same five minutes after you start racing. The viscosity grade tells you nothing about the oil's lubrication properties, its resistance to foaming or how well the viscosity is maintained when the oil gets hot. Temperatures around 200°C are possible in hard-worked units. Only specially designed damper oils will do the job correctly and they are worth paying for.

Track testing

Giving general advice on damping adjustment and other suspension settings is always a risky business because the same problem on two different bikes fitted with different tyres can require totally different forms of correction. Even I have gone fast enough to confirm this!

Perhaps the first thing to say is that it is easy to get carried away with these things and I am glad that I started out when suspension units had no adjustment apart from spring rate and preload. Riders have lapped the Isle of Man at an average speed of well over 161km/hr (100miles/hr) using nothing more exotic than a pair of unadjustable Girling twin shocks and Norton 'Roadholder' forks, yet every week we read in the press about how difficult it is to negotiate the roundabout on the way to work with anything less than GP suspension. I appreciate that tyre and power development has imposed impossible demands on the suspension but there is certainly a lot of 'hype' about in recent years.

If you have a range of adjustment then it is sensible to start with minimum values and investigate the effects all the way through to maximum, irrespective of whether the best results surface early on. This will give you a good idea of what the changes do. It will also tell you if the adjusters actually work! Provided you only change one thing at a time and write it all down you can always go back to any particular situation.

Try to sort out the springing and preload first because the damping required will relate to this. If you change it significantly then you will have to start all over again. Use any moderate levels of damping and do this first as discussed earlier. Once you know the springing is reasonable you can start looking at the damping in more detail but first make sure you have checked the more obvious things. Are the tyre pressures right? Are the wheels lined up? If you have made the bike yourself, check this with the swinging arm at both extreme positions. Check the steering head and swinging arm pivot bearings. Try to eliminate all such problems before you work on the damping otherwise you may well be trying to achieve the impossible.

If you start on minimal damping the lack of damping at low damper speeds should be immediately apparent. This mainly affects movements of the sprung mass irrespective of road speed. Pulling yourself slowly forwards and backwards on the seat at any speed sets up a see-saw motion as will momentary bursts of gradual acceleration followed by shutting off. Rebound damping at both front and rear can be increased until this mild pogo action just ceases. This may well take you half way through the range of possible adjustment so you start off with negligible compression damping and useful amount of rebound.

Now try some braking, though nothing too dramatic. Typically, the front will dive hard but the rear end may also extend straight to top-out fairly quickly. This is often easier for an observer to see than you. If the back end tends to shoot up making the wheel hop and skip very easily, try increasing the rear rebound damping until there is an obvious change. Once this happens gradually increase the compression damping at the front to help kill the dive. How much you can use depends very much on your riding style and spring stiffness, but if you go too far the front feels very solid and the front wheel tends to judder as you pitch into the corners.

At this stage you should have only relatively light damping in all its forms and can attempt more drastic tests. Brake very hard from a reasonable speed and let the brakes off suddenly. If the front end shoots up quickly, increase the rebound damping at the front until it is more controlled, then try flicking into corners immediately afterwards. It is easy to go too far with this increase and it is unlikely to show up on the local airfield. It will show up on long fast corners of the race track that have a few ripples because the forks will probably pump down, ie there is too much rebound damping for them to extend properly between bumps.

At the rear, hard acceleration at the test track will usually show up a lack of rebound damping as a 'chatter' at the wheel. Again, if you go too far the back end will be prone to pump down on fast bumpy corners just like the front forks.

I have never been really sure about compression damping at the back end other than to keep it as small as possible. Riders of large capacity bikes can control traction via compression damping but too much appears to be as bad, if not worse, than too little. Since my own interest was always focussed on small bikes which do not have the same power problems, I cannot comment further. If you find yourself developing a liking for adjustments that are both close to the limits of adjustment then more drastic action is required. If you are close to maximum rebound and compression then a thicker oil should be tried. Similarly, when close to minimum values a thinner oil should be tried. The problems arise when the adjustments are going in opposite directions because changing the oil will make one setting better and the other worse. In this case you need to consider re-valving the suspension.

Adjustment is a lot easier to talk about than it is to do because there are springs and preload to consider as well. Everything interacts and I would be the first to admit that I am rarely sure initially where the problems lie. I always found using an experienced observer very useful, even more so when they were armed with a cine-camera or camcorder. Most riders of average ability are busy trying to stay on the bike under extreme conditions and only very obvious problems find space in the brain cells. My own approach to this was simply to experiment, often with settings that were awful, just to see what happened. A more efficient method is to get a specialist to help you though this obviously costs money. Whatever the case the ground rules are the same. Once you have a basic set-up, explore only one thing at a time and write down everything that happens.

Another problem you will encounter is the variation in set-up required when riding at a different pace. When the damping is correct for serious racing it will be a lot greater overall than is necessary for road riding or the early stages of practice. This means that you will generally need more damping as you go faster and throw the bike about more quickly. During the first few laps of practice, a good set-up can feel extremely harsh. Some basic ideas are given in Table 5.10.

Advanced problems

Although it hurts to admit it, the vast majority of us cannot go fast enough to out-ride any reasonably adjusted suspension system that is produced for racing purposes. At GP level this is not the case. Riders reach limits imposed by the tyres, suspension and chassis and the GP engineers then have to try and find ways of removing those limits. If they succeed the riders go faster until the next problem arrives, at which point the whole process repeats itself. In this way the riders reach speed and skill levels that few can comprehend. It also leads to problems that are sensitive to the most minute adjustments.

Winning the odd club or National race is about as far removed from this as you can get so I cannot comment with any authority. However I do know a man who can and I am indebted to Eric Lindeman, one of WP Suspension's GP engineers, for the following comments on the sort of problems that GP riders face. Since he has to solve many of these problems there is no one better qualified to offer suggestions.

Chattering

This is frequently a problem when riders release the brakes in mid-corner and start to open the throttle. A data logger display showing this precise problem was given previously in Fig 5.72.

Chatter limits the rider's mid-corner speed. If they push it, they move off line and are passed though I am assured that they never fall off as a direct result of the chatter! The problem with chatter is that the solution is totally dependent on the make of tyre as well as the type of tyre. I was given three examples of the same problem. In the first case the problem was cured by reducing the low speed damping. In the second, this made matters worse and a solution was found by in-

Right Table 5.10 *Some of the problems related to suspension and possible solutions. This guide is adequate for average riders but at GP level the bike is very well set up initially and adjustments can go either way for the same type of problem.*

Front suspension problems	**Possible cures**
Laden sag too great	increase preload
Laden sag too small	reduce preload
Forks dive too fast	more compression damping
Forks dive too far (bottom)	stiffer springs, less air gap, possibly more preload
Forks judder when braking in straight line	less compression damping
Front wheel skips on bumps	soften springs, reduce compression damping, larger air gap
Always losing front end on corner entry	soften springs, check weight distribution
Front end shakes, not chatters, in corners	more rebound damping
Front end chatters out of corners	soften rebound springs or main springs, reduce compression damping
Front end shoots up too fast after braking	more rebound damping
Forks compress too much on smooth turns	stiffen springs, increase preload
Forks pump down on fast bumpy turns	reduce rebound damping
Excessive pogo action through chicanes	small increase in rebound damping
Bike difficult to turn in	soften springs, less preload or compression damping, alter steering

Rear suspension problems	**Possible cures**
Laden sag too great	increase preload
Laden sag too small	reduce preload
Rear squats on acceleration	stiffer spring, more anti-squat, increase compression damping slightly
Bike wallows	increase rebound damping
Rear jacks up too fast on braking	increase rebound damping
Rear end chatters leaving slow corners	increase rebound damping
Rear end pumps down on bumpy corners	reduce rebound damping
Very harsh ride on ripples	reduce compression damping
Bike kicks off ripples, bounces on bumps	increase rebound damping

creasing the low speed damping. Finally, for the Assen example given earlier, damping changes did not provide a cure but a change in tyre pressures did. Clearly there are no simple answers to this sort of problem at this level.

Pumping

Another type of corner that causes a lot of problems is the high speed uphill corner taken with a lot of power on and the front end rather light. You can be well cranked over and still the tyres only just touch the road - Fig 5.81. Under these conditions the bike is extremely sensitive to the low-speed (damper speed) damping and the rear end can start to move up and down slightly. This is called pumping and, because of the angle of lean the back end starts to weave a bit. The first solution to look at here is an increase in the low-speed compression damping of the rear unit. When the front tyre is just pattering on the track the spring stiffness includes that of the top-out springs and these may also require alteration to get the best adhesion.

High-speed damping problems

Although it is the low-speed compression damping that gives the rider maximum feedback about the track surface and tyre activity, high-speed damping can cause, or solve, many problems.

Braking is the obvious case but high-speed chicanes, when the suspension loads and unloads very rapidly, can push the damper speeds fairly high. If there are ripples or bumps in the chicane then the shape of the high-speed damping characteristic at the rear becomes critical.

If the overall level of high-speed damping, ie rebound damping plus compression damping, is too great, then the tyre will lose grip very easily

Fig 5.81 *Even in mid-corner, there is often a gap between the tyres and the track. Under these conditions the damping is critical, as is the stiffness of the fork's top-out (rebound) springs (photograph WP Suspension).*

Fig 5.82 *Pushing to the limit, Thunderbike style (photograph by Pan Images).*

and the rider may crash or highside. There is a lot of energy exchange under these conditions but grip must have priority.

On braking, there must be sufficient compression damping at the forks to keep the peak compression speed below about 300mm/s. If it is allowed to exceed this the front end is likely to tuck under when braking at GP levels. Provided this is prevented, the compression damping on the forks should be fairly light. If it is too heavy the front wheel will skip on the bumps instead of following them. Again the front end can tuck under and this is one of the most common causes of GP crashes. Similarly, the rebound should be minimal to control the rise but this is a low to medium speed activity rather than a high speed one.

High-speed corners

Fast corners are particularly important because it is easy to lose a lot of time on them. GP riders have a priority of getting up to speed on them and they are much faster than normal club racers. They will work on these corners even at the expense of other slower corners.

Entry speed is vital and if the corner is one that does not require any braking, ie the throttle is just backed off momentarily, then it is common to go for slightly softer springs or less preload. This makes the bike dip into the turn more than normal so that the front end steepens and it is easier to turn in at very high speed.

Rain

Sometimes it rains between final practice and the race. In England it just rains! This places a lot of pressure on the riders and engineers to achieve the best settings without a chance to try them. Typical changes are as follows.

- Nearly all wets raise the rear of the bike. This may require that the bike is lowered. It depends on whether you want to retain the original geometry.

- The gearing will alter a) due to the change in tyre size and b) if corner exit speed onto the fastest part of the circuit is going to reduce.

- Although the wet tyre compounds are very soft, the carcase is not much different in some cases. If it is too flexible, the rain slots close up. It is therefore not usual to compensate with increased spring rates.

- In general fork springs remain unchanged. It may be necessary to soften the rear slightly when grip is a problem, particularly on bumps.

- Low-speed compression damping is normally reduced slightly to help the tyres follow the bumps. Sometimes, a small amount of low-speed rebound damping is also removed from the rear.

All of the solutions to problems encountered at this level are a compromise because most systems are essentially fixed, ie one setting has to suit the complete lap, though some systems do have adjusters that the rider can alter during the lap. Assuming that this is not the case, the settings that are best on one corner will not be optimal on another so the balance that leads to the best lap times is critical. Riders concentrate on high-speed corners and those which are critical to straight line speed. We should do the same, though short circuit racing is often about who is blocking the track rather than who is going fastest. There is often a clash with settings that suit corners which are 'tactically critical', particularly at the end of the race, but without quick lap times this aspect is of little use.

In my experience, many riders do not need extreme finesse and can go as fast as they would wish to using relatively simple, but well set-up equipment. There is something to be said for not having all sorts of adjustment available but perhaps I am just showing my age!

6.1 Weight and inertia

Introduction

The performance of a motorcycle is measured in terms of its ability to complete a race in the shortest possible time under normal racing conditions. This is determined by a vast number of different factors. Some relate to the bike, some relate to the rider and others are determined by chance or things totally beyond your control.

Despite the fact that there will be aspects beyond your control involved, it is necessary to make the most of things you can control. Throughout this book I have identified a number of different aspects that will influence performance. What I have not done is to prioritise them. It is not possible to do this unless all the data for a specific bike is known. For example, your bike may have adequate power and suitable gearing. It may be light and aerodynamically efficient but if it does not go round corners quickly you will not win races. In this case it is obvious where the effort has to be directed but for an apparently similar bike it may be the aerodynamics that requires the most effort. To sort this out for your own bike, you must analyse it in detail, identify the weak points and then work on those, starting with the areas that will give maximum return for minimum outlay and effort.

Despite the complexity of the situation there are certain things that are common to all bikes and we can at least make some attempt to estimate the straight-line performance capabilities.

The purpose of doing this is not to arrive at some specific numbers. You will never do this exactly because of the variations in rider technique and ability. If you manage to predict that your bike will cover the standing quarter mile (402m) in 10.9s and it actually takes 11.2s then you should be very pleased. You should be even more pleased if your top speed estimate is also of the right order because this is telling you that the predictions are reasonable.

Once you know that your sums make sense you can then start to change things (on paper) and see what effect it has. By using figures that represent the sort of changes you might be able to achieve in practice, you can see roughly how they will influence the straight-line performance and hence make better decisions about what to work on. Not everyone will want to do this sort of thing and many people are much happier with a hacksaw than a calculator. Nevertheless, some sort of compromise between metal bashing and sums is better than no sums at all.

If you have any experience of racing motorcycles you will know how important weight is. What you may not be aware of is what the 'effective' weight of the motorcycle really is and in this chapter I hope to convey the basic ideas together with a few specific examples. This may help you decide how much money to spend in this area and where, or where not, to spend it!

Weight

There is no doubt whatsoever that reducing weight has to be a top priority and significant weight savings will yield performance improvements. In general, the weight will influence the acceleration, braking and cornering ability which seems like a good start!

Normal reductions in weight will not change the ultimate top speed significantly because the only mechanism by which the weight can do this is to lower the rolling resistance. Taken as a percentage of the total resistance, the reduction in rolling resistance that could be achieved by removing weight will be small unless you want to risk the whole bike falling apart.

However, because less weight is easier to accelerate, the speed you reach over any particular distance will increase, assuming that the bike is not at its limit. The general effect of reduced weight is therefore to alter the bike's speed-time history as shown in Fig 6.1 overleaf. It 'pads out' the curve and effectively makes the bike faster on short circuits, even though the ultimate top speed is much the same.

For a given engine and total resistance, the acceleration from all speeds is inversely proportional to the mass, hence weight. If you halve the weight you can, in theory, double the acceleration from any speed. In practice, the low speed improvement will be severely limited by the geometry of the bike which has to balance the needs of acceleration with those of braking and cornering. At anything much above 1.1g the rear tyre will spin or the front wheel will lift. Once below these limits the gains will be real.

To find the gain you might make in terms of acceleration figures, you need to calculate the percentage of weight saved. Unfortunately, this is not quite as simple as it might appear because the 'real' weight that the engine has to deal with is actually rather more than the apparent weight you will see on a set of scales.

Ignoring this problem for a moment, the first point to make is that the weight of the bike on its own is meaningless. You need to include the rider complete with all riding gear, the fuel, oil, water etc, everything that the engine has to drag around the circuit.

Doing this can be depressing but it represents the first step towards reality and there is no point in kidding yourself.

Example. A 125cc bike weighs 78kgf ready to race with fuel, oil and water. The rider weighs 70kgf and his leathers, helmet, boots, gloves and body armour weigh a further 7kgf. What is the percentage weight saving if 4kgf can be removed?

Total weight = 78 + 70 +7 = 155kgf

$$\%\text{ change in weight} = \frac{\text{change in wt. x 100}}{\text{original weight}}$$

Fig 6.1 *Reducing the weight will improve acceleration from any given speed. Since the acceleration starts at high values and eventually falls to zero, a weight reduction will fill out the graph as shown but it has negligible effect on the ultimate top speed. It will improve the speed reached on a restricted length of track but that then requires extra braking time!*

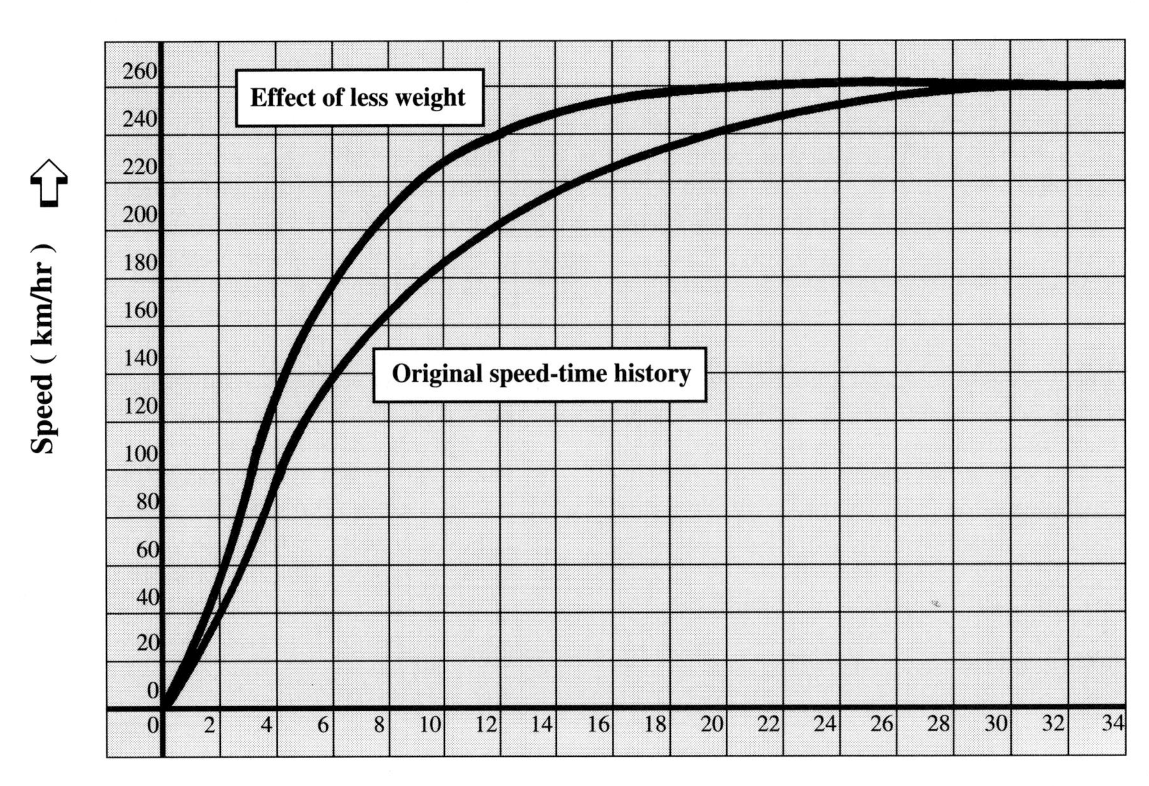

Fig 6.2 *The Aprilia RSV400 is about as light as it is possible to make such a bike. Riders of the calibre of Loris Reggiani can make use of any weight advantage they are given (photograph WP Suspension).*

$$\% \text{ change in weight} = \frac{4 \times 100}{155}$$

$$= 2.58\%$$

Thus the reduction is 2.58% even though, as a percentage of the bike's weight, 4kgf is 5.13%. On a heavier bike, a similar weight saving is even less impressive.

Example. A 1000cc bike weighs 430lbf ready to race with fuel, oil and water. The rider weighs 196lbf and his leathers, helmet, boots, gloves and body armour weigh a further 18lbf. How much will a weight saving of 10lbf improve the acceleration figures, assuming they are not limited?

$$\text{Total weight} = 430 + 196 + 18 = 644\text{lbf}$$

$$\% \text{ change in weight} = \frac{10 \times 100}{644}$$

$$= 1.55\%$$

On a good racing bike it can cost a lot of money to save a few pounds and, although everything counts, the figures are not wonderful. If you want a real weight saving, you simply change the rider. Changing the rider of the 125cc bike used in the example to one weighing 50kgf gives an improvement of 18% due to the rider alone. Doing the same on the larger bike gives a saving of 13.4%.

This is far from the end of the weight story. Firstly, a given increase in the acceleration possible from any given road speed will not yield the same percentage reduction in lap times, far from it, and lap times are what counts. Secondly, from a scientific point of view, we don't yet have the true weight of the bike.

Despite these limitations any reductions in the basic weight of the bike will improve it to some degree. The best way to achieve minimum weight is to design for it. This gives a much more cost effective result than trying to lighten something that already exists. For example, you could replace a heavy frame with a lighter copy and then find that all the bolts and spindles weigh even more than the frame itself. Reducing the weight of the bolts and spindles will be very expensive because it requires materials with a better strength:weight ratio. It will also be very frustrating if you know that some of the bolts could have been eliminated by a better design.

To reduce weight successfully you have to be committed to it, almost obsessed with it. Treat every single component as if it were the only component and work at it until you believe you are at the limit of strength or expense. If you do this with the thousand or so parts that make up the complete motorcycle, a few grams saved on each one makes a very impressive final total!

Inertia of rotating parts

Inertia is the reluctance of something to be accelerated. I used the same definition for mass earlier on but mass is only an effective representation of inertia when something has pure linear motion. The fact that the wheels, gears, crank and clutch rotate means that some of the engine power is used to accelerate them around their spindles. The acceleration of the bike along the road is determined by the power that is left over.

If a component is rotating then mass alone does not adequately represent its resistance to acceleration. Most people are aware of this even if they have not considered it formally. The two objects in Fig 6.3 are both assumed to have equal weight, hence mass, but the larger wheel type object is much harder to accelerate than the shaft. Clearly there is more than mass involved.

The effects of this can be quite dramatic and there is nothing like doing the job practically to prove it. If you have access to a mountain bike with state-of-the-art alloy wheels, thin spokes etc, then try riding it with these fitted and then with a pair of heavy steel wheels fitted. Even if you tie some lead on the frame to make up the difference, you will still notice how much easier the bike is to get going with the light wheels on.

The reluctance of rotating components to be accelerated depends on both the mass and where the mass is located. The greater the radius at which the bulk of the mass is concentrated, the harder the object is to accelerate about its centre. A value that incorporates both factors is called the moment of inertia (I).

For the simple shapes shown in Fig 6.3 the moment of inertia is easily calculated using,

$$\text{Moment of Inertia} = \frac{\text{mass x radius}^2}{2}$$

This shows that the moment of inertia is proportional to $(\text{radius})^2$ so if you double the radius the moment of inertia goes up by a factor 4 even if the mass remains the same. Note that the length of the component does not appear because it is effectively incorporated in the mass value.

How does this affect the bike? There are many rotating components on the bike and the engine has to accelerate them all. However, when I discussed the driving force at the rear wheel in Section 2, this aspect was ignored and I assumed that the net power at the back wheel was all used to accelerate the mass of the bike. No change to

Fig 6.3 *These rotating components have the same weight, hence mass, but the one with the larger diameter is harder to accelerate about its spindle.*

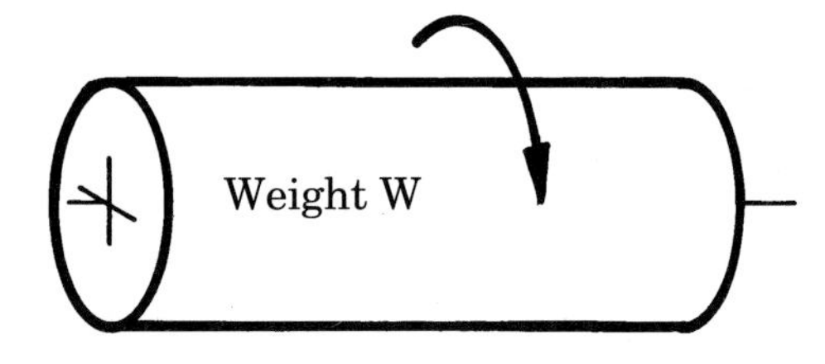

Relatively easy to accelerate

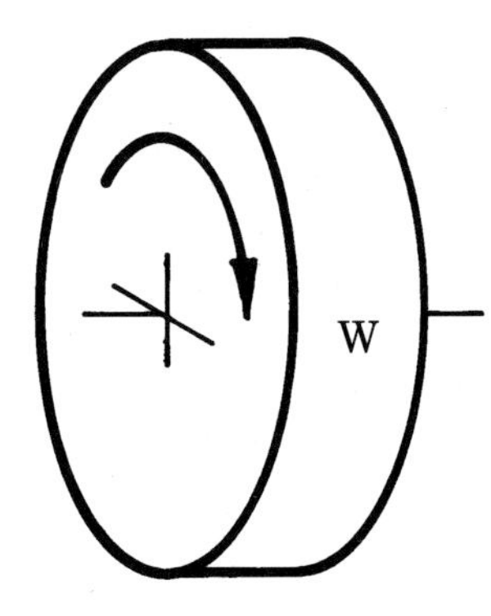

More difficult to accelerate if weights are equal

this is needed but, if any reasonable accuracy is required, we must ensure that the mass of the bike and rider includes a suitable allowance to represent the inertia of rotating parts. The mass representing the inertia of rotating parts is called an equivalent mass.

The wheels are the most straightforward components to deal with so I will consider them first. If we assume that the wheels are simple solid discs as shown in Fig 6.3 then we can easily calculate their moment of inertia. Once the moment of inertia is known an equivalent mass can be found. To obtain the equivalent mass that would have the same effect, you divide the moment of inertia by the (rolling tyre radius)^2. This is very convenient for the solid disk because it gives an equivalent mass of,

$$\text{Equivalent mass} = \frac{\text{moment of inertia}}{\text{radius}^2} = \frac{\text{mass x radius}^2}{2 \text{ x radius}^2} = \frac{\text{mass}}{2}$$

This means we have to add half the weight of each solid wheel to the original total. If the wheels are the same, the weight of the bike has to be increased by the weight of one wheel to get a true reflection of the inertia of the wheels.

For example, assume the bike and rider weigh 160kgf. If each wheel assembly has an equivalent weight of 4kgf then the weight to be accelerated is 168kgf, not 160kgf. The actual weight of the wheels is of course included in the original 160kgf. The figure of 168kgf will further increase when the other rotating parts are included.

Real bikes do not have solid wheels and the wheels they do have vary considerably. To assess their effect we need the moment of inertia of everything that rotates with the wheel, ie the wheel, tyre, sprocket, brake disc etc. Heavy tyres and/or rims will have the greatest influence because they are at a large radius. Any weight you can save on rotating parts will give an extra gain because it comes off the original total and the inertia equivalent. Calculating the moment of inertia of a complete motorcycle wheel assembly is not for the faint hearted. The sums do get a bit heavy but fortunately you do not need to do this. Instead, you can find the moment of inertia of your wheels by experiment. Having done so, dividing the result by the (rolling radius)^2 will give the equivalent mass to add to the original value.

To find the moment of inertia use the data in Fig 6.4 overleaf and the examples that follow. To determine its moment of inertia, the wheel has to roll down a slight incline on a spindle. The inertia of the spindle will be included in the result but it is very small. I use two pieces of angle iron off an old bed frame to make the runway as shown. The slope should only be shallow, typically one in ten, and it takes a bit of experience to stop the wheel veering off to one side before the end of the run. A few practice rolls will do the trick but this whole procedure requires great care. The following are all important.

- The wheel must be well balanced, statically at least. Imbalance will affect the roll speed and produce errors in the result.
- The wheel must rotate on the spindle, not the bearings. It is best to arrange a light fixing to the sprocket carrier bolts but you can usually get away with using Blu-Tack to hold the spindle, bearing inner and bearing outer together.
- If you are prepared to take the trouble, a special spindle giving rolling diameters of about 30mm on each side runs much better than a small diameter spindle.
- The spindle must not slip down the incline, it must roll. Watch carefully to detect this. You need smooth but not polished surfaces.
- The tracks must be straight. They need to be set up accurately using a spirit level or the wheel will veer off easily.
- I generally allow the wheel to run 500mm down a slope of about 6 deg, occasionally slightly steeper.

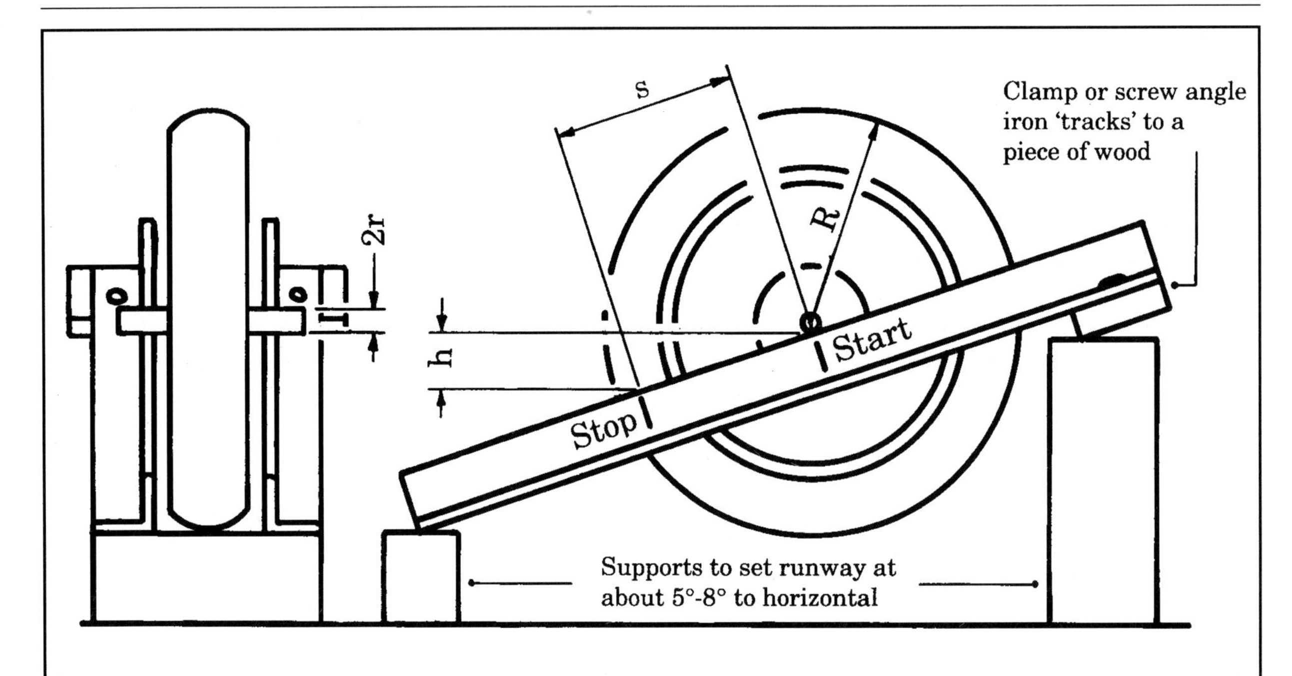

$I\ (kg.mm^2) = mr^2\left[\dfrac{4905ht^2}{s^2} - 1\right]$ **OR** **$I\ (lb.in^2) = mr^2\left[\dfrac{193.2ht^2}{s^2} - 1\right]$**

where

I = moment of inertia in $kg.mm^2$
m = mass in kg (reading on the scales)
r = spindle radius in mm
h = height of roll in mm
s = distance of roll in mm
t = time to roll in seconds

where

I = moment of inertia in $lb.in^2$
m = mass in lb (reading on the scales)
r = spindle radius in ins
h = height of roll in ins
s = distance of roll in ins
t = time to roll in seconds

$$\text{Equivalent mass} = \frac{\text{moment of inertia}}{(\text{rolling tyre radius})^2}$$

Equivalent mass is in kg if the moment of inertia is $kg.mm^2$ and the radius is mm.

In Imperial units, the mass is in pounds if the moment of inertia is in $lb.in^2$ and the radius is inches.

- Timing is critical. Do at least three runs and take an average. If the figures vary by more than 1%, eg 0.2s in 20s, your set-up is not good enough.

Begin by placing the wheel on scales. The reading gives the mass (m) in kg or lb as appropriate. Measure the tyre's rolling radius (R) and the spindle radius (r), then sort out the basic roll down a suitable shallow slope. The roll needs to be slow and consistent, you don't want the wheel hurtling down the slope. When this is good, mark a known distance (s) down the slope and measure the height difference (h) between these points. Do this by placing a piece of wood that is horizontal below the track and measure the height to the start and finish, then subtract the readings to give (h).

Release the wheel from the highest point, starting the stopwatch as you do so. Record the time to reach the lower point. Do not stop the wheel until it has passed this point and you have stopped the watch.

The moment of inertia is then calculated using the formula given with the diagram. Dividing the result by the (rolling radius of the wheel)^2 gives the equivalent mass, hence weight.

Example. The following data was obtained for a cast magnesium wheel off a 125cc bike when complete with tyre, sprocket and lightweight disc.

mass (m)	= 6.1kg
radius (r)	= 7.5mm
height (h)	= 55mm
distance (s)	= 500mm
rolling rad (R)	= 292mm
time to roll (t)	= 27.3s, 27.3s, 27.5s, 27.3s
	= 27.35 average

Left. Fig 6.4 *Method and calculation for finding the moment of inertia of a complete wheel assembly, together with its equivalent weight. The 'runway' must be straight. It must be level when viewed end on. This test has to be done carefully or it is useless. Spend some time setting up the track with a spirit level before you bother taking measurements. Once the roll is good, it usually stays that way provided you align the wheel correctly before releasing it.*

Using the formula for metric units,

$$I(\text{kg.mm}^2) = 6.1 \times 7.5^2 \left[\frac{4905 \text{x} 55 \text{x} 27.35^2}{500^2} - 1\right]$$

$$= 343.125 \left[\ 807.19 - 1\right]$$

$$= 276623.94\text{kg.mm}^2$$

To determine the equivalent weight, divide this result by the rolling tyre radius (R)^2, ie

$$\text{Equiv. mass} = \frac{276623.94 \text{ kg.mm}^2}{292^2 \text{ mm}^2}$$

$$= \frac{276623.94}{85264} \text{ kg}$$

$$= 3.24\text{kg}$$

Thus for this wheel, its inertia can be represented by an extra mass of 3.24kg which is about 53% of its actual mass. This is typical, the common range being 35% to 55% and for normal wheels with tyres fitted you could do a lot worse than to simply assume that adding 50% of the weight of each complete wheel assembly will provide a reasonable allowance for the rotational inertia of these parts.

When working out the total weight of the bike you need to include this in the total, ie the wheel in the example effectively weighs 6.1kgf + 3.24kgf = 9.34kgf. With two similar wheels the bike is effectively 6.48kgf heavier when the inertia of both is included. In this specific case, it represents 9% of the basic bike weight and these are small, light wheels. Here is an example in Imperial units.

Example. The following data was obtained for a 19in spoked wheel off a grass track bike. The wheel has a magnesium hub and a particularly light tyre and rim for this application.

mass (m)	= 19lb
radius (r)	= 0.335in
height (h)	= 2.625in
distance (s)	= 20in
rolling rad (R)	= 12.76in
time to roll (t)	= 19.8s average

Using the formula,

$$I(lb.in^2) = 19x0.335^2\left[\frac{193.2x2.625x19.8^2}{20^2} - 1\right]$$

$$= 2.13 \left[497.06 - 1\right]$$

$$= 1056.6lb.in^2$$

To determine the equivalent weight, divide this result by the rolling tyre radius $(R)^2$, ie

$$\text{Equiv. mass} = \frac{1056.6lb.in^2}{12.76^2\ in^2}$$

$$= \frac{1056.6}{162.82}\ lb$$

$$= 6.49lb$$

The inertia of this example is equivalent to only 34% of the basic mass and the effective weight of this wheel is about 25.5lbf. Experiments like this are usually quite interesting and you will frequently find that the results do not agree with your expectations that are based on the cost of the wheels! The inertia of spoked wheels can be suprisingly low if they have been 'worked on' and one often has to justify the cost of cast wheels in terms of stiffness, looks and the ability to run tubeless tyres. Table 6.1 gives some examples.

Other rotating parts

The wheels are not the only part the engine has to rotate. It also has to rotate the crankshaft, clutch and gearbox internals. These also have inertia but things are considerably more complicated here because of the effect of the gearbox.

An interesting property of inertia is that it changes according to where you view it from when gearing is present. Fig 6.5 illustrates this. The moments of inertia of the two shafts are I_A and I_B. The gear ratio is n, with shaft B running slower than shaft A.

If shaft A is the driver, then the inertia it has to deal with is its own, I_A, plus the inertia of B as seen at shaft A. This will be I_B/n^2, ie I_B is reduced by the square of the gear ratio.

However, if shaft B does the driving then, because shaft A runs faster, B will see its own inertia I_B plus $I_A n^2$. In this case the inertia of A appears to be greater than it really is. When large speed changes are involved the effects are dramatic. A 15:1 ratio makes the inertia greater or smaller by a factor of 225 (15^2) according to which shaft is doing the driving.

You can easily verify these findings on the bike. Spinning the back wheel in first gear takes a lot of

Table 6.1 *Inertia data for various wheels.*

Wheel configuration	Weight (kgf)	Moment of inertia (kg mm^2)	Tyre rolling radius (mm)	Equivalent weight (kgf)	Total effective weight (kgf)
Dymag 18in front + tyre for 125cc bike	4.54	198411	286	2.43	6.97
Astralite (thin) 18in front + tyre for 125cc	5.44	195473	286	2.39	7.83
Dymag 18in rear + tyre for 125cc bike	6.1	277029	292	3.25	9.35
Astralite (thin) 18in rear + tyre + disc for 125	7.03	278167	292	3.26	10.29
Light 19in spoked rear + tyre for grass track	8.62	320336	324	3.05	11.67
500cc classic racer front,120-80x18 tyre + disc	9.5	554212	307	5.9	15.4
500cc classic racer rear, 2.75-5.00x18 tyre + disc	11.34	648644	327	6.07	17.41

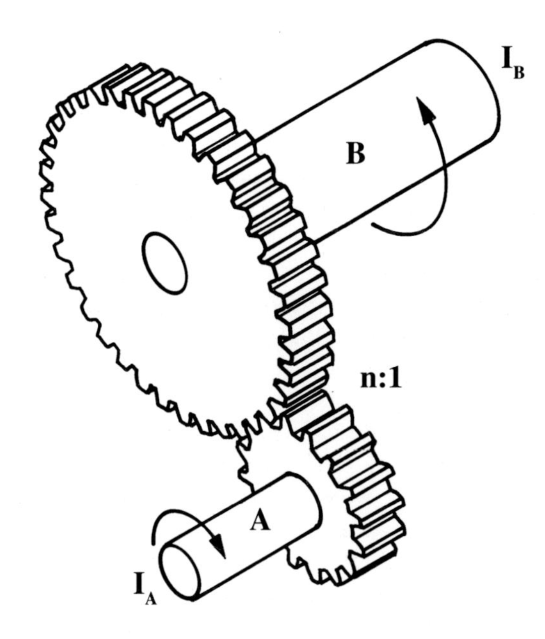

Fig 6.5 *When gearing is involved, the inertia of the components, as seen by the driving shaft, can change dramatically. If the driven component runs faster than the driver, its inertia appears to increase by a factor of n^2 where n is the gear ratio. If the driven component runs slower than the driver, its inertia appears to reduce by a factor of n^2.*

effort to accelerate the wheel compared to doing it in top gear. The reason is that you are accelerating the wheel's inertia plus that of the crankshaft, clutch and gearbox, all of which are running at a higher speed. Their inertia is therefore magnified by gearing and that of the crankshaft and clutch is greatly increased when in first gear (high numerical ratio value).

Viewed from the crankshaft, the reverse situation applies. The engine sees its own crankshaft inertia directly. That of the clutch, gearbox and rear wheel appears to be much less than it actually is because the gearing makes them run at lower speeds than the crankshaft.

For the purpose of investigating the effect of this on the bike, we can work from either the back wheel or crankshaft. I will work from the wheel because we have figures for driving force at the wheel (F) and the resistance to motion (R) (Sections 2 and 4). The acceleration will depend on the net driving force at any speed, ie (F - R) and the total equivalent mass seen by this force.

Our total mass is gradually getting larger! We started with the bike and then remembered there was a rider as well. Adding all the riding gear, fuel, oil and water gave a much higher figure. On top of this an allowance had to be made for the rotational inertia of the wheels and this probably added another 5%. Finally, we have just discovered that all the other rotating parts have their inertia magnified by the gearing as far as the torque at the back wheel is concerned so they will effectively add even more mass to the current total.

This last element is very influential at low speeds because the first gear ratio has a large numerical value. In top gear it is far less significant. I have not done the sums on enough bikes to give a general guide but when I was racing a 125cc bike several years ago, calculations showed that the inertia of the crank and transmission had an equivalent weight that was about three times the actual weight of the complete rear wheel assembly when in bottom gear. In top gear it was about 85% of the weight of the back wheel.

On a car, with its heavy rotating parts, the total rotational inertia can be equivalent to a 100% increase in the vehicle's weight when in a low first gear. In top gear it might account for an extra 5%. Unless you have nothing better to do, you are unlikely to work all this out. Each of the major components is connected to the wheel by a different ratio and some of them change with the gear selected - Fig 6.6 overleaf. It is all rather complicated but it does have an effect on low speed performance. If you wish to pursue it, the shafts, pinions, crankshaft and clutch can all be approximated reasonably well as individual discs for which $I = mr^2/2$ as discussed earlier. The problem is deciding on the value of r! There is too much work to include here but Fig 6.6 does cover the general idea.

Summary

Whatever the amount of work you decide to do on this area the basic idea is very simple. Things that rotate need to be accounted for. They will reduce the actual acceleration that the bike can achieve. Any weight saved on rotating parts reduces both the basic weight and the extra equivalent weight due to rotation. Do bear in mind that there are other considerations such as the effects of crankshaft inertia mentioned in Section 2. If you want

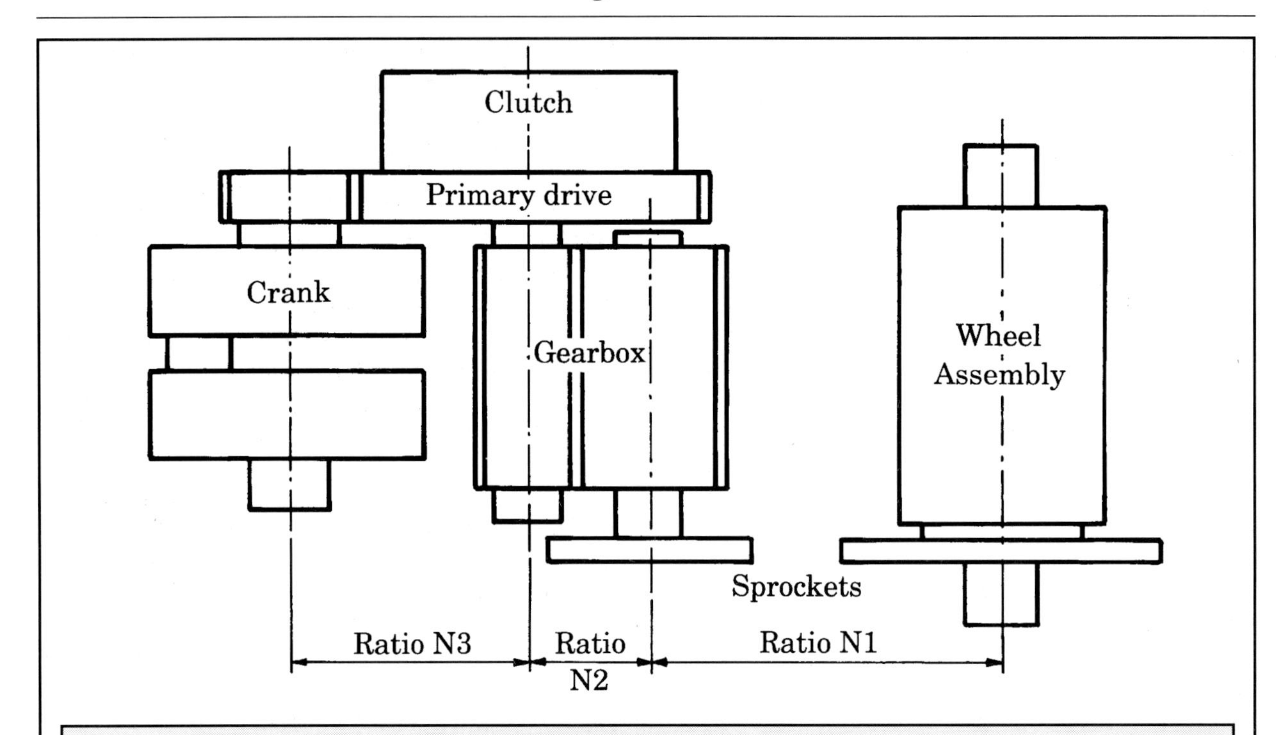

$$\mathbf{I_{WRef} = I_W + (N1)^2 I_{GO} + (N1N2)^2 I_{CL} + (N1N2N3)^2 I_C}$$

where

- I_{WRef} = **Total moment of inertia seen by the torque at the wheel**
- I_W = **Moment of inertia of everything on the wheel**
- I_{GO} = **Moment of inertia of everything on gearbox output shaft**
- I_{CL} = **Moment of inertia of everything on the clutch shaft**
- I_C = **Moment of inertia of everything on the crankshaft**
- **N1 = Final drive ratio = teeth on rear/teeth on gearbox**
- **N2 = Internal ratio = teeth on output shaft/teeth on input (clutch) shaft**
- **N3 = Primary ratio = teeth on clutch/teeth on crank**

Example. The data that follows applies to a 125cc bike. What is the total effective weight in each gear? (first gear is given as an example). Weight of bike and rider = 153kgf, equivalent weight due to front wheel inertia = 2.7kgf, moments of inertia as follows: Complete rear wheel = 280000kg mm^2, everything on gearbox output shaft = 1250kg mm^2, everything on clutch shaft = 10200kg mm^2, everything on crankshaft = 7400kg mm^2. Rolling rear tyre radius = 292mm. Final drive ratio = 2.4:1, primary = 3.28:1, internals (first to top) = 1.842, 1.455, 1.250, 1.120, 1.038, 0.963.

In first gear,

Total I $= 280000 + 2.4^2 x1250 + (2.4x1.842)^2 x10200 + (2.4x1.842x3.28)^2 x7400$ kg mm^2

$= 2042442$kg mm^2, thus equivalent weight of rotating parts = $2042442/292^2 = 24$kgf

Total effective weight of bike and rider in first gear = 153 + 2.7 + 24 = 179.7kgf

This is a 17% increase over the basic weight. In top gear the total is 164.7kgf, ie + 7.6%

to estimate the speed-time history of the bike, then the mass you use must include an allowance for rotating parts or the results will be optimistic, especially at low speed. If you don't like the sums just add on 10%, though in first and second gear it will not be enough.

In the performance estimates that follow in the next chapter I will neglect the inertia of the engine/gearbox components but include the wheels. This will result in an over-optimistic acceleration at low road speeds but not sufficiently over-optimistic to render the calculation worthless. In any event, if the purpose of the exercise is to compare possible improvements then, if you keep the engine and gearbox parts as they are, other comparisons will be perfectly valid.

Power to weight ratio

Having stood at the edge of a numerical abyss, I will now step back to the simple but very useful idea of power to weight ratio. This is a commonly quoted performance indicator that relates to acceleration. The big advantage of power to weight ratio is that it is very easy to work out though its usefulness is clearly limited by its simplicity. It is indicative of acceleration potential for the following reasons. If we had an infinitely variable gearbox, peak power would tell us the maximum driving force available at any road speed. If there was no rolling resistance or air resistance then dividing the driving force by the mass would give the acceleration possible at the chosen speed. Since weight is proportional to mass, power divided by weight does indicate acceleration potential subject to the restrictions below.

- It assumes all bikes have no resistance to motion or, if you like, equal resistance to motion. This is not the case.

- It neglects limits imposed by tyres, front wheel lift and chassis design.

- It assumes that the bike always delivers peak power. This is not true either. The shape of the torque curve and the choice of gear ratios are highly influential in practice.

My own view of power to weight ratio is that it represents a most important starting point. Although it fails to account for numerous things, if you have achieved a good power to weight ratio then that is the first step. If you can subsequently develop better aerodynamics and power delivery than the competition you will be well on the way towards being at the front.

Power to weight ratio is generally obtained by dividing the gross power produced by the engine by the weight of the unladen motorcycle. This gives a figure that is easy to compare but one which is very optimistic in real terms. Even if you do not attempt to calculate a true equivalent weight that includes an allowance for inertia, you must at least include a fully kitted rider and a tank of fuel. Without such allowances, the ratio assumes we are all the same and anyone who has raced small capacity bikes knows the difference rider weight can make.

Similarly, transmission losses vary and a net power figure at the back wheel is what you should be using. Whatever the case, the only really important aspect is that you know how the power to weight ratios are determined if you make comparisons with any published data.

Figures can be given in any suitable units of power and weight. All sorts of figures are in use and you can choose from units such as kW/N, kW/kgf, kW/tonne, bhp/lbf, bhp/tonf etc. Some conversions are given in Table 6.2.

Example. A 250cc roadracer produces 61kW and weighs 99kgf. What is the power to weight ratio of the bike?

$$\text{Power: weight ratio} = \frac{\text{power}}{\text{weight}}$$

$$= \frac{61\text{kW}}{99\text{ kgf}}$$

$$= 0.616\text{kW/kgf}$$

Left. Fig 6.6 *Referred inertia of transmission components as seen at the back wheel of the bike. The calculations do become rather lengthy but the example given may help the more enthusiastic readers.*

Example. A 750cc roadracer produces 120bhp and weighs 400lbf. What is the power to weight ratio a) in bhp/lbf b) in bhp/tonf c) in bhp/kgf?

$$\text{Power: weight ratio} = \frac{\text{power}}{\text{weight}}$$

$$= \frac{120\text{bhp}}{400\text{lbf}}$$

$$= 0.3\text{bhp/lbf}$$

b) using Table 6.2,

bhp/tonf = 0.3 x 2240 = 672bhp/tonf

bhp/kgf = 0.3 x 2.2046 = 0.66bhp/kgf

Example. A 125cc racer produces 44bhp gross, 38bhp at the rear wheel. The bike weighs162lbf including fuel and an allowance for inertia. The rider weighs 140lbf ready to race. What are the gross, net and laden power to weight ratios?

$$\text{Gross power: weight ratio} = \frac{\text{power}}{\text{weight}}$$

$$= \frac{44\text{bhp}}{162\text{lbf}}$$

$$= 0.272\text{bhp/lbf}$$

$$\text{Net power: weight ratio} = \frac{38\text{bhp}}{162\text{lbf}}$$

$$= 0.235\text{bhp/lbf}$$

$$\text{Laden, net value} = \frac{38\text{bhp}}{302\text{lbf}} = 0.126\text{bhp/lbf}$$

There is little point in quoting large numbers of power to weight ratios. They are only a baseline for a specific type of bike and there are many other factors that need to be considered as far as performance is concerned. You can obviously correlate power to weight ratio with standing quarter mile (402m) times but the scatter of results is vast, mainly due to all the other factors. Once you have obtained a power to weight ratio that is typical for the class you race in, other things are much more important, particularly aerodynamics.

Table 6.2 *Conversion factors for power:weight ratios. Note that 1tonne is 1000kg and therefore a mass unit, however its use for weight is common on the same basis as kgf. For the young, 1tonf = 2240lbf!*

To convert	To	Multiply by
kW/N	bhp/lbf	5.962
kW/tonne(f)	bhp/tonf	1.362
kW/kgf	bhp/lbf	0.608
bhp/lbf	bhp/tonf	2240
bhp/lbf	bhp/kgf	2.2046
bhp/lbf	kW/N	0.1677
bhp/lbf	kW/kgf	1.645
bhp/tonf	kW/tonne(f)	0.734

6.2 Straight-line performance

Introduction

On short circuits most respectable racing bikes are rarely going to reach the true top speed of which they are capable because the straights are too short and there are corners to negotiate. This means that the lap times are going to be determined by the ability of the bike to accelerate, brake and corner.

Cornering speed is the key to winning races once the basic performance of the bike is adequate. However, although it is possible to work out the speeds at which the bike should be capable of cornering this is very much a case of sums for the sake of it as far as normal riders are concerned. The difference in cornering speed between a club racer and a GP rider on the same bike is considerable, especially on corners taken at high speed, so the main factor controlling the speed is the rider, until one gets to GP level.

Additionally, although it is easy to decide what the maximum cornering forces should be, the road is not smooth and neither is the delivery of power. This means that the suspension, weight distribution and squat characteristics are all extremely influential. In short, reality is a long way from any simple sums that could be included here. The best way to develop cornering speed is to try harder!

Braking

Braking has not been discussed in this book, other than to acknowledge the problem of cg location which will influence the balance of rear wheel lift and front end slide during braking. Braking is one of the most important areas of performance but I have chosen to leave most of the discussion out of this particular book for the following reason.

Braking is an area where the rider is very much in control and there are considerable differences between riders. It is possible to buy superb braking systems off the shelf for a relatively modest outlay. Current brakes of race quality are easily capable of more stopping power than the tyres can deal with and they can maintain this level of performance throughout short circuit events. Few constructors will actually make the components involved because those available are of such high quality. Given this situation, it is the way the rider feels about the brakes and tyres that matters and this comes down to selecting components of a suitable type for the individual's style of riding. Factors such as pad compounds, relative areas of master cylinder and caliper cylinders, disc size etc are all dominated by the feel required by the rider. For example, when Kevin Schwantz was riding for Suzuki he normally used harder pads and a larger master cylinder bore than most of the other riders. The combination chosen was what Kevin required to match his outstanding braking ability and aggressive style of riding. To another rider, his brake set-up would probably feel awful, indeed a less aggressive rider may fail to get the brakes up to temperature.

Finally, the ability to dissipate heat and maintain performance is mainly a function of design and materials, in other words, the whole business of braking is largely one of selecting suitable standard parts. For this reason, I hope to cover brakes along with all the other standard parts in a second book. As far as this chapter is concerned, I will briefly discuss the deceleration figures achieved by good brakes because any bike that accelerates better also needs to stop!

Once you have braking components that suit you then there are two things that matter, the ability of the rider to use them and the limits imposed by the design of the bike and conditions.

In the dry, the maximum deceleration is probably around 1g for a quick National racer. GP riders with the best of everything push these figures to around 1.1g, possibly 1.2g but that is about it according to all the data logger traces I have. Also note that these are the figures for the most intense braking.

If you take an average over the whole braking event then the figures will be lower. For the majority of riders, 0.6g-0.9g is a good average. One thing that clearly separates the GP front runners from everyone else is the lack of build-up time, ie they are able to hit peak deceleration almost instantly and then maintain it. This pushes their average deceleration up close to the peak values, ie their level of deceleration remains more constant when conditions allow.

To illustrate this, Fig 6.7 is a repeat of one data logging trace given earlier. The deceleration figures shown in the lower trace do shoot up and down with every minor undulation in the speed trace. The reasons for this were given earlier. Ignoring these, the peak level of deceleration is around 12m/s^2, apart from the momentary region of overbraking. Taken as an average over the period C to G, the rider reduces his speed by 93km/hr (58miles/hr) in 2.5s. This gives an average deceleration of 10.3m/s^2 or 1.05g which is typical at this level. Beyond point G, he is easing off the brakes slightly as he turns into the corner.

In the wet everything is different and tyres dominate the issue, together with the rider's ability to seek out the limit. On top quality road tyres, figures around 0.5g-0.6g are possible but I do not have any accurate data for racing bikes using the latest breed of rain tyres. Common sense suggests that the figures are somewhat better than those just given.

All the figures quoted relate to an upright bike with a skilled rider so they can be used to give a reasonable reflection of the time taken to brake between various speeds. I will use this facility later on.

Fig 6.7 *Data logging is the only way to be really sure what is happening to the bike. Timing over set distances from the side of the track is very difficult to do accurately and it can only show average results over a significant period of time. This data from Jerez reveals just how rapidly a GP rider can slow the bike down.*

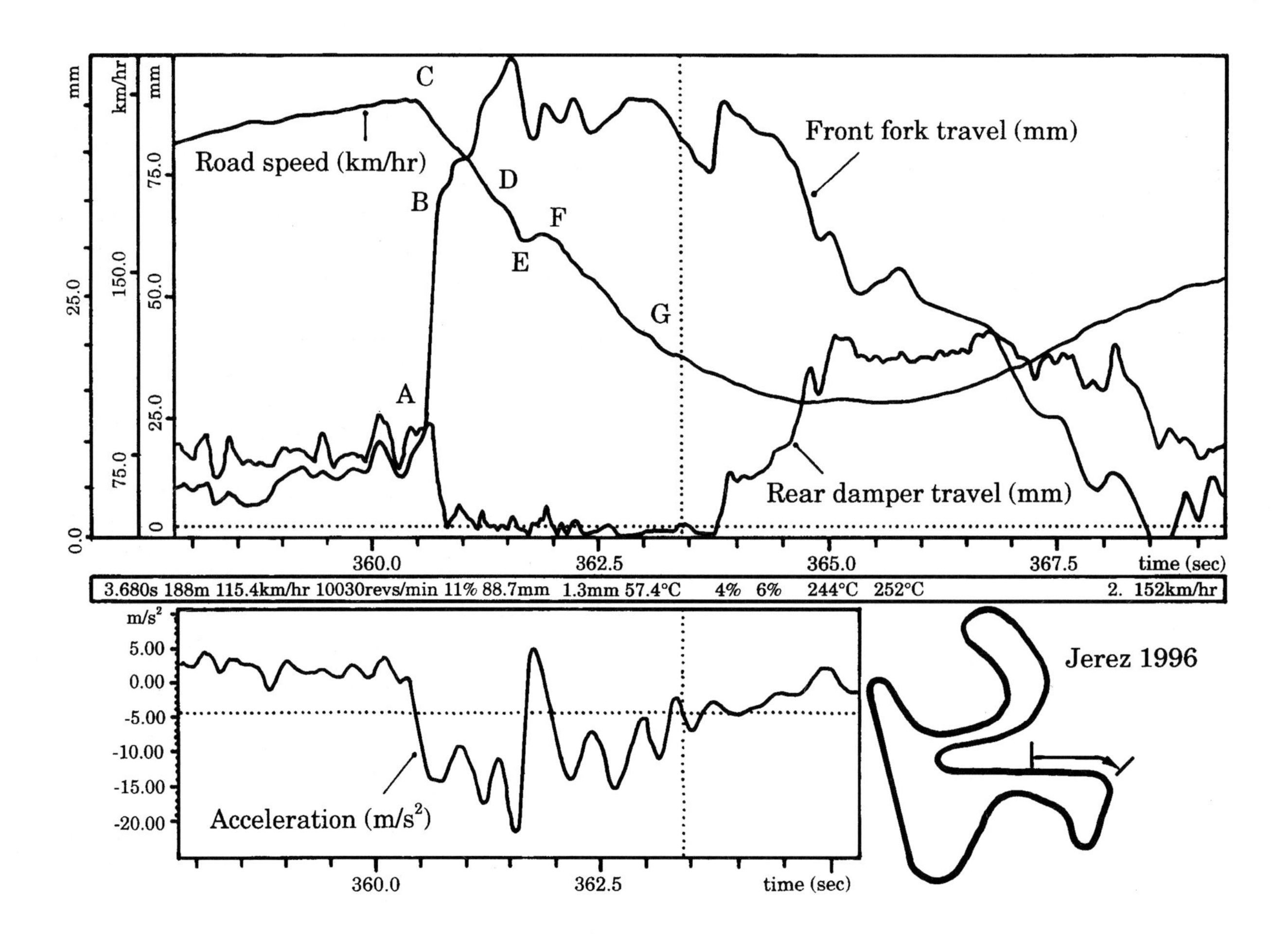

Acceleration

Acceleration is particularly important because it not only covers straight line activities but also a significant portion of cornering, especially on small bikes. If you are actually able to keep on full throttle and work up through the gears then it is the bike's ability to accelerate that controls the time you are taking even if the track happens to have a bend in it! The same can be said of braking though to a lesser extent.

For two riders of similar ability small differences in acceleration can produce vital gains. It might just amount to a wheel in front at the end of the straight or it could mean putting a back marker behind you before the next corner. Whatever the case, any small gains will add up. The basic idea of acceleration was covered in Chapter 3.2 and you may wish to refer to this.

The acceleration of the motorcycle is determined by many factors but they are conveniently divided into two groups, those which have a direct effect in generating the acceleration and those which limit what we can actually achieve. In the first group we have,

- The potential driving force at the rear wheel assuming there is grip.
- The total resistance to motion.
- The total mass of the bike, rider, fuel, riding gear etc.
- The total referred inertia of all the rotating components.

In the second group we must include,

- Rider skill.
- Tyre characteristics.
- The road surface and conditions.
- The tendency of the rear wheel to spin or the front wheel to lift.
- The compliance of the suspension and its reaction to the acceleration.

Limiting factors will have their biggest influence at low road speeds because that is where the acceleration is potentially greatest. How wide the range of speeds affected will be depends on the size and type of bike but we are certainly looking at the first 100km/hr (63miles/hr) in most cases. It could be a lot more.

Because of these limiting factors, the low speed acceleration of many racing motorcycles is surprisingly similar. Given normal race tyres (if there is such a thing), a dry track and a skilled rider, a limiting value somewhere close to 1.1g is likely to exist if the bike is well designed and is going to handle sensibly when braking or cornering. Exactly what this means in terms of design and how you compromise between front wheel lift and rear wheel spin was covered in Section 3.

If you are able to restrict yourself to straight line motion and not worry too much about cornering then considerably higher values can be achieved. This is the realm of sprinters and dragsters. Even the awesome GP 500's do not come up with anything much different to a 1.1g limit and many smaller capacity bikes will stay with them for one or two seconds, however the difference then starts to become rather obvious. At low speed, say 80km/hr (50miles/hr), the acceleration potential of the 500cc bike with perhaps 142kW (190bhp) driving a laden weight of some 225kgf (496lbf) is 2.9g but the rider cannot achieve this and keep the front wheel down. However, the bike can be kept at whatever the limit is and it will still be accelerating at close to 1g when it is going at 200km/hr (124miles/hr). It will of course reach zero acceleration like everything else but not until perhaps 320km/hr (200miles/hr). In contrast, even a 250cc GP bike is unlikely to be able to accelerate at its limiting values when the road speeds are above 115km/hr (71miles/hr).

Most people reading this book will never have access to any form of GP bike, let alone a 500 and therefore once the initial euphoria of the first couple of seconds is over the desire for more acceleration will be present, backed by the knowledge that the bike is no longer at any form of limit. How any increase in acceleration will convert into reduced lap times is something of a disappointment and I will leave it until the end of this chapter. For the moment, it is sufficient to summarise the requirements as follows.

Speed (km/hr)
260
240
220
200
180
160
140
120
100
80
60
40
20
0
0 2 4 6 8 10 12 14 16 18 20 22 24 26 28 30 32 34
Time from rest (s)

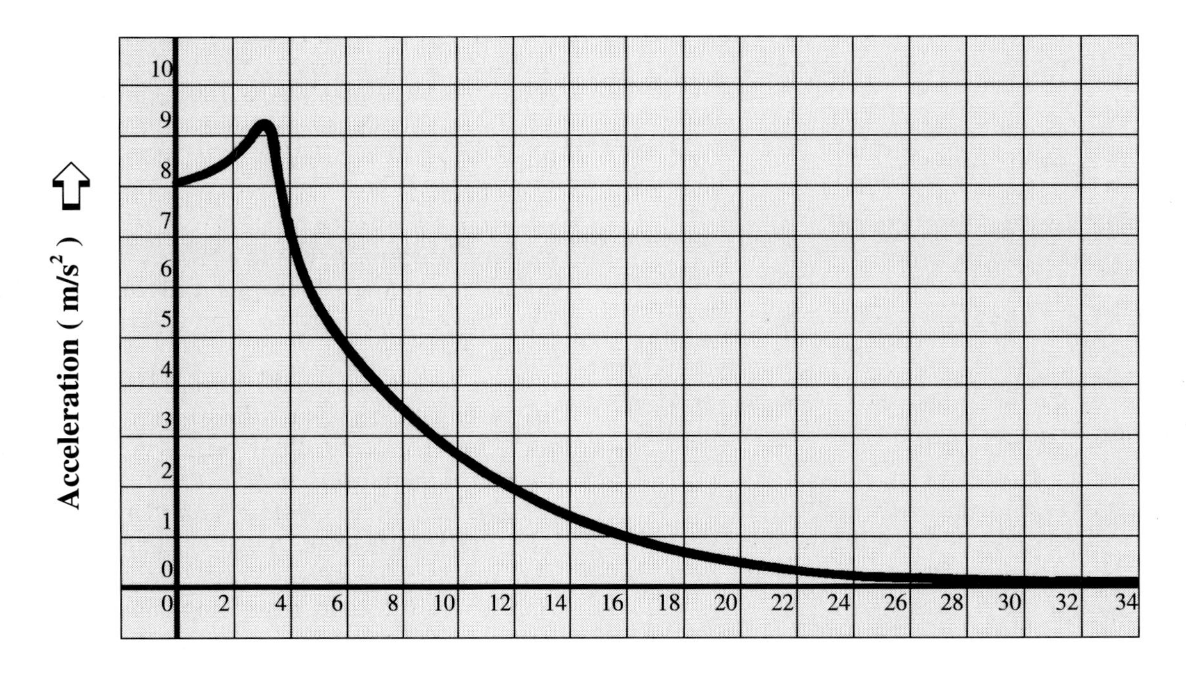
Acceleration (m/s^2)
10
9
8
7
6
5
4
3
2
1
0
0 2 4 6 8 10 12 14 16 18 20 22 24 26 28 30 32 34
Time from rest (s)

- Maximise the driving force. The general ideas associated with this have been covered in Chapter 2.4. Gearing is crucial to acceleration.

- Minimise the resistance to motion at all road speeds, especially high ones. Section 4 dealt with this.

- Minimise the laden weight of the bike and rider. Diet time!

- Minimise the inertia of rotating parts. In practice this boils down to using the best wheels/discs you can afford and, possibly, looking at crankshafts and clutches. The previous chapter outlined the basic ideas.

- Design the bike so that the weight distribution gives the best compromise between traction and front wheel lift. This was discussed in Chapter 3.2.

- Sort out some acceptable swinging arm geometry and suspension so that the rear end behaves itself, ie not too much squat or jacking up, Chapter 3.3.

If you do all these things then you will get the best result you can within your budget and you may not care what the actual acceleration is.

Left. Fig 6.8 *The acceleration of a motorcycle can be derived from the speed-time history. In all cases the acceleration reaches a peak value shortly after the start and then begins to tail off, eventually reaching zero at maximum speed.*

Acceleration potential

The acceleration of a motorcycle starts at a relatively high value and then gradually falls off to zero when top speed has been reached. If you have a speed-time history such as those shown previously from GP bikes then you can determine the average acceleration over a series of small time intervals using the formula given in Chapter 3.2. The result is of the general form shown in Fig 6.8, though detailed analysis will show lots of minor variations about the mean level, just as with braking. What I intend to do here is to discuss the problems of working the other way, ie using the ideas already covered to predict the speed-time history of the bike.

There are two major problems associated with doing this. The first is the sheer amount of data required to generate reasonable answers and, though not impossible, it is basically impractical to attempt any such calculation without the assistance of a computer system. By the time all the limiting factors have been introduced, and the net driving force has been determined every 2km/hr or so, you will have enough numbers to fill the room! It is better that they are left inside a computer's memory where they can easily be modified as required.

For this reason alone, I am not going to work through the whole procedure. If you do not have a computer system and some programming ability it is better to concentrate on track tests and the sources of improvement just listed. If there is sufficient demand, I will produce some software to cover all of the sums in this book. Alternatively, Motorcycle Tuning (chassis) by John Robinson contains several relevant program listings, and most of your requirements can be met by any good spreadsheet program.

The second major problem is the need to tailor the program to the type of bikes you are involved with. This is particularly true for the initial 'launch' of the bike and the limits set by front wheel lift or rear wheel spin. A small capacity bike with a razor sharp powerband does not get off the line in the same way as something that is both powerful and flexible. For best results, the calculations performed need to be refined on the basis of experimental data.

Despite these difficulties, some general comments and a simplified example may help readers to create their own programs for this purpose.

General Method

There are several ways of doing this job but the first stage is as follows.

- Generate a series of driving force cascades (for the chosen gearing) and a suitable resistance curve like that shown in Fig 6.9. Refer to the methods in Sections 2 and 4.

- From these curves you can find the net driving force available at a series of road speeds by subtracting the resistance from the driving force. To get reliable results this should be done at 2km/hr or 1mile/hr intervals, hence the need for a computer. If the curves are very smooth you can use wider intervals but in most cases you will then miss out important changes and the errors build up.

- If you are determined to pursue this by hand, then the best way to obtain these values from a set of graphs is to measure the force difference using a ruler as shown in Fig 6.10, then convert the readings. For example, the force scale in Fig 6.9 is 160mm long and covers 4000N. The scale is thus 25N/mm and a ruler measurement of say 60mm would equate to 1500N.

The launch and limits

In attempting the above, several decisions have to be made. Firstly, you must decide where to change gear. In general this will be where the cascades intersect to achieve maximum acceleration. Secondly, there is no data at low road speeds and the clutch is slipping. The best way to deal with this is to do some tests and determine the engine speed, or road speed, at the point where the clutch is fully engaged. This varies a lot between road bikes and race bikes, the latter usually having rather high first gears. Once you know this, you then have to decide what force is available at speeds below this and there are no simple, exact answers. I usually assume the driving force remains constant up to clutch engagement. For example, if the clutch is fully engaged at 50km/hr on the YZR750R (Fig 6.9) then I would assume that the driving force is about 2500N up to this point. It then climbs with the force curve and you can read all the remaining values directly. This is usually an underestimate, there is often sufficient force to maintain 1g, but it all depends on the rider's ability to launch the bike off the line.

Right. Fig 6.9 *Driving force cascades and probable resistance to motion for a Yamaha YZF750R.*

Below. Fig 6.10 *The best way to find the net driving force at regular speed intervals is to measure the gap with a ruler and then multiply this by the force scale factor. In the example, the net force in 3rd gear is being checked at 160km/hr.*

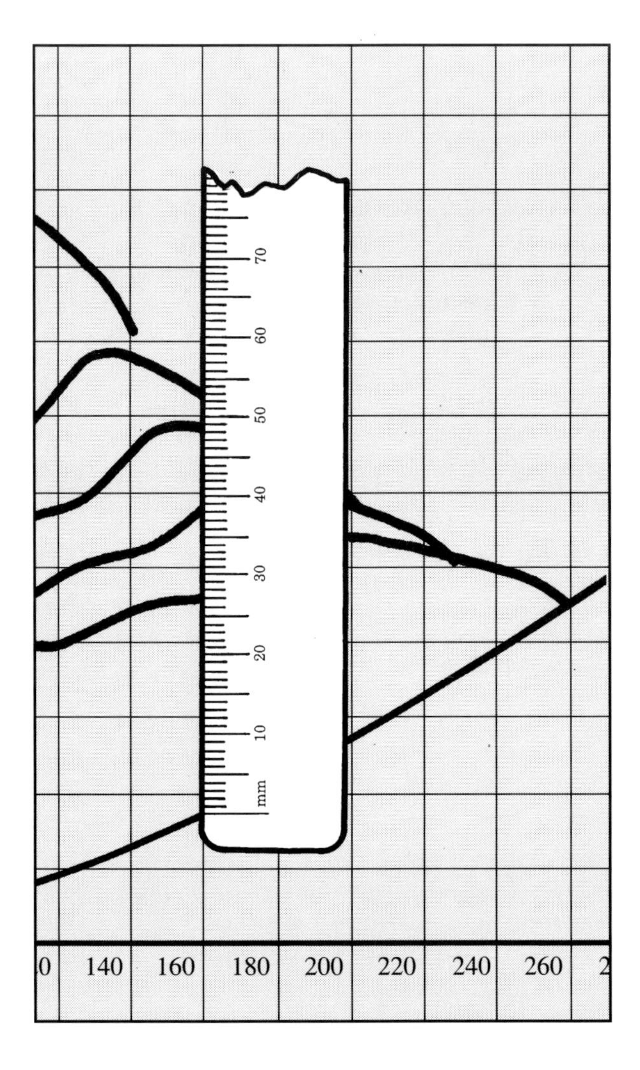

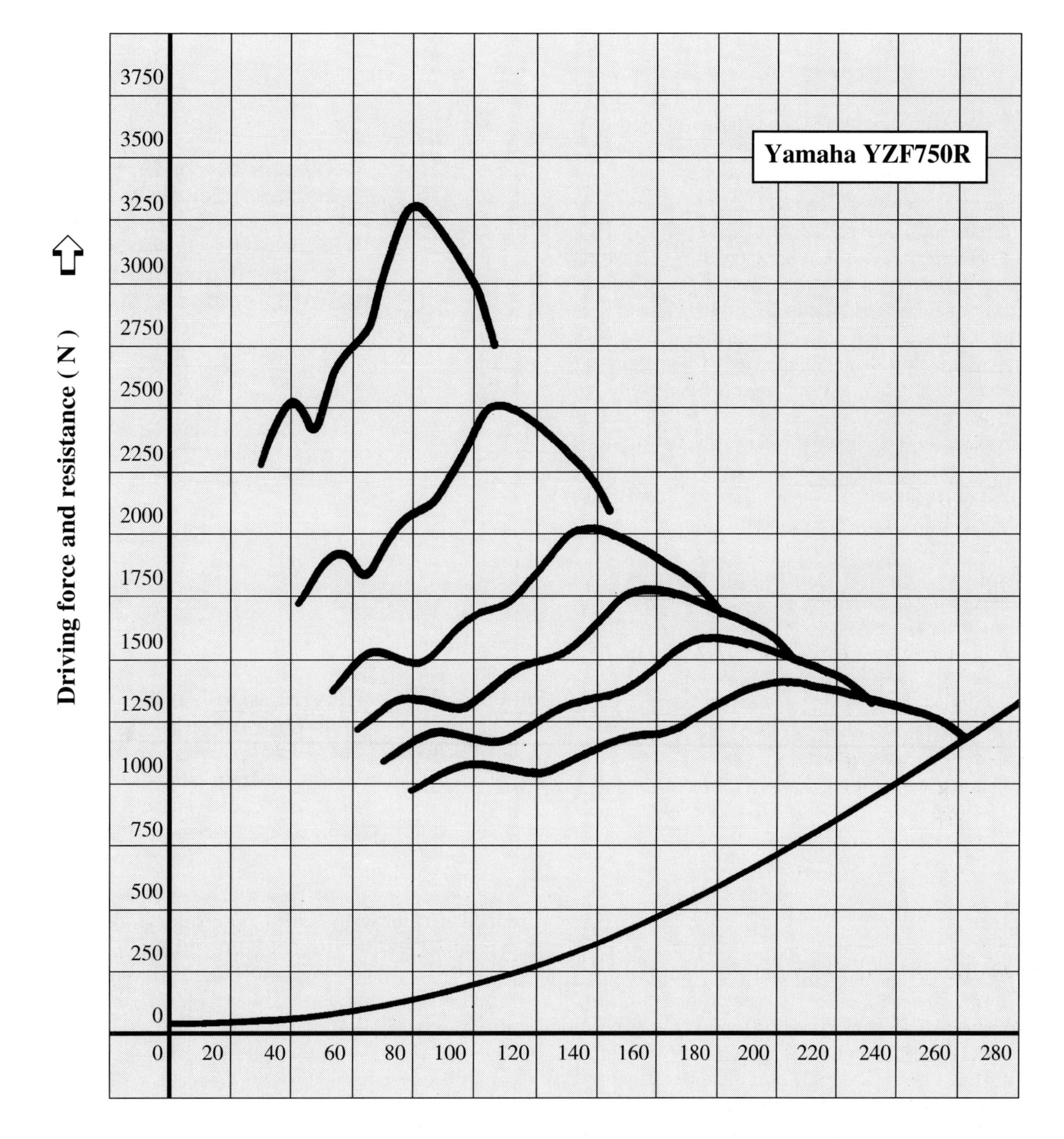
Yamaha YZF750R
Driving force and resistance (N)
3750
3500
3250
3000
2750
2500
2250
2000
1750
1500
1250
1000
750
500
250
0
0
20
40
60
80
100
120
140
160
180
200
220
240
260
280
Road speed (km/hr)

Once you have done this for the whole speed range you can then calculate the potential acceleration at any speed. To do this, use one of the formulae on the right. The mass figure should include the bike, fuel, oil, rider, clothing and an equivalent mass of the rotating parts.

The rotating parts are extremely important in all this. In first and second gear they will considerably increase the effective weight of the bike and if you do not include them your figures will be very optimistic once several seconds have passed. This is a problem that can be dealt with in two ways. The first option is to work out the equivalent weights in each gear, as described in the previous chapter. This is then added to the laden mass and your calculation is performed with a mass that reduces each time a new gear is selected. An alternative method is to incorporate an allowance for the inertia into the original graph of resistance vs road speed. Both options involve more work than it is practical to cover here so I will just assume a total figure does exist.

Example. The driving force and resistance plots for a certain bike show that at 160km/hr the driving force is 1800N and the resistance is 450N. What is the potential acceleration at this speed if the total effective mass is 300kg?

$$\text{Acceleration (m/s}^2) = \frac{F - R}{m} = \frac{1800 - 450}{300} = 4.5\text{m/s}^2\ (0.5g)$$

Example. At 20miles/hr a bike produces a driving force of 680lbf and the resistance is 10lbf. What is the potential acceleration at this speed if the total effective weight is 680lbf?

If the laden weight is 600lbf then the mass is 600lb.

$$\text{Acceleration (ft/s}^2) = 32.2\ \frac{(680 - 10)}{600} = 35.95\text{ft/s}^2\ (1.17g)$$

$$\text{Acceleration (m/s}^2) = \frac{F - R}{m}$$

where

F = driving force in N
R = resisting force in N
m = total laden mass in kg (the reading on scales) plus any allowance for rotating components

or

$$\text{Acceleration (ft/s}^2) = 32.2\ \frac{F - R}{m}$$

where

F = driving force in lbf
R = resisting force in lbf
m = total laden mass in lb (the reading on scales) plus any allowance for rotating components

The second example raises the question of low-speed acceleration limits. The bike may not be capable of accelerating at 1.17g, either because of front wheel lift or because of wheelspin. You therefore need to calculate the acceleration that is possible using the ideas in Section 3 and impose these on the results. For example, if a 1g limit is considered realistic then the figure of 1.17g needs to be replaced with 1g. This does of course assume that the rider has the skill to maintain this. I can only comment from my limited experience but I think it is more likely that you will overestimate the possible acceleration than underestimate it. The acceleration needs to be calculated for every net force figure and this gives another mass of values. Table 6.3 gives a sample of the data for the YZR750R, using 10km/hr intervals.

Speed (km/hr)	Gear	Net force (N)	Acceleration (m/s^2)
0	1	2500	8.039
10	1	2500	8.039
20	1	2500	8.039
30	1	2500	8.039
40	1	2500	8.039
50	1	2500	8.039
60	1	2650	8.521
70	1	2850	9.164
80	1	3175	9.81lim
90	1	3000	9.646
100	1	2800	9.003
110	2	2275	7.315
120	2	2175	6.994
130	2	2000	6.431
140	2	1800	5.788
150	2	1550	4.984
160	3	1425	4.582
170	3	1300	4.180
180	4	1100	3.537
190	4	975	3.135
200	4	775	2.492
210	5	675	2.170
220	5	575	1.849
230	5	425	1.367
240	6	300	0.965
250	6	150	0.482
260	6	0	0

Table 6.3 *Sample values of the net driving force (F - R) taken at 10km/hr intervals for the Yamaha YZF750R road bike. The acceleration figures in the last column are calculated as described in the text using a nominal mass of 311kg. This is the main approximation. One of the accelerations is limited to 1g.*

Once the acceleration figures have been calculated, there are several ways of turning them into a speed-time history. The most straightforward is as follows. Starting from rest, the acceleration is known but, in general, it is changing. By the time the bike has increased its speed slightly, a new acceleration figure applies. If the interval is extremely small, you can assume that the acceleration remains at its original value but, for anything but the shortest speed interval, it is more reasonable to assume that the acceleration over this period is an average of two values, the initial one and the final one. Even this will produce a lot of error if the speed interval is too great or the power curve has lots of sharp peaks and troughs. If you do not have a computer there is no question of working this out accurately but, for the YZR example which has a relatively smooth force delivery, a reasonable result can be obtained using the figures in Table 6.3 and averaging them over each speed interval, eg 0-10km/hr, 10-20km/hr, etc.

The time taken to achieve a specified speed change at a particular average acceleration can be found using the following formulae.

$$\text{Time interval (s)} = \frac{V_{step}}{3.6\,A_{av}}$$

where V_{step} = **the speed interval in km/hr**

A_{av} = **the average acceleration during the interval in m/s^2**

or

$$\text{Time interval (s)} = \frac{1.467V_{step}}{A_{av}}$$

where V_{step} = **the speed interval in miles/hr**

A_{av} = **the average acceleration during the interval in ft/s^2**

Speed (km/hr)	Gear	Net force (N)	Acceleration (m/s^2)	Speed interval (km/hr)	Average acceleration (m/s^2)	Time increment (s)	Total time (s)
0	1	2500	8.039	-	-	-	
10	1	2500	8.039	0 - 10	8.039	0.346	0.346
20	1	2500	8.039	10 - 20	8.039	0.346	0.692
30	1	2500	8.039	20 - 30	8.039	0.346	1.038
40	1	2500	8.039	30 - 40	8.039	0.346	1.384
50	1	2500	8.039	40 - 50	8.039	0.346	1.730
60	1	2650	8.521	50 - 60	8.280	0.335	2.065
70	1	2850	9.164	60 - 70	8.843	0.314	2.379
80	1	3175	9.81lim	70 - 80	9.487	0.293	2.672
90	1	3000	9.646	80 - 90	9.728	0.286	2.958
100	1	2800	9.003	90 - 100	9.325	0.298	3.256
110	2	2275	7.315	100 - 110	8.159	0.340	3.596
120	2	2175	6.994	110 - 120	7.155	0.388	3.984
130	2	2000	6.431	120 - 130	6.713	0.414	4.398
140	2	1800	5.788	130 - 140	6.110	0.455	4.853
150	2	1550	4.984	140 - 150	5.386	0.516	5.369
160	3	1425	4.582	150 - 160	4.581	0.606	5.975
170	3	1300	4.180	160 - 170	4.381	0.634	6.609
180	4	1100	3.537	170 - 180	3.859	0.720	7.329
190	4	975	3.135	180 - 190	3.336	0.833	8.162
200	4	775	2.492	190 - 200	2.814	0.987	9.149
210	5	675	2.170	200 - 210	2.331	1.192	10.341
220	5	575	1.849	210 - 220	2.010	1.382	11.723
230	5	425	1.367	220 - 230	1.608	1.727	13.450
240	6	300	0.965	230 - 240	1.166	2.382	15.832
250	6	150	0.482	240 - 250	0.724	3.837	19.670
260	6	0	0	250 - 260	0.241	11.526	31.195

Table 6.4 shows the figures calculated for the Yamaha using the approximate data given. No allowance for gearchanges has been included. It is difficult to assess this exactly. If you dip the clutch then the bike will immediately start to slow down, though you will not notice it unless you fail to select the next gear quickly. A reasonable approximation for the time involved would be to assume that the speed remains constant for a brief period and some 'dead time' then has to be included. This is clearly not very thorough because there is probably more of a delay due to interrupting the engine's stable airflow than there is due to the bare mechanics of it. If the purpose of these calculations is purely comparison of different weights, drag, gears, etc then it is perfectly acceptable to ignore this aspect.

The final results are shown overleaf in Fig 6.11 where they are compared with a variety of road test figures. Given the limited amount of data used for illustration, and the uncertainty of many factors, they are quite reasonable. Overall, there is far too much work involved to justify this unless you can program it all. This will then allow you to change any of the variables and see what happens. In the absence of anything more concrete, you would then pursue the changes that show the best return on paper.

Effect on lap times

The final aspect I am going to consider is the effect of acceleration on lap times. This is rarely as much as you expect and it is worth exploring some of the reasons. Taken in isolation, any improvement in acceleration will reduce the time taken to cover a certain length of track. For example, assume that the bike leaves a corner at 100km/hr and accelerates at an average of 0.5g over 300m. The time to do this can be calculated as 6.77s.

If the acceleration could be increased to 0.7g during this period then the time taken will fall to 6.14s but before getting too excited you should note that this is a 40% increase in acceleration that has produced a 9% reduction in time. Obviously the figures are a simplification but the general behaviour is correct. The gain is still very important, even if it only amounts to 1%, because it applies during each period of acceleration and it may also allow you to overtake people and hence dominate the track at the next corner. However, this raises another source of disappointment. Each track is basically corners connected by straights with the following constraints.

Firstly, cornering speed. There will be a maximum speed at which any particular combination of bike and rider can enter a corner without falling off or drifting off-line. Once through the corner the rider accelerates towards the next corner and, if the acceleration is increased, the speed will be higher at any point along the straight.

This is very exciting, except that you have to be able to slow down again for the next corner! Since your corner entry speed is fixed and you still have the same brakes, you will have to start braking earlier. Because of this, the time saved by better acceleration is reduced still further.

To find out what really happens you need to subtract the extra time spent braking from the saving you have already made while accelerating. This will immediately tell you that Grandad was correct when he said that a faster bike needs better brakes!

The sums are a bit tedious, even with a constant, average, acceleration, but I do think a sample result is informative. The figures are given in Fig 6.12 overleaf. In this particular case, the final result is a time saving of only 2.37% from an acceleration increase of 40%. If you can save 2.37% on every section of track it is a massive result but it is much less than the increase in acceleration implied.

The figure arises as follows. With 0.5g acceleration, the bike covers 173.6m before the brakes have to go on. This takes 3.825s and the bike reaches 197km/hr. With 0.7g acceleration the speed rises much more rapidly and is 210km/hr after 153.6m. Only 3.25s have elapsed but the brakes have to go on at this point because the extra speed demands another 20m to slow the bike down. This adds 0.4s to the time spent braking. When you add up the acceleration and braking times in each case, the result is rather sad.

If nothing else, these examples do show how you have to work at every aspect of the bike in order to achieve good results and I hope that this book has helped to identify some of the more important areas.

Left. Table 6.4 *Calculated speed-time history for the YZF750R using simplified data at 10km/hr intervals.*

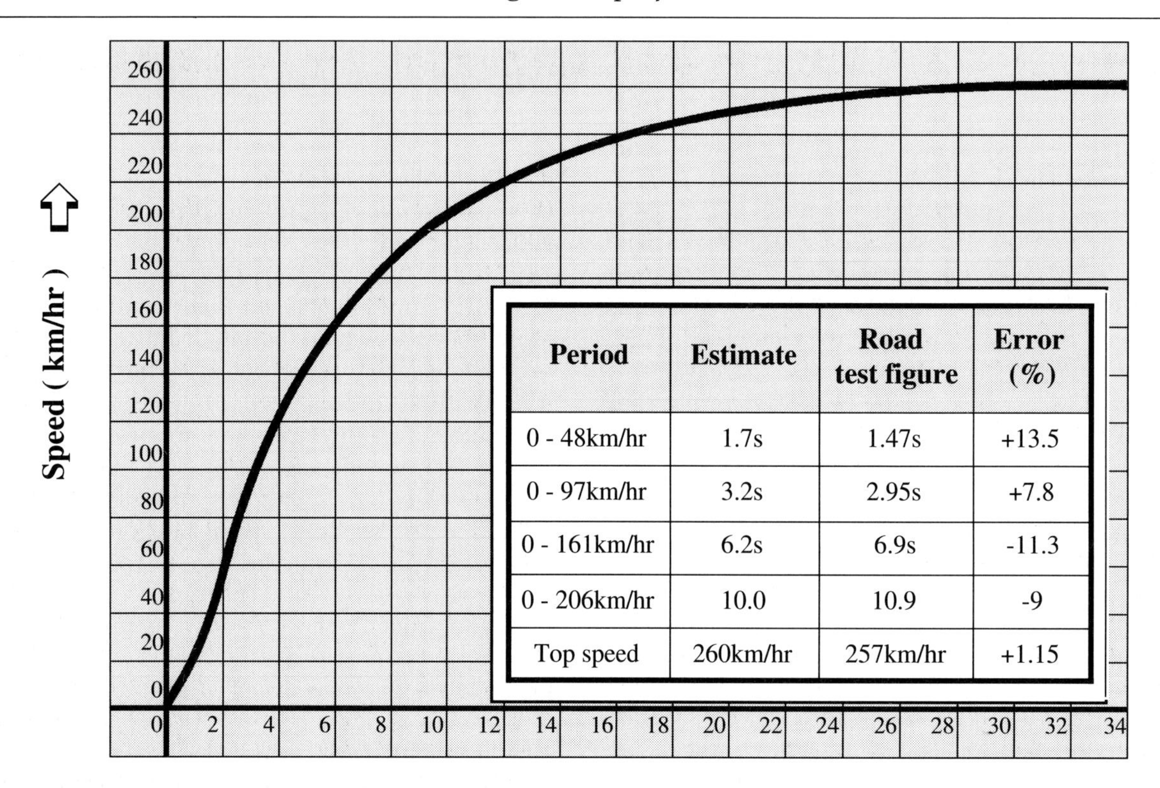

Period	Estimate	Road test figure	Error (%)
0 - 48km/hr	1.7s	1.47s	+13.5
0 - 97km/hr	3.2s	2.95s	+7.8
0 - 161km/hr	6.2s	6.9s	-11.3
0 - 206km/hr	10.0	10.9	-9
Top speed	260km/hr	257km/hr	+1.15

Time from rest (s)

Fig 6.11 *Estimated speed-time history for the YZF750R, together with road test data from several sources as a comparison.*

Fig 6.12 Example of the time saved by improved acceleration

A bike leaves a corner at 130km/hr (81miles/hr) and accelerates down a straight at 0.5g. Entry to the next corner is at 100km/hr (63miles/hr) and this is 300m away (984ft). If the brakes allow the bike to be decelerated at an average of 0.9g, how much time can be saved on this section of track if the acceleration is increased to 0.7g?

Although it sounds trivial, this is fairly tedious to work out and only the results are given here.

With 0.5g acceleration

time accelerating	= 3.825s
distance covered accelerating	= 173.6m
maximum speed reached	= 197km/hr
time spent braking	= 3.063s
distance covered braking	= 126.4m
total time to cover 300m	= 6.888s

With 0.7g acceleration

time accelerating	= 3.255s
distance covered accelerating	= 153.57m
maximum speed reached	= 210km/hr
time spent braking	= 3.469s
distance covered braking	= 146.43m
total time to cover 300m	= 6.725s

The final saving is thus 6.888s - 6.725s =0.163s which is 2.37% of the original time

Appendix A.1 Metric and Imperial units

Introduction

The purpose of this short appendix is to outline briefly the metric and Imperial units of measure that have been used throughout this book. The subject of units is vast and therefore I can only cover a very limited number of relevant topics.

Some understanding of units is essential in engineering. Performing calculations without this is rather like making components and measuring them with a vernier that you do not know how to read. Units are fundamental and much more important than the numbers they relate to since, if the units are wrong, the numbers are also likely to be incorrect. Sums are easy to check on a simple calculator but units are more difficult to deal with.

There are many systems of units in use. Some are metric and others are Imperial but they are all based on the need to measure certain fundamental quantities. As far as this book is concerned the most important quantities are mass, length, time temperature and angle. Other quantities such as electric current, luminous intensity etc apply to other applications but the final list is still very short because most quantities are derived from the few fundamental ones. For example, area has units of $(\text{length})^2$, speed is (length/time) and so on. Force, power, torque, speed, acceleration, pressure, energy etc are all derived quantities.

Any system of units has to define the fundamental quantities and relate them to a standard. Although it may be interesting, a knowledge of fundamental standards is unlikely to be of any practical use as far as motorcycles are concerned. The fact that one second is the duration of 9192631770 periods of radiation emission from caesium-133 is unlikely to change your approach to motorcycle development and I will therefore move on to the practical implications.

Imperial and metric

Broadly speaking there are still two basic systems in use, those which are based on metric quantities, eg kilogram and metre, and those based on Imperial quantities, eg pounds and feet. Within these two systems there are several variations but for many years the scientific community has being trying to achieve one universally agreed system based on certain metric units. Not everyone likes this idea, especially Americans who are unlikely ever to adopt anything metric. The whole business is a very sore point for a lot of people. You are certainly not alone if you have no idea what 10kg physically represents and so it is important that I make some distinctions here.

You do not find certain units more acceptable because of what they are but because you were brought up with them. I know exactly what a ten thou step feels like in a piece of metal but the metric equivalent does not leap to mind without some serious thought. 50bhp always had more meaning than 37kW but, to prove the point, I can immediately visualise a 250cm^3 engine while the equivalent, 15.3in^3, has little meaning. I am sure many people can identify with this.

However, this has nothing whatsoever to do with establishing a scientific system of units that is easy to use for engineering purposes. If you had to do that job you would try to make everything relate as simply and consistently as possible. This is exactly what the current SI (System International) system of units is designed to do. It is much more simple than any of the Imperial systems and easier to use though that does not mean you will have a 'feel' for the units.

Personally, I have no doubt that the metric system is scientifically better. I have used both systems simultaneously in industry for thirty years and the metric one is more straightforward. Despite this, I still 'think' Imperial because that is what I was brought up with initially. My children think metric and the idea of having 12ins in 1ft, 3ft in 1yard or 1760yards in 1mile just bemuses them.

Mass and weight

Mass is a fundamental quantity but unlike time and length we rarely use it. Because of this it has a certain mystique. Mass is a measure of the reluctance of an object to be accelerated, ie the more mass something has the greater the force required to increase its speed. This does sound rather abstract but then so are most other quantities when you look at them closely. Many other definitions of mass are used, things like 'the quantity of matter in an object', but they all sound even more abstract. Why bother? Mass is mass just as time is time and the metric unit for it, the kilogram, is deemed to be that of a particular block of platinum kept in Paris.

Our dislike of mass is largely due to the related term weight which we use with negligible thought because we have grown up with it. Despite this, weight is much more complicated than mass. Weight is a force and therefore a derived quantity. It is the force exerted on a mass by virtue of gravity, another can of worms! If these aspects interest you then further reading is essential but the most basic ideas are as follows.

Mass is fundamental. The mass of an object remains the same on earth, the moon, Mars or anywhere else. That is why it is chosen. When masses are close together there is an attraction between them. A large mass, like the earth, gives a strong attraction which we call gravity and gravity causes objects close to the earth to accelerate towards it. The product of the mass and the gravitational acceleration is a force called weight which we accept with no problems. As you can see weight is more involved than mass. It changes with gravity so weight varies slightly at different points on the earth and is dramatically different on other planets. You may not like the idea of mass but it is very clear why scientists do not want weight as a fundamental quantity.

The metric system

In the preferred (SI) metric system the fundamental units of general interest are as follows.

- Mass: The kilogram (kg).
- Length: The metre (m).
- Time: The second (s).
- Temperature: Degree kelvin (K).
- Angle: The radian (rad). Strictly speaking this is a supplementary unit.

You might expect temperature to be in Celsius (°C) but this is just another arbitrary scale that has found favour. If you do not think such things can be arbitrary you might contemplate the fact that 0°C was once the boiling point of water and 100°C was its freezing point! A change in temperature of 1K is the same as a change of 1°C but 0°C corresponds to 273.15K. The kelvin scale is much more scientifically based but the details are too involved to include here, as is the saga of degrees (angle) and radians. Centigrade should not be used for temperature because in some countries centigrade is a measure of angle. The complete list is given in Table A1.1.

Derived quantities are made up from combinations of the fundamental ones and some common examples are also given in Table A1.1. Note that there are no peculiar numbers involved, everything is related by 'ones', eg a force of 1N is defined as the force required to give a mass of 1kg an acceleration of 1m/s^2. 1J is the work done when 1N acts through a distance of 1m and so on. To cope with large or small quantities, the system uses a series of multipliers that are all powers of ten as given in Table A1.2 overleaf. It is all very logical and easy to remember once you get used to it. The only anomaly is the use of kg as a fundamental value rather than the gram (g) but the reason is that the gram is extremely small in everyday terms and its symbol can be confused with that used for gravitational acceleration.

Weight

The metric unit of force, and hence weight, is the newton (N). 1N is the weight of a mass of 1kg when the gravitational acceleration is 1m/s^2. This is simple and logical but unfortunately the gravitational acceleration on earth is typically 9.81m/s^2. This means that a mass of 1kg will weigh 9.81N on earth. This is neither here nor there for scientists but goes down like a lead balloon with the public at large.

Enter the kilogram-force (kgf), a unit much despised by scientists and adored by the public

Table A1.1 *SI base units, supplementary units, and examples of derived units. Note that all values are related by 'ones', there are no peculiar constants.*

SI base units		
Quantity	**Name**	**Symbol**
length	metre	m
mass	kilogram	kg
time	second	s
electric current	ampere	A
thermodynamic temperature	kelvin	K
amount of substance	mole	mol
luminous intensity	candela	cd
SI supplementary units		
Quantity	**Name**	**Symbol**
plane angle	radian	rad
solid angle	steradian	sr

Examples of derived units			
Quantity	**Name**	**Symbol**	**As other SI units**
area	square metre	m^2	
volume	cubic metre	m^3	
speed or velocity	metres per second	m/s	
acceleration	metres per second per second	m/s^2	
density	kilogram per cubic metre	kg/m^3	
force	newton	N	kgm/s^2
torque	newton metre	Nm	kgm^2/s^2
energy	joule	J	$Nm = kgm^2/s^2$
power	watt	W	$J/s = Nm/s = kgm^2/s^3$
pressure	pascal	Pa	N/m^2
electrical voltage	volt	V	$W/A = kgm^2/s^3A$
electrical resistance	ohm	Ω	$V/A = kgm^2/s^3A^2$
frequency	hertz	Hz	1/s

Prefix	Symbol	Factor by which unit is multiplied
exa	E	1 000 000 000 000 000 000
peta	P	1 000 000 000 000 000
tera	T	1 000 000 000 000
giga	G	1 000 000 000
mega	M	1 000 000
kilo	k	1 000
hecto	h	100
deca	da	10
deci	d	0.1
centi	c	0.01
milli	m	0.001
micro	μ	0.000 001
nano	n	0.000 000 001
pico	p	0.000 000 000 001
femto	f	0.000 000 000 000 001
atto	a	0.000 000 000 000 000 001

Table A1.2 *Multiplying factors used to scale the SI units. The most common multipliers are those from milli to giga. The others apply to very large or very small measurements. Examples. kg =1000g, mm = 0.001m, MN = 1000000N, km = 1000m etc.*

though they don't realise it. A kilogram-force, which is not an SI unit, is defined as the force acting on a mass of 1kg when the acceleration is 9.81m/s^2. As such, a mass of 1kg weighs 1kgf on earth! If you 'weigh' yourself and the scales say 80kg then you are a mass of 80kg which weighs 80kgf on earth (but nowhere else). The public are not really into this and the 'f' gets dropped. You then 'weigh' 80kg even though the kg is not a unit of weight. Your correct weight is 784.8N but it won't say that on the bathroom scales. This is just one example of scientific units being degraded by everyday use and it has nothing to do with the fact that the units are metric. The imperial units are even worse.

From a practical point of view there are no real problems unless they decide to build a race track on the moon. Always follow these rules.

- If your bathroom scales read kg then the value obtained is the weight in kgf or the mass in kg. If you need the weight in newtons multiply by 9.81.

- If the scales read in newtons (unlikely for domestic scales but common with scientific ones) then this is the weight in N. To find the mass in kg divide the reading by 9.81.

In general I have arranged the formulae in this book so that you do not have to think about this. Just enter the scale reading as detailed with the formulae.

The Imperial system

If you are quietly thinking what a ridiculous idea the metric system is, you will be sad to learn that the Imperial system is even more complicated. Indeed, some of the problems are so significant that general engineers, aircraft engineers and scientists never managed to agree on one coherent system. At least three variations were (are?) in common use.

In the metric system you can at least be sure that a newton is force. In Imperial a pound can be mass or weight. Alternatively, the mass might be in slugs! Add to this the fact that quantities are 'scaled' by a seemingly random series of numbers, eg 1mile = 1760yds = 5280ft = 63360in etc, and you can see that this system is very much one that evolved over a period of time, rather than one that was designed on a scientific basis. If you had used only the SI metric system for 40 years, this would also go down like a lead balloon!

Apart from the historical scaling factors, the Imperial system is based on exactly the same concepts as the metric version. Mass and weight cause similar problems and Table A1.3 indicates several adaptations. Poundals were favoured by scientists for force using the logical relationship of 1poundal = 1lb(mass) x 1ft/s^2(acceleration). This never caught on with the public and is now generally dead because scientists use metric. The system that has caught on is the definition that a mass of 1lb weighs 1lbf when the acceleration due to gravity is 32.2ft/s^2. The is exactly the same idea as the kgf, ie the mass and weight have the same numerical value on earth. The 'f' gets lost and everyone is suitably confused! This is the system I have used in this book but I have tried put the f in where it is appropriate, eg kg is mass but kgf is weight. Similarly lb is mass but lbf is weight. The fact that each pair of values will be numerically equal on earth is no excuse for leaving the f out.

In aeronautics, the difference between mass and weight is of vital importance, so much so that a unit of mass called the 'slug' was introduced by the late Professor Perry. The sole purpose of this was to avoid the use of the word pound where mass was concerned and hence remove the source of confusion. In this case, a force of 1lbf acting on a mass of 1slug will give an acceleration of 1ft/^{2}.

I was fortunate(?) enough to be involved in engineering research when all these systems, and several others, were in use together. It meant that we had to learn formal methods of dealing with units, though unfortunately space precludes any discussion of these methods here. If you are not involved with these things it must be a nightmare every time you have to work something out. Do you divide the weight by gravity to get mass? What are the units? When I weigh myself it says kg. I thought that was mass and so on.

I hope the approach I have used will help. A mass of 1lb weighs 1lbf on earth and a mass of 1kg weighs 1kgf on earth. Be careful with newtons. The number on the bathroom scales can be used for either mass or weight providing you stick to lb and lbf or kg and kgf as appropriate. Using these values, all the formulae in this book should work out correctly.

The derived units are more complicated with Imperial values generating yet another set of numbers to relate things. For example, the metric unit of power, the watt, is effectively 1Nm/s, ie all ones again, but the Imperial horse power is equivalent to 550ft.lbf/s. In general, the Imperial system has more constants to be remembered or looked up than the metric system.

There are numerous other units I would like to discuss but again space precludes this. Weight and mass are probably the cause of most confusion so I have concentrated on them. It is possible you are now even more confused but unless you have to calculate a variety of engineering quantities you can get by using whatever common units appeal to you.

Unless there is a revolution, all sorts of unit systems will persist for many years to come. The 'official' line may be metric but many do not comply and you are therefore faced with the problem of unit conversions between different systems. Appendix A.2 provides some of the more common conversions and there are several other tables in the appropriate chapters.

Table A1.3 *Three variations of the Imperial force and mass units. Scientists used poundals, general engineers used lbf with lb mass, aircraft engineers used lbf with slugs for mass. Everyone else is confused!*

Imperial force systems (In each case force is defined from mass x acceleration)		
Force (F)	**Mass (m)**	**Acceleration (a)**
poundal (1pdl)	pound mass (1lb)	1ft/s^2
pound force (1lbf)	pound mass (1lb)	32.2ft/s^2
pound force (1lbf)	1 slug	1ft/s^2

Appendix A.2 Unit conversion factors

To convert	to	multiply by	To convert	to	multiply by	To convert	to	multiply by
Length			**Volume and capacity**			**Force and weight**		
µm	thou	0.03937	cm^3	in^3	0.061024	kgf	lbf	2.2046
mm	in	0.03937	litres	ft^3	0.0353146	N	kgf	0.1019368
cm	in	0.3937	litres	gallons	0.2199736	N	lbf	0.224809
m	in	39.37	gallons	litres	4.546	kN	tonf	0.100361
m	ft	3.28083	in^3	mm^3	16387.064	lbf	kgf	0.45359
km	miles	0.62137	in^3	litres	0.016387	lbf	N	4.44822
thou	µm	25.4	ft^3	litres	28.31685	tonf	kN	9.96402
in	mm	25.4	fl.oz	cm^3	28.4131	**Pressure**		
in	cm	2.54	**Volume flowrate**			N/m^2	lbf/in^2	0.000145
in	m	0.0254	litres/s	gall/hr	791.905	kgf/cm^2	lbf/in^2	14.2233
ft	m	0.3048	litres/min	gall/hr	13.1984	N/mm^2	tonf/in^2	0.06475
miles	km	1.60934	m^3/s	ft^3/s	35.3143	bar	N/m^2	100000
Area			gall/hr	litres/min	0.075767	bar	lbf/in^2	14.5
mm^2	in^2	0.00155	gall/hr	litres/s	0.0012627	lbf/in^2	N/m^2	6894.76
cm^2	in^2	0.155	ft^3/s	m^3/s	0.0283171	lbf/in^2	kgf/cm^2	0.070307
m^2	ft^2	10.7639	**Mass**			lbf/in^2	bar	0.068965
ft^2	in^2	144	kg	lb	2.2046	tonf/in^2	N/mm^2	15.4443
ft^2	mm^2	92903.04	g	oz	0.0352739	**Torque**		
ft^2	cm^2	929.0304	lb	kg	0.45359	lbf ft	N m	1.3558
ft^2	m^2	0.092903	tons	kg	1016.05	lbf in	N m	0.1130
Viscosity			oz	g	28.3495	kgf cm	N m	0.0981
N s/m^2	lbf.s/ft^2	0.0208854	slugs	kg	14.5939	kgf m	N m	9.8100
Pa s	N s/m^2	1	**Temperature**			N m	lbf ft	0.7376
m^2/s	ft^2/s	10.763915	°F = 32 + (9C/5)			lbf in	lbf ft	0.0833
Pa s	cP	1000				kgf cm	lbf ft	0.07233
cSt	mm^2/s	1	°C = 5(F - 32)/9			kgf m	lbf ft	7.2330
m^2/s	mm^2/s	1000000						

To convert	to	multiply by
Speed and velocity		
km/hr	miles/hr	0.62137
km/hr	ft/s	0.9113426
m/s	ft/s	3.28083
m/s	miles/hr	2.23693
miles/hr	km/hr	1.60934
miles/hr	ft/s	1.466667
miles/hr	m/s	0.4470388
ft/s	m/s	0.3048
Acceleration		
m/s^2	ft/s^2	3.28083
m/s^2	'g'	0.1019368
ft/s^2	m/s^2	0.3048
ft/s^2	'g'	0.0310559
km/hr/s	m/s^2	0.2777777
miles/hr/s	ft/s^2	1.46666667

To convert	to	multiply by
Stiffness		
kgf/cm	kgf/mm	0.1
kgf/cm	lbf/in	5.5997
kgf/mm	kgf/cm	10
kgf/mm	N/mm	9.81
kgf/mm	lbf/in	55.997
N/mm	lbf/in	5.71
N/mm	kgf/mm	0.1019
N/mm	kgf/cm	1.0194
lbf/in	N/mm	0.175
lbf/in	kgf/mm	0.01786
N m/deg	lbf ft/deg	0.7376
lbf ft/deg	N m/deg	1.35578
Density		
kg/m^3	lb/ft^3	0.0624
lb/ft^3	kg/m^3	16.0185

To convert	to	multiply by
Power		
bhp	kW	0.746
bhp	PS	1.015
kW	bhp	1.340
kW	PS	1.361
PS	kW	0.735
PS	bhp	0.985
Moment of Inertia		
kg cm^2	lb in^2	0.3417136
kg cm^2	lb ft^2	0.002373
lb in^2	kg cm^2	2.926426
lb ft^2	kg cm^2	421.4075

Formula finder

About the author

John Bradley BSc.(Hons), C.Eng., M.I.Mech.E., M.Inst.M.C., A.I.E.D. is a professional engineer who built and raced motorcycles as a hobby for more than 25 years. He started grass track racing in the 1960's using a bike he had made at school for a 500cc AJS engine. This was quickly followed by several JAP and JAWA based specials. He rode in grass track and speedway events for seven years and was a member of the Birmingham British League side. He started roadracing after being encouraged to do so by his great friend, the late Peter McKinley. After starting with a bike built by Jack Machin he built a variety of bikes to his own design and was a regular top three finisher. He was also a National winner and lap record holder, finishing third in the ACU Clubman's Championship. John's bikes were always simple and inexpensive but they were carefully refined using the ideas presented in this book. He is an experienced engineer, lecturer and author with more than 40 books, manuals and papers to his credit. This is his first book relating to motorcycle engineering and he is currently writing a second volume on practical construction.

Index